NON-STOICHIOMETRIC COMPOUNDS

NON-STOICHIOMETRIC COMPOUNDS

Edited by

L. MANDELCORN

WESTINGHOUSE ELECTRIC CORPORATION

RESEARCH AND DEVELOPMENT CENTER

PITTSBURGH, PENNSYLVANIA

ACADEMIC PRESS   New York and London   1964

ACADEMIC PRESS INC.
111 Fifth Avenue, New York 3, New York

United Kingdom Edition published by
ACADEMIC PRESS INC. (LONDON) LTD.
Berkeley Square House, London W.1

LIBRARY OF CONGRESS CATALOG CARD NUMBER: 63-16968

PRINTED IN THE UNITED STATES OF AMERICA

CONTRIBUTORS

R. M. BARRER,
Chemistry Department, Imperial College of Science and Technology, London, England

STIG R. ERLANDER,
Northern Regional Research Laboratory, Peoria, Illinois

HENRY EYRING,
Institute for the Study of Rate Processes, University of Utah, Salt Lake City, Utah

LLOYD C. FETTERLY,
Shell Development Co., Emeryville, California

E. A. GULBRANSEN,
Westinghouse Research Laboratories, Pittsburgh, Pennsylvania

DOUGLAS HENDERSON,*
Institute for the Study of Rate Processes, University of Utah, Salt Lake City, Utah

O. M. KATZ,†
Westinghouse Research Laboratories, Pittsburgh, Pennsylvania

H. M. POWELL,
Chemical Crystallography Laboratory, Oxford University, England

J. MONTEATH ROBERTSON,
Chemistry Department, The University of Glasgow, Scotland

FREDERIC R. SENTI,
Northern Regional Research Laboratory, Peoria, Illinois

L. A. K. STAVELEY,
Inorganic Chemistry Laboratory, Oxford University, England

E. C. SUBBARAO,
Westinghouse Research Laboratories, Pittsburgh, Pennsylvania

A. D. WADSLEY,
Division of Mineral Chemistry, C.S.I.R.O., Melbourne, Australia

* Present address: Department of Physics, Arizona State University, Tempe, Arizona.
† Present address: Westinghouse Bettis Atomic Power Laboratory, Pittsburgh, Pennsylvania.

PREFACE

The science of non-stoichiometric compounds has developed rapidly during the past 15 years. This has been due in part to improvements in methods of x-ray crystal structure analysis and to the use of high speed computers in analyzing crystal structure data. Since non-stoichiometric compounds are complex, they are usually difficult to define and to study. In defining the atomic geometry and composition of these compounds and in understanding their physical properties, x-ray crystal structure analysis is essential.

Theoretical investigations of non-stoichiometric compounds have been aided by the establishment of their structure and the arrangement of the several atoms which often had little chemical affinity for one another. Thus, in the non-stoichiometric oxides a major advance was made regarding their physical properties and the valence state of the ions when their modes of coordination were understood. In addition, basic study and practical utilization of inclusion complexes such as clathrates have been greatly aided by crystal structure analyses.

The composition and structure of a non-stoichiometric compound is best considered in terms of the geometrical disposition of one or more of its components. The components may be molecular, atomic, or ionic species. A molecular compound of the *host-guest* type consists of one component comprising the host structure which contains spaces or cavities that can accommodate the guest molecules. The guest molecules have limited ranges in size and shape to fit the geometry of the cavities. The cavities need not have a simple numerical relationship with the host molecules or atoms.

Non-stoichiometric compounds cover a wide range of chemical bonding. A liquid solution, for example, may be classed as a simple type of non-stoichiometric compound. A solid surface containing an adsorbed layer of gas may also be classed as a non-stoichiometric compound. The close relationships of adsorbed gases on surfaces, liquid solutions, and non-stoichiometric compounds can be demonstrated by the fact that theories of liquid solutions and of surface adsorption can be applied to various non-stoichiometric compounds.

Assemblies of solid substrate layers having molecular dimensions in thickness may be used to illustrate many of the non-stoichiometric structures. First, a stacked group of these may comprise a host structure. The second component, or guest molecules, may be accommodated between any two adjacent layers. In some cases the guest molecules, atoms, or ions may be preferentially bound to one layer. This type of structure is termed a *layer* structure.

A host structure also may be visualized as composed of two layer structures intersecting each other. This arrangement gives *channel* or *tunnel* structures. The channels are long compared to molecular dimensions. However, the cross-sectional dimensions allow limited space for guest atoms, molecules, or ions. There are also channel-type non-stoichiometric compounds in solution.

The intersection of three layer structures gives a *cage* structure. These cage structures contain three-dimensionally enclosed cavities. In these cavities one or more guest molecules may be located.

The rigidity of the layer structures, channel structures, and cage structures when guest molecules, atoms, or ions are added is an important property which distinguishes various individual complexes. Many layer structures swell perpendicular to the layers during inclusion of the guest component. The increase in interlayer distance is dependent on the size of the guest molecules or ions. Most channel structures, in contrast, are inflexible. One set of cross-sectional dimensions of potential guest molecules must be compatible with the cross-sectional geometry of the host channel. However, some channel structures adjust somewhat to the size and shape of the guest. In cage structures all three dimensions of the guest molecules are restricted by the size and shape of the enclosing cavities, with some leeway, occasionally, due to possible distortion of the host structure.

These considerations pertain to upper limits of dimensions of molecules or ions which may be accommodated in various host structures. In cage structures containing neutral molecules, i.e., clathrates, where the interaction between the host and guest component is small, molecules below a certain size may readily escape through the host structure. In certain channel structures one or more of the dimensions of the guest molecules are restricted by the necessity for a close fit to exist between a rather inflexible channel and the host molecule.

The above models for layer, channel, and cage structures built up from combinations of surfaces or intersecting surfaces are probably unrealistic. The true representation of the host structures should be given in terms of various interstitial structures. Some of the important properties may be understood readily from the simplified models and the concept of surface adsorption. One example is a molecular compound with a guest component consisting of neutral molecules or atoms.

When there is one guest molecule per site in the host structure, as in the adsorption of a monolayer on a surface, the equilibrium may be represented by a Langmuir-type of isotherm. The adsorption model implies a continuous composition range for the guest component, complete saturation of sites being possible at only infinite concentration or pressure of the guest component. In some cases the neutral guest molecules appear to occupy all the available sites. However, a small fraction of the spaces may be unoccupied, but the methods of analysis may not have been capable of revealing this.

A host-guest composition range may be interrupted by a phase change of the host structure. At this composition, one may have equilibrium between the terminal solid solution of the guest component in the original host structure with the new phase of host plus guest. For the general case a particular host phase exists only over a certain concentration range of the guest component. In defining the system, this concentration range, as well as temperature and pressure, should be given.

In addition to the layer, channel, and cage types of non-stoichiometric compounds there are two types where the geometry factor is important. They are not of the typical host-guest variety.

The first type consists of two or more distinct structures which follow a certain stacking sequence, or the structures may be interlaced with each other in a regular fashion. The second type is essentially one structure with planes of discontinuity (crystallographic shear) interspaced at regular intervals. These two types may be classed as distinct cases of ordered non-stoichiometric compounds. Here variations may occur only in entire structural sequences or in discrete changes of thickness of the structural block between two successive discontinuities. The corresponding effects on composition occur according to the same integral, non-continuous relationship. The graphite-metal inclusion compounds, of the host-guest layer type, are analogous to these in some ways. Here metal atoms are added continuously to graphite, with the addition occurring in a set of regularly separated interlayer spaces. When these are effectively saturated another set of interlayer spaces may be filled.

Certain physical properties of non-stoichiometric compounds of the host-guest type reflect essentially the presence of the guest component and its interaction with its environment. The Lennard-Jones and Devonshire free-volume theory has been applied to the thermodynamic properties of clathrates of non-polar compounds. Excellent agreement between experiment and theory has been achieved. Interactions between host and guest in some clathrates are very small. As a result it has been possible to study the behavior of individual gas molecules physically isolated from each other. Dielectric, electromotive force, electrical conductivity, ferroelectric, magnetic, diffusion, spectral, heat capacity, and Mössbauer shift measurements have been variously related to the interactions of the guest with the host, the orientation of the guest molecules, and the form they assume in these structures.

The stability of non-stoichiometric compounds is a function of the degree of isolation of the guest component, the contribution of the guest component to the over-all structure stability, and the modification of the reactivity of the guest component by the host environment. There are two energy barriers when non-stoichiometric compounds decompose into host and guest components. One is due to interaction between the host and guest; the other results from the constraint imposed by the host structure on the guest molecules once the first energy barrier is overcome. In cage structures containing neutral molecules the energy barrier imposed by the host itself predominates. Host-guest interaction may predominate where ions are the included species and in the channel and layer types of non-stoichiometric compounds. These interactions in channel compounds in solution also affects the reactivity of some guest compounds.

The foregoing paragraphs have dealt very briefly with some of the topics discussed in this volume. Both structural details and physical properties of various non-stoichiometric compounds are emphasized. The first two chapters are on structural analysis and statistical thermodynamics, and theories related to non-stoichiometry were specially selected. These chapters should provide a basis for understanding the experimental material and the interpretation of results given in succeeding chapters. Both organic and inorganic non-stoichiometric compounds are included. Since there are good books on the subject of "doped" semiconductors, they are not included in this book.

The development of this volume was marked by active cooperation among the authors to assure proper continuity of topics and to avoid serious overlap. They enlarged the scope of the book beyond that which was originally intended, and helped one another to enrich their contributions by providing vital and timely information. The editor wishes to express his sincere appreciation to Dr. J. Swiss and Dr. T. W. Dakin of the Westinghouse Research Laboratories for their constant support rendered whenever scientific advice or material help was requested. To Dr. A. Taylor, of the Laboratories, the editor is also grateful for valuable consultation and guidance.

LYON MANDELCORN

November, 1963   Westinghouse Research Laboratories

CONTENTS

CONTRIBUTORS   v

PREFACE   vii

Chapter 1

X-RAY STRUCTURAL ANALYSIS

J. MONTEATH ROBERTSON

I.	Introduction	2
II.	Classical Crystallography	7
III.	Departures from the Classical Lattice	14
IV.	X-Ray Diffraction	23
V.	Structure Determination	31
VI.	Diffraction by Neutrons and Electrons	41
	References	47

Chapter 2

STATISTICAL THERMODYNAMICS AND REACTION RATE THEORY

DOUGLAS HENDERSON AND HENRY EYRING

I.	Statistical Thermodynamics and Its Relation to Classical Thermodynamics	50
II.	The Theory of Absolute Reaction Rates	63
III.	The Lennard-Jones and Devonshire Free Volume Theory of Liquids and Dense Gases	68
IV.	Thermodynamics and Kinetics of Imperfections in Stoichiometric Solids	78
V.	Non-Stoichiometric Solids	87
VI.	Concluding Remarks	93
	References	95

Chapter 3

INORGANIC NON-STOICHIOMETRIC COMPOUNDS

A. D. WADSLEY

I.	Introduction	99
II.	Oxides	104
III.	Chalcogenides (Sulfides, Selenides, Tellurides)	165
IV.	Classification According to Structure	197
	References	201

Chapter 4

OCCLUDED GASES IN TRANSITION METALS

O. M. KATZ AND E. A. GULBRANSEN

I.	Introduction	211
II.	Crystal Structures of the Interstitial Compounds	211
III.	Materials	214
IV.	Adsorption, Hydride Formation, and Hydrogen Solution Processes	216
V.	Diffusion of Hydrogen	218
VI.	Effect of Oxide Films and Pretreatments on the Occlusion of Hydrogen	225
VII.	Thermodynamic Analyses	233
VIII.	Crystal Structure and Phase Diagram Studies of Zr–H	250
	Text References	258
	Additional Bibliography on Hydrogen in Metals	261

Chapter 5

PHYSICAL PROPERTIES OF NON-STOICHIOMETRIC INORGANIC COMPOUNDS

E. C. SUBBARAO

I.	Introduction	268
II.	Ionic Conductivity	270
III.	Electrical Conductivity	281
IV.	Ferroelectricity	294
V.	Magnetic Properties	298
VI.	Concluding Remarks	304
	References	305

Chapter 6

INORGANIC INCLUSION COMPLEXES

R. M. BARRER

I.	Introduction	310
II.	Guest Molecules in Isolated Cavities	313
III.	Guest Molecules in Parallel Channels: Cancrinites and Fibrous Clays	327
IV.	Guest Molecules between Chains	330
V.	Guest Molecules between Layers	333
VI.	Some Additonal Complexes	363
VII.	Zeolites with Intersecting Channel Networks	367
VIII.	Inclusion Isotherms	399
IX.	Thermochemistry	412
X.	Molecule Diffusion in Some Porous Crystals	421
XI.	Conclusion	429
	References	430

Chapter 7

CLATHRATES

H. M. POWELL

I.	Molecular Imprisonment	438
II.	Early Observations on Clathrates	439
III.	Crystal Structures of Clathrates	450
IV.	Equilibrium Relationships and Non-Stoichiometry in Clathrates	484
	References	489

Chapter 8

ORGANIC ADDUCTS

LLOYD C. FETTERLY

I.	Introduction	491
II.	Historical	494
III.	Urea Channel Adducts	497
IV.	Thiourea Channel Adducts	530
V.	Other Channel Inclusion Complexes	538
VI.	Soluble "Complex" Phenomena	541
VII.	Applications of Inclusion Complexes	551
	References	563

Chapter 9

CARBOHYDRATES

FREDERIC R. SENTI AND STIG R. ERLANDER

I.	Introduction	568
II.	Amylose Inclusion Compounds	569
III.	Iodine-Iodide Complexes of Glycogen and Amylopectin	587
IV.	Schardinger Dextrin Complexes	588
V.	Adsorption and Addition Complexes of Polysaccharides	601
	References	602

Chapter 10

PHYSICS AND CHEMISTRY OF INCLUSION COMPLEXES

L. A. K. STAVELEY

I.	Introduction	606
II.	Dielectric Properties	608
III.	Magnetic Susceptibility Studies	616
IV.	Spectroscopic Studies	620
V.	Thermodynamic Studies of the Movement of the Guest Molecules in Hydroquinone Clathrates	626
VI.	Changes in the Chemical Behavior of Guest Molecules	629
VII.	The Stability and Decomposition of Inclusion Complexes	632
	References	634

AUTHOR INDEX	637
SUBJECT INDEX	659
CHEMICAL AND MINERAL INDEX	671

CHAPTER **1**

J. Monteath Robertson

*Chemistry Department, The University of Glasgow,
Scotland*

X-Ray Structural Analysis

I.	Introduction	2
II.	Classical Crystallography	7
	A. Fundamental Laws	7
	B. Symmetry	8
	C. Limitation of Symmetry in a Crystal	9
	D. Point Groups	10
	E. The Lattice Theory	11
	F. Space Groups	13
III.	Departures from the Classical Lattice	14
	A. Dislocations	14
	B. Point Defects	20
	C. Non-Stoichiometry	22
IV.	X-Ray Diffraction	23
	A. Laue and Bragg Equations	23
	B. Experimental Methods	24
	C. The Reciprocal Lattice	25
	D. Space Group Determination	27
	E. Powder Photographs	29
	F. Superlattices and Solid Solutions	30
V.	Structure Determination	31
	A. The Intensity of X-Ray Reflections	31
	B. Scattering by Electrons, Atoms, and Crystals	32
	C. The Structure Factor and Electron Density Distribution	34
	D. The Phase Problem	36
VI.	Diffraction by Neutrons and Electrons	41
	A. Neutron Diffraction	41
	B. Electron Diffraction	45
	References	47

I. INTRODUCTION

Fifty years have now elapsed since the discovery of x-ray diffraction by M. von Laue in 1912, but crystallography and the theory of crystal symmetry is a much older subject than this, and had its first beginnings in the 17th century. Robert Hooke in 1665 and Christiaan Huygens in 1690 provided very clear models and drawings of three-dimensional crystal lattices (25). Further evidence for the lattice theory of crystals was provided by Nicolaus Steno (1669), Romé de l'Isle (1772), and particularly by Abbé René Just Haüy in his famous treatise published in 1784 which referred to chemical atoms of definite and constant form, and which preceded Dalton's atomic theory by several decades. The geometrical implications of this theory were developed most notably by Bravais in 1850, who established the 14 possible types of space lattice, and by Sohncke whose 65 regular point systems give all the possible distinct systems of symmetrical repetition of identical objects. The theory was completed between 1885 and 1894 by Fedorov, Schoenflies, and Barlow by the inclusion not only of identity but also the enantiomorphous similarities which are exhibited in certain crystals, and they derived the 230 space groups with which all crystallographers are now familiar. It is not always realized that this mathematical theory was so fully and completely developed long before the discovery of x-ray diffraction, and indeed before the discovery of x-rays by Röntgen. Our first few sections are therefore devoted to summarizing a little of this basic theory.

Although all this earlier work was quite fully established and proved mathematically, it may be said that it was only verified experimentally with the discovery of x-ray diffraction in 1912. The immense importance of this discovery was immediately recognized. As well as establishing the true nature of x-radiation, with all the repercussions that this had on atomic theory, it provided for the first time the means for actually finding the positions of atoms in crystals, and accurately measuring the distances between them. As nearly all matter can be made crystalline under some conditions, the field of application thus embraced not only the whole of structural chemistry but quite a lot of biology as well.

Progress was at first rapid and many simple and fundamentally important structures were determined. Some of the concepts of inorganic chemistry were completely changed when it now for the first time became possible to discover the true arrangement of the atoms in space. The importance of geometrical packing in crystals became clear. Some structures were found to depend, not so much on questions of bonds or charges as on the sizes of the units concerned and on how they could best fit together. The stoichiometric compound was thus not the only possibility, and what has accrued from the further development of this concept is explained in the other chapters of this book.

The early years of the science of x-ray analysis were remarkable not only for the rapid elucidation of many simple but fundamentally important inorganic structures, but also for the equally rapid development of the basic physical theory underlying the new method. Already by 1915 Darwin had shown that only rarely can crystals be perfect lattice structures, and had developed the concept of the mosaic crystal; W. H. Bragg had suggested that the distribution of the scattering matter composing a crystal might be represented mathematically by a Fourier series. By this time Debye had also given a quantitative theoretical treatment of the effect of thermal motion on the intensities of x-ray reflections, and soon afterwards, with Scherrer and Hull, devised the simple but important method of using powders instead of single crystals. Ewald's quantitative treatment of the intensities of x-ray reflections was also made about this time, and a little later he developed the beautiful idea of the reciprocal lattice.

By the end of the 1920's it was possible to formulate the problem of x-ray crystal analysis very concisely and completely by the expression

$$\rho(xyz) = \sum_{-\infty}^{+\infty}\sum\sum \frac{F(hkl)}{V} \exp\left[-2\pi i(hx/a + ky/b + lz/c)\right] \qquad (1)$$

$\rho(xyz)$ is the distribution of electron density in the unit cell of sides a, b, and c, and volume V. $F(hkl)$ is the structure factor of the plane whose Miller indices are h, k, l. This quantity F is a number which represents the ratio of the wave which is scattered or reflected from this particular plane to the wave which would be scattered if the contents of the unit cell were replaced by a single classical electron. Its magnitude can be derived in a straightforward way from a measurement of intensity of the reflected ray compared to that of the incident beam, using the formulas derived by Darwin and Ewald.

At first sight, therefore, it would appear that all the quantities in this expression are known, and that the problem is completely solved. We have only to measure the intensities of all the observed reflections, calculate the corresponding F's, and insert them in this expression, which can then be evaluated at as many points x, y, z as are required to plot out the complete electron distribution in the unit cell. The maxima obtained in this distribution will represent the atoms.

Further consideration, however, shows that there is still something missing. The F's represent the scattered waves, and these are complex quantities characterized not only by an amplitude, which can be measured, but also by a phase constant, which cannot be directly measured.

The determination of these constants is the well known *phase problem*, which is the central problem in crystal analysis.

This problem was not clearly formulated till about 1930. If the structure is comparatively simple, and likely positions for the atoms can be postulated, then the structure factors including the phase constants may be calculated. The calculated amplitudes can then be compared with those observed, and adjustments made. In this trial and error method the Fourier series approach can be used, with observed amplitudes and calculated phases, as a most valuable means of refinement and successive approximation.

During the 1930's and 1940's a very large number of structures, some of them quite complex, were accurately solved in this way. However, in the field of organic chemistry it is true to say that although many structures were solved and much valuable information about bond lengths and stereochemical problems obtained, yet very few structures were determined for which the chemist did not already know the structural formula. If nothing or very little is known about the probable arrangement of the atoms, then for a complex molecule it is clearly impossible even to formulate a trial structure. A more powerful and fundamental approach was necessary before such problems could be tackled.

During the 1930's such methods began to be developed. The Patterson vector method expresses in an elegant way all the information that can be obtained about a structure from a knowledge of the amplitudes only, without any phase constants. The result, by a Fourier method analogous to that described above, gives not a picture of the atomic positions but of a superposition of all the interatomic vectors in the structure. If there are not too many atoms in the unit cell the result can be fully interpreted, and this is a most valuable approach which is now used in practically every structure investigation. But when the number of atoms increases to a dozen or more it is usually impossible to isolate the individual vectors, whose number unfortunately increases with the square of the number of atoms. During the past 25 years many intricate mathematical investigations have been made in an attempt to solve the phase problem more completely. Although much progress has been made with several different approaches, the results are not of very general application if more than about 20 atoms are involved in general positions.

A more direct approach of a chemical nature is, however, possible, and this was developed soon after Patterson's discovery of the vector method. These methods are known as the isomorphous substitution and the heavy atom methods, and were first extensively developed in studies of the phthalocyanine structures. If by a chemical process another atom can be added to or substituted in a structure without greatly disturbing what is already there, the contribution from the new atom will alter the resultant amplitude in a way which depends on the phase constant of that particular structure factor. By observing the amplitude before and after the substitution the unknown phase constant can often be deduced. In what is known as the heavy atom method, the substituted derivative alone is used, on the assumption that the phase constant is governed mainly by the contributions of the additional atom or atoms, these atoms being preferably ones of fairly high scattering power. Although phase constant determination by these methods is often far from complete, it does provide a starting point. Some very badly resolved picture of what is otherwise a completely unknown structure is obtained, and from this beginning various powerful methods of successive approximation can commence.

It is perhaps worth noting here that such methods are in principle particularly applicable to many complex structures of the kind described elsewhere in this book, where a host molecule may accommodate other molecules or atoms in gaps in the structure. These additional atoms may often be varied at will without greatly disturbing the remainder of the structure, and in a manner that can lead to a very direct application of the above methods of direct phase constant determination. On the other hand these structures are often so complex that many of them have not yet been fully elucidated. In principle, however, there is no reason now why they should not all be completely determined.

The phthalocyanine structures were a particularly simple case for the application of these methods of phase constant determination, and all the atoms were completely and accurately resolved in two-dimensional projections. It then seemed that this was the obvious and perhaps the only way to determine complex structures of unknown chemical formula, but during the next 15 years progress was rather slow. To explain the reason for this we must now refer to another less profound but equally difficult problem of x-ray crystal analysis. This is the problem of computation.

To resolve atoms by the Fourier method their centers must usually be separated by about 0.6 Å. (This depends on the wavelength used, the perfection of the crystal, and the number of observable reflections.) Now, the atoms in the phthalocyanine molecule could be resolved in a single two-dimensional projection because the molecules are planar and inclined to the projection plane at a suitable angle. But most complex structures are three-dimensional, and in any projection the atoms will in general overlap to such an extent that individual resolution is impossible. The resulting diagrams, although correct, cannot be interpreted. The same problem, in a more acute form, prevents us from using the Patterson method when many atoms are involved.

The solution to this problem is very simple. Let us do all the work in three dimensions. Then every atom (but not every Patterson vector) can always be resolved, because the real distance between atoms is fortunately always greater than 0.75 Å, and usually greater than 1 Å. The only remaining difficulty is one of computation, but this is certainly a formidable one. For the main phthalocyanine projections the two-dimensional series corresponding to Eq. (1) contained about 200 terms, the number of observed reflections in the zones concerned. To plot out a good electron density distribution over the asymmetric crystal unit (half a molecule), this series had to be evaluated at about 1000 points (different values of x and z). This gives a total of about 200,000 quantities that have to be evaluated and added in groups. Some shortening devices are possible, but on the other hand the work has generally to be repeated many times as successive approximations are made. With the kind of desk equipment available in the 1930's this kind of computation took about a month of fairly hard labor.

However, when we move into three dimensions, using the full Eq. (1), a moderately complex crystal may give a total of about 4000 measurable reflections. To plot this throughout the volume of the asymmetric unit means evaluating this series of 4000 terms at a minimum of some 50,000 points, giving a total of some 200,000,000 quantities to be evaluated and added in groups. If the two-dimensional operation required a month, then at this rate the three-dimensional one would take more than 80 years to complete!

This explains the comparatively slow progress made up until about the mid-1950's with complex and chemically undetermined structures. The principles required for solving the problems were known, but the calculations were too laborious. Within the last few years the invention and general availability of fast electronic digital computers has solved all this, and calculations of the type outlined above can now be carried out in hours instead of years. After all, the ratio of a microsecond to a minute is about the same as the ratio of a minute to a hundred years!

This is, however, a much oversimplified account of events. It would be a mistake to imagine that for the solving of a complex structure nothing more is required than a fast electronic computer and a suitable program. Phase constant determination by the methods described is seldom complete. Much judgment and sometimes intuition are required in interpreting the first badly resolved electron density distributions. And with moving into three dimensions a whole new strategy and tactics had to be developed and new techniques devised. Already, however, a great deal has been accomplished. When it comes to ordinary chemical compounds it is safe to say that we now know how to solve structures accurately for molecules containing up to 100 or more atoms, without counting hydrogen, provided that suitable crystalline derivatives can be prepared. And we know enough chemistry to be able to prepare these derivatives almost without fail. It is also possible, or it will shortly be possible, to solve problems of this magnitude in a comparatively short time. The collection of the experimental data is being speeded up, and computers are becoming faster. Already we can solve the structure of a complex alkaloid in less time than we used to devote to the crystal structure of a simple benzene derivative in the 1930's.

In the case of the special compounds that are the main concern of this book, the same is true provided that true single crystals are available. Very often, however, some disorder may be present, and this may be of various complicated kinds. If the crystal gives sharp reflections and shows proper periodicities in three dimensions, there may still be disorder in the sense that the contents of successive unit cells are not identical. p-Chlorobromobenzene is a simple example. Crystallographically the molecule exhibits a center of symmetry. When packed together to form a crystal a chlorine and a bromine atom are not significantly different in this case and the result is a random arrangement. Such structures can be solved quite accurately, but what we get (and indeed what we get with every crystal structure determination) is a picture showing the contents of the unit cell averaged over all the unit cells. Crystalline hydrates are another example, where the sites of the water molecules are not always occupied. We often find "weak" water molecules, and by counting the electrons, in a quantitative study, the percentage occupation of the site can be determined. In such work, however, some caution is required in distinguishing between incomplete occupation of a site and unusually large thermal movement of the atom concerned. It is better to count electrons by integration rather than by measuring the height of an electron density peak.

II. CLASSICAL CRYSTALLOGRAPHY

A. Fundamental Laws

We have already seen that the mathematical theory of crystallography was completed long before the discovery of x-ray diffraction. This early work was inspired by the remarkable external appearance of crystals. With their sharp edges and smooth, geometrically plane faces they are quite unlike any other naturally occurring objects. When allowed to grow in an unconfined space, a crystal forms a polyhedron. Through accidents of growth the faces may be very unequal, but the crystal can easily be generalized into a regular geometrical figure, and in spite of variations in habit it was soon found (by Steno in 1669) that for a given crystalline substance the angles between corresponding faces are constant. This is the first law of crystallography, and points to a constancy of underlying structure.

To name the faces on a crystal a set of reference axes may be chosen as the intersections of any three nonparallel faces. If a fourth face is now chosen to cut these axes to give lengths a, b, and c, we have a natural system of reference axes of defined relative lengths to which every face on the crystal may be referred. If any such face makes intercepts with the chosen reference axes of a/h, b/k, c/l, it is said to have the Miller indices h, k, l. A plane parallel to any axis has an intercept at infinity and the corresponding Miller index is zero. These reciprocal relations used in defining indices are very useful in crystallography.

The most fundamental law in crystallography, which followed directly from Haüy's work in 1784, can now be stated. It is that the ratios of the indices of any face of any crystal, defined in this way, are always small whole numbers. In practice these numbers are seldom as high as 6 for naturally occurring crystal faces.

B. Symmetry

One of the most striking features of crystals is the symmetry that they display. When we say a figure has symmetry we mean that some movement or operation applied to the figure will bring every point of it into some position that was previously occupied by some other point of the figure. Or more generally, a body may be said to have symmetry if its properties are invariant under a transformation which preserves all its linear dimensions.

These symmetry operations may be of various kinds. Thus, a figure may have a plane of symmetry, one half of the figure being the reflection of the other half in the plane. This operation is denoted by the symbol m. Again there may be various axes of symmetry, 2-fold, 3-fold, $\cdots$, n-fold, where a rotation of $2\pi/n$ brings the figure into self coincidence. The symbols for these operations are 1, 2, 3, $\cdots$, n, where 1 denotes the identity operation, possessed by all figures. Another kind of symmetry operation is reflection through a point instead of in a plane, and this is called a center of symmetry or a center of inversion and is denoted by the symbol $\bar{1}$. In general, centers of symmetry may be combined with the rotation axes to give axes of rotary inversion which are denoted by the symbols $\bar{1}$, $\bar{2}$, $\bar{3}$, $\cdots$, $\bar{n}$. A little consideration will show that $\bar{2} = m$ (see Fig. 2), so this latter symbol, although convenient and frequently used, is really unnecessary. All the symmetry that any figure can have may thus be represented by the symbols 1, 2, 3, $\cdots$, n, and $\bar{1}$, $\bar{2}$, $\bar{3}$, $\cdots$, $\bar{n}$, or combinations of these.

It may be noted that there are two very distinct kinds of symmetry operation, those involving pure rotations and producing congruent figures, and those involving reflection and producing enantiomorphous figures. Both kinds of operation when applied to an unsymmetrical figure leave the distance between any two given points the same.

C. Limitation of Symmetry in a Crystal

Although the symmetry that can be given to a geometrical figure is of unlimited multiplicity (up to $n = \infty$), that possessed by crystals is confined to certain quite narrow limits, and this explains the limited number of crystal systems, crystal classes, and space groups that are found to occur in nature. This important limitation can be shown to follow as a necessary consequence from the law of rational indices, and this law itself is, of course, a consequence of the underlying lattice structure of crystals.

Suppose we have a crystal with an n-fold rotation axis perpendicular to the plane of the paper at 0 (Fig. 1). The plane of the paper itself may be taken as a crystal plane, and 0A, 0A′, and 0A″ are the traces of other planes perpendicular to the plane of the paper and generated by successive operations of the n-fold rotation axis. We now wish to consider the indices of the plane whose trace is 0A″ (or any parallel plane). For reference axes we may choose the symmetry axis through 0 and the two equal axes 0A and 0A′ which may be taken as of unit length. Through A′ draw a plane A′B parallel to the plane 0A″ whose indices we wish to find. Then the intercepts made by this plane on the chosen axes are

∞ on the symmetry axis through 0

1 on the axis 0A′

$1/(2 \cos 2\pi/n)$ on the axis 0A.

The indices required are the reciprocals of these numbers, namely 0, 1, and $2 \cos 2\pi/n$, and these must be integers.

Hence

$$2 \cos 2\pi/n = \pm 2, \pm 1, \text{ or } 0$$

$$\cos 2\pi/n = \pm 1, \pm \tfrac{1}{2}, \text{ or } 0$$

$$n = 1, 2, 3, 4, \text{ or } 6$$

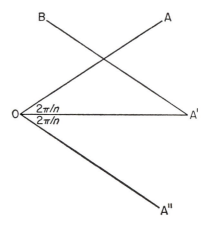

FIG. 1. Limitation of symmetry.

D. Point Groups

The symmetry elements possible in a crystal are thus limited to 1-, 2-, 3-, 4-, or 6-fold rotation axes, and these may be combined with centers of symmetry to give a similar set of axes of rotary inversion, namely $\bar{1}$, $\bar{2}$, $\bar{3}$, $\bar{4}$, and $\bar{6}$. It is obvious that this limited number of symmetry operations which are applicable to crystals can be combined together in a limited number of ways, and will lead to a certain distinct number of crystal classes to one or other of which every crystal occurring in nature must belong.

The collection of symmetry operations present in any given crystal forms a self-consistent set, or a group in the mathematical sense. Thus, the product of any two, or the square of any one of these operations is

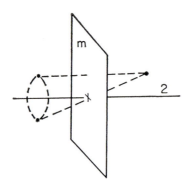

FIG. 2. The group $2m\bar{1}$.

equivalent to some other member of the series, and the series always contains the reverse operation A^{-1} if it contains the operation A, the product $A \cdot A^{-1}$ being the identity operation 1.

Such relations may be illustrated for the simple group $2m\bar{1}$ (Fig. 2) from which it can be seen that

$$2.m = \bar{1}, \quad 2.\bar{1} = m, \quad m\bar{1} = 2, \quad m^2 = 1, \quad \bar{1}^2 = 1, \quad 2^2 = 1.$$

Now it is a matter of pure mathematics to work out all the possible different ways of combining these symmetry elements, and this analysis

TABLE I

The 32 Point Groups

Triclinic	1	$\bar{1}$					
Monoclinic	2	m	$2/m$				
Orthorhombic	222	$mm2$	mmm				
Tetragonal	4	$\bar{4}$	$4/m$	422	$4mm$	$\bar{4}2m$	$4/mmm$
Trigonal	3	$\bar{3}$	32	$3m$	$\bar{3}m$		
Hexagonal	6	$\bar{6}$	$6/m$	622	$6mm$	$\bar{6}m2$	$6/mmm$
Cubic	23	$m3$	432	$\bar{4}3m$	$m3m$		

was first performed by Hessel in 1830. It is found that 32 distinct classes of symmetry are possible, and these are known as the 32 point groups. They constitute finite groups of operations in the mathematical sense (unlike the space groups which contain infinite groups of operations) and they are called point groups because the operations are always such as to leave one fixed point, the center of the group, unmoved.

Crystals are generally classified into seven systems according to the most convenient choice of reference axes. The 32 point groups, arranged in these systems, are given in Table I. The symbols for the point groups are given in the Hermann-Mauguin notation, which enumerates only the essential elements of symmetry present. Additional elements of symmetry, such as $\bar{1}$, 2, are often present although not enumerated, especially in the higher symmetry classes.

E. The Lattice Theory

All the arguments so far have been derived from a study of the idealized external form of crystals, using the law of rational indices to limit the number of possible symmetry elements. We have as yet made no use of any physical theory as to the nature of crystals. This we must now do, and consider what kind of underlying structure can account for all the various facts and laws.

A very simple explanation is in fact possible, and was perceived almost three centuries ago by Hooke and Huygens. It is that the ultimate units of a crystal (atoms, molecules, or groups of molecules) must be arranged according to a regular geometrical pattern. A regularly spaced row of points, extending indefinitely in both directions, is called a row, and is fully described by one parameter a, the interval separating two neighboring points. A regular, planar series of parallel rows, described by the two parameters a and b, and an arbitrary angle γ, is called a net. An indefinitely extended regular series of parallel nets, defined by six parameters, a, b, c, α, β, γ, is called a lattice. The smallest identically repeated parallelopiped in the lattice is called the unit cell.

The next step is to consider the number of distinct geometrical types of lattice that are possible, and this problem was solved by Bravais in 1848. In this connection the fundamental criterion, in addition to the regular spacing of rows and columns, is that none of the individual lattice points can be distinguished from any other by any uniqueness of relative position.

First of all there will be one simple type, called primitive and denoted by the symbol P, corresponding to each of the seven systems already described, with points at the corners of the unit cells. These all have the full symmetry of the highest point group in each system, $\bar{1}$, $2/m$, mmm, etc. (Table I), and they are, of course, distinguished from each other by their symmetry. Other arrangements are, however, possible which still have the full symmetry of these types. These may have an identical point at the center of the unit cell (body-centered, denoted by the symbol I) or at the centers of one pair of opposite faces (symbols A, B, or C depending on the naming of the reference axes) or at the centers of all the faces (face-centered lattice, denoted by the symbol F). However, these do not constitute distinct types in all the systems. Thus, in the triclinic system there can be only a primitive lattice because the choice of the reference axes is quite arbitrary. In the monoclinic system there are two types only, the primitive and what is generally taken to be opposite end pairs of faces centered. A little consideration will show that body-centered is here not a distinct type, because we have only to select a different set of monoclinic axes, which are chosen arbitrarily, to change this into a lattice with opposite pairs of end faces centered.

In all it is found that 14 distinct types of lattice are possible which can be distinguished from one another. These are given, with their symmetry and their symbols, in Table II.

TABLE II

THE 14 BRAVAIS LATTICES

Triclinic	$\bar{1}$	P
Monoclinic	$2/m$	P, $[ABC]$
Orthorhombic	mmm	P, $[ABC]$, F, I
Tetragonal	$4/mmm$	P, I
Trigonal	$\bar{3}/m$	P
Hexagonal	$6/mmm$	P
Cubic	$m3m$	P, F, I

F. Space Groups

So far we have studied the symmetry of crystals as geometrical figures and have found an explanation for the 32 crystal classes that occur in nature. It is now necessary to deal with the symmetry properties of structures which are based on regular lattices. The lattice consists of an infinite number of regularly spaced identical units, typified by the lattice points. Hence if the structure contains, say, an axis of symmetry through a lattice point, then it must contain an infinite number of parallel axes.

Further, the structure can be brought into self-coincidence by another set of movements not yet considered, namely, by translations along the lattice directions. As the lattice units are by definition identical, such movements leave the structure unchanged. By combining reflections and rotations with translations we obtain certain new types of symmetry operation which are applicable to lattice structures and hence to crystals.

Two successive reflections in a plane, or two successive operations of a twofold axis, or three successive operations of a threefold axis, etc., bring a figure back to its original position; but a lattice may be brought back to its original position, or to a position one translation removed. This latter state is achieved if the twofold axis is a screw axis (symbol 2_1) i.e., a rotation of π accompanied by a translation equal to half the primitive translation of the lattice. A rotation of 2π then brings the structure to self-coincidence in a position one translation removed, while a rotation of π brings it to a position which cannot be distinguished from this or from its original position. Similarly we have the screw axes 3_1, 3_2; 4_1, 4_2, 4_3; 6_1, 6_2, 6_3, 6_4, 6_5. In general, the symbol p_q means a rotation of $2\pi/p$ accompanied by a translation of q/p.

The corresponding operation of reflection is a glide plane, which denotes reflection in a plane accompanied by a half translation in some direction. The symbol used for the glide plane, a, b, c, n, or d, depends on the direction of the translation which may be $a/2$, $b/2$, $c/2$, a half diagonal translation, or a quarter diagonal translation, this last case arising with centered lattices.

The number of possible symmetry operations is thus greatly increased, although the axes are of course still limited to 2-, 3-, 4-, or 6-fold types, either pure rotation or screw. All the operations which can be present again must form a self-consistent set, or a group in the mathematical sense. However, these are now infinite, although discontinuous, groups, and there is no unique point or origin. They are therefore termed space groups. The investigation of all the possibilities is a lengthy mathematical operation, which was accomplished between 1885 and 1894 independently by Fedorov, Schoenflies, and Barlow, who found that there are 230 distinct space groups, to one or other of which every crystal must conform. It is an interesting thought that at that time there must have seemed no possibility of ever discovering the physical existence of a screw axis or glide plane or finding to which space group a crystal belonged. The whole matter was one of abstract theory with no obvious practical application. Yet today the derivation of the space group is the first practical task which the crystal analyst now undertakes.

Table III gives a complete list of the 230 space groups in the older Schoenflies notation and also in the modern Hermann-Mauguin notation which specifies the essential but not, of course, all the symmetry elements present. The capital letter at the beginning of the Hermann-Mauguin symbol specifies the type of Bravais lattice present. Diagrams illustrating the distribution of symmetry elements in the space groups, the coordinates of the equivalent positions, and a great deal of other practical data concerning them are given in the International Tables for the Determination of Crystal Structure (17).

III. DEPARTURES FROM THE CLASSICAL LATTICE

A. Dislocations

Since we have now discussed the general theory of the ideal crystal structure, it is important to point out immediately that such crystals seldom, if ever, exist in nature. Soon after the discovery of x-ray diffraction a quantitative study of the intensities of the reflections (which is discussed in a later section) showed that in most crystals the perfect

TABLE III

THE 230 SPACE GROUPS[a]

(The eleven classes of distinct Laue symmetry are separated by double rulings.)

System	Point groups		Space groups						
	Schfl.	H.-M.							
Triclinic	C_1	1	$P1$						
	C_i	$\bar{1}$	$P\bar{1}$						
Monoclinic	$C_2^{(1-3)}$	2	$P2$	$P2_1$	$C2$				
	$C_s^{(1-4)}$	m	Pm	Pc	Cm	Cc			
	$C_{2h}^{(1-6)}$	$2/m$	$P2/m$	$P2_1/m$	$C2/m$	$P2/c$	$P2_1/c$	$C2/c$	
Orthorhombic	$D_2^{(1-9)}$	222	$P222$ $I222$	$P222_1$ $I2_12_12_1$	$P2_12_12$	$P2_12_12_1$	$C222_1$	$C222$	$F222$
	$C_{2v}^{(1-22)}$	$mm2$	$Pmm2$ $Pba2$ $Abm2$ $Ima2$	$Pmc2_1$ $Pna2_1$ $Ama2$	$Pcc2$ $Pnn2$ $Aba2$	$Pma2$ $Cmm2$ $Fmm2$	$Pca2_1$ $Cmc2_1$ $Fdd2$	$Pnc2$ $Ccc2$ $Imm2$	$Pmn2_1$ $Amm2$ $Iba2$
	$D_{2h}^{(1-28)}$	mmm	$Pmmm$ $Pcca$ $Pbca$ $Ccca$	$Pnnn$ $Pbam$ $Pnma$ $Fmmm$	$Pccm$ $Pccn$ $Cmcm$ $Fddd$	$Pban$ $Pbcm$ $Cmca$ $Immm$	$Pmma$ $Pnnm$ $Cmmm$ $Ibam$	$Pnna$ $Pmmn$ $Cccm$ $Ibca$	$Pmna$ $Pbcn$ $Cmma$ $Imma$

TABLE III—*Continued*

System	Point groups		Space groups						
	Schfl.	**H.-M.**							
Tetragonal	$C_4^{(1-6)}$	4	$P4$	$P4_1$	$P4_2$	$P4_3$	$I4$	$I4_1$	
	$S_4^{(1-2)}$	$\bar{4}$	$P\bar{4}$	$I\bar{4}$					
	$C_{4h}^{(1-6)}$	$4/m$	$P4/m$	$P4_2/m$	$P4/n$	$P4_2/n$	$I4/m$	$I4_1/a$	
	$D_4^{(1-10)}$	422	$P422$ $P4_32_12$	$P42_12$ $I422$	$P4_122$ $I4_122$	$P4_12_12$	$P4_222$	$P4_22_12$	$P4_322$
	$C_{4v}^{(1-12)}$	$4mm$	$P4mm$ $P4_2bc$	$P4bm$ $I4mm$	$P4_2cm$ $I4cm$	$P4_2nm$ $I4_1md$	$P4cc$ $I4_1cd$	$P4nc$	$P4_2mc$
	$D_{2d}^{(1-12)}$	$\bar{4}2m$	$P\bar{4}2m$ $P\bar{4}n2$	$P\bar{4}2c$ $I\bar{4}m2$	$P\bar{4}2_1m$ $I\bar{4}c2$	$P\bar{4}2_1c$ $I\bar{4}2m$	$P\bar{4}m2$ $I\bar{4}2d$	$P\bar{4}c2$	$P\bar{4}b2$
	$D_{4h}^{(1-20)}$	$4/mmm$	$P4/mmm$ $P4/ncc$ $P4_2/nmc$	$P4/mcc$ $P4_2/mmc$ $P4_2/ncm$	$P4/nbm$ $P4_2/mcm$ $I4/mmm$	$P4/nnc$ $P4_2/nbc$ $I4/mcm$	$P4/mbm$ $P4_2/nnm$ $I4_1/amd$	$P4/mmc$ $P4_2/mbc$ $I4_1/acd$	$P4/nmm$ $P4_2/mnm$
Trigonal	$C_3^{(1-4)}$	3	$P3$	$P3_1$	$P3_2$	$R3$			
	$C_{3i}^{(1-2)}$	$\bar{3}$	$P\bar{3}$	$R\bar{3}$					
	$D_3^{(1-7)}$	32	$P312$	$P321$	$P3_112$	$P3_121$	$P3_212$	$P3_221$	$R32$
	$C_{3v}^{(1-6)}$	$3m$	$P3m1$	$P31m$	$P3c1$	$P31c$	$R3m$	$R3c$	
	$D_{3d}^{(1-6)}$	$\bar{3}m$	$P\bar{3}1m$	$P\bar{3}1c$	$P\bar{3}m1$	$P\bar{3}c1$	$R\bar{3}m$	$R\bar{3}c$	

System								
Hexagonal	$C_6^{(1-6)}$	6	$P6$	$P6_1$	$P6_5$	$P6_2$	$P6_4$	$P6_3$
	$C_{3h}^{(1)}$	$\bar{6}$	$P\bar{6}$					
	$C_{6h}^{(1-2)}$	$6/m$	$P6/m$	$P6_3/m$				
	$D_6^{(1-6)}$	622	$P622$	$P6_122$	$P6_522$	$P6_222$	$P6_422$	$P6_322$
	$C_{6v}^{(1-4)}$	$6mm$	$P6mm$	$P6cc$	$P6_3cm$	$P6_3mc$		
	$D_{3h}^{(1-4)}$	$\bar{6}m2$	$P\bar{6}m2$	$P\bar{6}c2$	$P\bar{6}2m$	$P\bar{6}2c$		
	$D_{6h}^{(1-4)}$	$6/mmm$	$P6/mmm$	$P6/mcc$	$P6_3/mcm$	$P6_3/mmc$		
Cubic	$T^{(1-5)}$	23	$P23$	$F23$	$I23$	$P2_13$	$I2_13$	
	$T_h^{(1-7)}$	$m3$	$Pm3$	$Pn3$	$Fm3$	$Fd3$	$Im3$	$Pa3$	$Ia3$
	$O^{(1-8)}$	432	$P432$ / $I4_132$	$P4_232$	$F432$	$F4_132$	$I432$	$P4_332$	$P4_132$
	$T_d^{(1-6)}$	$\bar{4}3m$	$P\bar{4}3m$	$F\bar{4}3m$	$I\bar{4}3m$	$P\bar{4}3n$	$F\bar{4}3c$	$I\bar{4}3d$	
	$O_h^{(1-10)}$	$m3m$	$Pm3m$ / $Fd3c$	$Pn3n$ / $Im3m$	$Pm3n$ / $Ia3d$	$Pn3m$	$Fm3m$	$Fm3c$	$Fd3m$

lattice could extend only over very small regions before being interrupted in some way. To explain the observed intensities Darwin (9) introduced the concept of the ideally imperfect crystal consisting of a mosaic of small blocks "each block a perfect crystal, but the adjacent blocks not accurately fitted together."

The real nature of crystal imperfections, however, was not elucidated until much later. The mechanical properties of crystals, the ease with which they can be deformed, and the study of such phenomena as plastic deformation, especially of metals, has led to the recognition of *dislocations* of various types, where the perfection of the lattice is interrupted. The discovery of dislocations has explained many phenomena and has provided an important mechanism for the understanding of crystal growth. Recently, very direct evidence of the existence of dislocations has been provided in the electron microscope studies of long chain compounds by Dawson (10) and especially in the very beautiful direct photographs of the lattice in platinum phthalocyanine and other crystals by Menter (18), where the interruption of the regular lattice planes by the insertion of an additional row of molecules can be clearly seen and measured at a magnification of about 1,500,000 times.

Dislocations are of two basic types, although intermediate varieties and combinations of these types are known to exist. The first type is known as the *edge dislocation*, or Taylor-Orowan dislocation. Here the edge referred to is the edge of an additional lattice plane that has been inserted part way into the crystal, as at A in Fig. 3, distorting the regular-

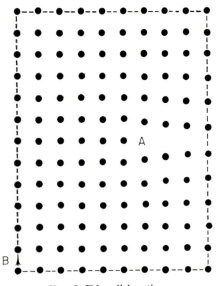

Fig. 3. Edge dislocation.

ity of the immediately surrounding lattice. Each of the lattice points (atoms or molecules) on this edge, as at A, is faced by a gap instead of an adjacent lattice point, and so has a smaller immediate coordination number.

The dislocation edge or line is vertical at A, and if we trace a loop or circuit around it and at some distance from it (the dotted boundary of the diagram) this circuit will close at B, but it contains one lattice translation less than a corresponding circuit in an undistorted perfect lattice. The vector translation closing the gap, and indicated by the small arrow

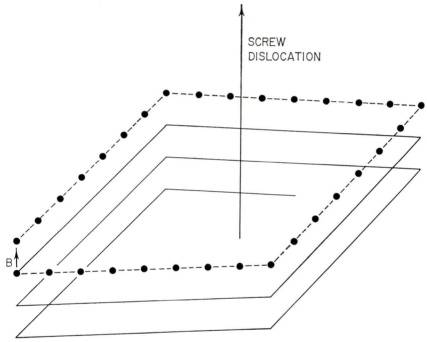

FIG. 4. Screw dislocation.

at B, is called the Buergers vector, and its direction is *perpendicular* to the direction of the dislocation line or edge. This construction provides a convenient method for specifying the nature of the dislocation.

The second basic type of dislocation is known as a *screw dislocation* or Buergers dislocation, and here there is no abrupt termination of a lattice plane, and there is no change in the number of coordinating points around those on the dislocation axis, but merely a distortion in their mean positions. If we imagine a section as in Fig. 3 of a now regular three-dimensional lattice we may suppose that successive points on a circuit around the axis are displaced slightly downwards, so that the loop fails to close. A helical arrangement like the thread of a screw will result (Fig. 4) and the Buergers vector required to close the circuit (arrow) will have a vertical direction, *parallel* to the screw dislocation axis. This type of dislocation is of widespread occurrence and is of particular importance in explaining the phenomenon of crystal growth, as the work of Frank (*13*) and others has shown. The point of emergence of a screw dislocation on a crystal face provides a step which is the edge of a lattice layer and to which new molecules can be added. This step is indestructible, and as growth continues the advancing edge lags behind as the distance from the screw axis increases, and so it winds itself into a spiral pattern which can often be seen on crystal faces viewed under a high power microscope.

Other more major types of discontinuity and various kinds of stacking faults can occur in crystals. Evidence concerning such disorder is sometimes found on x-ray diffraction photographs when the reflections become diffuse and may be drawn out into streaks instead of sharp spots, due to the interruption of the regular periodicity.

B. Point Defects

Another and very important class of imperfections known as *point defects* occurs on an atomic or molecular scale, where the region of disturbance is localized about an individual lattice position. The existence of properties such as electrolytic conductivity and diffusion requires explanations of this kind, with the possibility of the creation of vacancies in the lattice. Non-stoichiometry in crystals can also be associated with lattice vacancies of various kinds.

There are at least three well recognized types of process by which lattice vacancies can be formed. These will be considered for simple ionic arrays as in Fig. 5, but similar situations can occur in other kinds of crystal.

One possible mode is by the displacement of an ion from its lattice position to an interstitial position. This is known as the Frenkel (*14*) defect, and is shown in Fig. 6. A second possibility, proposed by Schottky (*27*), is that ions may be removed from their normal positions to new

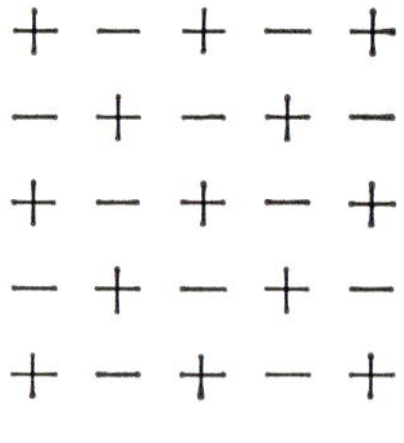

FIG. 5. Perfect ionic crystal.

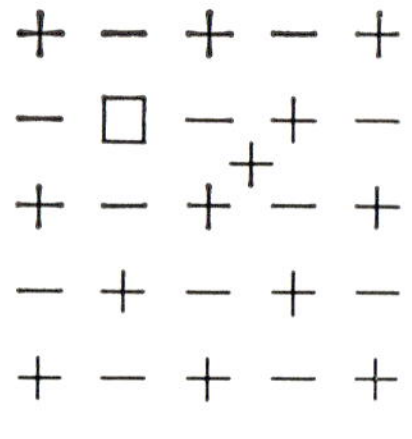

FIG. 6. Frenkel defect.

positions on an external or internal surface boundary, as indicated in Fig. 7. As over-all electrical neutrality must be maintained, the number of positive and negative ion vacancies produced in these ways must be equal.

The Frenkel and Schottky defects are intrinsic lattice defects which will be present in any pure ionic crystal above $0°K$. The concentration of these defects depends on temperature, and a theoretical thermodynamic treatment is given in Chapter 2, Section IV, B and in reference (30). For example, in the NaCl crystal at room temperature there will be on the average about one Schottky defect for each 10^{16} ions. Although in general both types of defect occur, the respective energies for formation are usually sufficiently different in any given crystal to make one type predominate over the other. Thus, the Frenkel defects are more probable

FIG. 7. Schottky defect.   FIG. 8. Vacancy caused by impurity.

in the silver halides, and the Schottky defects more probable in the alkali halides.

A third important type of defect is that caused by the presence of foreign ions in normal lattice positions in a crystal. The presence of an impurity ion with a different charge will lead to the production of vacancies in order that the crystal may remain electrically neutral. For example, the presence of a divalent metal ion in a sodium chloride crystal will cause an extra positive ion vacancy as shown in Fig. 8 if electrical neutrality is to be maintained.

When a vacancy is created in a crystal, it obviously requires very little energy for a neighboring ion to shift from its proper position into the vacancy. The process of ionic transport in crystals can be explained on this basis, and the model can also account for the phenomena attributed to *color centers* which have been observed in many crystals. These are discussed in Chapter 2, Sections IV, C and V, A, and in Chapter 5, Section II.

C. Non-Stoichiometry

Point defects of the kind we have described can be responsible for non-stoichiometry, but for significant departures from stoichiometry the concentration of the defects must be large compared to those of the inherent Frenkel and Schottky thermal defects considered above.

In a binary compound BX, if there are lattice vacancies for the component B but not for X, or vice versa, it is clear that non-stoichiometry will result. Non-stoichiometry will also occur where both types of vacancies are present and one may be in excess of the other. The same will also be true if interstitial positions are preferentially occupied by one of the components.

In ionic crystals, however, it is impossible for this simple situation to exist. If there is an excess of cations, for example, the whole crystal will

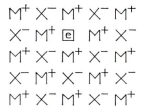

FIG. 9. Excess metal with anion vacancy.

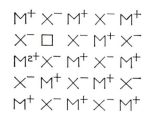

FIG. 10 Excess nonmetal with cation vacancy.

be positively charged. Non-stoichiometry may still occur, however, if with any excess of cations there is a corresponding excess of electrons trapped within the crystal, or with an excess of anions a corresponding deficit of electrons. To achieve non-stoichiometry in ionic crystals a mechanism for dealing with an excess or deficit of electrons is necessary.

Figure 9, for example, shows a structure with an excess of metal and with electrical neutrality preserved by an electron being trapped at the anion vacancy, or somewhere in the environment of the surrounding cations. Similarly, in Fig. 10, there is an excess of nonmetal because of vacant cation sites, and in this case the electrical neutrality is maintained by an extra positive charge on a cation adjacent to the vacant site. When the excess of one component is located in an interstitial position in the lattice, similar methods of preserving electrical neutrality may apply. Examples of all these types of non-stoichiometry are known, some of which are discussed in the following chapters.

IV. X-RAY DIFFRACTION

A. Laue and Bragg Equations

Diffraction effects in crystals arise when the x-ray waves scattered by successive layers of atoms reinforce each other according to the usual principles of optional interference. The study is thus a branch of optics, with the regularly spaced atoms of the crystal lattice acting as a three-dimensional diffraction grating. At the time of the original discovery in 1912 von Laue set out quite fully the conditions for diffraction in the equations

$$a (\cos \alpha_0 - \cos \alpha) = n_1\lambda$$

$$b (\cos \beta_0 - \cos \beta) = n_2\lambda \tag{2}$$

$$c (\cos \gamma_0 - \cos \gamma) = n_3\lambda$$

a, b, and c are the lattice translations, while α_0, β_0, γ_0, and α, β, γ are the angles which the incident and diffracted beams make with these directions, the condition stated in the equations being that the path difference between waves scattered from successive points should equal a whole number of wavelengths, $n\lambda$.

In the original Laue experiments the crystal was stationary and the direction of the incident beam fixed. Each crystal plane then gives rise to a diffracted beam because, from the continuous range of wavelengths present in the general radiation, there will always be one of length to suit the spacing of each particular plane. The result is the well known Laue photograph, where the array of spots often reveals in a beautiful way the symmetry of the crystal. Although detailed interpretation is possible, this method is not in general very suitable for crystal structure analysis.

The idea of obtaining *reflections* from crystal planes, using homogeneous or monochromatic x-rays and turning the crystal slowly through the appropriate angle for each plane, was evolved by the work of W. L. and W. H. Bragg. They gave the very simple Bragg law

$$n\lambda = 2d \sin \theta \tag{3}$$

where d is the spacing of the plane in question and θ the angle of incidence and angle of reflection of the x-ray beam. It is not difficult to show that this relation is equivalent to the Laue conditions. The use of monochromatic rays and this simple relation leads to a variety of elegant experimental methods which are invaluable in the determination of crystal structures.

B. Experimental Methods

A monochromatic x-ray beam incident on a crystal at X (Fig. 11) will not in general give rise to any reflection. But if the crystal is rotated until a particular plane, of spacing d, makes an angle θ ($= \sin^{-1}\lambda/2d$) with the incident beam, then a reflection will occur at angle 2θ and this diffracted ray may be recorded on an ionization chamber or Geiger counter, as in Fig. 11a or on a photographic film surrounding the crystal, as in Fig. 11b. If the crystal continues to rotate, other planes will come into their reflecting positions and the complete diffraction pattern will be recorded.

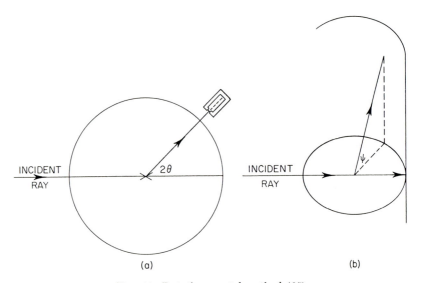

(a)   (b)

FIG. 11. Rotating crystal method (25).

If the crystal is rotated about some prominent zone axis, a characteristic pattern of spots is obtained, known as a *rotation photograph*. All those planes parallel to the rotation axis will give a line of spots on the equator, known as the *equatorial layer line*, and their spacings can be determined by measuring the distances of these spots from the origin (where the direct beam hits the film) which gives 2θ.

A number of higher layer lines generally appear on the photograph, these being the reflections from planes that are inclined at definite angles to the rotation axis. For example, if the crystal is rotated about the a lattice direction, the equatorial layer line consists of the $(0kl)$ reflections, the first and higher layer lines then being due to the $(1kl)$, $(2kl)$, $(3kl)$ reflections, and so on. The distances between these layer lines give a direct measure of the fundamental lattice translation a. This can be seen by considering the Laue equation for diffraction from a row of points of periodicity a, with the incident beam normal to the row. In the equation

$$a (\cos \alpha_0 - \cos \alpha) = n\lambda$$

α_0 is now $90°$ and the angle which the diffracted beam makes with the row (see Fig. 11b) is $(90 - \psi)°$. The equation becomes

$$a \sin \psi = n\lambda \tag{4}$$

ψ being the angle subtended from the crystal to the nth layer line.

The great importance of the rotation photograph is that it can be used in this way to measure the true lattice periodicities. The measurement of spacings, although more convenient and more accurate, does not necessarily give this information. For example, the spacing of the (100) plane may very often give $a/2$ or $a/4$ owing to a centered lattice, or the presence of glide planes or screw axes. But the rotation photograph is unequivocal.

For a moderately complex crystal the rotation photograph may contain many hundreds or even thousands of spots, and their separate identification presents a difficulty. This can be overcome by taking *oscillation photographs*, where the crystal is oscillated to and fro over a few degrees instead of being completely rotated. The small number of planes that now come into a reflecting position produce a few widely separated spots that can be easily identified. An even more useful method is that of the moving film, or *Weissenberg photograph*. Here the film is moved slowly parallel to the rotation axis while the crystal is rotated. The movements are synchronized, so that the angular setting of the crystal for each reflection can be read off from the position of the spot on the film. A separate exposure is given for each layer line, the unwanted reflections being cut off by a screen as shown in Fig. 12.

C. The Reciprocal Lattice

By these various means the diffracted beams can be recorded and indices assigned to all the reflections. The detailed analytical and graphical methods employed for doing this cannot be described here, but it may be mentioned that the work is greatly simplified by employing the concept of the *reciprocal lattice* (*12*). It is difficult to visualize the complex intersecting array of planes which can be drawn in a crystal lattice and it is much easier to deal with the plane normals rather than the planes themselves. If we choose a lattice point as origin and from this origin draw

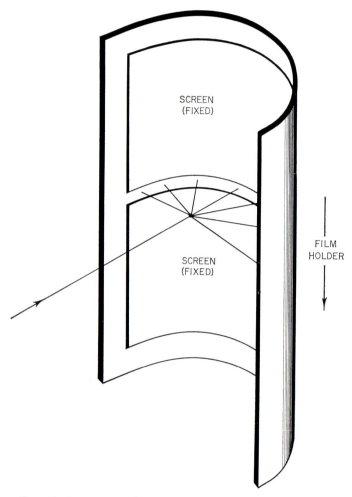

SCREEN
(FIXED)

SCREEN
(FIXED)

FILM
HOLDER

Fig. 12. Arrangement for taking moving film photographs (25).

a normal to each plane, then we may represent each plane by a point on its normal at a distance ρ from the origin which is the reciprocal of the Bragg spacing. It is convenient to introduce the wavelength as a constant in this construction, so that

$$\rho = \lambda/d = 2 \sin \theta \tag{5}$$

The array of points generated in this way is found to form a new lattice which is called the reciprocal lattice. By means of this construction, diffraction phenomena can be interpreted in a simple geometrical way. For example, it is clear that the maximum value of ρ is 2 (when $\theta = 90°$) and all the planes which can give reflections must lie on the reciprocal lattice within a sphere of this radius, which is called the *limiting sphere*.

The spots on an x-ray photograph themselves form a kind of distorted reciprocal lattice, those furthest from the origin having the smallest spacings. By oscillating the crystal and simultaneously moving the film holder in certain modified ways in an apparatus known as a *precession goniometer*, one can obtain completely undistorted pictures of various levels in the reciprocal lattice. From these pictures the crystallographic constants may be measured and the reflections indexed directly.

D. Space Group Determination

When the unit cell has been measured and all the reflections indexed, it is possible to complete the first stage of structure analysis by determining the space group to which the crystal belongs. An examination of the recorded spectra will generally show that certain sets of reflections are systematically absent. These absences, or halvings as they are called, are of three main kinds. First there may be systematic halvings in the general hkl reflections due to the lattice being body-centered or face-centered. The spectra are then absent when $h + k + l$ is odd, or when $h + k$ is odd, because the odd index planes are interleaved with identical scattering units, as indicated in Fig. 13.

Next, there may be halvings in certain zones of reflections due to the presence of glide planes. Thus, all the $hk0$ reflections may be absent when $h + k$ is odd, because a glide plane n, for example, will produce a molecule in the center which is identical *in projection* with the corner molecules,

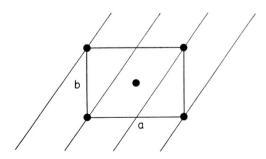

FIG. 13. General halving due to centered lattice (25).

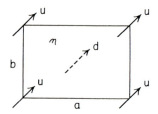

Fig. 14. Zonal halving due to glide plane (25).

as shown in Fig. 14. If the standard molecules at the corners are pointing up, the reflected molecule in the center, due to the operation of the glide plane parallel to the plane of the paper, will be pointing down; but in this projection, and in this projection only, these are identical.

Finally, the odd orders of reflection from a certain plane, such as 100, may be systematically absent. This axial halving is due to a screw axis, e.g., 2_1, and is illustrated in Fig. 15. In this case the operation of the two-fold screw axis produces a rotated molecule displaced half-way along a, and in projection on the a axis this rotated molecule is identical with the standard molecules. This identity applies only to this line projection, and so only the orders of the 100 reflections are affected, the observed reflections being 200, 400, 600, etc. Other screw axes, such as 3_1 or 4_1, will leave only every third order or every fourth order, and so on.

We see, therefore, that systematic absences in the x-ray spectra enable us to detect the presence of those symmetry elements which are peculiar to lattice structures, the glide plane, and screw axis. From this information the space group may be determined, and the absent spectra which occur in each space group have been systematically classified in the International Tables for X-Ray Crystallography (17). Unfortunately, space group determination based on absent spectra is very often not unique. In particular, it is usually necessary to decide by some other means (morphology, statistical tests, etc.) to which crystal class, or point group, the

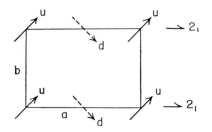

Fig. 15. Axial halving due to screw axis, 2_1 (25).

crystal belongs. If doubt remains it is generally the best policy to assume the lowest possible symmetry. Any higher symmetry is then likely to emerge as the analysis proceeds.

It is an interesting thought that in the days of classical crystallography, before the discovery of x-ray diffraction, the only elements of symmetry that could be observed from morphological studies were those involving pure reflection planes and pure rotation axes, and these were often uncertain. Now, from a study of the x-ray spectra we get direct positive evidence concerning the glide planes and screw axes, but none concerning pure reflections and pure rotations, as far as the systematically absent spectra are concerned.

E. Powder Photographs

The methods so far described assume that single crystals of the substance are available so that all the possible x-ray reflections may be examined individually. Sometimes, however, a substance may be crystalline yet the separate crystals of which it is composed are only of microscopic or even submicroscopic dimensions. Metals and alloys, for example, often belong to this class and it may be extremely difficult or impossible to obtain single crystals.

For dealing with powders a powerful and simple method is available, which was first devised by Debye, et al. (11). A monochromatic x-ray beam is passed through the powder specimen, which may be contained in a fine thin walled tube, or attached by adhesive to a fine hair or glass fiber. As the specimen consists of many thousands of minute crystals, randomly oriented, there will always be a number correctly set with respect to the direction of the beam to give a reflection from every plane. But instead of a single spot on the plate or film for every reflection there will now be a complete line or ring of minute microscopic spots for each reflection. The distance of the line or ring from the center will of course give 2θ, and hence d for every plane.

Unfortunately these lines will often overlap, especially for complex structures of low symmetry, and this is the chief limitation of the method. In the general case it will often happen that planes of quite different indices and orientation will have the same, or very nearly the same, spacings, and so they cannot be separately observed in the powder photograph. In the cubic, hexagonal, trigonal, and tetragonal system it is possible to index the lines systematically by various graphical methods, and determine the dimensions of the unit cell. Even in these cases, however, the reflections from a number of crystallographically distinct planes will coincide on the same powder line and it is not possible to estimate their separate intensities. For systems of lower symmetry it is very difficult even to determine the dimensions of the unit cell unequivocally unless some other data are available.

These limitations usually prevent any really detailed structure determination if only a powder photograph is available. However, for purposes of characterization and identification, and for the accurate measurement of spacings, the method is extremely valuable.

F. Superlattices and Solid Solutions

Reference has already been made to cases where equivalent sites within a crystal may be occupied indiscriminately by different kinds of atoms. In organic crystals the difference between a substituent chlorine or bromine atom in a molecule, or between a chlorine atom and a methyl group, may not be significant from the point of view of packing, and a random arrangement may occur. Solid solution formation is also common with both organic and inorganic substances when the structures of the pure substances are closely analogous, as in the case of potassium and ammonium sulfates.

With metals and alloys the replacement of one atom by another is still more easily effected as no strong electrostatic effects are involved. If the atoms are of comparable size, as in the case of copper and gold, substitutional solid solutions of any composition can be formed. Such alloys, however, can be obtained only by quenching from a high temperature. If, on the other hand, the alloy is cooled slowly, or annealed at a suitable temperature, the atoms will sort themselves out to form a more regular arrangement, which is generally characterized by the appearance of additional lines or reflections on the x-ray diffraction pattern. In alloy systems these more highly ordered structures which are obtained from solid solutions by annealing are called *superlattices*.

In the copper gold system (*31*), for example, the random or disordered high temperature structure is face-centered cubic with four atoms to the unit cell and from the x-ray evidence all the atoms appear identical. This means that the lattice points are occupied indiscriminately by the two types of atom. When ordering occurs, however, and the superlattice is formed, the lattice is primitive, the corners of the cube being occupied by gold and the face centers by copper, forming the alloy Cu_3Au. Additional lines appear on the diffraction pattern because there are no longer any systematic absences or halvings. In the general case, as the name implies, the superlattice will comprise a larger and more complex ordered arrangement with every atom in a uniquely defined position.

Another class of structure arises when two kinds of atom of very markedly different size are present, as in compounds of boron, carbon, etc., with various heavy metals. In these cases, instead of the substitutional solid solutions discussed above, *interstitial* solid solutions may be formed where the atoms of the solute element are incorporated between the atoms of the main constituent, and various non-stoichiometric possibilities arise.

V. STRUCTURE DETERMINATION

A. The Intensity of X-Ray Reflections

So far we have assumed that x-rays are scattered in a uniform manner by each lattice point, and that reinforcement of the waves by the principles of optical interference produces diffracted beams in certain directions as the crystal is turned through the appropriate reflecting angles. If the planes are interleaved midway by identical lattice points, then cancellation occurs and the reflection is absent. In this purely geometrical way, by measuring the positions of the spots on the film, and noting their presence or absence, the dimensions of the unit cell, the symmetry, and very often the space group can be deduced. If by chemical analysis and measurement of density it is then found that each lattice point, or perhaps the asymmetric crystal unit, corresponds to a single atom, the structure is completely solved.

However, this is very seldom the case. The repeating unit in the crystal is very rarely a single atom. It is usually a group of atoms, perhaps a molecule containing many atoms, or even a group of molecules. To find the positions of all the atoms then requires a more detailed analysis in which we must take account not only of the positions but also the intensities of all the x-ray reflections.

It is the electrons in the atom that are responsible for scattering x-rays, the small heavy nucleus having no significant effect. But as most of the bound electrons are highly concentrated at very small distances from the nucleus, the atom may for the present be regarded as the scattering source. Atoms lying on the crystal planes will scatter in phase for the Bragg reflection, the path difference for the contributing scattered waves being $2a \sin \theta = \lambda$ for the first order 100 reflection, or generally $2a \sin \theta = h\lambda$ for the $h00$ reflections. But if an atom lies at a distance x from the crystal plane the path difference for the wave from this atom, compared to that from the atom on the plane, will be $2x \sin \theta = hx\lambda/a$, the phase difference in angular measure for these waves being $2\pi hx/a$. This contribution being out of phase, the resultant amplitude will be reduced compared to what it would have been if the extra atom had been situated on the crystal plane.

Waves scattered by different kinds of atoms will have different amplitudes, which we may denote by f_1, f_2, $\cdots$. If there are now a number of atoms lying at various distances, x_1, x_2, $\cdots$ from the crystal plane, the phase differences of the contributed waves compared to the standard wave will be $2\pi h x_1/a$, $2\pi h x_2/a$, $\cdots$. These waves may be treated as vectors of amplitudes f_1, f_2, $\cdots$, and angles $2\pi h x_1/a$, $2\pi h x_2/a$, $\cdots$. The resultant wave, denoted by F and called the *structure factor*, is obtained by adding these vector quantities

$$F(h00) = \sum f_j \exp (2\pi i h x_j/a) \tag{6}$$

For the general plane hkl and atoms situated at $x_1 y_1 z_1$, $x_2 y_2 z_2$, $\cdots$ we have

$$F(hkl) = \sum f_j \exp [2\pi i (h x_j/a + k y_j/b + l z_j/c)] \tag{7}$$

The structure factor is thus a complex quantity, and it can be expressed as an amplitude $|F|$ and a phase constant α such that

$$|F(hkl)| = \sqrt{A^2 + B^2} \tag{8}$$

$$\alpha(hkl) = \tan^{-1} B/A \tag{9}$$

where

$$A = \sum f_j \cos 2\pi (h x_j/a + k y_j/b + l z_j/c) \tag{10}$$

$$B = \sum f_j \sin 2\pi (h x_j/a + k y_j/b + l z_j/c) \tag{11}$$

In each space group there are a number of symmetry related equivalent positions. The coordinates of these positions are given in the International Tables for X-Ray Crystallography (17). When the expression for the structure factor is summed over these positions, there is often some simplification, and the results of such summations for each of the 230 space groups are also given in the International Tables.

One common simplification which is quite frequently encountered may be noted. If the structure contains a center of symmetry and this is chosen as the origin for coordinates, then for every atom at x, y, z there is another at $-x$, $-y$, $-z$. The expression for B in the above relations therefore vanishes, and the phase angle α can have only the values 0 or π.

B. Scattering by Electrons, Atoms, and Crystals

If the positions of the atoms in a crystal are known or can be guessed, the structure amplitudes may be calculated by these formulas. These structure amplitudes are obviously related to the intensities, so any postulated structure can be immediately tested. However, the precise relation between the intensity and the structure amplitude, and the way it varies with the angle of reflection, the nature of the atoms and their thermal motion, and the state of perfection of the crystal, are complicated matters on which a great deal of detailed work has been carried out.

It can be shown from classical electromagnetic theory that the amplitude A of the wave scattered by a single electron is given by

$$A = A_0 e^2 / mrc^2 \tag{12}$$

at a distance r, where A_0 is the amplitude of the incident wave, with electric vector perpendicular to the plane of the incident and scattered rays. The fundamental constants have their usual meaning. For an extended electron cloud, represented by a probability function, the scattering can be treated as proportional to the density of the cloud at each point.

In an atom containing z electrons the scattered amplitude will be zA for zero or very small scattering angles, but this amplitude will decrease rapidly by interference as the scattering angle (2θ) increases. If the electrons could be given definite positions in the atoms the resultant amplitude could be calculated in the way described in the previous section. The actual scattering factor f will, however, depend on the average distribution of electrons in the atom, and these distributions can now be calculated with fair certainty by theoretical methods. From these distributions the atomic scattering factors, or f-curves, which decrease rapidly with angle, have been calculated and are tabulated for most atoms (17).

Another factor which causes a still further and sometimes rapid decrease in the scattering with increasing angle is thermal motion. It can easily be seen that this effectively increases the size of atom and so decreases the resultant amplitude still further by interference as the scattering angle increases. If f_0 is the scattering factor for the atom at rest, then the temperature corrected factor f can be written as

$$f = f_0 \exp\left[-B(\sin\theta/\lambda)^2\right] \tag{13}$$

where B is known as the Debye factor. It can easily be shown that

$$B = 8\pi^2\bar{\mu}^2 \tag{14}$$

where $\bar{\mu}^2$ is the mean square displacement of the atom across the reflecting plane.

When a crystal structure has been solved and the mean positions of the atoms determined, the temperature factor and hence the state of thermal motion of each atom may be deduced by comparing the observed scattering factors (f-curves) with those deduced from the theoretical electron distributions.

Finally there is the problem of the quantitative relation between the intensity of reflection from a real crystal of finite size and the structure factor. Difficult calculations are involved, but the problem was solved very soon after the discovery of x-ray diffraction. When rotated in a monochromatic x-ray beam most crystals reflect over an appreciable angle which may vary from a few minutes of arc to a degree or more. What is called the integrated reflection can be defined as the quantity $E\omega/I_0$ where E is the total reflected energy, ω the angular velocity of rotation, and I_0 the intensity of the incident beam (energy per second per cm^2 at the crystal).

For a very small crystal of volume δV, for which absorption can be neglected, it can then be shown (9) that

$$\frac{E\omega}{I_0} = \left[N \frac{e^2}{mc^2} F(hkl) \right]^2 \lambda^3 \frac{1 + \cos^2 2\theta}{2 \sin 2\theta} \delta V \qquad (15)$$

N is the number of unit cells per unit volume of the crystal and the other constants have their usual meaning. The incident radiation is assumed to be unpolarized.

In theory this expression should hold only for extremely minute, almost submicroscopic crystals. For ordinary macroscopic crystals, if the lattice were perfect and uninterrupted, the theory shows that reflection should be total over a very narrow range of glancing angle, and that the integrated reflection should be proportional to the first power of the structure factor. In practice, however, Eq. (15) is found to hold (when allowance is made for absorption) for many comparatively large single crystals. From this it must follow, as first pointed out by Darwin (9) that for most real crystals the lattice is not perfect and uninterrupted throughout their whole volume. They must consist of some kind of conglomerate or mosaic of small regions which may themselves be perfect but which are not quite accurately fitted together. Modern views on crystal growth and direct studies with the electron microscope show that this early theoretical deduction is indeed true (10, 18).

C. The Structure Factor and Electron Density Distribution

We have now seen how the structure factor can be obtained from the observed intensities of the x-ray reflections, and also how it may be calculated from a knowledge of the atomic positions and their respective scattering factors (f), corrected for thermal motion. It is now desirable, however, to give a more comprehensive and simple definition of the structure factor in terms of the general electron distribution in the crystal, because this alone is responsible for all the x-ray scattering. We represent the density of electrons at any point in the crystal by $\rho(xyz)$, so that $\rho(xyz)dxdydz$ gives the number of electrons in the volume element $dxdydz$. Each volume element will make a contribution to the structure amplitude from the whole unit cell, and for the general plane hkl the phase change between the origin and the point xyz is $2\pi(hx/a + ky/b + lz/c)$ where a, b, and c are the sides of the unit cell whose volume is V. The total resultant structure factor is then given by

$$F(hkl) = \frac{V}{abc} \int_0^a \int_0^b \int_0^c \rho(xyz) \exp [2\pi i(hx/a + ky/b + lz/c)]dxdydz \quad (16)$$

The factor V/abc is included to take account of the case where the axes a, b, c are not orthogonal. The structure factor can thus be simply defined as the ratio of the amplitude given by the whole contents of the unit cell to that which would be given if these contents were replaced by a single classical electron. The units involved are numbers of electrons, and the zero term in the structure factor series, $F(000)$, is simply the total number of electrons (z) in the unit cell, because

$$F(000) = \frac{V}{abc} \int_0^a \int_0^b \int_0^c \rho(xyz)dxdydz = z \quad (17)$$

Now, in the determination of a crystal structure, the quantities that we can measure are the magnitudes of $F(hkl)$, but the quantity which we wish to calculate is $\rho(xyz)$. This can readily be done if we represent $\rho(xyz)$, which is of course a periodic function, by a Fourier series

$$\rho(xyz) = \sum_{-\infty}^{+\infty} \sum \sum A(pqr) \exp [2\pi i(px/a + qy/b + rz/c)]$$

where p, q, and r are integers and $A(pqr)$ is the coefficient of the general term. To find these coefficients we may now substitute this series for $\rho(xyz)$ in the expression for the structure factor (Eq. 16). On carrying out the integration it will be found that every term is zero except that for which $p = -h$, $q = -k$, and $r = -l$, which gives

$$F(hkl) = \frac{V}{abc} \int_0^a \int_0^b \int_0^c A(\bar{h}\bar{k}\bar{l})dxdydz = VA(\bar{h}\bar{k}\bar{l})$$

Hence

$$A(\bar{h}\bar{k}\bar{l}) = \frac{F(hkl)}{V} \tag{18}$$

and

$$\rho(xyz) = \sum \sum_{-\infty}^{+\infty} \sum \frac{F(hkl)}{V} \exp[-2\pi i(hx/a + ky/b + lz/c)] \tag{1}$$

We therefore obtain the very beautiful result that if the distribution of the scattering matter in the crystal is represented by a triple Fourier series, then the coefficients of the terms in this series are the structure factors of the crystal planes divided by the volume of the unit cell.

In Eq. (1) the quantity $F(hkl)$ is complex, consisting of an amplitude and a phase constant. For many purposes it is conveniently written in the form

$$\rho(xyz) = \sum \sum_{-\infty}^{+\infty} \sum \frac{|F(hkl)|}{V} \cos[2\pi hx/a + 2\pi ky/b + 2\pi lz/c - \alpha(hkl)] \tag{19}$$

where $|F(hkl)|$ is now the amplitude only, which can be measured, and $\alpha(hkl)$ is the associated phase constant. In this form these quantities have the same significance as in Eqs. (8) and (9).

D. The Phase Problem

1. STRUCTURE FACTOR RELATIONS

With the derivation of Eq. (1) it would now appear, as we have already stated in our introduction, that the problem of crystal structure determination is formally solved. The evaluation of this expression at every point in the unit cell is a lengthy process, but one which can now be conveniently programmed for electronic digital computers, or solved by some analog process. The measurement of $|F(hkl)|$, however, does not in general carry with it any information concerning the associated phase constant $\alpha(hkl)$. As the x-ray reflections occur at different times with the crystal in different positions, all information concerning the relative phase constants appears to be necessarily lost in making the experiment.

This phase problem has now been the subject of intensive study for many years. In the absence of any direct knowledge of the phase constants, a solution would at first sight appear to be impossible. Each different set of phase constants will lead to a different electron density distribution, and all these different distributions will explain the observed structure amplitudes. However, the *true* electron density distribution is one to which severe restrictions can be attached. It can never be negative, and it must consist of a number of well separated, almost spherically symmetrical maxima corresponding to the number and kind of atoms which are known to be present from elementary chemical analysis and density measurement.

Based on this criterion, a number of rather different approaches have been formulated. Some of the earliest were sets of inequality relations between the structure factors discovered by Harker and Kasper (15) which relate the phases of certain structure factors to the magnitudes and phases of others. Further developments have led to formulas of a statistical nature (16) and the development of a structure factor algebra (4). The formulas are complicated, but some progress has been made in programming such approaches for electronic computers (7). The success of such methods has in some cases been quite considerable, but if there are more than about a dozen unrelated atoms in general positions the possibility of applying these methods successfully is uncertain. With the development of much larger and faster computers, however, more progress may be made.

2. Patterson Vector Methods

One of the most powerful methods in crystal analysis was discovered at an early date by Patterson (20). It does not attempt to solve the phase problem directly, but shows in an elegant way all the information that can be obtained when we know only the magnitudes of the structure factors. If the squares of the structure factors are used as coefficients in a Fourier series

$$A(uvw) = \frac{1}{V^2} \sum \sum_{-\infty}^{+\infty} \sum F^2(hkl) \exp\left[-2\pi i(hu/a + kv/b + lw/c)\right] \quad (20)$$

it can then be shown that the peaks in the distribution $A(uvw)$ correspond not to atomic positions in the crystal but to interatomic distances defined by vectors whose components are (uvw). The picture obtained is a super-position of all the interatomic vectors in the crystal.

Such distributions are always centrosymmetrical, with a large peak at the origin expressing the fact that every atom is at zero distance from itself. The heights of the other peaks depend on the product of the scattering powers of the pairs of atoms concerned. If there are only a few heavy atoms in the structure, the vectors between them and hence the position of the atoms in the structure can readily be found.

Unfortunately, the number of vectors in a structure depends on the square of the number of atoms, and so in a complex structure containing many atoms it is generally impossible to resolve the separate vector peaks. The degree of resolution in any structure depends on the wavelength and on the number of observed reflections, and in general detail cannot be distinguished unless it is on a coarser scale than about

$$R = 0.6\lambda/2 \sin \theta_{max} \qquad (21)$$

where θ_{max} is the limiting glancing angle up to which spectra are measured. For $\lambda = 1.54$ Å (copper radiation) and $\theta_{max} = 90°$, this distance is about 0.5 Å. This means that if we know the phases, atoms can always be resolved in a three-dimensional analysis, because their true distances from each other are always considerably greater than 0.5 Å. But the vector peaks, whose number depends on the square of the number of atoms, will often be crowded together making individual resolution impossible.

Elaborate and systematic methods for analyzing Patterson vector maps have been devised (6) and a great deal of progress has been made. In fact the information that can be obtained from a three-dimensional Patterson vector analysis generally takes us about as far towards solving a structure as the various other statistical and probability methods already mentioned. But the difficulty goes up rapidly with the number of atoms present in unrelated general positions, and a solution is often not possible if this number exceeds about twelve atoms.

3. Heavy Atom and Isomorphous Replacement Methods

In spite of these limitations in the so-called direct methods of phase constant determination, many crystal structures containing molecules with up to 100 atoms in quite unknown chemical configurations have been successfully solved during the last 10 years. This has been achieved in almost every case by the application of what are known as the heavy atom (26) and isomorphous substitution methods (24). These methods are more chemical in nature than the other approaches we have described, but their effect is to provide direct knowledge of the unknown phases which cannot be measured and so in this sense they alone deserve to be called direct phase constant determining methods. These methods are correspondingly more powerful, and in fact there is no obvious limit to their application. Indeed, the structures of many complex protein molecules, containing thousands of atoms, are now being studied by these methods with a very considerable measure of success.

The problem before us is to determine the phase of the resultant wave which is scattered by the whole contents of the unit cell and for which we can measure only the amplitude. Now suppose that by some ingenious chemical experiment we are able to insert one more atom in the unit cell without disturbing, or greatly disturbing, the structure which is there already. If we choose a reference point or origin at the site of this new atom, its contribution will be positive ($\alpha = 0°$). Now if the wave which is scattered by the remainder of the unit cell is also positive, the two contributions will add and the total resultant amplitude will increase. If, however, the contribution from the remainder is negative ($\alpha = 180°$) there will be mutual cancellation between these two contributions, and the total resultant amplitude will decrease. By observing these amplitudes it is therefore possible to make deductions concerning the phases due to the unknown part of the structure.

In isomorphous replacement it will more often be a case of replacing one atom (A_1) by another (A_2). Let the remainder of the structure be represented by O. Then in the simple centrosymmetric case that we have considered, the contribution from O remains constant, and we have

$$F(A_1O) - F(A_2O) = F(A_1) - F(A_2) = \Delta F \qquad (22)$$

Here ΔF represents the difference in scattering power of the two replaceable atoms and this is known for each reflection. A knowledge of ΔF is then usually sufficient to determine the signs of $F(A_1O)$ and $F(A_2O)$ if their magnitudes can be accurately measured. A practical difficulty is the accurate determination of these amplitudes on an absolute scale.

In the case of noncentrosymmetric structures this equation still holds, but the quantities are vectors with the phase angle no longer restricted to 0° or 180°. The vector equation can be solved for the phase angles, but there remains an ambiguity of sign of the angle. This can be overcome in various ways, but the equations can be solved completely if a third isomorphous derivative is available.

With the heavy atom method only one derivative containing an atom of fairly high atomic number relative to the other atoms need be used. Halogen derivatives of organic compounds, or the heavy metal salts are often suitable. The position of the heavy atom or atoms can then be determined by a Patterson vector analysis, and their contributions to structure amplitudes calculated. If these contributions are considerable, as will generally be the case, then the phase angles due to the heavy atoms may be used in effecting a first Fourier synthesis. This will in general result in a rather badly resolved and distorted map of the structure, but usually one from which various powerful processes of successive approximation can begin.

In practice one is often surprised by the small amount of phase determination that is necessary in order to commence a structure determination. If only a few other atoms are resolved with certainty, these can then be included in the phasing calculations and better resolution is obtained in the next round of calculations. The successful application of the method, however, often requires a great deal of judgment and experience. If a false atom is included in the phasing calculations it will appear on the maps and its unreality is often difficult to detect. If the analysis goes wrong, sometimes a completely fresh start has to be made. It will be clear that in work of this kind, involving repeated lengthy three-dimensional Fourier syntheses and structure factor calculations, access to a fast electronic computer is usually essential.

Many difficulties and ambiguities can arise in this work, which will not be considered in detail here. These depend on the space group symmetry and the positions of the heavy atoms, and they frequently involve a false center of symmetry with duplication of every peak. Such difficulties can be overcome in most cases, but if they arise in the solution of an organic structure it is usually worthwhile to consider preparing a new derivative of the compound and making a fresh start. The chemical effort required for this is usually small compared with the effort required to resolve a difficult phase ambiguity; and from the new derivative just as valuable information concerning the structure of the parent compound can usually be obtained.

In certain molecular compounds and non-stoichiometric compounds of the clathrate type heavy atom methods should often be relatively easy to apply. The structures may be complex, involving a number of molecules, but there is no reason why they should not be completely solved.

4. ANOMALOUS DISPERSION

What is called a *phase lag* in scattering may be introduced by the use of a heavy atom which can itself be excited if the incident radiation is of a wavelength near the absorption edge of the atom concerned. This effect has been used to distinguish between the 111 and $\overline{1}\overline{1}\overline{1}$ reflections of the polar zinc blende crystal (8), and more recently has been employed extensively by Bijvoet (5) in determining the absolute configurations of various inorganic and organic compounds. This phase lag can be used to resolve the ambiguity of the sign of the phase angle to which we have already referred, and it is this which makes the determination of absolute configuration possible. The observed effects are generally quite small changes in the intensities of reflections which would otherwise be identical.

More recently the method has been further developed as a promising tool for the direct determination of the structures as well as the absolute configurations of noncentrosymmetrical crystals (*19*). It is perhaps too early as yet to assess the full potency of the method, but much important development work is in progress. Accurate methods for measuring intensities are required, but this is also being developed in the construction of single crystal photon-counting instruments.

VI. DIFFRACTION BY NEUTRONS AND ELECTRONS

A. Neutron Diffraction

1. PRINCIPLES

Neutron diffraction and electron diffraction are entirely different problems of different scope and with quite different limitations. But although the neutron and electron are commonly thought of as particles, both have wave properties and their wavelengths can be made comparable with the distances between atoms in crystals. Hence in both cases diffraction phenomena occur, of much the same general type as with x-rays and the same principles of optical interference apply. But the tools are different, and the kind of information which these tools are best adapted to provide is also different.

The neutron is a particle of approximately the same mass as the hydrogen atom, and when moving with a velocity v it can be described as a wave of length

$$\lambda = h/mv \qquad (23)$$

where h is Planck's constant and m the neutron mass. High energy neutrons such as those generated in nuclear reactors move with enormous velocities and have extremely short wavelengths. But it is fairly easy by arranging collisions with moderating material to slow these neutrons down to 'thermal' energy, and at 20°C this amounts to 0.03 ev. The wavelengths will then mostly lie in the range of from 1 to 2 Å, and they are therefore suitable for crystal diffraction studies.

It is indeed a fortunate circumstance that the wavelengths of thermal neutrons lie in the range that is just right for crystal diffraction work. But in contrast to x-rays there is no easy way of getting a truly monochromatic beam. A diffraction process, using a crystal as monochromator, is perhaps the easiest method, but even then owing to difficulties in collimation, a certain spread of wavelengths will be obtained. The outstanding difficulty in neutron diffraction work, however, is to obtain a beam of sufficient strength. The work can only be done at all in those places where a large and powerful atomic pile is available, with space to accommodate bulky shielding apparatus. Even then the beam finally obtained is very weak by x-ray standards, the number of neutrons per second passing through a given area being less by a factor of about 10^5 than the number of quanta from a standard x-ray tube (1). It follows that the crystal specimens employed in neutron diffraction work must usually be very large compared with those required for x-ray work, measuring perhaps inches instead of fractions of a millimeter. For single crystal work this imposes a severe difficulty, because although large single crystals can often be obtained from simple substances, yet in the case of many interesting and important compounds suitable specimens can be obtained only with great difficulty, if at all.

These various limitations mean that neutron diffraction will not be employed for any initial or routine measurement of crystals, and a thorough x-ray investigation will first be made in all cases. But neutron diffraction can supply a great deal of vital and important new information concerning the structure of crystals which cannot be obtained in any other way. To appreciate these special applications we must first consider briefly the process of neutron scattering.

In general this scattering is by the atomic nuclei, and as the order of size here is only about 10^{-12} cm, the atoms act as point scattering sources, with no fall-off in intensity with increasing angle of incidence. There is an important exception in the case of atoms of the transition elements and rare earths, which have a magnetic moment and where there is additional scattering due to the interaction of magnetic dipoles. This additional scattering does fall away in a complicated manner with increasing angle. For most of the elements, however, there is no such angular dependence. The normal scattering consists of two components. In the first, called "potential" scattering, the nucleus behaves as an impenetrable sphere whose radius increases only slowly with increasing atomic mass. The scattered amplitude therefore also increases only very slowly with increasing atomic weight.

Superimposed on this is a second process known as "resonance" scattering, which is due to the neutrons forming momentary combinations with the nuclei. This component of the scattering varies abruptly from element to element, and it may be of the same or opposite phase to that of the potential scattering, leading to abrupt increases or decreases in the total scattered amplitude as we pass from element to element. For a few elements, including the important case of hydrogen, the resultant amplitude is of opposite sign, and this is conventionally chosen as being negative for these few elements. One very striking fact is that the different isotopes of an element may sometimes have quite different scattering amplitudes due to different resonance scattering contributions. Ni^{58}, for example, has a scattering amplitude of $+1.44 \times 10^{-12}$ cm, while the value for Ni^{62} is -0.87×10^{-12} cm.

This behavior is in the most marked contrast to x-ray scattering, where there is a steady increase in scattering amplitude with increasing atomic number, and a very rapid decrease for every element as the scattering angle increases, owing to the spread of the electron cloud in the atom. The irregular variation of the neutron scattering amplitude with increasing atomic weight is shown in Fig. 16, where it is contrasted with the steady increase in x-ray scattering amplitude.

Another important aspect of the behavior of neutrons in crystal diffraction work is their extremely small absorption coefficient, which is generally hundreds of times less than for x-rays in the same material. This makes it easily possible to use the very large crystals that are required for neutron work, but at the same time it raises a difficulty. We have not dealt with the problem of *secondary extinction* in x-ray work. This is an apparent increase in absorption and decrease in reflected intensity due to the fact that for strong reflections some of the incident beam is reflected away and fails to reach the inner mosaic blocks of the crystal. In the x-ray case this is not usually very important if very small crystal specimens measuring only about 0.1 mm are employed. But for the large crystals used in neutron diffraction work it is of course very important, and very careful corrections for this effect must be attempted, although they are difficult to calculate.

2. APPLICATIONS

It will be clear from what has been said that one of the very important applications of neutron diffraction will be the location of light atoms, especially hydrogen, in crystal structures. It is true that hydrogen atoms can often be detected in accurate x-ray work, but only with difficulty and always with considerable uncertainty. With neutrons, however, the scattering amplitude for hydrogen, and especially for deuterium, is as large or larger than that for many heavy elements.

The location of hydrogen in hydrogen bonded structures has for long been a much discussed problem, which has now been solved in many cases by neutron diffraction work. Early studies of ice (*32*) showed that Pauling's structure with discrete water molecules but random hydrogen positions on the $O \cdots O$ bonds is correct. The central hydrogen in the $F \cdots H \cdots F$ bond in KHF_2 was established (*21*), and the hydrogen positions in KH_2PO_4 in the normal room temperature and in the ferro-electric state

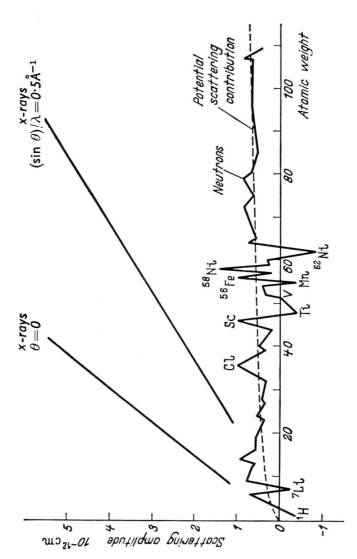

Fig. 16. Irregular variation of neutron scattering amplitude with atomic weight, compared with the steady increase for x-ray scattering (1).

were determined (*3*). A further very beautiful study of the hydrogen positions in the resorcinol crystal structure has been made by Bacon (*2*).

Another important application lies in the power of neutron diffraction to distinguish clearly between elements of closely similar atomic number. This occurs, for example, in the order-disorder study of certain alloys. In an ordered arrangement, superlattice lines can be detected, and this has been done for Ni_3Mn by neutron diffraction (*28*), whereas it is not possible by x-rays owing to the closely similar scattering power of manganese and nickel. Other examples are found in the study of *spinel* type structures where neutron diffraction can distinguish between magnesium and aluminium much more readily than x-rays can.

We have mentioned the additional scattering of a different kind which occurs when atoms have a magnetic moment. This magnetic scattering is complex, but there have already been important structural applications. For example, the antiferromagnetic structure of MnO at low temperature has been determined (*29*) and is characterized by the appearance of additional lines in the diffraction pattern due to *magnetic* reflections.

B. Electron Diffraction

The discovery of the wave nature of the electron was one of the very early triumphs of modern physics. Electrons of mass m and charge e accelerated by a potential V will have energy eV and a velocity v given by $eV = \frac{1}{2}mv^2$ or $v = (2eV/m)^{\frac{1}{2}}$. Equation (23) then becomes

$$\lambda = h/(2meV)^{\frac{1}{2}} \tag{24}$$

For an electron beam accelerated by a potential of the order of 40 kv, which is conveniently attained, the wavelength will be about 0.06 Å. This is shorter than the x-ray wavelengths usually employed in diffraction studies, but is still of the right order of magnitude.

Since the original discovery was made, electron beams have been extensively employed in gas or vapor phase diffraction studies, and also for direct imaging of small objects, and even in some cases large molecules and certain crystal lattices, in electron microscope work. These developments, however, are out of the scope of this article. In crystal diffraction studies most valuable results can be obtained, but the fully quantitative interpretation of the effects is surrounded by many difficulties and limitations which have hitherto tended to prevent any very widespread use of the method.

In some respects these limitations are precisely opposite to those of the neutron diffraction methods described above. The penetrating power of electrons is small, and a 50 kv electron beam can reach only about a hundred or so atomic planes before it is dissipated by inelastic scattering. This means that the method is very largely restricted to the study of surfaces or extremely small crystals. However, the elastic scattering, which gives rise to the diffraction effects, is extremely efficient, and is indeed greater by a factor of about 10^7 than the corresponding x-ray scattering. A considerable proportion of the incident energy thus appears in the diffracted beams.

As only extremely small crystals are effective, the type of diffraction pattern obtained generally consists of an array of spots which is known as a cross-grating pattern owing to its resemblance to the theoretical diffraction pattern from a two-dimensional grating. This pattern is usually a symmetry-true projection of a section of the reciprocal lattice. Its appearance can be explained in terms of Ewald's reciprocal lattice construction for diffraction conditions, where owing to the smallness of the crystal there is an effective spreading of the reciprocal lattice points in the direction of the smallest dimension of the crystal. This spreading, combined with the small wavelength generally employed, gives rise to an array of reflections corresponding to a near-plane sectioning of the reciprocal lattice.

Another feature of crystal electron diffraction patterns arises from the high efficiency of the scattering. Strong reflections coming from a few atomic planes may be rediffracted by underlying planes in another mosaic block of the same crystal, and this gives rise to many anomalous features consisting of extra spots or groups of spots, or rings in the case of polycrystalline material. This secondary scattering causes a modification of the intensities, but corrections for these effects can be calculated.

The early chemical applications of this method were mostly confined to the study of thin films, surface oxides, etc., and much valuable information concerning unit cell dimensions, crystal symmetry, and orientation was obtained which could not have been discovered in any other way. More complete structural investigations are obviously difficult owing to the complicating factors mentioned above, but considerable progress has recently been made. Efficient methods have been developed by Pinsker, Weinstein, and their colleagues (22) at the Institute of Crystallography of the Academy of Sciences of the U.S.S.R. in Moscow for dealing with polycrystalline materials, and later with single crystals. The use of single crystal data for structure analysis has been further and very fully developed by Cowley and Rees in the Chemical Physics Section of C.S.I.R.O. in Melbourne (23).

In this work Fourier methods have been employed and the results delineate potential distributions in molecules, either in the form of two-dimensional projections or three-dimensional sections. The difficulty of making accurate intensity measurements is greater than in x-ray analysis and for reliable results careful corrections for secondary scattering must be made. There is also more uncertainty regarding the form of the atom scattering curves for electrons. From the work that has been done, however, it is clear that electron diffraction is much more powerful than x-ray diffraction for the detection of light atoms in the presence of heavy atoms, for example, hydrogen atoms in organic molecules, or carbon, oxygen, and nitrogen in compounds containing lead or platinum.

It will be recalled that neutron diffraction has precisely the same advantages to an even more striking degree, but electron diffraction methods can, and in fact must be applied to extremely small crystals. It is in the field of very small crystal work that the most important applications of the method are likely to be found. This may be the only way to detect particular types of defect or even structural modifications that are closely related to crystalline size and which are completely obscured in the averaging processes that necessarily apply to x-ray or neutron diffraction studies of macroscopic single crystals.

REFERENCES

1. Bacon, G. E., *Research* 7, 257 (1954); "Neutron Diffraction," Oxford Univ. Press, London and New York, 1955.
2. Bacon, G. E., and Curry, N. A., *Proc. Roy. Soc.* A235, 552 (1956).
3. Bacon, G. E., and Pease, R. S., *Proc. Roy. Soc.* A220, 397 (1953); *Nature* 173, 443 (1954).
4. Bertaut, E. F., *in* "Computing Methods and the Phase Problem in X-Ray Crystal Analysis" (R. Pepinsky, J. M. Robertson, and J. C. Speakman, eds.), p. 202. Pergamon Press, New York, 1961.
5. Bijvoet, J. M., *Koninkl. Ned. Akad. Wetenschap.* 52, 313 (1949); Peerdeman, A. F., van Bommel, A. J., and Bijvoet, J. M., *ibid.* 54, 3 (1951).
6. Buerger, M. J., *Acta Cryst.* 3, 87 (1950).
7. Cochran, W., *in* "Computing Methods and the Phase Problem in X-Ray Crystal Analysis" (R. Pepinsky, J. M. Robertson, and J. C. Speakman, eds.), p. 218. Pergamon Press, New York, 1961; Woolfson, M. M., *ibid.* p. 220.
8. Coster, D., Knol, K. S., and Prins, J. A., *Z. Physik* 63, 345 (1930).
9. Darwin, C. G., *Phil. Mag.* [6] 27, 315, 675 (1914).
10. Dawson, I. M., and Vand, V., *Proc. Roy. Soc.* A206, 555 (1951).
11. Debye, P., and Scherrer, P., *Physik Z.* 17, 277 (1916); Hull, A. W., *Phys. Rev.* 10, 661 (1917); see also Peiser, H. S., Rooksby, H. P., and Wilson, A. J. C., "X-Ray Diffraction by Polycrystalline Materials." Institute of Physics, London, 1955.
12. Ewald, P. P., *Z. Krist.* 56, 148 (1921); Buerger, M. J., "X-Ray Crystallography." Wiley, New York, 1942.

13. Frank, F. C., *Discussions Faraday Soc.* **No. 5,** p. 48 (1949); Burton, W. K., Cabrera, N., and Frank, F. C., *Phil. Trans. Roy. Soc. (London)* **243,** 299 (1951); Frank, F. C., *Advances in Phys. (Phil. Mag. Suppl.)* **1,** 91 (1952).

14. Frenkel, J., *Z. Physik* **35,** 652 (1926).

15. Harker, D., and Kasper, J. S., *Acta Cryst.* **1,** 70 (1948).

16. Hauptman, H., and Karle, J., "Solution of the Phase Problem. 1. The Centrosymmetric Crystal." Am. Crystallographic Assoc. Monograph No. 3 (1954); Hauptman, H., *in* "Computing Methods and the Phase Problem in X-Ray Crystal Analysis" (R. Pepinsky, J. M. Robertson, and J. C. Speakman, eds.), p. 214. Pergamon Press, New York, 1961.

17. "International Tables for X-Ray Crystallography." Kynoch Press, Birmingham, England, 1952.

18. Menter, J. W., *Proc. Roy. Soc.* **A236,** 119 (1956).

19. Okaya, Y., and Pepinsky, R., *in* "Computing Methods and the Phase Problem in X-Ray Crystal Analysis" (R. Pepinsky, J. M. Robertson, and J. C. Speakman, eds.), p. 273. Pergamon Press, New York, 1961.

20. Patterson, A. L., *Phys. Rev.* **46,** 372 (1934); *Z. Krist.* **90,** 517 (1935).

21. Peterson, S. W., and Levy, H. A., *J. Chem. Phys.* **20,** 704 (1952).

22. Pinsker, Z. G., "Electron Diffraction" (translated by J. A. Spink and E. Feigl). Butterworths, London, 1953; Weinstein, B. K., "Structural Electron Diffraction." Academy of Sciences of the U.S.S.R., Moscow, 1956.

23. Rees, A. L. G., *J. Proc. Roy. Soc. N. S. Wales* **86,** 38 (1953); Cowley, J. M., and Rees, A. L. G., *Repts. Progr. in Phys.* **21,** 165 (1958).

24. Robertson, J. M., *J. Chem. Soc.* p. 615 (1935); p. 1195 (1936); Robertson, J. M., and Woodward, I., *ibid.* p. 219 (1937).

25. For references to this and other early work, see J. M. Robertson, "Organic Crystals and Molecules." Cornell Univ. Press, Ithaca, New York, 1953.

26. Robertson, J. M., and Woodward, I., *J. Chem. Soc.* p. 36 (1940).

27. Schottky, W., *Z. physik. Chem. (Leipzig)* **B29,** 335 (1935); Wagner, C., and Schottky, W., *ibid.* **B11,** 163 (1930).

28. Shull, C. G., and Siegel, S., *Phys. Rev.* **75,** 1008 (1949).

29. Shull, C. G., Strauser, W. A., and Wollan, E. O., *Phys. Rev.* **83,** 333 (1951).

30. Stone, F. S., *in* "Chemistry of the Solid State" (W. E. Garner, ed.), Chapter 2. Butterworths, London, 1955.

31. Taylor, A., "X-Ray Metallography," p. 442. Wiley, New York, 1961.

32. Wollan, E. O., Davidson, W. L., and Shull, C. G., *Phys. Rev.* **75,** 1348 (1949).

CHAPTER *2*

Douglas Henderson* and Henry Eyring

Institute for the Study of Rate Processes,
University of Utah, Salt Lake City, Utah

Statistical Thermodynamics and Reaction Rate Theory

I. Statistical Thermodynamics and Its Relation to Classical Thermodynamics... 50
   A. Introduction... 50
   B. Relation to Classical Thermodynamics..................... 52
   C. Approximate Partition Functions of Some Simple Systems..... 55
   D. Fermi-Dirac, Bose-Einstein, Boltzmann, and Intermediate Statistics... 58
II. The Theory of Absolute Reaction Rates....................... 63
   A. Equilibrium Constants and Partition Functions............. 63
   B. The Theory of Absolute Reaction Rates.................... 64
   C. Pressure and Temperature Effects......................... 67
III. The Lennard-Jones and Devonshire Free Volume Theory of Liquids and Dense Gases... 68
   A. Introduction... 68
   B. The Lennard-Jones and Devonshire Model.................. 73
   C. Equation of State; Comparison with Experiment............ 74
   D. Recent Modifications..................................... 77
IV. Thermodynamics and Kinetics of Imperfections in Stoichiometric Solids... 78
   A. The Boltzmann Factor for Entropy........................ 78
   B. Structural Imperfections................................. 80
   C. Diffusion and Ionic Conductivity......................... 83
V. Non-Stoichiometric Solids.................................. 87
   A. Color Centers in Non-Stoichiometric Ionic Crystals......... 87
   B. Oxidation of Metals at High Temperatures................. 89
VI. Concluding Remarks....................................... 93
   References.. 95

---

* *Present address*: Department of Physics, Arizona State University, Tempe, Arizona.

49

I. STATISTICAL THERMODYNAMICS AND ITS RELATION TO CLASSICAL THERMODYNAMICS

A. Introduction

Consider a system, A, consisting of N molecules each with f degrees of freedom. Classically the motion of these molecules is described by Hamilton's equations of motion (*15*)

$$\dot{q}_i = \frac{\partial H}{\partial p_i}, \qquad \dot{p}_i = -\frac{\partial H}{\partial q_i}, \qquad i = 1, \cdots, Nf \qquad (1)$$

which constitute $2Nf$ first order differential equations in $2Nf$ unknowns. Momenta and coordinates rather than velocities and coordinates are almost exclusively used as dynamical variables because of the symmetry that is gained thereby. Once all the values of the p_i and q_i are known at any one time the motion of these molecules is completely known for all time. Thus, in principle, the macroscopic properties of any system could be determined by a detailed investigation of the microscopic motion of the molecules constituting the system. However, if the system contains a large number of molecules such a procedure quickly loses its value. Furthermore, classical mechanics is not valid for such microscopic particles and because of such quantum mechanical considerations as the Heisenberg uncertainty relations the concept of a trajectory is inapplicable. Hence even if the mathematics involved in Eqs. (1) were tractable, the molecular motions could not be calculated exactly. For these reasons a quite different procedure will have to be adopted if the macroscopic properties of the system are to be theoretically obtained.

Consider the system A as being in thermodynamic equilibrium with another system B. The nature of the system B is immaterial because of the zeroth law of thermodynamics and therefore we can choose B so as to make our calculations simplest. Assume that B consists of s harmonic oscillators of frequency ν. Assuming the energy of the combined system A + B has the constant value E let us calculate the probability that the system A has the energy $\epsilon \ll E$ distributed in any unique allowed manner among its degrees of freedom. In order to do this we must make an assumption which is the foundation of all statistical mechanics: *any allowed way of distributing the energy E in the combined system $A + B$ is equally probable.* This assumption of equal *a priori* probabilities has as its justification the complete agreement of its applications with experimental findings. The energy of the system B is $E - \epsilon$ and therefore the number of quanta, n,

FIG. 1. A possible distribution of ten quanta among six oscillators.

to be distributed among the s oscillators is

$$n = \frac{E - \epsilon}{h\nu} \tag{2}$$

Thus the probability that A has an energy ϵ is proportional to the number of ways N of distributing n quanta among s oscillators. Figure 1 depicts one possible distribution for six oscillators and ten quanta. Since both the quanta and the oscillators are indistinguishable the number of ways of distributing n quanta among s oscillators is the number of combinations of n x's and $s - 1$ partitions. Therefore

$$N(n,s) = \frac{(n + s - 1)!}{n!(s - 1)!} \tag{3}$$

Equation (3) can be rewritten as

$$N(n,s) = \frac{1}{(s - 1)!} \prod_{i=1}^{s-1} (n + s - i) \tag{4}$$

From Eq. (2) we have

$$(n + s - i) = \left(\frac{E - \epsilon}{h\nu} + s - i \right)$$

$$= \left(\frac{E + (s - i)h\nu}{h\nu} \right) \left(1 - \frac{\epsilon}{E + (s - i)h\nu} \right) \tag{5}$$

Therefore Eq. (4) becomes

$$N(n,s) = \frac{1}{(s - 1)!} \prod_{i=1}^{s-1} \left(\frac{E + (s - i)h\nu}{h\nu} \right) \prod_{i=1}^{s-1} \left(1 - \frac{\epsilon}{E + (s - i)h\nu} \right) \tag{6}$$

Equation (6) is an exact expression which can be simplified for large values of n and s to give the form due to Boltzmann. Let $\gamma = (E - \epsilon)/s$ be the average energy of one of the s oscillators. If we assume $n \gg s$ then $\gamma = nh\nu/s \gg h\nu$ and

$$E + (s - i)h\nu \simeq s\gamma + (s - i)h\nu \simeq s\gamma \tag{7}$$

for all i. Therefore Eq. (6) becomes

$$N(n,s) = C \left(1 - \frac{\epsilon}{s\gamma} \right)^{s-1} \tag{8}$$

where C is a constant independent of ϵ. For s large this becomes

$$N(n,s) = Ce^{-\epsilon/\gamma} \tag{9}$$

Since the properties of the system A cannot depend on the particular properties of the substance we use for system B, we can take as this substance a hypothetical metal whose intermolecular forces are very weak so that the s oscillators behave classically as near as we please down to absolute zero. Dulong and Petit have found the molar heat capacity of a classical metal to be about 6.2 cal mole^{-1} deg^{-1} and therefore

$$\gamma = kT \tag{10}$$

where k is known as Boltzmann's constant and is given by

$$k = \frac{6.2 \times 4.183 \times 10^7}{3 \times 6.023 \times 10^{23}} = 1.4 \times 10^{-16} \text{ erg deg}^{-1}$$

If a more accurate evaluation is carried out one finds that $k = R/N = 1.3803 \times 10^{-16}$ erg deg^{-1}, where R is the gas constant and $N = 6.023 \times 10^{23}$ is Avogadro's number. Normalizing Eq. (9) and using Eq. (10) the probability that system A is in a particular state i with energy ϵ_i is

$$\rho_i = \frac{e^{-\epsilon_i/kT}}{\sum_i e^{-\epsilon_i/kT}} \tag{11}$$

where the summation is over all possible unique states of A. The sum $Z = \sum_i e^{-\epsilon_i/kT}$ is called the *partition function* and, as we shall see in Section I.B, is of great importance when thermodynamic properties are to be calculated.

B. Relation to Classical Thermodynamics

The average value of any property that can be expressed in terms of the momenta and coordinates of the system can be determined by means of Eq. (11). We define the average value $\bar{x}$ of the property x by the following relation

$$\bar{x} = \sum_i \rho_i x_i \tag{12}$$

where x_i is the value of the property in the ith state. For example, the internal energy of the system is

$$E = \sum_i \epsilon_i \rho_i = \frac{\sum_i \epsilon_i e^{-\epsilon_i/kT}}{\sum_i e^{-\epsilon_i/kT}}$$

$$= kT^2 \left[\frac{\partial}{\partial T} \left(\ln \sum_i e^{-\epsilon_i/kT} \right) \right]_V$$

$$= kT^2 \left(\frac{\partial \ln Z}{\partial T} \right)_V \tag{13}$$

The specific heat at constant volume will then be

$$C_V = \left(\frac{\partial E}{\partial T} \right)_V = \left[\frac{\partial}{\partial T} \left(kT^2 \frac{\partial \ln Z}{\partial T} \right) \right]_V \tag{14}$$

Thus the entropy of the system is

$$S - S_0 = \int_0^T \frac{C_V}{T} \, dT = \int_0^T \frac{1}{T} \frac{\partial}{\partial T} \left(kT^2 \frac{\partial \ln Z}{\partial T} \right) dT \tag{15}$$

Integrating by parts yields

$$S - S_0 = \frac{1}{T} kT^2 \left(\frac{\partial \ln Z}{\partial T} \right) + k \int_0^T \frac{\partial \ln Z}{\partial T} \, dT$$

$$= \frac{E}{T} + k \ln Z \Big|_0^T \tag{16}$$

The term $k \ln Z(0)$ may be identified with S_0 and therefore

$$S = \frac{E}{T} + k \ln Z \tag{17}$$

The Helmholtz free energy is defined as

$$A = E - TS \tag{18}$$

Therefore

$$A = -kT \ln Z \tag{19}$$

The pressure can also be obtained in terms of the partition function. Differentiating Eq. (18) gives

$$dA = dE - T \, dS - S \, dT \tag{20}$$

The first law of thermodynamics requires that

$$TdS = dE + PdV \tag{21}$$

and therefore Eq. (20) becomes

$$dA = -SdT - PdV \tag{22}$$

Hence

$$P = -\left(\frac{\partial A}{\partial V}\right)_T = kT\left(\frac{\partial \ln Z}{\partial V}\right)_T \tag{23}$$

Clearly if we know the energy levels of the system as functions of volume and temperature we can form the partition function and calculate the thermodynamic properties of the system by means of Eqs. (13), (14), (17), (19), and (23).

Classically the energy levels are not discrete but form a continuum and therefore the partition function would become an integral. If ω_i is the degeneracy of the ith energy level then, as was historically the case, the transition to an integral might be accomplished by

$$\epsilon_i \rightarrow H(p, q)$$

$$\omega_i \rightarrow dp_1 \cdots dp_f dq_1 \cdots dq_f \tag{24}$$

but this yields an integral with the dimensions of (gm cm^2 sec^{-1})^f = (erg sec)^f whereas the partition function is dimensionless. In order to investigate this anomaly further consider the case of a single one-dimensional harmonic oscillator, defined by the total energy

$$H(p, q) = \frac{p^2}{2m} + \tfrac{1}{2}aq^2 \tag{25}$$

and so the curves of constant energy are ellipses in p-q space (*phase space*), as is shown in Fig. 2, the area of the ellipse being given by

$$I = \oint pdq \tag{26}$$

The integration is carried over one complete period of the oscillator. Classically any ellipse in phase space would represent a state of the oscillator but in quantum mechanics the Wilson–Sommerfeld (56, 64) quantization rule requires that $I = nh$, where n is some integer. The allowed energy surfaces subdivide phase space into regions of area h. This result can be generalized to include systems with many degrees of freedom. For a molecule of f degrees of freedom the energy surfaces corresponding to allowed states subdivide phase space into regions of volume h^f. In other words we

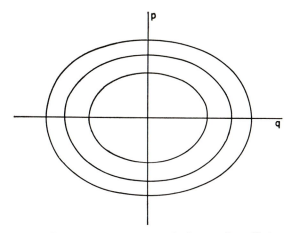

FIG. 2. Constant energy curves of a harmonic oscillator.

can associate a volume h^f with each quantum state and therefore the transition to an integral should be accomplished by

$$\epsilon_i = H(p, q)$$

$$\omega_i = \frac{1}{h^f} dp_1 \cdots dp_f dq_1 \cdots dq_f \tag{27}$$

The classical partition function is therefore

$$Z = \frac{1}{h^f} \int e^{-H/kT} dp_1 \cdots dp_f dq_1 \cdots dq_f \tag{28}$$

which is dimensionless.

The partition function, Z_N, for the system of N molecules is gained by raising the molecular partition function, Z, to the power N. This procedure is valid provided the molecules are distinguishable (as are the molecules in a crystal). However, if the molecules are indistinguishable then the number of distinct states has been overcounted by $N!$ and therefore

$$Z_N = Z^N \qquad \text{Distinguishable molecules}$$

$$Z_N = Z^N/N! \qquad \text{Indistinguishable molecules} \tag{29}$$

C. Approximate Partition Functions of Some Simple Systems

If the energy levels in a degree of freedom are independent of the state occupied in the other degrees of freedom then the ith level can be written as

$$\epsilon_i = \epsilon_i(t) + \epsilon_i(v) + \epsilon_i(r) + \epsilon_i(e) + \epsilon_i(n) \tag{30}$$

where $\epsilon_i(t)$, $\epsilon_i(v)$, $\epsilon_i(r)$, $\epsilon_i(e)$, $\epsilon_i(n)$ are the energy levels associated with translational, vibrational, rotational, electronic, and nuclear motions, respectively. To this approximation

$$Z = Z_t Z_v Z_r Z_e Z_n \tag{31}$$

where

$$Z_t = \sum_i e^{-\epsilon_i/kT} \tag{32}$$

If a molecule is rotating the centrifugal force will change the force constant and therefore will change the vibrational energy levels. Such refinements are usually unnecessary and the above considerations are valid for most applications.

The nuclear energy may be taken as zero and hence

$$Z_n = \omega_0(n) \tag{33}$$

where $\omega_0(n)$ is the degeneracy of the lowest nuclear state. The electronic partition function may usually be taken as

$$Z_e = \omega_0(e) \tag{34}$$

where $\omega_0(e)$ is the degeneracy of the lowest electronic state. The evaluation of the translational, vibrational, and rotational partition functions is a little more involved and will be considered in that order in the next three sections.

1. TRANSLATIONAL PARTITION FUNCTION

The energy levels of a particle in a rectangular box of edge l_1, l_2, and l_3 are known (15) to be given by

$$\epsilon_{n_1 n_2 n_3} = \frac{h^2}{8m} \left(\frac{n_1^2}{l_1^2} + \frac{n_2^2}{l_2^2} + \frac{n_3^2}{l_3^2} \right) \tag{35}$$

where n_1, n_2, $n_3 = 1, 2, 3, \cdots$. Therefore

$$Z_t = \sum_{n_1=1}^{\infty} \exp\left(-\frac{n_1^2 h^2}{8ml_1^2 kT}\right) \sum_{n_2=1}^{\infty} \exp\left(-\frac{n_2^2 h^2}{8ml_2^2 kT}\right) \sum_{n_3=1}^{\infty} \exp\left(-\frac{n_3^2 h^2}{8ml_3^2 kT}\right) \tag{36}$$

Except at extremely low temperatures where

$$\frac{h^2}{8ml_i^2} \gg kT,$$

the sums in Eq. (36) may be replaced by integrals, giving

$$Z_t = \int_0^\infty \exp\left(-\frac{n_1^2 h^2}{8ml_1^2 kT}\right) dn_1 \int_0^\infty \exp\left(-\frac{n_2^2 h^2}{8ml_2^2 kT}\right) dn_2$$

$$\times \int_0^\infty \exp\left(-\frac{n_2^2 h^2}{8ml_3^2 kT}\right) dn_3$$

$$= \frac{(2\pi mkT)^{1/2} l_1}{h} \frac{(2\pi mkT)^{1/2} l_2}{h} \frac{(2\pi mkT)^{1/2} l_3}{h} \tag{37}$$

$$= \left(\frac{2\pi mkT}{h^2}\right)^{3/2} V$$

2. VIBRATIONAL PARTITION FUNCTIONS

The energy levels of a harmonic oscillator are given by (15)

$$\epsilon_n = (n + \tfrac{1}{2}) h\nu \tag{38}$$

and therefore

$$Z_v = e^{-h\nu/2kT} \sum_{n=0}^\infty e^{-h\nu/kT}$$

$$= e^{-h\nu/2kT}\left[1 + e^{-h\nu/kT} + (e^{-h\nu/kT})^2 + \cdots\right] \tag{39}$$

$$= \frac{e^{-h\nu/kT}}{1 - e^{-h\nu/kT}}$$

The above expression is exact insofar as the vibrational energy levels can be represented by those of a harmonic oscillator.

3. ROTATIONAL PARTITION FUNCTIONS

The energy levels of a two-dimensional rigid rotator are given by (15)

$$\epsilon_n = n(n + 1) \frac{h^2}{8\pi^2 I} \tag{40}$$

where I is the moment of inertia of the rotator. These energy levels are $(2n + 1)$-fold degenerate and therefore the partition function of a two-dimensional rigid rotator is

$$Z_r = \sum_{n=0}^{\infty} (2n + 1) \exp\left(-\frac{n(n + 1)h^2}{8\pi^2 I k T}\right) \tag{41}$$

If $h^2/8\pi^2 I \ll kT$ we can replace this sum by an integral

$$Z_r = \int_0^{\infty} (2x + 1) \exp\left(-\frac{x(x + 1)h^2}{8\pi^2 I k T}\right) dx$$

$$= \frac{8\pi^2 I k T}{h^2} \int_0^{\infty} e^{-y} \, dy \tag{42}$$

$$= \frac{8\pi^2 I k T}{h^2}$$

Equation (42) must be divided by σ, the symmetry number, which is the number of indistinguishable ways of orienting the molecule in space. For a heteronuclear diatomic molecule $\sigma = 1$ and for a homonuclear diatomic molecule $\sigma = 2$.

A polyatomic molecule must be represented by a general rigid body. It is not possible to solve Schrödinger's equation for the energy levels of a nonsymmetrical rigid body and therefore the partition function for low temperatures cannot be obtained. It is, however, possible to obtain a high-temperature expression for the partition function by performing the integrations in Eq. (29). The result is (19)

$$Z_r = \frac{8\pi^2 (8\pi^3 ABC)^{1/2} (kT)^{3/2}}{\sigma h^3} \tag{43}$$

where A, B, and C are the principal moments of inertia and σ is the symmetry number whose value is tabulated for many molecules (19).

D. Fermi-Dirac, Bose-Einstein, Boltzmann, and Intermediate Statistics

1. Absolute Activity

The *chemical potential* is defined by

$$\mu_i = \left(\frac{\partial A}{\partial n_i}\right)_{V,T,n_j} = \left(\frac{\partial G}{\partial n_i}\right)_{P,T,n_j} = kT \ln \lambda_i \tag{44}$$

where λ_i is the *absolute activity*. Consider N identical molecules in the gaseous state or in solution. If Z is the partition function for a single molecule then

$$A = -kT \ln (Z^N/N!) = -kT \ln (Ze/N)^N \tag{45}$$

The chemical potential is then

$$\mu = -kT \ln (Ze/N) + kT$$

$$= -kT \ln (Z/N) \tag{46}$$

and therefore the absolute activity is

$$\lambda = N/Z \tag{47}$$

2. SATURATION (16) OR FERMI-DIRAC STATISTICS

Consider a system in which n_g gaseous molecules in a volume V are in equilibrium with a variety of sites of which ω_i are alike and each of which yields the energy ϵ_i per molecule absorbed. Figure 3 depicts a typical situation. At equilibrium adsorption and desorption balance and thus

$$n_g k_g (\omega_i - n_i) = n_i k_i \tag{48}$$

where n_i of the ω_i sites are filled at equilibrium and k_g and k_i are the rates at which adsorption and desorption take place. Solving for n_i

$$n_i = \frac{\omega_i}{(k_i/n_g k_g) + 1} \tag{49}$$

Dilute or Boltzmann statistics apply for the situation $\omega_i \gg n_i$. Under this condition, solving Eq. (48) for n_i gives

$$n_i = \omega_i \frac{n_g k_g}{k_i} \tag{50}$$

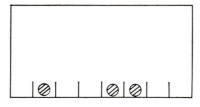

FIG. 3. Typical situation in saturation statistics.

Comparing with Eqs. (11) and (47) yields

$$n_i = \omega_i \lambda e^{-\epsilon_i/kT} \tag{51}$$

or

$$\frac{n_g k_g}{k_i} = \lambda e^{-\epsilon_i/kT} \tag{52}$$

Thus Eq. (49) takes the familiar form due to Fermi (18) and Dirac (9)

$$n_i = \frac{\omega_i}{\lambda^{-1} e^{\epsilon_i/kT} + 1} \tag{53}$$

The above procedure was used by Langmuir (35) for the adsorption of a gas on a solid surface. If we write $\theta = n_i/\omega_i$ for the fraction of the surface covered and $\lambda e^{-\epsilon_i/kT} = KP$ where K is the adsorption coefficient and P is the pressure then Eq. (53) takes on the well known Langmuir form

$$\theta = \frac{KP}{KP + 1} \tag{54}$$

3. CONDENSATION (16) OR BOSE-EINSTEIN STATISTICS

Again consider a system in which n_i molecules have condensed on ω_i sites but in this case there are no restrictions as to the number of molecules allowed on a given site (Fig. 4). At equilibrium

$$n_g k_g(\omega_i + n_i) = n_i k_i \tag{55}$$

since any of the n_i molecules is a candidate for removal, then by detailed balance, in addition to the original ω_i condensation sites each of the n_i molecules may be thought of as providing an additional condensation site above it. The $\omega_i + n_i$ sites may be thought of as all having the same reac-

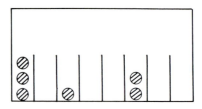

FIG. 4. Typical situation in condensation statistics.

tion rate since a catalyst may be introduced to assure this without affecting the equilibrium properties. Solving for n_i gives

$$n_i = \frac{\omega_i}{(k_i/n_g k_g) - 1} \tag{56}$$

Again dilute or Boltzmann statistics apply for the situation $\omega_i \gg n_i$ which means that Eq. (52) is valid and thus Eq. (56) takes the familiar form due to Bose (6) and Einstein (11)

$$n_i = \frac{\omega_i}{\lambda^{-1} e^{\epsilon_i/kT} - 1} \tag{57}$$

For the condensation of a liquid we have, as before, $\sigma = n_i/\omega_i$ as the ratio of adsorbed molecules to the original number of condensation sites and $\lambda e^{-\epsilon_i/kT} = KP$. Substituting into Eq. (57)

$$\sigma = \frac{KP}{1 - KP} \tag{58}$$

As long as $KP < 1$ in Eq. (58), positive finite values of σ are obtained. This corresponds to adsorption on the surface without condensation of the liquid phase. When $KP = 1$ the value of σ suddenly becomes infinite corresponding to the appearance of a new phase. For $KP > 1$ we have supersaturation for which no equilibrium is possible, as the physically impossible negative values of σ indicate.

4. Intermediate Statistics (21, 48)

Consider the intermediate case where d_i molecules saturate a site. The equilibrium condition is then

$$n_g k_g [\omega_i + n_i - \rho_i \omega_i (d_i + 1)] = k_i n_i \tag{59}$$

where ρ_i is the probability that a particular site has the d_i particles which would saturate it, in which case each such saturated site eliminates $d_i + 1$ prospective condensation loci.

For the case where d_i is infinite, ρ_i is necessarily zero and Bose–Einstein statistics result, while if $d_i = 1$, $\rho_i = n_i/\omega_i$ and Fermi–Dirac statistics result. If $A(\omega_i, n_i, d_i)$ is the number of ways that n_i molecules can be arranged on ω_i sites where d_i particles saturate any site, then

$$\rho = \frac{A(\omega_i - 1, n_i - d_i, d_i)}{A(\omega_i, n_i, d_i)} \tag{60}$$

The number $A(\omega_i, n_i, d_i)$ is the coefficient of z^{n_i} in the polynomial

$$(1 + z + \cdots + z^{d_i})^{\omega_i} \tag{61}$$

since the terms $1, z, \cdots, z^{d_i}$ may be thought of as proportional to the probability of introducing $0, 1, \cdots, d_i$ molecules in a particular site and there are ω_i such sites. Thus the coefficient of z^{n_i} includes all possible ways of introducing n_i particles on the sites. The coefficient of z^{n_i} is just

$$A(\omega_i, n_i, d_i) = \left[\frac{1}{n_i!} \frac{d^{n_i}}{dz^{n_i}} (1 + z + \cdots + z^{d_i})^{\omega_i} \right]_{z=0}$$

$$= \frac{1}{n_i!} \left\{ \frac{d^{n_i}}{dz^{n_i}} \left[\left(\frac{1 - z^{d_i+1}}{1 - z} \right)^{\omega_i} \right] \right\}_{z=0} \tag{62}$$

This differentiation may be performed by means of Leibnitz's rule

$$\frac{d^n(uv)}{dz^n} = v \frac{d^n u}{dz^n} + \cdots + \frac{n!}{(n-r)!r!} \frac{d^{n-r}u}{dz^{n-r}} \frac{d^r v}{dz^r} + \cdots \tag{63}$$

Performing the required differentiations yields

$$\left[\frac{d^{n_i-r}}{dz^{n_i-r}} (1 - z)^{-\omega_i} \right]_{z=0} = \frac{(\omega_i + n_i - r - 1)!}{(\omega_i - 1)!} \tag{64}$$

and

$$\left[\frac{d^r}{dz^r} (1 - z^{d_i+1})^{\omega_i} \right]_{z=0} = \frac{d^r}{dz^r} [1 - \omega_i z^{d_i+1} + \cdots + (-z^{d_i+1})^{\omega_i}] \tag{65}$$

It is evident that

$$\left[\frac{d^r}{dz^r} (1 - z^{d_i+1})^{\omega_i} \right]_{z=0} = 0 \tag{66}$$

except as r has the value $s(d_i + 1)$ where s is an integer. For this case

$$\left[\frac{d^{s(d_i+1)}}{dz^{s(d_i+1)}} (1 - z^{d_i+1})^{\omega_i} \right]_{z=0} = \frac{\omega_i!}{(\omega_i - s)!s!} (-1)^s [s(d_i + 1)]! \tag{67}$$

and therefore

$$A(\omega_i, n_i, d_i) = \sum_{s=0}^{m} \frac{(-1)^s \omega_i [\omega_i + n_i - s(d_i + 1) - 1]!}{[n_i - s(d_i + 1)]!s!(\omega_i - s)!} \tag{68}$$

where m is the largest integer less than $n_i/(d_i + 1)$.

As a further example to illustrate the generality of this method consider condensation in fissures formed by two parallel infinite planes (Fig.

5). There are $\omega_i/2$ sites opposite an equal number of like sites and the fissures can be filled by adding particles from above and below. The equilibrium condition is

$$n_g k_g \left[\omega_i + n_i - \rho_i \frac{\omega_i}{2} (d_i + 2) \right] = n_i k_i \tag{69}$$

where ρ_i is the probability that a site is saturated. In this case saturation withdraws two sites on the surface plus d_i condensation sites corresponding to the d_i molecules. As long as $l < d_i$ a fissure can accommodate l mole-

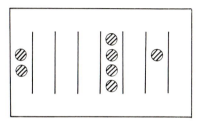

FIG. 5. Condensation in fissures.

cules in $l + 1$ ways since if r particles are added at the top site, the remaining $l - r$ particles can be added at the bottom site and r can take on all values between zero and l. Therefore, the number of ways, A, of distributing n_i molecules in $\omega_i/2$ fissures is given by

$$A(\omega_i, n_i, d_i) = \left[\frac{1}{n_i!} \frac{d^{n_i}}{dz^{n_i}} \left(\sum_{l=0}^{d_i} (l + 1) z^l \right)^{\omega_i/2} \right]_{z=0}$$

$$= \frac{1}{n_i!} \left[\frac{d^{n_i}}{dz^{n_i}} \left(\frac{d}{dz} \sum_{l=0}^{d_i} z^{l+1} \right)^{\omega_i/2} \right]_{z=0} \tag{70}$$

This expression can be evaluated in a manner similar to that used in obtaining Eq. (68). The resulting series will, however, be much more complicated.

It is clear that this is a general method of treating any type of statistics.

II. THE THEORY OF ABSOLUTE REACTION RATES

A. Equilibrium Constants and Partition Functions

Consider the reaction

$$aA + bB + \cdots = mM + nN + \cdots$$

$$\sum m_i M_i = 0 \tag{71}$$

where the m_i are positive or negative integers for the reactants and products respectively. If the reaction occurs at constant temperature and pressure, then at equilibrium the Gibbs free energy will be a minimum, i.e.,

$$dG = \sum_i \left(\frac{\partial G}{\partial N_i}\right)_{T,P,N_j} dN_i = 0$$

$$= \sum_i \mu_i dN_i = 0 \qquad (72)$$

where N_i is the number of molecules present of the ith species. Now

$$dN_i = m_i dn \qquad (73)$$

and therefore Eq. (72) becomes

$$0 = \sum_i \mu_i m_i \qquad (74)$$

For molecules in a gas or a solution the chemical potential is given by Eq. (46) and therefore

$$0 = -\sum_i m_i \ln\left(\frac{Z_i}{N_i}\right) \qquad (75)$$

Thus

$$\prod_i Z_i^{-m_i} = \prod_i N_i^{-m_i} \qquad (76)$$

Introducing the concentrations $[M_i] = N_i/V$, Eq. (76) becomes

$$K = \frac{[M]^m[N]^n \cdots}{[A]^a[B]^b \cdots} = \frac{[Z_m/V]^m[Z_n/V]^n \cdots}{[Z_a/V]^a[Z_b/V]^b \cdots} e^{-E_0/RT} \qquad (77)$$

where the exponential has been inserted to insure that all energies are measured from the same zero point, and K is known as the *equilibrium constant*.

B. The Theory of Absolute Reaction Rates (*13,22*)

The fundamental concept in the theory of absolute reaction rates is that reactants combine to form transition state structures called *activated complexes* to which equilibrium theory can be applied. If the potential energy is plotted as a function of the reaction coordinate a plot similar to Fig. 6 is obtained. The potential energy of the activated complex is a minimum with respect to all the coordinates but the reaction coordinate so that the

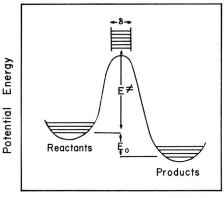

FIG. 6. Schematic plot of the potential energy for a reaction.

activated complexes lie on a saddle point or pass between the potential wells of the reactants and products. The activated complexes are assumed to be in equilibrium with the reactants and, therefore, the rate at which the reaction occurs is determined by the average velocity of the activated complexes over the top of the barrier. If the top of the barrier is of length δ the energy levels of an activated complex are given by

$$\epsilon_n = \frac{n^2 h^2}{8 m^{\ddagger} \delta^2} = \tfrac{1}{2} m^{\ddagger} v^2 \tag{78}$$

where $m^{\ddagger}$ is the effective mass of the activated complex and n is an integer. Therefore

$$v = \frac{nh}{2\delta m^{\ddagger}} \tag{79}$$

The average velocity in the forward direction is given by

$$\bar{v} = \frac{\displaystyle\int_0^{\infty} \frac{nh}{2\delta m^{\ddagger}} \exp\left(-\frac{n^2 h^2}{8\delta^2 m^{\ddagger} kT}\right) dn}{\displaystyle\int_{-\infty}^{\infty} \exp\left(-\frac{n^2 h^2}{8\delta^2 m^{\ddagger} kT}\right) dn}$$

$$= \left(\frac{kT}{2\pi m^{\ddagger}}\right)^{1/2} \tag{80}$$

The average time for an activated complex to cross the barrier is

$$\tau = \frac{\delta}{\bar{v}} = \delta \left(\frac{2\pi m^{\ddagger}}{kT}\right)^{1/2} \tag{81}$$

The rate of the reaction is then the number of activated complexes which cross the barrier in the forward direction per unit volume per unit time

$$\text{Rate of Reaction} = \frac{C^{\ddagger}}{\tau} = \frac{C^{\ddagger}}{\delta(2\pi m^{\ddagger}/kT)} \tag{82}$$

where $C^{\ddagger}$ is the concentration of complexes. Equation (82) should be multiplied by a factor κ, called the *transmission coefficient*, to account for the tendency for products to dissociate and move in a backward direction through the activated complex state and into the reactant well. The transmission coefficient is frequently very close to unity and unless there is evidence to the contrary κ will be assumed to equal unity. The *specific reaction rate* k' is defined by

$$\text{Rate of Reaction} = \frac{C^{\ddagger}}{\tau} = k'C_A C_B \cdots \tag{83}$$

where C_A, C_B, $\cdots$, etc., are the concentrations of the reactants.

Since it has been assumed that the reactants and activated complexes are in equilibrium, an equilibrium constant K_c may be introduced

$$K_c = \frac{C^{\ddagger}}{C_A C_B \cdots} = \frac{Z'^{\ddagger}}{Z_A Z_B \cdots} e^{-E^{\ddagger}/RT} \tag{84}$$

Substituting Eqs. (84) and (82) into Eq. (83) gives

$$k' = \kappa \frac{Z'^{\ddagger}}{Z_A Z_B \cdots} \left(\frac{kT}{2\pi m^{\ddagger}}\right)^{1/2} \frac{e^{-E^{\ddagger}/RT}}{\delta} \tag{85}$$

Instead of using the complete partition function for the activated complex, $Z'^{\ddagger}$, a new partition function, $Z^{\ddagger}$, which does not include the contribution due to translational motion along the reaction coordinate, is introduced.

$$Z'^{\ddagger} = Z^{\ddagger} Z'_t$$

$$= Z^{\ddagger} \frac{(2\pi m^{\ddagger} kT)^{1/2}}{h} \delta \tag{86}$$

Substituting (86) into (85) gives

$$k' = \kappa \frac{kT}{h} K^{\ddagger} \tag{87}$$

where

$$K^{\ddagger} = \frac{Z^{\ddagger}}{Z_A Z_B \cdots} e^{-E^{\ddagger}/RT} \tag{88}$$

As for any other equilibrium constant

$$-\Delta G^{\ddagger} = RT \ln K^{\ddagger} \tag{89}$$

so that

$$k' = \kappa \frac{kT}{h} \exp\left(-\frac{\Delta G^{\ddagger}}{RT}\right) \tag{90}$$

C. Pressure and Temperature Effects

Taking the logarithm of Eq. (90) gives

$$\ln k' = \ln T - \frac{\Delta G^{\ddagger}}{RT} + \begin{array}{l} \text{terms independent} \\ \text{of pressure and} \\ \text{temperature} \end{array} \tag{91}$$

The pressure dependence of the rate of a reaction may be obtained by differentiating Eq. (91) with respect to pressure

$$\left(\frac{\partial \ln k'}{\partial P}\right)_T = -\frac{1}{RT}\left(\frac{\partial \Delta G^{\ddagger}}{\partial P}\right)_T \tag{92}$$

But

$$\left(\frac{\partial G}{\partial P}\right)_T = V \tag{93}$$

And therefore

$$\left(\frac{\partial \ln k'}{\partial P}\right)_T = -\frac{\Delta V^{\ddagger}}{RT} \tag{94}$$

So that for all reactions, except unimolecular reactions for which $\Delta V^{\ddagger} = 0$, an increase in pressure will cause either a decrease or an increase in the reaction rate according as $\Delta V^{\ddagger}$ is greater or less than zero.

The temperature dependence of the rate of a reaction may be obtained by differentiating Eq. (95) with respect to temperature

$$\left(\frac{\partial \ln k'}{\partial T}\right)_P = \frac{1}{T} + \frac{\Delta G^{\ddagger}}{RT^2} - \frac{1}{RT}\left(\frac{\partial \Delta G^{\ddagger}}{\partial T}\right)_P$$

$$= \frac{1}{T} + \frac{\Delta G^{\ddagger}}{RT^2} + \frac{\Delta S^{\ddagger}}{RT}$$

$$= \frac{1}{T} + \frac{\Delta H^{\ddagger}}{RT^2} \tag{95}$$

Therefore as the temperature increases so does the rate of the reaction, unless $\Delta H^{\ddagger} < -RT$.

III. THE LENNARD-JONES AND DEVONSHIRE FREE VOLUME THEORY OF LIQUIDS AND DENSE GASES

A. Introduction

This theory has been applied quite successfully in studies of the thermodynamic properties of β-hydroquinone clathrates (Chapter 7, Section IV and Chapter 10, Section V) and of gas hydrates (Chapter 6, Section VIII). The present discussion will be limited, for simplicity, to liquids consisting of monatomic molecules of nonmetallic character. Further, this discussion will be limited to liquids whose molecules are sufficiently heavy and that exist only at temperatures which are sufficiently high so that quantum effects need not be considered. The incorporation of quantum liquids into this theory will, however, be briefly discussed.

A rigorous theory of liquids would involve the evaluation of the partition function

$$Z_N = \frac{1}{N!h^{3N}} \int e^{-H/kT} d\mathbf{r}_1 \cdots d\mathbf{r}_N d\mathbf{p}_1 \cdots d\mathbf{p}_N \tag{96}$$

where the integration is over all possible values of the momenta and coordinates. In order to facilitate the evaluation of this integral the forces between molecules are assumed to be central forces which are derivable from a potential function $\phi(r)$ and further that the potential function of two molecules is independent of the positions of the other molecules. Under these assumptions

$$H = \sum_i \frac{p_i^2}{2m} + \sum_{i>j} \phi(r_{ij}) \tag{97}$$

The integration over the momenta may be performed immediately giving

$$Z = \frac{1}{N!} \left(\frac{2\pi m k T}{h^2} \right)^{3N/2} \int \exp\left[-\frac{1}{kT} \sum_{i>j} \phi(r_{ij}) \right] d\mathbf{r}_1 \cdots d\mathbf{r}_N \quad (98)$$

The intermolecular potential is well described by the Lennard-Jones (6–12) potential

$$\phi(r) = 4\epsilon \left[\left(\frac{\sigma}{r} \right)^{12} - \left(\frac{\sigma}{r} \right)^{6} \right] \quad (99)$$

where ϵ is the maximum depth of the potential and σ is the *collision diameter*, the distance at which ϕ is zero. At large separations ($r \gg \sigma$) the attractive inverse sixth power component is dominant. This type of potential describes the induced dipole-dipole interaction between two nonpolar molecules.

TABLE I

FORCE CONSTANTS FOR THE LENNARD-JONES (6–12) POTENTIAL (*29*)

Substance	ϵ/k (°K)	σ (Å)
Ne	35.60	2.749
Ar	119.8	3.405
Kr	171	3.60
Xe	221	4.100

The choice of twelve for the repulsive interaction is somewhat arbitrary but is as good as any number in the region ten to fourteen. Moreover twelve has the distinct advantage of being twice six. The values of ϵ and σ can be determined from data on the second virial coefficient and are tabulated for the inert gases in Table I. Further tabulations of these parameters for other substance may be found in Hirschfelder *et al.* (*29*).

The parameters ϵ and σ can be used to define the following reduced quantities

$$T^* = \frac{kT}{\epsilon}, \qquad V^* = \frac{V}{N\sigma^3} \quad (100)$$

According to Eq. (23) the pressure is given by

$$P = kT \left\{ \frac{\partial}{\partial V} \ln \int \exp\left[-\frac{1}{kT} \sum_{i>j} \phi(r_{ij}) \right] d\mathbf{r}_1 \cdots d\mathbf{r}_N \right\}_T \quad (101)$$

The pressure depends only on the quantities kT, V, ϵ, and σ. Therefore, if the dimensionless quantity

$$P^* = \frac{P\sigma^3}{\epsilon} \tag{102}$$

is formed, then the law of corresponding states:

$$P^* = P^*(V^*, T^*) \tag{103}$$

follows, since a dimensionless quantity can be a function only of dimensionless quantities. In quantum theory the pressure will depend on h, m, kT, ϵ, and σ, and a new dimensionless quantity

$$\Lambda^* = \frac{h}{\sigma(m\epsilon)^{1/2}} \tag{104}$$

must be introduced. Equation (103) must therefore be corrected to

$$P^* = P^*(V^*, T^*, \Lambda^*) \tag{105}$$

The classical law of corresponding states is therefore correct for substances with sufficiently large mass so that Λ^* is negligibly small and may be neglected. The reduced triple and critical point properties for the inert gases are given in Table II and the reduced volumes and pressures are plotted in Figs. 7 and 8 respectively.

If it is assumed that each molecule is confined to a singly occupied cell formed by its nearest neighbors and that within its cell each molecule moves in a field $\psi(r)$ where $r = 0$ is located at the minimum in $\psi(r)$ then the partition function for such a liquid is given by

$$Z_N = \left(\frac{2\pi mkT}{h^2}\right)^{3N/2} \exp\left[-N\psi(o)/2kT\right]v_f{}^N \tag{106}$$

TABLE II

REDUCED TRIPLE POINT AND CRITICAL POINT PROPERTIES OF THE INERT GASES(17)

Substance	$T_t{}^*$	$P_t{}^* \times 10^3$	$V_t{}^*$	$T_c{}^*$	$P_c{}^*$	$V_c{}^*$	$P_c{}^* V_c{}^*/T_c{}^*$
Ne	0.690	1.83	1.29	1.25	0.111	3.33	0.296
Ar	0.699	1.65	1.18	1.26	0.116	3.16	0.292
Kr	0.678	1.44	1.21	1.22	0.109	3.28	0.291
Xe	0.730	1.84	1.03	1.31	0.132	2.86	0.290
Average	0.699	1.69	1.17	1.26	0.117	3.15	0.292

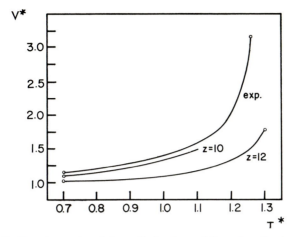

FIG. 7. Experimental and theoretical values of the reduced volume (3).

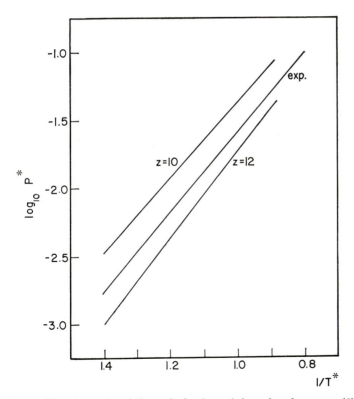

FIG. 8. Experimental and theoretical values of the reduced pressure (3).

where v_f is called the *free volume* and is given by

$$v_f = \int_{\text{cell}} \exp\{-[\psi(r) - \psi(o)]/kT\}4\pi r^2 dr \qquad (107)$$

A characteristic difficulty arises when the limit of low densities $(V \to \infty)$ is considered. In this limit $\psi(r) \to 0$ and $v_f = V/N$ giving

$$Z_N = \left(\frac{2\pi mkT}{h^2}\right)^{3N/2} \left(\frac{V}{N}\right)^N \qquad (108)$$

whereas the partition function of a perfect gas is, if Stirling's approximation, $N! = (N/e)^N$, is used

$$Z_N = \left(\frac{2\pi mkT}{h^2}\right)^{3N/2} \left(\frac{eV}{N}\right)^N \qquad (109)$$

The extra factor e^N arises because the gas molecules are indistinguishable whereas in the cell model of a liquid the molecules are confined to their respective cells and are therefore distinguishable. The extra factor e^N gives rise to an additional contribution Nk to the entropy which is called the *communal entropy*. Eyring *(14)* and later Lennard-Jones and Devonshire *(36)* suggested that the extra factor e^N should be added to Eq. (106) and that the communal entropy provides most of the entropy of melting. Recent modifications of the free volume theory of liquids *(8, 47, 49, 53)* obtain the extra entropy of liquid in more acceptable manner by considering the randomness introduced by empty cells. For this procedure Eq. (106) is used as the starting point. We also prefer this procedure but for historical reasons follow the earlier ideas of Lennard-Jones and Devonshire.

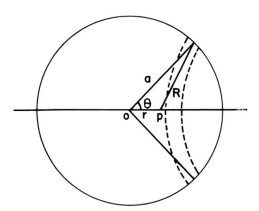

Fig. 9. Lennard-Jones and Devonshire calculation of $\psi(r)$.

B. The Lennard-Jones and Devonshire Model

Lennard-Jones and Devonshire (36) calculated $\psi(r)$ by assuming that each molecule moves within its cell in the potential field of its nearest neighbors fixed at the centers of their respective cells. To simplify the problem the z nearest neighbors are treated as uniformly smeared over a spherical surface of radius, a, equal to the nearest neighbor distance. Under these assumptions the field $\psi(r)$ in which a molecule moves in its cell is the molecular field of the surrounding molecules averaged over all directions (Fig. 9). The area of the ring is $2\pi a^2 \sin\theta d\theta$ and therefore the number of smeared nearest neighbors in the ring is $z/2 \sin\theta d\theta$. Hence

$$\psi(r) = \int_0^\pi 4\epsilon\left[\left(\frac{\sigma}{R}\right)^{12} - \left(\frac{\sigma}{R}\right)^6\right] \frac{z}{2} \sin\theta d\theta \qquad (110)$$

where $R^2 = r^2 + a^2 - 2ar\cos\theta$. For fixed r, $2RdR = 2ar\sin\theta d\theta$ and

$$\psi(r) = 2\frac{z\epsilon}{ar} \int_{a-r}^{a+r} \left\{\left(\frac{\sigma}{R}\right)^{12} - \left(\frac{\sigma}{R}\right)^6\right\} RdR$$

$$= z\epsilon\sigma^{12} \left\{\frac{1}{5ar}\left[\frac{1}{(a-r)^{10}} - \frac{1}{(a+r)^{10}}\right]\right\} \qquad (111)$$

$$+ z\epsilon\sigma^6 \left\{\frac{1}{2ar}\left[\frac{1}{(a+r)^4} - \frac{1}{(a-r)^4}\right]\right\}$$

But

$$\psi(o) = 4z\epsilon \left\{\left(\frac{\sigma}{a}\right)^{12} - \left(\frac{\sigma}{a}\right)^6\right\} \qquad (112)$$

and therefore

$$\psi(r) - \psi(o) = z\epsilon\sigma^{12} \left\{\frac{1}{5ar}\left[\frac{1}{(a-r)^{10}} - \frac{1}{(a+r)^{10}}\right] - \frac{4}{a^{12}}\right\}$$

$$+ z\epsilon\sigma^6 \left\{\frac{1}{2ar}\left[\frac{1}{(a+r)^4} - \frac{1}{(a-r)^4}\right] + \frac{4}{a^6}\right\} \qquad (113)$$

For a cubic close packed structure $z = 12$ and $v = V/N = a^3/\sqrt{2}$. Under these circumstances Eq. (113) can be expressed in the following more usual form

$$\psi(r) - \psi(o) = z\epsilon\left(\frac{l(y)}{v^{*4}} - \frac{2m(y)}{v^{*2}}\right) \qquad (114)$$

where

$$l(y) = (1 + 12y + 25.2y^2 + 12y^3 + y^4)(1 - y)^{-10} - 1$$

$$m(y) = (1 + y)(1 - y)^{-4} - 1 \tag{115}$$

and $y = (r/a)^2 = (r^*/a^*)^2$, $r^* = r/\sigma$, $a^* = a/\sigma$, and $v^* = v/\sigma^3 = V/N\sigma^3$.

Using Eq. (113) the partition function becomes

$$Z_N = \left(\frac{2\pi mkT}{h^2}\right)^{3N/2} \exp\left[-N\psi(o)/2kT\right](ev_f)^N \tag{116}$$

Choosing the volume of the cell so that it equals the volume per molecule, the free volume becomes

$$v_f = \int_0^{r_m} \exp[-\psi(r) - \psi(o)/kT]4\pi r^2 dr$$

$$= 2\pi a^3 g(v^*, T^*) \tag{117}$$

where

$$g(v^*, T^*) = \int_0^{y_m} \sqrt{y} \exp\left\{-\frac{z}{T^*}\left[\frac{l(y)}{v^{*4}} - \frac{2m(y)}{v^{*2}}\right]\right\} dy \tag{118}$$

and

$$y_m = \left(\frac{3}{4\pi\sqrt{2}}\right)^{2/3} \tag{119}$$

C. Equation of State; Comparison with Experiment

The Helmholtz free energy is thus given by

$$A = -kT \ln Z_N = -NkT \ln\left[\left(\frac{2\pi mkT}{h^2}\right)^{3/2} v_f\right] + \frac{N\psi(o)}{2} - NkT \tag{120}$$

The pressure then given by

$$\frac{PV}{NkT} = -\frac{v}{2kT}\left[\frac{\partial\psi(o)}{\partial v}\right]_T + v\left(\frac{\partial \ln v_f}{\partial v}\right)_T \tag{121}$$

The first term is the potential part of the pressure resulting from the potential energy of all the molecules placed at the centers of their cells and the second term is the thermal part of the pressure resulting from the motion of the molecules in their cells. Performing these differentiations yields, since $a^3 = \sqrt{2}v$,

$$\left(\frac{\partial \psi(o)}{\partial v}\right)_T = \frac{4z\epsilon}{v}\left(\frac{1}{v^{*2}} - \frac{1}{v^{*4}}\right) \tag{122}$$

$$\left(\frac{\partial \ln v_f}{\partial v}\right)_T = \frac{1}{v} + \frac{1}{g}\frac{1}{v}\frac{4z}{T^*}\int_0^{y_m}\left[\frac{l(y)}{v^{*4}} - \frac{m(y)}{v^{*2}}\right]\sqrt{y}$$

$$\times \exp\left\{-\frac{z}{T^*}\left[\frac{l(y)}{v^{*4}} - \frac{2m(y)}{v^{*2}}\right]\right\} dy \tag{123}$$

The equation of state in the Lennard-Jones and Devonshire theory is thus

$$\frac{PV}{NkT} = 1 + \frac{2z}{T^*}\left[\frac{1}{v^{*4}}\left(1 + \frac{2g_l}{g}\right) - \frac{1}{v^{*2}}\left(1 + \frac{2g_m}{g}\right)\right] \tag{124}$$

where

$$g(v^*, T^*) = \int_0^{y_m}\sqrt{y}\exp\left\{-\frac{z}{T^*}\left[\frac{l(y)}{v^{*4}} - \frac{2m(y)}{v^{*2}}\right]\right\} dy \tag{118}$$

$$g_l(v^*, T^*) = \int_0^{y_m}l(y)\sqrt{y}\left\{-\frac{z}{T^*}\left[\frac{l(y)}{v^{*4}} - \frac{2m(y)}{v^{*2}}\right]\right\} dy \tag{125}$$

$$g_m(v^*, T^*) = \int_0^{y_m}m(y)\sqrt{y}\left\{-\frac{z}{T^*}\left[\frac{l(y)}{v^{*4}} - \frac{2m(y)}{v^{*2}}\right]\right\} dy \tag{126}$$

These integrals have been tabulated by several authors (26, 36, 52). In the original papers of Lennard-Jones and Devonshire the effect of the 6 second nearest neighbors at a distance of $a\sqrt{2}$ and the 24 third nearest neighbors at a distance $a\sqrt{3}$ on the lattice energy (but not the free volume) was included resulting in a change in the coefficient of $1/v^{*2}$ in Eq. (124) to $(1.2 + 2g_m/g)$. The most extensive calculations on the Lennard-Jones and Devonshire equation of state are those of Wentorf et al. (63), who included the effect of the first 3 neighboring shells on both the lattice energy and the free volume and obtained the following equation of state

$$\frac{PV}{NkT} = 1 + \frac{2z}{T^*}\left[\frac{1}{v^{*4}}\left(1.0110 + \frac{2G_L}{G}\right) - \frac{1}{v^{*2}}\left(1.2045 + \frac{2G_M}{G}\right)\right] \tag{127}$$

where G, G_L, and G_M are integrals like g, g_l, and g_m except that $l(y)$ and

$m(y)$ are replaced by the functions

$$L(y) = l(y) + \tfrac{1}{128} l(\tfrac{1}{2}y) + \tfrac{2}{729} l(\tfrac{1}{3}y) \qquad (128)$$

$$M(y) = m(y) + \tfrac{1}{16} m(\tfrac{1}{2}y) + \tfrac{2}{27} m(\tfrac{1}{3}y) \qquad (129)$$

The expansion of Eq. (124) in powers of v^*/v has no first power term so that the second virial coefficient is zero.

The molar volumes of the liquid under its vapor pressure may be directly obtained, at low vapor pressures, from Eq. (124) by setting $P = 0$. The result of this calculation is compared with experimental results in Fig. 7. The agreement can be considerably improved by assuming a smaller coordination number, say $z = 10$. The vapor pressure of the liquid can be obtained by equating the Gibbs free energy of the liquid to that of the vapor. The contribution PV_{1iq} to the Gibbs free energy may be neglected and therefore

$$G_l = NkT \ln \left(\frac{h^2}{2\pi mkT}\right)^{3/2} + \frac{N\psi(o)}{2} - NkT \ln v_f - NkT \qquad (130)$$

Except in the critical region the vapor may be assumed to be ideal and therefore

$$G_g = NkT \ln \left(\frac{h^2}{2\pi mkT}\right)^{3/2} - NkT \ln \frac{eV}{N} + PV$$

$$= NkT \ln \left(\frac{h^2}{2\pi mkT}\right)^{3/2} - NkT \ln \frac{V}{N}$$

$$= NkT \ln \left(\frac{h^2}{2\pi mkT}\right)^{3/2} + NkT \ln P - NkT \ln kT \qquad (131)$$

Equating the two free energies gives

$$\ln P = \ln kT - \ln v_f + \frac{\psi(o)}{2kT} - 1 \qquad (132)$$

The theoretical values of the vapor pressure are compared with experiment in Fig. 8 and is seen to be somewhat too low. Using $z = 10$ gives vapor pressures which are somewhat too large.

Critical constants have been calculated by Wentorf et al. for the three shell modification and are tabulated in Table III. Only for T_c^* is the agreement satisfactory.

The above theory can be applied to quantum liquids. The only modification is that the integrations over momenta and coordinates used in evalu-

TABLE III

Reduced Critical Constants (63)

	T_c^*	V_c^*	P_c^*	$P_c^* V_c^*/T_c^*$
Experimental	1.26	3.15	0.117	0.292
L J D	1.30	1.77	0.434	0.591

ating Eq. (116) must be replaced by a sum over the energy levels which can be obtained by solving Schrödinger's equation. Levelt and Hurst (38) have recently done this for liquid hydrogen.

D. Recent Modifications

Janssens and Prigogine (30) and Pople (51) have studied the effects of multiple occupancy of cells. Their calculations showed some numerical improvement and made the theory conceptually more clear. In particular they found that in their model the communal entropy gradually increased from zero to Nk with decreasing density and did not appear abruptly on melting as Lennard-Jones and Devonshire had supposed. A second type of improvement is to allow the number of cells to exceed the number of molecules so that some of the cells are unoccupied or are *holes* in the liquid. This suggestion has been investigated by Cernuschi and Eyring (8) and successively refined by Ono (47), Peek and Hill (49), Rowlinson and Curtiss (53), deBoer (3), and Blomgren (1). These hole theories show little improvement over the treatment of Lennard-Jones and Devonshire. It is interesting to note, though, that these theories provide a non-zero second virial coefficient which shows surprisingly good agreement with the experimental values. Again it is found that the communal entropy appears gradually. These theories also have the conceptual advantage of accounting for the decrease in coordination numbers. Mayer and co-workers (40) have proposed a related hole theory with similar results. It should not be surprising that these hole theories yield little improvement over the Lennard-Jones and Devonshire model since the assumption of a spherically symmetric potential in the cells is even more inadequate if empty cells are considered. Recent work of de Boer, Cohen, and co-workers (4) on a cell cluster model has at least formally been able to consider the effect of correlations of motions of neighboring molecules but has not yet yielded numerical results for any realistic intermolecular potentials.

It is possible that these extensions of the Lennard-Jones and Devonshire theory may be applied in thermodynamic studies of more complex clathrate type systems than those (Chapters 6, 7, and 10) in which the cells are spherically symmetrical and contain only one molecule.

In addition to the above free volume theories, two quite different approaches have proved illuminating in describing the thermodynamic properties of liquids. These are firstly the Significant Structure Theory (17) which considers the liquid as being much like a solid except that there is a large number of holes present which confer gas-like degrees of freedom on neighboring molecules, and secondly theories based on the evaluation of the radial distribution function (5, 34). The evaluation of the radial distribution function involves the solution of some very complex integral equations and for this reason the method has progressed but little beyond the superposition principle of Kirkwood (33) until the recent work of Meeron (41), de Boer (37), Morita (45), and others.

IV. THERMODYNAMICS AND KINETICS OF IMPERFECTIONS IN STOICHIOMETRIC SOLIDS

A. The Boltzmann Factor for Entropy

It is well known from thermodynamics that if one mole each of two different perfect gases, at the same temperature and pressure, are allowed to diffuse into one another, the temperature and pressure remaining constant, the entropy is increased by an amount $2R \ln 2$. As a result of the diffusion a certain degree of knowledge has been lost, since before the diffusion the position of a molecule also gave knowledge of its species whereas after the diffusion this is no longer true. In other words an element of randomness has been introduced. Because of this it is reasonable to postulate a relationship between the entropy of a system and the randomness or degree of disorder of the system in the given state. Therefore

$$S = f(W) \tag{133}$$

where W is the number of a priori equally probable states accessible to the system.

The form of the function $f(W)$ may be obtained by means of the following argument. Consider two separate systems with entropies S_1 and S_2.

$$S_1 = f(W_1), \qquad S_2 = f(W_2) \tag{134}$$

The entropy of the combined system is

$$S_1 + S_2 \tag{135}$$

And since the systems are independent

$$W = W_1 W_2 \tag{136}$$

Thus

$$S_1 + S_2 = f(W_1 W_2) \tag{137}$$

The only functional relationship that can exist between S and W which satisfies Eq. (137) is

$$S = k' \ln W + C \tag{138}$$

where k' and C are some constants. Assuming that W is 1 at absolute zero then C is equal to zero because of the third law of thermodynamics. The only remaining difficulty is to evaluate the constant k'. To do this it is first necessary to calculate W. Assume that there are n_i molecules in the system occupying the energy level ϵ_i which has degeneracy ω_i. The number of ways of realizing this situation is

$$W\{n_i\} = N! \prod_i \frac{\omega_i{}^{n_i}}{n_i!} \tag{139}$$

Therefore,

$$W = \sum_{\{n_i\}} W\{n_i\} = \sum_{\{n_i\}} N! \prod_i \frac{\omega_i{}^{n_i}}{n_i!} \tag{140}$$

The equilibrium distribution of the n_i, Eq. (11), is overwhelmingly more probable than any other distribution and therefore the sum in Eq. (140) may be replaced by the dominant term corresponding to the equilibrium distribution. The entropy then becomes

$$S = k'[\ln N! + \sum_i (n_i \ln \omega_i - \ln n_i!)] \tag{141}$$

If Stirling's approximation is used

$$S = k'[N \ln N + \sum_i n_i(\ln \omega_i - \ln n_i)] \tag{142}$$

where

$$\sum_i n_i = N \tag{143}$$

has been used. Substituting for the values of the n_i yields

$$S = k'\left[N \ln \sum_i \omega_i e^{-\epsilon_i/kT} + \frac{\sum_i n_i \epsilon_i}{kT} \right] \tag{144}$$

Comparison with Eq. (17) shows that k' is the Boltzmann constant so that Eq. (138) becomes

$$S = k \ln W \tag{145}$$

B. Structural Imperfections

There are two ways in which lattice vacancies can arise in a crystal. Firstly, a lattice site may be vacant. This type of imperfection is usually called a *Schottky defect*. Secondly, an atom may migrate from a lattice site to an intersitial lattice position forming a vacancy and an interstitial atom. This type of imperfection is called a *Frenkel defect*. These two types of imperfections are illustrated in Figs. 6 and 7 of Chapter 1.

1. SCHOTTKY DEFECT (54, 59)

The number of Schottky defects in a crystal may be calculated as follows. Let W_s be the energy necessary to form a Schottky defect and let ΔV_s be the volume associated with the formation of a Schottky defect. This volume change will not necessarily equal one atomic volume because the lattice will tend to relax around the vacancy site. Further let n be the number of Schottky defects and N the total number of atoms in the crystal. The configurational entropy due to the n vacancies is

$$S_{\text{conf}} = k \ln \frac{N!}{(N-n)!n!} \tag{146}$$

Therefore, provided no two vacancies are nearest neighbors

$$G_s = nW_s - kT \ln \frac{N!}{(N-n)!n!} - nT\Delta S_{\text{th}} + Pn\Delta V_s \tag{147}$$

where P is the pressure and ΔS_{th} is the increase in thermal entropy per vacancy. Applying Stirling's approximation

$$G_s = n(W_s - T\Delta S_{\text{th}} + P\Delta V_s)$$
$$- kT(N \ln N - (N-n) \ln (N-n) - n \ln n) \tag{148}$$

At equilibrium $\partial G/\partial n = 0$ and therefore

$$W_s - T\Delta S_{\text{th}} + P\Delta V_s - kT \ln \frac{N-n}{n} = 0$$

$$\frac{n}{N-n} = \exp\left(-\frac{W_s - T\Delta S_{\text{th}} + P\Delta V_s}{kT}\right) \tag{149}$$

At all except very high pressures $P\Delta V_s$ is negligible. Also $n \ll N$ and therefore Eq. (149) becomes

$$n/N = e^{\Delta S_{\text{th}}/k}e^{-W_s/kT} \tag{150}$$

To obtain the form of ΔS_{th} assume the crystal to be an Einstein solid. That is a crystal in which all the atoms vibrate harmonically with a single frequency ν. At high temperatures $kT \gg h\nu$: the partition function for a single harmonic oscillator becomes

$$Z = \frac{kT}{h\nu} \tag{151}$$

and therefore the thermal entropy is given by

$$S = 3Nk\left(1 + \ln\frac{kT}{h\nu}\right) \tag{152}$$

In the imperfect crystal atoms neighboring a vacancy will have a vibrational frequency smaller than ν because the restoring forces are reduced. This will be particularly true along the direction of the line joining the atom and the vacancy. For convenience assume that each of the three vibrational modes of an atom next to a vacancy have frequency $\nu' < \nu$. If z is the number of nearest neighbors then in the imperfect crystal there are $3nz$ oscillators of frequency ν', and $3N - 3nz$ oscillators of frequency ν. On this basis

$$\Delta S_{th} = 3zk\left(1 + \ln\frac{kT}{h\nu'}\right) + 3\left(\frac{N}{n} - z\right)k\left(1 + \ln\frac{kT}{h\nu}\right)$$

$$- 3\frac{N}{n}k\left(1 + \ln\frac{kT}{h\nu}\right) \tag{153}$$

$$= 3zk\ln\left(\nu/\nu'\right)$$

so that

$$n/N = (\nu/\nu')^{3z}e^{-W_s/kT} \tag{154}$$

In the above analysis it has been assumed that W_s is not temperature dependent. Further details about this problem can be found in the books by Mott and Gurney (44) and by Van Bueren (7).

2. FRENKEL DEFECT (20)

Let W_f be the energy necessary to form a Frenkel defect and ΔV_f be the volume associated with the formation of a Frenkel defect. Further let N be the number of atoms and N' the number of interstitial positions in the crystal. The configurational entropy is then

$$S_{con} = k\ln\frac{N!}{(N-n)!n!}\frac{N'!}{(N'-n)!n!} \tag{155}$$

Therefore

$$G_f = n(W_f - T\Delta S_{th} + P\Delta V_f) - kT[N \ln N - (N - n) \ln (N - n)$$
$$- n \ln n + N' \ln N' - (N' - n) \ln (N' - n) - n \ln n] \quad (156)$$

where Stirling's approximation has been applied.
At equilibrium $\partial G_f/\partial n = 0$ and thus

$$W_f - T\Delta S_{th} + P\Delta V_f = kT \ln \frac{(N - n)(N' - n)}{n^2}$$

$$\frac{n^2}{(N - n)(N' - n)} = \exp\left[-\frac{W_f - T\Delta S_{th} + P\Delta V_f}{kT}\right] \quad (157)$$

As before if one neglects the pressure effects then

$$\frac{n}{\sqrt{NN'}} = e^{\Delta S_{th}/2k}e^{-W_f/2kT} \quad (158)$$

where n has been neglected with respect to N and N'.

In a crystal both types of imperfections will exist but the one with lower energy will in general predominate.

3. Structural Imperfections in Ionic Crystals

Consider the formation of Schottky defects in the ionic crystal B^+X^-. In contrast to the crystals considered above two kinds of vacancies can be formed: positive ion and negative ion vacancies. Suppose that positive ion vacancies were formed in the crystal by transporting positive ions from the interior to the surface of the crystal and that no negative ion vacancies were formed. The surface of the crystal would then become positively charged and the interior would become negatively charged. Space charges would be set up which would oppose the formation of more positive ion vacancies but would favor the formation of negative ion vacancies. As a result it is to be expected that an ionic crystal would have nearly equal numbers of positive ion and negative ion vacancies. The Gibbs free energy of the imperfect crystal is then, in the absence of pressure effects,

$$G_F = n[W_1 + W_2 - T\Delta S_{th}]$$
$$- 2kT[N \ln N - (N - n) \ln (N - n) - n \ln n] \quad (159)$$

where Stirling's approximation has been applied. The symbols W_1 and W_2 represent respectively the energies required to form positive and negative ion vacancies and N is the number of positive or negative ions. The factor

2 arises because the positive and negative ion vacancies make equal contributions to the configurational entropy. At equilibrium

$$W_1 + W_2 - T\Delta S_{\text{th}} + 2kT \ln \frac{N - n}{n} = 0 \tag{160}$$

Neglecting n with respect to N

$$\frac{n}{N} = e^{\Delta S_{\text{th}}/2k}e^{-W/2kT} \tag{161}$$

where $W = W_1 + W_2$

In the case of Frenkel defects in an ionic crystal it is not necessary that there be equal numbers of positive and negative ion Frenkel defects. In general either the positive or negative ion Frenkel defects will predominate and therefore Eq. (158) is applicable.

On the basis of theoretical and experimental evidence (*31, 32, 43, 58*) it is generally thought that Schottky defects predominate in the alkali halides whereas Frenkel defects predominate in the silver halides. It is to be noted that the production of Schottky defects results in an increase in volume of the crystal with no change in mass and therefore results in a lowering of the density. The production of Frenkel defects does not at least to first order, change the density of the crystal.

C. Diffusion and Ionic Conductivity

1. DIFFUSION

Atoms will migrate in a crystal due to a difference in the chemical potential. This process is called diffusion. The driving force, f_{ix}, for the diffusion of atoms of species i in the x direction is usually assumed to be given by

$$f_{ix} = -\frac{1}{N}\left(\frac{\partial \mu_i}{\partial x}\right)_T \tag{162}$$

where μ_i is the chemical potential for one mole of atoms of species i and has hence been divided by N. The net flow, J_{ix}, is then

$$J_{ix} = -u_i \frac{C_i}{N} \frac{\partial \mu_i}{\partial x} \tag{163}$$

where C_i is the number of atoms of species i per unit volume and u_i is their average drift velocity for unit driving force for a dilute concentration of atoms of species i, $\mu_i = RT \ln C_i + \mu°_i$. Therefore

$$J_{ix} = -kTu_i \frac{\partial C_i}{\partial x} \tag{164}$$

The coefficient, kTu_i, is usually constant so that

$$J_{ix} = -D_i \frac{\partial C_i}{\partial x} \tag{165}$$

where D_i is the *diffusion coefficient*. Eq. (165) is known as *Fick's law*. D_i will only be a scalar in an isotropic medium and will in general be a tensor.

Comparing Eqs. (164) and (165) yields $D_i = kTu_i$. Defining the electric mobility, l_i, as $l_i = z_i e u_i$, where $z_i e$ is the charge on an atom of species i, gives the Nernst–Einstein relation

$$D_i = \frac{kT}{z_i e} l_i \tag{166}$$

It is to be emphasized that the above definition of the electric mobility is sensible only if diffusion and conduction are due to the same mechanism. Thus the Nernst–Einstein relation is applicable only under these circumstances.

Three simple mechanisms for diffusion in a solid have been proposed. These are illustrated in Fig. 10. Firstly, two atoms may interchange positions. This is not a common process since large intermediate distortions are involved resulting in a rather high energy barrier. Secondly, an atom may wander as an interstitial atom. This process is important in many metals and the alkali halides. More complicated mechanisms for diffusion have been proposed but will not be considered here.

An expression for the diffusion coefficient may be obtained from the theory of absolute reaction rates. Consider Fig. 11. The wells represent the

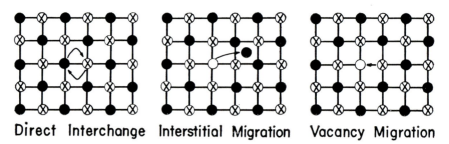

Direct Interchange   Interstitial Migration   Vacancy Migration

Fig. 10. Mechanisms for diffusion in crystals.

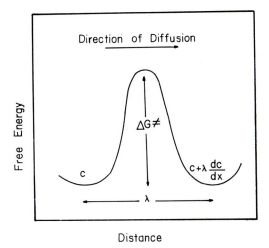

Distance

FIG. 11. Schematic plot of the potential energy for diffusion.

stable positions separated by the lattice constant. If the concentrations of diffusing atoms in the two wells are respectively C and $C + \lambda dC/dx$ then the number jumping forward per unit time per unit volume is

$$k'\lambda C \qquad (167)$$

and the number jumping backward per unit time per unit volume is

$$k'\lambda \left(C + \lambda \frac{dC}{dx} \right) \qquad (168)$$

where k' is the specific rate constant and is given by

$$k' = \frac{kT}{h} \exp\left(-\Delta G^{\ddagger}/RT \right) \qquad (169)$$

Therefore

$$D - \frac{dC}{dx} = \lambda k'C - \lambda k'\left(C + \lambda \frac{dC}{dx} \right) \qquad (170)$$

$$D = \lambda^2 k' = \lambda^2 \frac{kT}{h} \exp\left(-\Delta G^{\ddagger}/RT \right) \qquad (171)$$

Equation (171) should be multiplied by a factor determined by the geometry of the lattice and the mechanism involved in the diffusion. For example, for vacancy diffusion Eq. (171) should be multiplied by the probability that an adjacent lattice site will be vacant. Therefore, for vacancy diffusion in an alkali halide

$$D = \tfrac{1}{3}\lambda^2 \frac{kT}{h} \frac{n}{N} \exp\left(-\Delta G^{\ddagger}/RT\right)$$

$$= \tfrac{1}{3}\lambda^2 \frac{kT}{h} \exp\left(\Delta S_{th}/2k\right) \exp\left(-\frac{W/2 + \Delta g^{\ddagger}}{kT}\right) \tag{172}$$

where $\Delta g^{\ddagger}$ is the Gibbs free energy of activation per particle. The factor $1/3$ is inserted because in a face-centered cubic lattice only four of twelve nearest neighbor positions lie in the forward direction.

2. Ionic Conductivity

If a potential difference is applied to an alkali or silver halide crystal an electric current can be measured. The current is much too large to be explained in terms of electron motions since for the temperatures involved the number of electrons in the conduction band is too small. Since Faraday's law is obeyed the current must be due to the motion of ions under the influence of the field.

In the alkali halides ionic conductivity, like diffusion, can be explained in terms of the motion of vacancies. Experiments have shown that the positive ion vacancies are much more mobile than the negative ion vacancies. The electric conductivity, σ, may be related to the electric mobility by

$$\sigma = Czel \tag{173}$$

Hence combining Eqs. (166), (172), and (173) gives

$$\sigma = \frac{z^2 e^2}{6h} e^{\Delta S_{th}/2k} \exp\left(-\frac{W/2 + \Delta g^{\ddagger}}{kT}\right) \tag{174}$$

since $C = 1/2\lambda^2$ for a face-centered cubic lattice.

If small amounts of the halides of divalent metals are added to alkali halide crystals then at lower temperatures the ionic conductivity departs from the relationship expressed in Eq. (174), and the ionic conductivity at a given temperature is proportional to the concentration of divalent metal indicating that the vacancies introduced by the divalent metals are responsible for the conduction.

V. NON-STOICHIOMETRIC SOLIDS

A. Color Centers in Non-Stoichiometric Ionic Crystals

Pure alkali halide crystals are transparent throughout the entire visible spectrum. However, it has been known for many years that an alkali halide heated in the presence of the vapor of its alkali metal and then quickly cooled becomes colored. For example, a sodium chloride crystal heated in the presence of sodium vapor becomes yellow and a potassium chloride crystal heated in the presence of potassium vapor becomes violet.

The generally accepted explanation of this phenomenon is due to de Boer (2). The excess alkali atoms are believed to ionize at the surface and diffuse into the crystal where they occupy cation lattice positions. An equal number of anion vacancies are created. Each of these anion vacancies behaves like a positive charge and can trap one of the electrons freed by the ionization of the excess alkali metal atoms. An electron bound to an anion vacancy is called an *F center* (the German word for color is *Farbe*). There are a number of experimental facts which support this view.

(1) The absorption band is characteristic of the crystal and not of the alkali metal in the vapor. The *F* band in potassium chloride is unchanged if the crystal is heated in sodium vapor rather than potassium. Moreover, the same *F* band is formed when the stoichiometric crystal is irradiated with x-rays or some other type of radiation which produces free electrons. These free electrons are then bound by anion vacancies forming *F* centers.

(2) The colored crystal is less dense than the stoichiometric crystal which rules out the possibility of the absorption band being due to an electron bound to an interstitial cation.

(3) The paramagnetic susceptibility of an *F* center corresponds closely to the spin contribution of a relatively free electron.

The concentration of *F* centers in an alkali halide crystal in equilibrium with the vapor of an alkali metal may be calculated in the following manner. Assuming the vapor to be monatomic, the Gibbs free energy of the vapor is

$$G_V = -N_V kT \left[\ln \left(\frac{2\pi mkT}{h^2} \right)^{3/2} \frac{V}{N_V} \right] \tag{175}$$

where N_V is the number of atoms of the vapor which are contained in a volume V. The increase in free energy if one atom is removed from the vapor is

$$kT \left[\ln \left(\frac{2\pi mkT}{h^2} \right)^{3/2} \frac{V}{N_V} \right] \tag{176}$$

If the solid contains N ion pairs and n_F F centers then the configurational entropy is

$$S_{\text{conf}} = k \ln \frac{(N + n_F)!}{N!n_F!} \tag{177}$$

Therefore if W_0 is the energy required to add an alkali atom to the crystal and form an F center then using Stirling's approximation and neglecting pressure effects

$$G = n_F \left[W_0 + kT \ln \left(\frac{2\pi mkT}{h^2} \right)^{3/2} \frac{V}{N_V} \right]$$

$$- kT[(N + n_F) \ln (N + n_F) - N \ln N - n_F \ln n_F] \tag{178}$$

at equilibrium $\partial G/\partial n_F = 0$ and therefore

$$W_0 + kT \ln \left(\frac{2\pi mkT}{h^2} \right)^{3/2} \frac{V}{N_V} - kT \ln \frac{N + n_F}{n_F} = 0 \tag{179}$$

Therefore

$$\frac{n_F}{N} = \frac{N_V}{V} \left(\frac{2\pi mkT}{h^2} \right)^{-3/2} e^{-W_0/kT} \tag{180}$$

In deriving Eq. (180) the change in the thermal entropy due to the formation of F centers has not been considered.

The F center absorption is believed to be due to the excitation of the F center electron into an excited state below the conduction band rather than into the conduction band. The width of the absorption band is believed to be due to the lattice vibrations of the ions.

There is evidence for other types of color centers involving trapped electrons. For example, if a crystal already containing F centers is irradiated with light in the F band a broad band on the red side of the F band appears. This new band is called the F' band. Since, experimentally, two F centers disappear for each incident quantum it is believed that the quantum ionizes an F center and that the free electron so produced wanders through the crystal until it is trapped by another F center. Such an anion vacancy with two trapped electrons is called an F' center. F' centers are long-lived only at low temperatures. Other centers believed to cause optical absorption bands in alkali halide crystals are the R_1 center which has one electron bound to two anion vacancies, the R_2 center which has two electrons bound to two anion vacancies, and the M center which has one electron bound to two anion vacancies and one cation vacancy, these groups of vacancies being close together. In some cases it is possible to heat an alkali halide crystal in a halogen vapor and produce a series of color centers analogous to the centers discussed above. Such centers are called *V centers* and should consist of holes bound to cation vacancies. The exact models for these *V* centers are, however, somewhat in doubt. For a more complete discussion of color centers in alkali halide crystals the reader is referred to the review by Seitz (*55*) and to the book by Mott and Gurney (*44*).

B. Oxidation of Metals at High Temperatures

1. INTRODUCTION

In solids like cuprous oxide there are cation vacancies. To compensate for the smaller number of cations and the consequent loss of positive charge a Cu^+ ion must be transformed into a Cu^{2+} ion for each vacancy formed, resulting in a departure from stoichiometry. The departure from stoichiometry may be reflected by writing the formula for cuprous oxide as $Cu_{2-x}O$. Other similar examples are $Fe_{1-x}O$, $Fe_{1-x}S$, $Co_{1-x}O$, and $Ni_{1-x}O$ (see Chapter 3). The formation of these cation vacancies may be considered simply as a solution of CuO in Cu_2O. However, the electron holes $\oplus$ associated with the valency differences are frequently not fixed at one specific ion site but readily migrate. For this reason the electron hole is frequently represented separately in the reaction, i.e.,

$$\tfrac{1}{2}O_2(g) \rightleftharpoons Cu_2O + 2\square_{Cu^+} + 2\oplus \tag{181}$$

where $\square_{Cu^+}$ represents a cation vacancy.

Applying the law of mass action

$$\frac{C_\square^2 C_\oplus^2}{P_{O_2}^{1/2}} = K \tag{182}$$

Since the concentrations of cation vacancies and the concentration of electron holes are equal and the electrical conductivity is proportional to $C_\oplus$, we have

$$\sigma_\oplus = \text{constant } P_{O_2}^{1/8} \tag{183}$$

which has been observed to be essentially correct (*10*). The case of $Fe_{1-x}O$ is similarly dealt with in Chapter 5, Section III, B. Compounds with interstitial anions are less common but an example is UO_{2+x} (see Chapter 3, Section II.C.2).

Similarly there are compounds with anion vacancies such as ZrO_{2-x} and TiO_{2-x}. Also oxides occur in which there are interstitial cations. Examples are $Zn_{1+x}O$, $Cr_{2+x}O_3$, $Cd_{1+x}O$. At high temperatures ZnO dissociates as follows

$$ZnO \rightleftharpoons O_{Zn^+} + \ominus + \tfrac{1}{2}O_2(g) \tag{184a}$$

or

$$ZnO \rightleftharpoons O_{Zn^{2+}} + 2\ominus + \tfrac{1}{2}O_2(g) \tag{184b}$$

where $\ominus$ represents a free electron and O_{Zn^+} and $O_{Zn^{2+}}$ represent interstitial cations. Applying the law of mass action gives

$$\sigma_\ominus = \text{constant } P_{O_2}^{-1/4} \tag{185a}$$

$$\sigma_\ominus = \text{constant } P_{O_2}^{-1/6} \tag{185b}$$

respectively, which have been observed to be essentially correct (42).

2. The Parabolic Rate Law

This discussion will be limited to metals which form a thick compact layer of oxide on the metal surface. Under these conditions the reaction will proceed only as fast as the reactants diffuse across the oxide layer. Inasmuch as the layer is compact it will be assumed that there is no diffusion through pores or grain boundaries and therefore only cations and anions diffuse through the oxide layer. For thick layers the concentrations of the reactants at the two boundaries will be independent of time and thermodynamic equilibrium at the respective interfaces is practically established. Diffusion across the oxide layer is then the only rate-determining process. Therefore, it follows that the rate of increase in thickness of the oxide layer is inversely proportional to the instantaneous thickness Δx

$$\frac{d(\Delta x)}{dt} = \frac{k'}{\Delta x} \tag{186}$$

Integrating

$$(\Delta x)^2 = 2k't \tag{187}$$

This is the parabolic rate law (50, 57).

3. Wagner's Theory of Oxidation

Again this discussion will be limited to metals which form a thick compact layer of oxide on their surface. Assuming that the ions and electrons diffuse across the oxide layer independently then the average drift velocity of ions of type i is

$$v_i = -u_i \left(\frac{1}{N} \frac{d\mu_i}{dx} + z_i e \frac{dV}{dx} \right) \tag{188}$$

where z_i is the valence of an ion of type i, e is the electronic charge and V is the electric potential. If $\dot{n}_i/A$ is the number of moles migrating per unit time per unit area then

$$\frac{\dot{n}_i}{A} = C_i v_i = -C_i u_i \left(\frac{1}{N} \frac{d\mu_i}{dx} + z_i e \frac{dV}{dx} \right) \tag{189}$$

where C_i is the concentration of ions of type i in molecules per unit volume.

It is possible to express the u_i in terms of the electrical conductivity and the transport number, t_i, of the ions of the ith type. The transport numbers are the portions of the total current carried by a given ion. The current is given by

$$I = 300 A \sigma \left| \frac{dV}{dx} \right| \tag{190}$$

where the factor of 300 has been inserted so that I is in amperes. In the case of electrolysis the contribution of $d\mu_i/dx$ is relatively negligible and hence

$$\left(\frac{\dot{n}_i}{A} \right)_{\text{electrolysis}} = \frac{300}{96,500} t_i \sigma \left| \frac{dV}{dx} \right| \tag{191}$$

Comparing Eqs. (189) and (191) gives

$$\frac{\dot{n}_i}{A} = \frac{300}{96,500} \frac{t_i \sigma}{|z_i| eN} \left(-\frac{d\mu_i}{dx} - z_i eN \frac{dV}{dx} \right) \tag{192}$$

If we let $i = 1, 2$, and 3 for the cations, anions, and electrons respectively then

$$\dot{n}_1 = \dot{n}_2 + \dot{n}_3 \tag{193}$$

Therefore

$$\frac{dV}{dx} = \frac{1}{Ne} \left(-\frac{t_1}{|z_1|} \frac{d\mu_1}{dx} + \frac{t_2}{|z_2|} \frac{d\mu_2}{dx} + \frac{t_3}{|z_3|} \frac{d\mu_3}{dx} \right) \tag{194}$$

In view of the chemical equilibrium between ions, electrons, and neutral atoms, we have

$$\mu_B = \mu_1 + z_1 \mu_3 \tag{195}$$

$$\mu_X = \mu_2 + z_2 \mu_3 \tag{196}$$

where μ_B and μ_X are respectively the chemical potentials of the metal B and the nonmetal X. These potentials are related by the Gibbs-Duhem equation

$$n_B d\mu_B + n_X d\mu_X = 0 \tag{197}$$

If the deviation from stoichiometry is only slight then Eq. (197) becomes

$$d\mu_B \simeq - \left| \frac{z_1}{z_2} \right| d\mu_X \tag{198}$$

Substituting Eqs. (194), (195), (196), and (198) into Eq. (162) gives

$$\frac{\dot{n}_1}{A} = \frac{300}{96,500} \frac{t_1 t_3 \sigma}{Ne} \frac{1}{|z_1|} \frac{d\mu_X}{dx} \tag{199}$$

$$\frac{\dot{n}_2}{A} = -\frac{300}{96,500} \frac{t_2 t_3 \sigma}{Ne} \frac{1}{|z_2|} \frac{d\mu_X}{dx} \tag{200}$$

$$\frac{\dot{n}_3}{A} = \frac{300}{96,500} \frac{(t_1 + t_2) t_3 \sigma}{Ne} \frac{1}{|z_2|} \frac{d\mu_X}{dx} \tag{201}$$

Therefore

$$\frac{\dot{n}_{equ}}{A} = \frac{|\dot{n}_1|}{A} + \frac{|\dot{n}_2|}{A} = \frac{|\dot{n}_3|}{A}$$

$$= \frac{300}{96,500} \frac{(t_1 + t_2) t_3 \sigma}{Ne} \frac{1}{|z_2|} \left| \frac{d\mu_X}{dx} \right| \tag{202}$$

where $\dot{n}_{equ}/A$ is the rate of both outward diffusion of metal ions and inward diffusion of nonmetal ions expressed in equivalents per cm per sec. Integrating over x yields

$$\frac{\dot{n}_{equ}}{A} = \left[\frac{300}{96,500} \frac{1}{Ne} \int_{\mu_X^{(i)}}^{\mu_X^{(a)}} \frac{1}{|z_2|} (t_1 + t_2) t_3 \sigma d\mu_X \right] \frac{1}{\Delta x}$$

$$= k_r \frac{1}{\Delta x} \tag{203}$$

where the superscripts (i) and (a) denote the inner and outer boundaries. Equation (203) was first obtained by Wagner (60). Hauffe (25) has recently obtained Eq. (203) in a different manner. Wagner (61) has also obtained an equation similar to Eq. (203) which does not contain the transport numbers or the conductivity but depends on the diffusion coefficients, D_1 and D_2, of the metal and nonmetal ions.

For further applications of Wagner's theory of oxidation the reader is referred to the above references and to an excellent review by Hauffe (24).

Other examples of processes in crystals involving non-stoichiometry are to be found in the reduction of metallic oxides and in phase changes in oxides and sulfides.

VI. CONCLUDING REMARKS

It is evident from the above discussion that statistical mechanics and reaction rate theory provide a broad theoretical basis for discussing the thermodynamics and kinetics of solids. The theory not only includes stoichiometric solids but can be extended without difficulty to non-stoichiometric solids. The theory is exact in so far as the transmission coefficient κ can be calculated.

In this connection it is of interest to consider the following calculation of Hirschfelder and Wigner (28). Consider an adiabatic reaction in which the system of reactants and products are in thermal equilibrium. Therefore equal numbers of activated complexes will be moving in each direction across the top of the barrier. Suppose that A is the number of systems per unit time arriving at the activated state directly from the initial state and that B is the number of systems per unit time arriving at the activated state directly from the final state. Further suppose that ρ_i and ρ_f are the probabilities for reflection from the forward to the backward direction and from the backward to the forward direction respectively. The resulting situation is depicted in Fig. 12 on the assumption that the probability of crossing is independent of the number of times the system has previously crossed the barrier. The total number of crossings in the forward direction (i.e., from left to right) is given by

$$N_{l \to r} = A(1 + \rho_i\rho_f + \rho_i^2\rho_f^2 + \cdots) + B\rho_i(1 + \rho_i\rho_f + \rho_i^2\rho_f^2 + \cdots)$$
$$= \frac{A + B\rho_i}{1 - \rho_i\rho_f} \tag{204}$$

while the number of crossings in the backward direction is given by

$$N_{r \to l} = A\rho_f(1 + \rho_i\rho_f + \rho_i^2\rho_f^2 + \cdots) + B(1 + \rho_i\rho_f + \rho_i^2\rho_f^2 + \cdots)$$
$$= \frac{A\rho_f + B}{1 - \rho_i\rho_f} \tag{205}$$

At equilibrium the two rates are equal and therefore

$$B = A\frac{1 - \rho_f}{1 - \rho_i} \tag{206}$$

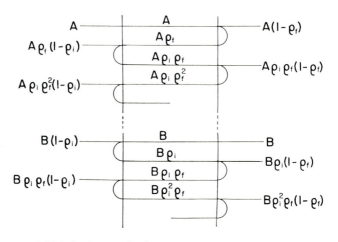

Initial State   Activated State   Final State

FIG. 12. Calculation of the transmission coefficient (28).

Substituting Eq. (206) into (204) gives

$$N_{l \to r} = \frac{A}{1 - \rho_i} \tag{207}$$

The net number of systems crossing from the initial to the final states is given by

$$N_{i \to f} = A(1 - \rho_f)(1 + \rho_i \rho_f + \rho_i^2 \rho_f^2 + \cdots)$$
$$= \frac{A(1 - \rho_f)}{1 - \rho_i \rho_f} \tag{208}$$

The transmission coefficient is therefore

$$\kappa = \frac{N_{i \to f}}{N_{l \to r}} = \frac{(1 - \rho_i)(1 - \rho_f)}{1 - \rho_i \rho_f} \tag{209}$$

For κ to be of the order of unity it is necessary that ρ_i and ρ_f both be small.

Nonadiabatic reactions are considered in the book of Glasstone, *et al.* (22).

More recently Wall *et al.* (62), have numerically solved the classical equations of motion using the London-Eyring-Polanyi (12, 39) form for the potential energy of the colinear system $H + H_2$ and have obtained values for the transmission coefficient. Quantum mechanical calculations are being carried out by Mortensen and Pitzer (46).

With the increasing availability of high speed digital computers more attention should be focused on the problem of obtaining values for the transmission coefficient.

ACKNOWLEDGMENTS

The authors wish to acknowledge the useful discussions they have had with Professors Milton Wadsworth and Peter Gibbs of the University of Utah and Professor LeRoy Eyring of Arizona State University.

One of the authors (D.H.) wishes to thank the Corning Glass Foundation for a research fellowship awarded him during the period 1959–1961.

REFERENCES

1. Blomgrem, G., *J. Chem. Phys.* **34**, 1307 (1961).
2. de Boer, J., *Rec. trav. chim.* **56**, 301 (1937).
3. de Boer, J., *Proc. Roy. Soc.* **A215**, 4 (1952).
4. de Boer, J., *Physica* **20**, 655 (1954); Cohen, E. G. D., de Boer, J., and Salsburg, Z. W., *ibid.* **21**, 137 (1955); **23**, 389 (1957); Salsburg, Z. W., Cohen, E. G. D., Rethmeier, B. C., and de Boer, J., *ibid.* **23**, 407 (1957); Cohen, E. G. D., and Rethmeier, B. C., *ibid.* **24**, 959 (1958); Dahler, J. S., and Cohen, E. G. D., *ibid.* **26**, 81 (1960).
5. Born, M., and Green, H. S., *Proc. Roy. Soc.* **A188**, 10 (1946).
6. Bose, S. N., *Z. Physik* **26**, 178 (1924).
7. van Bueren, H. G., "Imperfections in Crystals." North-Holland, Publ., Amsterdam, 1960.
8. Cernuschi, F., and Eyring, H., *J. Chem. Phys.* **7**, 547 (1939).
9. Dirac, P. A. M., *Proc. Roy. Soc.* **A112**, 661 (1926).
10. Dunwald, H., and Wagner, C., *Z. physik. Chem.* (*Leipzig*) **B17**, 467 (1932).
11. Einstein, A., *Sitzber. preuss. Akad. Wiss. Berlin, Physik.-math. Kl.* **1924**, 261; **1925**, 3, 18.
12. Eyring, H., and Polanyi, M., *Z. physik. Chem.* (*Leipzig*) **B12**, 279 (1931).
13. Eyring, H., *J. Chem. Phys.* **3**, 107 (1935).
14. Eyring, H., *J. Chem. Phys.* **4**, 283 (1936); Eyring, H., and Hirschfelder, J. O., *J. Phys. Chem.* **41**, 249 (1937).
15. Eyring, H., Walter, J., and Kimball, G. E., "Quantum Chemistry." Wiley, New York, 1944.
16. Eyring, H., and Wallenstein, M., *Proc. Natl. Acad. Sci. U.S.* **39**, 138 (1953).
17. Eyring, H., Ree, T., and Hirai, N., *Proc. Natl. Acad. Sci. U.S.* **44**, 683 (1958); Eyring, H., and Ree, T., *ibid.* **47**, 526 (1961).
18. Fermi, E., *Z. Physik* **36**, 902 (1926).
19. Fowler, R., and Guggenheim, E. A., "Statistical Thermodynamics." Cambridge Univ. Press, London and New York, 1939.
20. Frenkel, J., *Z. Physik* **35**, 652 (1926).
21. Gentile, G., *Nuovo cimento* [8] **17**, 493 (1940).
22. Glasstone, S., Laidler, K. J., and Eyring, H., "The Theory of Rate Processes." McGraw-Hill, New York, 1941.
23. ter Haar, D., "Elements of Statistical Mechanics." Holt, Rinehart & Winston, New York, 1955.
24. Hauffe, K., *Progr. in Metal Phys.* **4**, 71 (1953).
25. Hauffe, K., *in* "The Surface Chemistry of Metals and Semi-Conductors" (H. C. Gatos, ed.), pp. 439-482. Wiley, New York, 1959.

26. Hill, T. L., *J. Phys. Chem.* **51**, 1219 (1947).
27. Hirschfelder, J. O., Stevenson, D., and Eyring, H., *J. Chem. Phys.* **5**, 896 (1937).
28. Hirschfelder, J. O., and Wigner, E. P., *J. Chem. Phys.* **7**, 616 (1939).
29. Hirschfelder, J. O., Curtiss, C. F., and Bird, R. B., "Molecular Theory of Gases and Liquids." Wiley, New York, 1954.
30. Janssens, P., and Prigogine, I., *Physica* **16**, 851 (1950).
31. Jost, W., *J. Chem. Phys.* **1**, 466 (1933); *Trans. Faraday Soc.* **34**, 860 (1938).
32. Jost, W., and Nehlep, G., *Z. physik. Chem.* (*Leipzig*) **B32**, 1 (1936); **B34**, 348 (1938).
33. Kirkwood, J. G., *J. Chem. Phys.* **3**, 300 (1935); Kirkwood, J. G., and Boggs, E. M., *ibid.* **10**, 394 (1942).
34. Kirkwood, J. G., Maun, E. K., and Alder, B. J., *J. Chem. Phys.* **18**, 1040 (1950); Kirkwood, J. G., Lewison, V. A., and Alder, B. J., *ibid.* **20**, 929 (1952).
35. Langmuir, I., *J. Am. Chem. Soc.* **40**, 1361 (1918).
36. Lennard-Jones, J. E., and Devonshire, A. F., *Proc. Roy. Soc.* **A163**, 53 (1939); **A165**, 1 (1938).
37. van Leewuen, J. M. J., Groeneveld, J., and de Boer, J., *Physica* **25**, 792 (1959).
38. Levelt, J. M. H., and Hurst, R. P., *J. Chem. Phys.* **32**, 961 (1960).
39. London, F., *Z. Elecktrochem.* **35**, 552 (1929).
40. Mayer, J. E., and Careri, G., *J. Chem. Phys.* **20**, 1001 (1952); Levine, H. B., Mayer, J. E., and Aroeste, H., *ibid.* **26**, 201, 207 (1957); Levine, H. B., *ibid.* **27**, 335 (1957).
41. Meeron, E., *Phys. of Fluids* **1**, 139 (1958); *J. Chem. Phys.* **28**, 505 (1958); **29**, 444 (1958); Meeron, E., and Rodemich, E. R., *Phys. of Fluids* **1**, 246 (1958); Meeron, E., *J. Math. Phys.* **1**, 192 (1960); *Physica* **26**, 445 (1960).
42. Miller, P., *Phys. Rev.* **60**, 890 (1941).
43. Mott, N. F., and Littleton, M. J., *Trans. Faraday Soc.* **34**, 485 (1938).
44. Mott, N. F., and Gurney, R. W., "Electronic Processes in Ionic Crystals," 2nd ed. Cambridge Univ. Press, London and New York, 1948.
45. Morita, T., *Progr. in Theoret. Phys.* (*Kyoto*) **20**, 920 (1958); **21**, 361 (1959); **23**, 175, 829 (1960); Morita, T., and Hiroike, K., *ibid.* **23**, 1003; **24**, 679 (1960); Hiroike, K., *ibid.* **24**, 317 (1960); *J. Phys. Soc. Japan* **15**, 771 (1960).
46. Mortensen, E. M., and Pitzer, K. S., Private communication.
47. Ono, S., *Mem. Fac. Eng. Kyushu Univ.* **10**, 190 (1947).
48. Parlin, R. B., Wallenstein, M. B., Zwolinski, B. J., and Eyring, H., in "Catalysis" (P. H. Emmett, ed.), Vol. II, pp. 368-370. Reinhold, New York, 1955.
49. Peek, H. M., and Hill, T. L., *J. Chem. Phys.* **18**, 1252 (1952).
50. Pilling, N. B., and Bedworth, R. E., *J. Inst. Metals* **29**, 529 (1923).
51. Pople, J. A., *Phil. Mag.* [7] **42**, 459 (1951).
52. Prigogine, I., and Raulier, S., *Physica* **9**, 396 (1942); Prigogine, I., and Garikian, G., *J. chim. phys.* **45**, 273 (1948).
53. Rowlinson, J. S., and Curtiss, C. F., *J. Chem. Phys.* **19**, 1519 (1951).
54. Schottky, W., *Z. physik. Chem.* (*Leipzig*) **B29**, 353 (1935).
55. Seitz, F., *Revs. Modern Phys.* **26**, 7 (1954).

56. Sommerfeld, A., *Sitzber. bayer. Akad. Wiss. München, Math.-naturw. Kl.* **1915**, 425, 459; **1916**, 131.
57. Tamman, G., *Z. anorg. Chem.* **111**, 78 (1920).
58. Tetlow, J., *Ann. Physik* [6] **5**, 63, 71 (1949); *Z. physik. Chem. (Leipzig)* **195**, 197, 213 (1950).
59. Wagner, C., and Schottky, W., *Z. physik. Chem. (Leipzig)* **B11**, 163 (1930).
60. Wagner, C., *Z. physik. Chem. (Leipzig)* **B21**, 25 (1933).
61. Wagner, C., *in* "Atom Movements" (J. Holloman, ed.), pp. 153-173. American Society for Metals, Cleveland, Ohio, 1951.
62. Wall, F. T., Hiller, L. A., Jr., and Mezur, J., *J. Chem. Phys.* **29**, 255 (1958).
63. Wentorf, R. H., Buehler, R. H., Hirschfelder, J. O., and Curtiss, C. F., *J. Chem. Phys.* **18**, 1484 (1950).
64. Wilson, W., *Phil. Mag.* [6] **29**, 795 (1915).

CHAPTER 3

A. D. Wadsley
Division of Mineral Chemistry, C.S.I.R.O.,
Melbourne, Australia

Inorganic
Non-Stoichiometric Compounds

I. Introduction.. 99
  A. Historical.. 99
  B. Scope.. 100
  C. Techniques of Study; Uses and Limitations.................. 101
  D. Order and Disorder of Structural Anomalies................. 102
  E. Structural Causes of Variability of Composition............. 104
II. Oxides.. 104
  A. Binary Oxides and Sulfides BO_x; the $B1$ (NaCl-Type) Structure. 105
  B. Oxides Derived from the $C4$ (Rutile-Type) Structure.......... 108
  C. $BO_{2\pm x}$ Derived from the $C1$ (Fluorite-Type) Structure....... 115
  D. Uranium Oxides UO_{3-x}.................................... 123
  E. Oxides Derived from the DO_9 (ReO$_3$-Type) Structure........ 125
  F. Oxides A_xBO_3 with Tetragonal and Hexagonal Structures...... 136
  G. Multiple Oxides of Mixed Structure with Perovskite-Like
     Fragments.. 140
  H. Hexagonal Oxides ABO_{3-x}................................ 143
  J. Oxides Based upon the Spinel $H1_1$ Structure................. 147
  K. Ternary "Bronzes" $A_xB_3O_4$.............................. 151
  L. Ternary Alkali Titanates.................................... 152
  M. Oxides with the Approximate Formula B_2O_5................ 156
  N. Hydrous Oxides.. 161
III. Chalcogenides (Sulfides, Selenides, Tellurides)................. 165
  A. Chalcogenides BX-BX$_2$ Intermediate between $B8$ and $C6$...... 165
  B. Chalcogenides with B_h (Tungsten Carbide) Structure.......... 177
  C. Copper Chalcogenides BX_x, $0.5 < x < 1$, Related to the Anti-$C1$
     Structure.. 179
  D. Compounds in the Range $BX_{0.5}$–$BX_{1.0}$ Intermediate in Struc-
     ture between $C38$ and Anti-$B10$........................... 182

E. Chalcogenides BX_x, $1.0 < x < 1.5$, with the $B3$ (Zinc Blende)
Structure.. 184
F. Compounds BX_x, $1.33 < x < 1.50$, with the $D7_3$ (Th_3P_4)
Structure.. 185
G. Compounds BX_x, $1.0 < x < 1.8$, Related to the $C33$ (Bi_2Te_2S)
Structure.. 186
H. Compounds Based upon the $D5_8$ (Bi_2S_3) Structure: Copper in
Interstitial Tetrahedral Positions........................ 188
J. Phases Which May Represent Structures Intermediate between
the $B1$ (BX) and $D5_8$ (B_2X_3) Types: The Mineral Sulfosalts.. 190
IV. Classification According to Structure.......................... 197
A. Substitution.. 197
B. Interpolation... 198
C. Subtraction.. 199
D. Shear... 200
E. Intergrowth.. 200
References... 201

I. INTRODUCTION

A. Historical

Chemical thought is traditionally influenced by Dalton's laws of constant and multiple proportions, based originally upon the study of simple ionic and molecular species. These experimental rules are not necessarily all-embracing, however, and Berthollet suggested that compounds might well exist to which they did not apply. It has since become customary to distinguish the *daltonides*, which conform, from the *berthollides*, which do not.

The name berthollide was first used by Kurnakow (*206*) to describe certain alloy phases with a range of composition where the maxima or minima of properties do not coincide with a simple and characteristic formula. The chemistry of metals and their compounds received impetus from an important paper by Wagner and Schottky (*283*) on the statistical thermodynamics of ordered solid phases, where it was suggested that daltonides are a special and perhaps limiting class of compound. The development of experimental techniques in the period that followed provided ample evidence that many different kinds of compound are variable in composition, the evidence being largely derived from the Scandinavian and German schools of inorganic chemistry where the extensive use of x-ray diffraction and phase analysis resulted in long and important series of publications. Interest in inorganic berthollides was revived in the postwar period. Anderson (*5*) in 1946 reviewed all the evidence on oxides and the chalcogenides (sulfides, selenides, and tellurides), and the Institut

International de Chimie Solvay in 1956 held its tenth conference on problems of solid state chemistry. The emphasis placed upon the properties of solids by current trends of scientific enquiry has led to much recent work, but the gradual refinement of techniques as well as the introduction of new ideas has reopened the question of the status of berthollide compounds at ordinary temperatures. This is what we propose to examine.

B. Scope

Solid state chemistry is a term now largely used to describe compounds between the metals and non-metals, and includes the various disciplines of metallurgy, mineralogy, and solid state physics. Berthollides reported as such in the literature include hydrides, borides, carbides, nitrides, oxides, silicides, phosphides, and chalcogenides, as well as intermetallic compounds and isolated halides of the transition metals. The interstitial nitrides, carbides, and suboxides were recently reviewed by Bénard (39) and will not be included here; some mention of them is also made in an authoritative article on borides and silicides by Aronsson (23), and these are also omitted. In this account we shall follow the examples of Anderson (5) and Bénard (40) by discussing the oxides and chalcogenides of the transition metals in terms of their crystal structures and by expanding the list of phases it is customary to include in this group. These compounds consist of networks of atoms bonded together and terminating only at the boundaries of the crystal or at some other discontinuity. The crystal structure is the characteristic arrangements of the atoms, and the density, dimensions of the unit cell, its symmetry, space group, and structural type provide an obvious method of comparing compounds with each other, rather than some "ideal" formula which is so difficult to define (143). Many of the simpler berthollides can be classified in this way, and the shorthand *Strukturbericht* notation, where it exists, is used as a matter of convenience, and the nomenclature rules recommended by the International Union of Pure and Applied Chemistry [see *J. Am. Chem. Soc.* **82**, 5523 (1960)] are followed where possible.

The reader's attention is also directed to Chapter 5, where some of the physical properties, notably electrical and magnetic, of a number of the systems presented in the present chapter are discussed.

It is important to know precisely what is meant by "a range of composition." Here we define it as a solid solution where one or more kinds of atom are gained or lost, and a binary compound BX_x (B is the cation species and X the anion) is a berthollide provided x is variable. Klemm (200) pointed out that in order to achieve this, the expenditure of energy must be small, the energy difference between the two valency states in the case of the transition metals also needs to be small, and the sizes of the corresponding ions must be of the same order of magnitude if a stable structure is to be formed.

The isomorphous substitution of a third ion A can result in a range of composition in one of two ways. If it has a different valency from B, then (A + B) will change the value of x if the anion lattice X is unaltered, and the phase is a berthollide. On the other hand, the introduction of A may be compensated by a valency adjustment in B without changing the numbers of (A + B) and X in the unit cell, and these controlled dual-valency compounds, which may be only stoichiometric solid solutions, are often erroneously classified as berthollides.

C. Techniques of Study; Uses and Limitations

The techniques of study are covered in Chapter 4 and need not be re-iterated except for one or two comments. The evidence to be presented here was largely derived from combinations of phase equilibria studies and diffraction measurements. In straightforward cases, a berthollide and its composition limits are recognizable by a change of unit cell volume with composition (Fig. 1), and the over-all mechanism by comparing observed densities with values calculated on the assumptions that atoms of one kind or another are added to, or subtracted from, the structure.

A good deal of the early work was done before the introduction of high resolution diffraction equipment, and the Debye-Scherrer techniques available at that time may well have failed to record much of the fine detail at present being recognized. The very ease with which powder patterns can be recorded, and indexed for phases of high symmetry in terms of a particular unit cell, does not in itself mean that a structure is satisfactorily determined by analogy with others of similar composition and crystallographic constants; it is of equal importance to calculate the structure factors for a particular arrangement of atoms and to compare them with the observed data even in the simplest case. This is not always done.

The compounds of the heavier metals dominate the literature of the berthollides, and while more refined x-ray procedures enable the metal atoms to be located with relative ease, the lighter ones are often difficult or even impossible to find with direct methods. In simple cases this can be avoided, but not really solved, by fitting them into available spaces in the most likely way, but as problems of increasing complexity are tackled by the newer methods of structure determination, it is often possible only to guess the likeliest arrangement of anions of low atomic number which usually occupy the greatest volume in the structure. Since the metals in their various valency states may have more than one kind of coordination, the light atoms assume a position of considerable importance in describing a structure with some assurance. If a berthollide containing a metal with a high atomic number is examined at a number of composition intervals, it is more than likely that x-ray data, particularly those obtained with the powder camera, will fail to disclose anomalies in the non-metal lattice, and a simple interpretation may be given to what is really a series of complex events. In other words a composition region which appears to be a berthollide may contain a number of discrete, stoichiometric phases of seemingly irrational formulas, where the metal lattices are closely related to each other in a simple way. In these circumstances the systematic use of single crystal techniques is not merely an advantage but indeed is imperative if crystals can be prepared, and neutron diffraction, where the relative scattering of elements is not a function of atomic number, will assume increasing importance in straightforward problems of structure determination.

D. Order and Disorder of Structural Anomalies

Although structural anomalies are often regarded as being randomized in a structure, refinements of the Schottky-Wagner treatment (see Chapter 2, Section IV), which include the attractive interaction between defects, reproduce additional features of berthollides. However, a final theoretical solution has still not been reached.

The occupant of a lattice position can be expected to influence the selection of its immediate neighbors provided attractive forces exist between them, complete or long-range order being achieved at low temperatures when the system has the lowest possible free energy of formation. At higher temperatures the increased energies of the atoms together with their associated thermal motions make it easier for them to adopt alternative positions or to interchange with others, either of the same or of different kinds. This local ordering eventually leads to the state where two or more adjacent ordered regions are out of step, and these anti-phase domains are separated by boundaries where disorder reaches a maximum, propagating still further when the temperature is raised. The combination of these factors leads to a rapid decrease in order near a critical temperature where long-range order ceases altogether. All these events can take place in a single crystal, and the domains, which should not be confused with individual crystallites in a polycrystal, are regions where order is limited to a few unit cells.

There is abundant experimental evidence that the homogeneity range of a berthollide varies with temperature and may be represented by Fig. 1 for a simple case. Classical methods of phase analysis, quenching from the

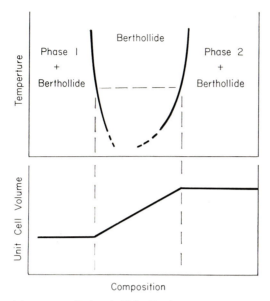

FIG. 1. Composition range of a berthollide. In the upper part the composition varies with temperature, and in the lower the phase boundaries are determined from measurements of the unit cell volume.

liquid where fusion is possible, or plotting vapor pressure equilibrium diagrams when one of the components is volatile weight the evidence in favor of the solid having a high temperature disordered structure while in many cases the minimum of Fig. 1 extends below room temperature, a purely arbitrary reference point. Below the curve the berthollide is unstable, and will disproportionate into other phases with smaller homogeneity ranges. In some cases this unmixing is extremely slow, and prolonged periods of heat treatment or annealing are needed to encourage the formation of ordered phases from berthollides prepared at high temperatures. For this reason many studies are now made by reaction in the solid state at temperatures well below the solidus.

When the concentration of the anomaly is large enough to influence the lattice parameters and the unit cell volume, the diffraction evidence should reveal it, either by altering the scatter from some of the lattice components in favorable cases if disordered, or by differences in the size of the unit cell and its symmetry if ordered. Annealing a berthollide can result in the separation of two phases unrelated to it, but may on the other hand lead to ordered compounds, falling within the composition range, where order-disorder is recognizable by the general similarity of the diffraction data of the two forms. An ordered phase contains reflections in addition to those of the disordered form, and the *superstructure*, caused by the resolution of the structural anomaly, persists in all probability as *microstructure* in the berthollide. If more than one ordered compound is found in a narrow composition interval, it is possible that the same anomaly is present in all of them, and the structures, having the same subcell, are related to each other in simple ways. Conversely if a number of ordered phases such as these are recognizable, they can be expected to form a berthollide above some order-disorder temperature.

E. Structural Causes of Variability of Composition

It was believed for some time that berthollides could be regarded as the logical extensions of solids whose optical, electrical, and kinetic properties can be interpreted by mechanisms first put forward by Schottky (*282*) and by Frenkel (*115*) for extremely dilute defect concentrations. In oxide and chalcogenide systems where the concentration is large enough to affect the formula and unit cell volume, some amplification is clearly required as the structure of the compound itself influences, or is affected by, changes of composition.

The emphasis placed upon the results obtained by structural crystallography enables a series of pictorial reasons to be given, and these five general ways, enumerated without additional discussion at this point, precede the detailed examination of the available evidence.

(1) An excess of component B can be situated on sites vacated by X, the other—*substitution*.

(2) Additional atoms B or X may occupy sites, normally vacant, which afford them a reasonable stereochemical environment. *Interpolation* is also achieved by the addition of a third element into suitable positions of the host lattice BX_x.

(3) Ions of either sort, or both simultaneously in unequal and variable amounts, may be absent from the structure—*subtraction*.

(4) Adjacent blocks of a parent structure may be out of step with each other, reducing the number of anions by changes of polyhedral grouping—*shear structures*.

(5) Intergrowth of two phases of different composition can occur if they are related in structure—*mixed* or *intergrowth structures*.

In Section IV these will be dealt with in more detail.

II. OXIDES

Grouping together composition and structural type is the simplest way of dealing with the extensive literature pertaining to this subject; but the order in which the subdivisions are presented is another matter. No particular sequence has been adopted, each part being complete in itself. Oxides and chalcogenides rarely have the same kinds of structure; when they do they are discussed together.

A. Binary Oxides and Sulfides BO_x; the $B1$ (NaCl-Type) Structure

The oxides BO of the alkaline earths, the transition metals of the first series, as well as niobium, tantalum, and several of the actinides, together with many sulfides, selenides, and tellurides of the Group IV metals and the metals of the lanthanide and actinide series, crystallize with the simple $B1$ (NaCl-type) structure. A list of those reported to have a composition range is given in Table I, in many ways an interesting and unusual group.

The first of these studied in any detail is TiO_x which was shown by Ehrlich (92) to be a substance where both metal and non-metal absences occur simultaneously over a very wide composition range. At the metal-rich end, the titanium positions are completely occupied but three out of every ten oxygen atoms are missing, $Ti_{1.0}O_{0.7}$, and at the oxygen-rich end the oxygen lattice is complete and two out of ten of the metals are now absent, $Ti_{0.8}O_{1.0}$. The stoichiometry at any intermediate composition depends upon the relative occupancy of the positions which are never both completely filled. The exact composition TiO is only achieved by design,

TABLE I

NON-STOICHIOMETRIC OXIDES AND CHALCOGENIDES WITH THE $B1$ (NaCl-TYPE)
STRUCTURE IN WHICH METAL AND NON-METAL ABSENCES OCCUR SIMULTANEOUSLY

Compound	Approx. composition range x in BX_x	Unit cell dimension Å at composition $BX_{1.0}$	Fraction of atoms of both kinds at composition $BX_{1.0}$[a]	Reference
ZrS_x	0.9–1.0	5.24	∼4/5	(149)
$ZrSe_x$	1.0–1.4	5.34, $\alpha = 89.4°$ [b]	∼5/6	(152)
YS_x	0.9–1.0	5.47	∼9/10	(105)
TiO_x	0.7–1.25	4.18	∼6/7	(92)
VO_x	0.9–1.20	4.09	∼6/7	(201, 333)
NbO_x	0.9–1.04	4.20	3/4	(52)

[a] The fraction of atoms determined by equating the observed and the calculated densities.

[b] Rhombohedral distortion.

the formula then being $Ti_{0.85}O_{0.85}$; this means that one position in every seven is vacated by both elements. Since the vacancies are randomized, the structure appears to be cubic over the entire range of composition. Klemm and Grimm (201), with a sub-solidus "phase diagram" not unlike that of Fig. 1, showed that the regions of homogeneity are really a function of the temperature at which the specimens are annealed, supporting their arguments with a study of the compound VO_x which has a remarkable resemblance to TiO_x.

Niobium monoxide, zirconium monosulfide and monoselenide and yttrium sulfide all follow a somewhat similar pattern. At the chance composition BX both metal and nonmetal absences occur together, but the fraction of them, varying widely from one substance to another, is nevertheless a simple one and ranges from 1 in 10 for YS to 1 in 4 for NbO and also for ordered ZrS (Table II). The lower composition limit for YS and disordered ZrS approximates to B_9S_8 (Table I), but there is no evidence to suggest a relationship to the cubic $D8_9$ (Co_9S_8 type) structure formed by several sulfides, etc. of the transition and ruthenium metals where tetrahedral and octahedral coordination exist together, and which do not appear to have wide ranges of composition. The nonmetal-rich limit of composition corresponds to a completed nonmetal lattice for each compound, and the larger the percentage of vacated sites the greater is the expected region of homogeneity.

Annealing these high temperature phases can yield a superlattice, which in the case of $Nb_{3/4}O_{3/4}$ is an extremely simple one, differing from the B1 structure by having the same cubic unit cell dimension but a lower symmetry group. This is caused by the ordered omission of one niobium and one

TABLE II

SUPERLATTICES OF NON-STOICHIOMETRIC OXIDES AND CHALCOGENIDES WITH THE B1 (NaCl-TYPE) STRUCTURE

Compound	Range of composition	Unit cell (a, b, and c in terms of the cubic subcell edge a)	Formula (in terms of fractional occupancy)	Reference
ZrS_x	$1.0 < x < 1.5$	2a (cubic)	$Zr_{3/4}S_{3/4}$ at $x = 1$ to $Zr_{2/3}S_{1.0}$ at $x = 1.5$	(149, 220)
TiO_x	$x = 1.0$	$3a\sqrt{2}, 3a\sqrt{2}, 2a$ (orthorhombic?)	$Ti_{6/7}O_{6/7}$	(15)
VO_x	$x = 1.27$	4a, 4a, 4a (B. C. tetragonal)	$V_{4/5}O_{1.0}$	(333)

oxygen atom from each unit cell, which ideally has four atoms of both kinds, resulting in a square planar co-ordination around the metal (Fig. 2). A random structure cannot be prepared (*10*, *52*).

The superlattices found for ordered TiO and VO are extremely large, and the detailed crystal structure analyses are very formidable problems. Attempts to solve ordered TiO in terms of a regular *B1* type with periodic vacancies have been unsuccessful (*12*), and it may well be that minor but nevertheless complicated shifts of atoms from the ideal positions will be found, leading in all probability to changes of coordination number for the metal atoms adjacent to vacancies of both kinds. $VO_{1.27}$, the composition at which the superstructure occurs, has been examined in rather more detail. The oxygen positions are all filled and the vacant metal sites are grouped together as "cartwheels" of seven in the form of a centered hexagonal disc (*332*), probably persisting at concentrations which cannot be ordered at other compositions. The change in composition $Zr_{3/4}S_{3/4}$ to $Zr_{2/3}S$ also represents a difficult crystallographic problem. The superlattice is a cube with twice the unit cell edge of the sub cell. The region $Zr_{3/4}S_{3/4}-Zr_{3/4}S$ might represent the filling of the sulfur vacancies, and the additional composition range to the removal of the metals from certain positions; this needs careful study by single crystal methods, as some unpublished experiments by the writer gave evidence that even larger superlattices can be expected. These could correspond to a case where the cation vacancies, for example, are capable of grouping with as little reduction of symmetry as possible. It is interesting to note that at the composition B_7X_8 the *B1* lattice provides regular cation vacancies with little loss of symmetry, illustrated by the structure of the compound $MnMg_6O_8$ (*192*) (Fig. 3). This could represent a limit to the "doping" of semiconduct-

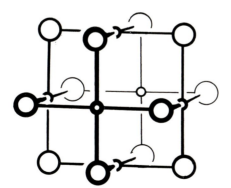

Fɪɢ. 2. Crystal structure of NbO: Nb, smaller circles; oxygen, larger circles. The resemblance to the *B1* structure is illusory.

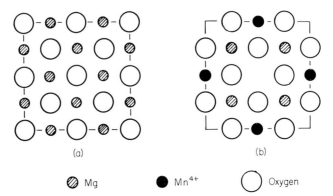

FIG. 3. (a) A sheet of the *B1* structure. (b) A sheet of the same kind with systematic ionic replacements and the simultaneous appearance of cation vacancies. The complete structure of $MnMg_6O_8$ contains sheets of both kinds alternating, with successive displacements of the origin.

ing crystals with the *B1* structure as, for example, the solid solutions of the rare earth sulfides in strontium sulfide (*338*).

The ferromagnetic or antiferromagnetic oxides Mn, Fe, Co, and Ni all have ranges of homogeneity, and FeO_x, $1.0 < x < 1.19$, which has received the most attention, has a complete oxygen lattice with iron vacancies (*188*). Variability of composition is achieved not only by the removal of iron, but by the insertion of some of these atoms into interstitial positions (*38*) which recent studies of the crystal and magnetic structures by neutron diffraction identified as tetrahedral, the region of a defect resembling a localized domain of the spinel Fe_3O_4 (*271*).

B. Oxides Derived from the *C4* (Rutile-Type) Structure

The *C4* structure, formed by several of the transition metal dioxides (and divalent metal fluorides), ideally has a simple tetragonal unit cell where the metal atoms are octahedrally coordinated to oxygen, and the octahedra are joined together in a characteristic way by sharing edges and corners (Fig. 4). There are several distorted but nevertheless related dioxides, low VO_2, MoO_2, WO_2, TcO_2, ReO_2, and NbO_2, containing displacements of atoms which result in metal-to-metal bond formation, as well as the ternary oxides AB_2O_6 where the metals A^{2+} and B^{5+} are ordered in the larger unit cell of the trirutile structure.

1. BINARY OXYGEN DEFICIENT OXIDES BO_{2-x} DERIVED FROM $C4$

Variability of composition has been noted only for the dioxides of Ti, V, Mn, Pb, and possibly Cr (Table III); CrO_2 is prepared only with difficulty.

MnO_2 and PbO_2 both decompose at low temperatures to oxides with lower oxidation states differing in atomic arrangement; disordered phases are all that can be expected as it is difficult to establish equilibrium conditions with any certainty.

TiO_2 lends itself much more readily to study, but the literature is particularly rich in contradictory experimental evidence. The composition range quoted in Table III is perhaps the largest that has been given, and more recent estimates have narrowed the formula limits of TiO_x to $1.98 < x < 2.0$ (295). Hauffe (162) reviewed the literature up to 1954 on this phase, and concluded that the mechanism of the composition variation is due to the random removal of some of the oxygen atoms, but Hurlen (179)

TABLE III

NON-STOICHIOMETRIC COMPOUNDS WITH THE $C4$ (RUTILE FORM OF TiO_2) STRUCTURE

Compound	Possible composition range	Reference
TiO_x	$1.9 < x < 2.0$	(92)
	also $1.7 < x < 1.8$	(92)
	(closely related)	
VO_x	$1.8 < x < 2.0$	(174)
MnO_x	$1.93 < x < 2.0$	(321)
CrO_x	$x \cong 2$ [a]	(284)
PbO_x	$1.87 < x < 2.0$	(193)

[a] A wide homogeneity range $1.7 < x < 1.9$ was reported for CrO_x by Cameron et al. (71). No x-ray diffraction examination was made.

took the opposite view and suggested that substantially better agreement with physical and crystallographic properties could be reached if it is assumed that additional titanium atoms enters the octahedral holes present in the $C4$ structure. Two recent studies (13, 295), independently made on oxygen deficient TiO_2 with precision x-ray powder methods, failed to agree and, therefore, to give an unequivocal answer to this problem, and it might be profitable to examine it from another point of view.

The interval TiO_x ($1.7 < x < 1.9$), which Ehrlich (92) showed to contain a low symmetry phase, is now known to include at least seven stable titanium oxides, all prepared by reacting TiO_2 with metallic titanium in the solid state or by direct fusion in a controlled atmosphere followed by annealing. These have a common formula Ti_nO_{2n-1}, n having whole number values from 4 to 10 inclusive (13), and the diffraction data of any one phase bears a remarkable resemblance to all the others as well as to the $C4$ modification of TiO_2 itself, the unit cell of which may be regarded as the subcell (14) of this whole system. Preparations made at compositions in between those of adjacent phases consist of mixtures, and each member of this structural *series* appears to be strictly stoichiometric if the conditions of formation are carefully controlled. The removal of the valency anomaly in the titanium series by the substitution of trivalent chromium also led to the formation of four of the compounds (16, 208). A similar series V_nO_{2n-1} ($n = 4$ to 8 inclusive) of the same kind had been found earlier (9).

The structure determination of Ti_5O_9, recently reported by Andersson (11), enabled the crystal chemistry of the whole of the series Ti_nO_{2n-1} as well as V_nO_{2n-1} to be clarified (14). Ti_5O_9 contains domains, or blocks, of the $C4$ structure extending indefinitely in two dimensions but with a finite width of five octahedra. Each phase in the series has its own characteristic width of 4, 5, 6, 7, 8, 9, or 10 octahedra (the number appearing in its formula), which distinguishes it from the others, and an infinite width gives the structure and the formula of the $C4$ form of TiO_2.

For any one compound the octahedra at the finite ends of a block have faces in common with those of adjacent blocks, so that the $C4$ structure is interrupted by parallel and equidistant planes of discontinuity, or in other words the domains are regularly out of phase with one another (Figs. 4 and 5). This phenomenon, occurring in several other kinds of structure discussed elsewhere in this chapter, may be likened to a process of *crystallographic shearing* (317). Face sharing of octahedra brings the metal atoms bordering the junctions of the blocks closer together, and reduces the oxygen-to-titanium ratio without changing the coordination number of the metal ion or creating vacant oxygen positions.

The limiting phase is $Ti_{10}O_{19}$. Additional members might exist in the interval $TiO_{1.90}$–$TiO_{2.0}$ but it is difficult to establish experimental equi-

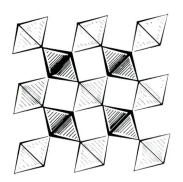 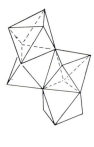

FIG. 4. The $C4$ structure, as octahedra projected down the edges. The discontinuity present in Ti_5O_9, drawn in perspective, is shown on the right-hand side. Octahedral faces, as well as edges, are shared.

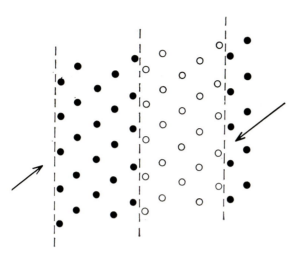

Fig. 5. The metal atoms of Ti_5O_9 projected in a direction equivalent to $(\bar{1}01)$ for TiO_2. The vertical dotted lines separate TiO_2 blocks, five atoms thick (the direction marked by arrows). Atoms of adjacent blocks are drawn as filled and open circles.

librium, and the interpretation of the diffraction evidence from the very large oblique unit cells, which can be predicted, is limited by the lack of resolving power of even the most precise x-ray focusing camera. The isomorphous chromium-substituted series $(Ti_{n-2}Cr_2)O_{2n-1}$ shows a continuous transition between $BO_{1.89}$ [ordered $(Ti_7Cr_2)O_{17}$], and $BO_{1.95}$ which is disordered and approaches the $C4$ structure (16). In this region it seems likely that the discontinuities, where octahedra share faces, now appear only at irregular intervals, and coherent scattering of x-rays arises solely from the $C4$-like domains now no longer ordered and in phase with one another. Quenching from high temperatures will induce disorder which could be interpreted as an extension of the homogeneity range (55).

These arguments support Hurlen's (179) views on the structure of TiO_x in the region where the $C4$ diffraction pattern alone is found. It implies that the interstitial holes occupied by additional titanium atoms lie in certain planes, *and these atoms are in the normal octahedral positions of the adjacent domain.* When the level of defect concentration is high, the planes of discontinuity become ordered in three dimensions to result in a group of phases constituting an homologous series.

2. Ternary Interstitial Oxides A_xBO_2 Derived from $C4$ Type

The group of four linear strings of octahedra sharing corners that continues indefinitely to form the $C4$ structure, may combine with itself in another way by sharing edges to give a host framework also having the formula BX_2. The squares seen in Fig. 6, formed by the doubled octahedral strings, are the projections of open spaces running right through the crystal in one particular direction. This is called a *tunnel* structure, and the tunnels or closed channels constitute potential positions for ions or molecules of the appropriate size. A single site in a tunnel is a cube, and if these are all filled the ternary ionic compound has the formula $A_2B_8X_{16}$, i.e., $A_{0.25}BX_2$.

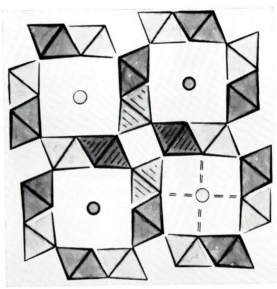

FIG. 6. The hollandite structure in projection, the A ions appearing as circles. The central group of four shaded octahedra appears also in Figs. 4 (the *C4* type) and 7 (psilomelane).

This structure was first found for the hollandite group of minerals $A_xMn_8O_{16}$ (*70*), where A is one of the ions Ba^{2+}, K^+, or Pb^{2+}, and is recognized in laboratory preparations of the so-called α-MnO_2 (*75*), where the foreign ion can also be Rb^+ and possibly $(NH_4)^+$ (*68*). The cubic positions in the tunnels are seldom more than half filled by these ions, but on the other hand may be almost entirely empty (*66*). The diffraction data give no evidence of any kind of order in the tunnels, and it is therefore assumed that they are distributed at random over all possible positions.

TiO_2 forms the same host structure, with K^+ as the foreign ion, in the mineral priderite (*239*) where valency anomalies introduced into the host are adjusted by the substitution of trivalent metals for Ti^{4+}, and also as a metal oxide "bronze" (Section II,L,1) of the same composition (*320*) where the anomalies are retained. Single crystals of the isomorphous non-stoichiometric phase $Ba_x(Ti_{8-x}Mg_x)O_{16}$, $0.67 < x < 1.14$, readily made by the flame fusion technique, have been studied by additional physical techniques in an attempt to clarify the role of the impurity ions (89). At the composition $x = 1$, the Ba ions and vacancies are present in equal numbers, and strong dielectric absorption, which was only found parallel to the direction of the tunnels, was associated with the movement of the ions to the empty positions adjacent to them, agreeing with a model where the sequence in a particular tunnel is ordered:

$$-vacancy-Ba^{2+}-vacancy-Ba^{2+}-$$

At the composition $x = 0.67$ the ratio of ions to vacancies is $1:2$, but as the absorption characteristics were virtually unchanged, the ions in the tunnels obviously do not form a new arrangement:

$$-vacancy-vacancy-Ba^{2+}-vacancy-vacancy-Ba^{2+}-$$

The first sequence must therefore be present in some of the tunnels with others completely empty, and from this it can be argued that the phase contains different numbers of half filled and of completely empty tunnels in the composition region $0.67 < x < 1.0$. These sequences in the tunnels need not be in phase with each other, and only in this sense is the compound a disordered one.

FeOOH, of indefinite composition, always contains chlorine and free water (328) and is now known to have the hollandite structure, iron–oxygen octahedra forming the host framework enclosing chlorine ions (221). These are presumably bonded through hydrogen atoms to the oxygens bordering the tunnels, which are large enough to enclose water molecules as well. Considerable flexibility of composition is associated with the relative proportions of water and of chlorine, in turn affecting the number of hydrogen bonds.

The host structure of the mineral psilomelane, $Ba_xMn_5O_{10}(2 - x)H_2O$, $0.5 < x < 0.75$ (107), a framework of manganese-oxygen octahedra with the formula BX_2, contains double and treble octahedral strings, the junctions again being the residual $C4$ fragments present in hollandite (Fig. 7). The large tunnels, rectangular in cross section, contain double rows of barium ions and water molecules, and the crystal structure was solved only by assuming that the two substitute isomorphously for each other (311). This led to the strange formula $(Ba, H_2O)_2Mn_5O_{10}$ where the ideal ratio $Ba^{2+}:H_2O$ is $1:2$.

By analogy with hollandite and its related compounds, to which it bears obvious similarities, it may be assumed that order exists in any one

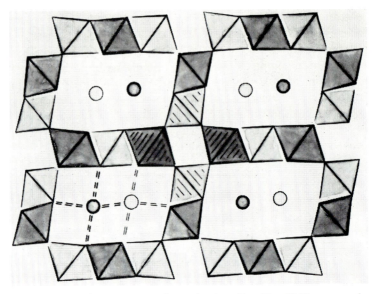

Fɪɢ. 7. The psilomelane structure in projection, the (Ba, H_2O) groups drawn as circles.

tunnel unrelated, however, to the same ordered arrangement in any other one. The most probable sequence that can be expected is

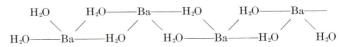

where $Ba^{2+}:H_2O$ is $1:2$. Barium is combined to four water molecules, two being in the adjacent row of the tunnel, and completes its tenfold coordination with oxygens from the framework, providing a model whereby water may be readily lost and regained. Variability of composition is due to the replacement of barium by water in the tunnels. Whether this is a random event averaged out over all possible positions, or whether some tunnels are completely filled with water, is unknown.

No other substance having this particular crystal structure has been reported. The wide variety of ill-defined manganese dioxides of variable composition and unknown structure, recently reviewed in the literature (*121, 123*), often containing substantial quantities of water as well as small amounts of foreign ions, may be more closely related to the two barium-containing tunnel structures than to the dimorphs of manganese dioxide with which they are often compared. If water alone is present in the tunnels, the diffraction patterns of the host phases will alter considerably. Disordered phases of no fixed composition or structure could arise from the irregular intergrowth of one tunnel compound with the other, a likely possibility in view of the exact correspondence of the two in certain directions and of the presence of the residual fragments of the $C4$ structure in both.

C. $BO_{2 \pm x}$ Derived from the $C1$ (Fluorite-Type) Structure

The $C1$ structure, consisting of metal atoms B coordinated to eight X atoms situated at the corners of a cube and with the cubes sharing edges, is adopted by many fluorides and oxyfluorides as well as the dioxides of Ce, Pr, Tb, and the actinides from Th to Am. Nonstoichiometric compounds based upon $C1$ may vary in composition either by increasing or decreasing the oxygen-to-metal ratio.

1. BO_{2-x} Intermediate between $C1$, $E8_1$, and $D5_3$ or $D5_2$

The crystal structures of the rare earth sesquioxides B_2X_3 form three groups; from La through to Nd having the hexagonal $D5_2$ structure where the metal atom has the sevenfold coordination found in ZrO_2, Sm Eu and Gd form a low symmetry structure (81), and the remainder, including Y_2O_3, the cubic $D5_3$. The arrangement of atoms in the latter resembles that in $C1$, and may be considered to form a simple superlattice where the axial length is doubled due to the ordered omission of one-quarter of the oxygens. The coordination of the metal atoms is of two kinds; each has six oxygens as ligands at the corners of the cubes, but two atoms of a face diagonal of one, and two of a body diagonal of the other are omitted (Fig. 8) (253). Although it was recently suggested (82) that these groups are in a more symmetrical arrangement of octahedra, the $D5_3$ structure has nevertheless been verified by neutron diffraction studies on Ho_2O_3 (204), a typical member.

A large number of studies have been made of the solid solutions formed between the $C1$ dioxides and rare earth sesquioxides with $D5_2$ and $D5_3$ structures, where a reduction in the net valency of the filled metal lattice of $C1$ leads to the creation of oxygen vacancies (344). Despite the over-all similarity between $C1$ and $D5_3$, a complete solid solution is achieved in only a few cases, notably for CeO_2–Y_2O_3 and PrO_2–Y_2O_3 (54, 218) where the superlattice lines of $D5_3$ appearing at the composition $(Ce_{0.85}Y_{0.15})O_{1.925}$ indicate that some ordering of the defective oxygen lattice is present even at very low vacancy concentrations. For the other remaining systems, where the dioxide is Ce, Pr, Th, or U, the region of homogeneity of $C1$ varies in a rather arbitrary fashion up to the limiting case which appears to be $(Ce, Sm)O_{1.67}$ (218), although the composition range might perhaps

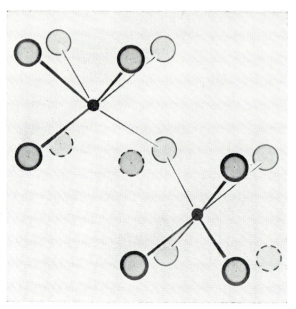

FIG. 8. The six-coordinated groups characteristic of the $D5_3$ structure resulting from the omission of a pair of face- and body-diagonal atoms (dotted) from a cubic coordination of oxygens.

be influenced by the size of the rare earth ion. UO_2 forms defective solid solutions at high temperatures with $CaUO_3$, which also has the $D5_3$ structure, where the two metals are randomized over the one set of positions (3). In systems of UO_2 with the alkali earths or with MgO (7) some precaution must be taken to prevent the oxidation of U^{4+} to higher valencies; CaU_2O_6 and the corresponding Mg and Sr compounds have the $C1$ arrangement and should be formulated $(Ca_{1/3}U_{2/3})O_2$ (167).

The pyrochlore structure, $E8_1$, is frequently found in compositions $A_2B_2X_7$, where the metals A and B have valencies of 2 and 5, or 3 and 4, the additional criterion being a geometrical one that can be expressed in terms of ionic size (181). The length of the cubic or pseudocubic cell edge is double that of $C1$. A and B are mostly ordered into their own sets of positions where they form an orthogonal sublattice; here one anion in every eight is regularly missing and the remainder are shifted by substantial distances from the ideal $C1$ positions. The larger metal ion A is surrounded as in $C1$ by eight oxygens now in a deformed cube, and B by a cube where the two atoms forming a body diagonal are removed. The structure, intermediate between $C1$ and $D5_3$, consists of a host framework, B_2O_6, of the distorted octahedra, and the two A ions, together with the seventh oxygen, are not essential for its stability. The number of oxygens

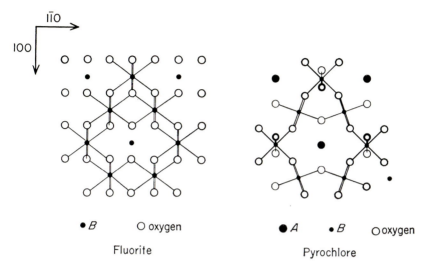

FIG. 9. Sections of the *C1* (fluorite) and *E8₁* (pyrochlore) structures. Bonds are drawn between metal and oxygen for equivalent portions.

varies from 6 to 7 if the number of A ions varies accordingly; this results in a general formula $A_{1+x}B_2O_{6+x}$ *(189)* when A is divalent, or $A_{1+x}B_2O_{6+y}$ when A is trivalent.

The combinations of elements giving this structure are very extensive, and a partial list is included in Table IV. ZrO_2, listed in this table, and HfO_2 are the only host oxides related to *C1*, but the metal atom adopts a sevenfold coordination *(219)*. The technical importance of converting ZrO_2 into a more symmetrical thermally-stable phase has led to an ex-

TABLE IV

COMBINATIONS OF METALS A AND B IN PHASES WITH THE $E8_1$ STRUCTURE

A	B
Y, Sm, Gd, Dy, Yb	Ti
La, Nd to Yb	Sn
La, Sm, Nd, Y, Ce³⁺	Zr
Y, Pr to Lu	Ru
Cd, Pb	Nb
Cd, Pb, Ca	Ta
Na, (Ca, Na, Mn, Fe),ᵃ Cd, Pb	Sb

ᵃ Isomorphous substituents in various minerals.

tensive examination of its binary and ternary phase systems with oxides of other elements (86). Although much of the early work can no doubt be criticized (266), it is nevertheless clear that the substitution of metal ions with valencies less than four, accompanied by anion vacancies of some kind, can result in a higher symmetry for "defective ZrO_2," but may lead to the formation of the $E8_1$ structure (72).

The phase diagram for part of the system ZrO_2–Gd_2O_3, shown in Fig. 10, contains a region where the random substitution of Gd for Zr gives a solid solution $(Zr_{1-x}, Gd_x)O_{2-x/2}$ of the $C1$–$D5_3$ type. At the boundary of an enclosed sub-solidus region there is an order-disorder transformation to

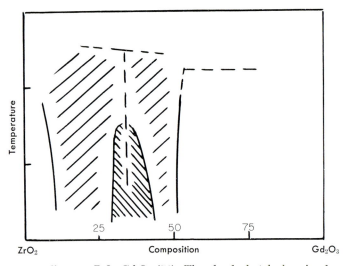

Fig. 10. Phase diagram ZrO_2–Gd_2O_3 (76). The closely hatched region has the $E8_1$ structure bordered by disordered defective $C1$.

the $E8_1$ structure which appears to vary between the approximate limits $Gd_{1.8}Zr_{2.2}O_{7.1}$ to $Gd_{2.4}Zr_{1.6}O_{6.8}$ (254). The pyrochlore phase also appears in the system ZrO_2–La_2O_3, but is entirely absent in the corresponding Nd and Yb systems (76) where the $C1$–$D5_3$ transition appears to be a smooth one. It must be emphasized that the use of x-ray powder diffraction patterns alone to distinguish between the two closely related structures at best only provides slender evidence, and such studies up to the present have not shown whether the ordering corresponds to the segregation of the ions A and B into their own positions, to the rearrangement of the oxygen lattice, or to both occurring simultaneously.

There is good reason to believe that ordering takes place in several steps. Several pyrochlore compounds were found in a phase analysis of

TABLE V

ORDERED PHASES RELATED TO PYROCHLORE, $E8_1$, IN THE SYSTEM $PbO–Nb_2O_5$ (*268*)

Composition	Symmetry	Unit cell dimensions
$Pb_3Nb_4O_{13}$, $(Pb, Nb)O_{1.86}$	Cubic	$a = 10.561$ Å
$\begin{cases} Pb_2Nb_2O_7,[a]\ (Pb, Nb)O_{1.75} \\ Pn_5Nb_4O_{15},\ (Pb, Nb)O_{1.67} \end{cases}$	Rhombohedral Rhombohedral	$a = 10.674$ Å, $\alpha = 88°\ 50'$ $a = 10.709$ Å, $\alpha = 88°\ 14'$
$Pb_3Nb_2O_8$, $(Pb, Nb)O_{1.60}$	Pseudotetragonal	$a = 10.66,\ c = 10.82$ Å

[a] A continuous solid solution between the bracketed compounds.

the system $PbO–Nb_2O_5$ (Table V), and only one of these appeared to be a berthollide. Density measurements were unfortunately not included in this work (*268*), and the population of A and B sites cannot be derived from the published data. Two interesting and parallel studies $CeO_2–Ce_2O_3$ (*46*) and $PrO_2–Pr_2O_3$ (*103*) were reported almost simultaneously, and in both cases a group of ordered phases which appeared to be of irrational composition were recognized (Table VI). These are closely related to each other and strikingly similar to the lead-niobium oxides of Table V. Bevan (*46*) showed that three of the four cerium oxides in one range of $2 < x < 1.5$ are virtually of fixed composition, and only one, CeO_x, $1.65 < x < 1.69$, gave the characteristic $D5_3$ diffraction pattern. The other phases containing rhombohedral deformations of the unit cells are nevertheless closely related to $C1$ or $D5_3$; the fixed formulas could be expressed in general terms $Ce_{32}O_{64-n}$ ($n = 6, 7,$ and 9), and the vacant oxygen positions are evidently ordered in different ways. It is possible that one or more of these phases has the $E8_1$ structure, where the oxygens are extensively regrouped and the Ce^{3+} and Ce^{4+} ions perhaps segregate into preferred positions of their own. This would, however, be a very difficult matter to prove.

The composition of the phase boundaries in $CeO_2–Ce_2O_3$ changes at high temperatures where disorder is rapidly achieved, and the interpretation, as in the case of $ZrO_2–Gd_2O_3$, may then be based upon the concept of the solid solution with a continuously variable fraction of vacant oxygen positions (*53*). Stepwise oxidation states in the upper limits of the system TbO_x, $1.5 < x < 1.81$, also show a marked similarity to the cerium and praseodymium oxides (*34*).

Some of the older work on the lead oxides of intermediate composition, summarized by Butler and Copp (*67*), claimed wide homogeneity ranges; but subsequent investigations, while agreeing on the identity of the stable phases which can be prepared, have tended to reduce the composition limits. PbO_2, which does not form the $C1$ structure, is readily decomposed

TABLE VI

Ordered Phases Intermediate between $C1$ and $D\delta_2$ or $D\delta_3$

	Cerium (46)			Terbium (34)		Praseodymium (103, 140)
CeO_x x	Unit cell contents	Unit cell dimensions	TbO_x x	Unit cell dimensions	PrO_x x	Unit cell dimensions
2.00	Ce_4O_8	$a = 5.409$ Å	1.95	$a = 5.220$ Å	1.833	$a = 5.468$ Å
1.812–1.805	$Ce_{32}O_{58}$	$a = 11.009$ Å[a] $\alpha = 89°58'$	1.823	$a = 5.283$ Å[b] $\alpha = 89°41'$	1.801	$a = 5.482$ Å
1.785	$Ce_{32}O_{57}$	$a = 11.001$ Å[a] $\alpha = 90°20'$	1.809	$a = b = c = 5.286$ Å $\alpha = \beta = 89°25'$, $\gamma = 90°$[c]		
1.722–1.710	$Ce_{32}O_{55}$	$a = 11.123$ Å[a] $\alpha = 89°40'$	1.715	$a = 5.319$ Å[a] $\alpha = 89°41'$	1.715	$a = 11.071$ Å $\alpha = 89°40'$
1.688–1.651	$Ce_{32}O_{54}$ to $Ce_{32}O_{53}$	$a = 11.1$ Å (variable)			1.700	$a = 11.071$ Å
1.52–1.50	Ce_2O_3	$a = 3.90$ Å $c = 6.05$ Å $(D\delta_2)$	1.500	$a = 10.728$ Å $(D\delta_3)$		

[a] Recalculated from Bevan's data (46).   [b] Subcell.   [c] Subcell, triclinic.

above 300°C. to an oxide α-PbO$_x$, $1.5 < x < 1.67$. The oxidation of tetragonal PbO at the same temperature gives a second fluorite-like non-stoichiometric phase which on annealing gives the diffraction pattern characteristics of β-PbO$_x$, $1.47 < x < 1.51$ (69). These have been represented as Pb$_{12}$O$_{19}$ and Pb$_{12}$O$_{17}$ (8), where five and seven oxygens in every twenty-four are systematically missing from the fluorite structure which is somewhat distorted (Table VII). This is not in complete accord with the detailed structures proposed by Byström (69) where, it must be admitted, the positions of the oxygens are only tentative. Anderson and Sterns (8) suggested an interesting topochemical mechanism whereby the unsymmetrical lead environment of the B10 structure is transformed to the cubic fluorite-

TABLE VII

ORDERED INTERMEDIATE LEAD OXIDES

| Compound | Composition range[a] | Unit cell dimensions (Å) | | | | |
		a	b	c	β	Reference
α-PbO$_x$	$1.5 < x < 1.67$	$\sqrt{2} \times 5.46$	2×5.40	$3\sqrt{2} \times 5.42$	88.7°	(69)
β-PbO$_x$	$1.47 < x < 1.51$	$\sqrt{2} \times 5.51$	5.50	$\sqrt{2} \times 5.42$	90°	(69)

[a] Anderson and Sterns (8) reported that α-PbO$_x$ had the invariant composition PbO$_{1.57}$, and β-PbO$_x$ the range $1.4 < x < 1.45$, probably PbO$_{1.41}$. They also suggested the b axis of β-PbO$_x$ should be doubled.

like group by the disordered intercalation of sheets of oxygen atoms, which are doubtless rearranged in the structure as a whole by prolonged annealing.

2. BO$_{2+x}$ INTERMEDIATE BETWEEN C1 AND DO$_3$ (BiF$_3$ TYPE)

Despite the diversity of three-dimensional networks theoretically possible in inorganic systems, there are remarkably few with secondary sites large enough to accommodate anions. It had been known for many years that naturally occurring CaF$_2$ often included substantial quantities of Y^{3+}, and this led Zintl and Udgård (345) to examine the chemical systems CaF$_2$-YF$_3$, SrF$_2$-LaF$_3$, and CaF$_2$-ThF$_4$ for evidence of solid solution formation, BF$_{2+x}$. They succeeded in proving by x-ray and density measurements that the C1 structure could include additional anions in "empty" positions formed by the function of six cubes (Fig. 11), each supernumerary ion then becoming part of the environment of all six metal atoms surrounding it. BiF$_3$, the DO$_3$ type, has the C1 structure with all of these positions occupied by fluorine (*161, 176*), and many fluoride, oxyfluoride, and oxide systems form non-stoichoimetric phases intermediate between the two*: representatives of these are given in Table VIII. For the most part the upper composition limit depends upon chemical constituents and falls within the region $BX_{2.2}$ to $BX_{2.4}$. The complete interval is spanned in the system PbF_2–BiF_3, while solid solutions of the rare earth sesquioxides in U_3O_8 cover a range where the *C1* structure is oxygen-deficient at one end and has an excess of oxygen at the other.

Provided the metal valency may exceed four, oxides with the fluorite structure readily take up additional oxygen, and the oxidation of UO_2 at

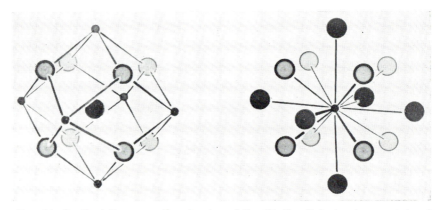

FIG. 11. On the left, perspective drawing of the *C1* (fluorite) structure; metal and non-metal, small and larger circles, respectively; the interstitial position being a large black circle. On the right the coordination of any one metal is increased from eight to fourteen by the additional anions.

low temperatures, which has been extensively studied, occurs in two stages. The first is complete at a composition around $UO_{2.33}(= U_3O_7)$ and the second at $UO_{2.67}(U_3O_8)$. Considerable disagreement in matters of detail has centered around the region from UO_2 to $UO_{2.33}$, where the existence of a solid solution region appears to be well established (*6, 135*), and where annealing at 300–400°C leads to the disproportionation into UO_2 and U_4O_9, while higher temperatures yield U_4O_9 and U_3O_8. Between $UO_{2.25}$ (U_4O_9) and $UO_{2.40}$, three tetragonal phases have been observed (*6, 255*), and the possibility that oxidation takes place by discrete structural increments must be stressed. These steps may be considered due to the ordering of interstitial oxygen atoms within the unit cell; for U_4O_9 one such position in every four is ordered, and the tetragonal superlattices are

---

* BiF_3 also exists in a hexagonal form (tysonite), and a defective variety BiO_xF_{3-2x} was reported (*33*).

caused by the regular incorporation of additional oxygen atoms into multiple U_4O_9 units. While the existence of these phases has recently been confirmed (*168*), some doubts have been thrown upon this structural model by the thermodynamic study of Aronson and Belle (*22*), who quote supporting but unpublished neutron diffraction experiments claiming that the oxygen lattice in U_4O_9 is quite different from that in UO_2. It was concluded from this that additional oxygens are unlikely to enter the interstitial positions of the *C1* structure. On the other hand, a specimen of U_4O_9 was claimed on x-ray examination to have a very large cubic superlattice, and from this it was deduced that interstitial oxygens are ordered in clusters (*37*). Solid solutions of mixed uranium-thorium dioxides were also oxidized, at low temperatures, to a composition limit (U, Th)$O_{2.33}$

TABLE VIII

C1 COMPOUNDS WITH EXCESS NON-METAL: REPRESENTATIVE SOLID SOLUTIONS

System	Compound	Composition range	Reference
PbF_2–BiF_3	(Pb, Bi)F_x	$2.0 < x < 3.0$	(*80*)
KF–ThF_4	(K, Th)F_x	$2.0 < x < 2.2$	(*342*)
LaF_3–La_2O_3	La(O, F)$_x$	$2.0 < x < 2.45$	(*202*)
La_2O_3–U_3O_8	(La, U)O_x	$1.8 < x < 2.4$	(*178*)
$SrCl_2$–$LaCl_3$	(Sr, La)Cl_x	$2.0 < x < 2.23$	(*56*)

(*177*). The crystal structure determination of the B_3X_7 phase is undoubtedly of considerable importance in future studies of this most complicated system, and it may be necessary to examine a crystallographically related compound that is chemically stable at high temperatures.

D. Uranium Oxides UO_{3-x}

The literature on the chemistry of the phases identified in the region U_3O_8 to UO_3 was summarized in a recent paper by Hoekstra and Siegel (*169*). The crystal structures of α- and δ-UO_3 are the only ones known, and the assignment of lattice parameters to the remainder of the five UO_3 phases is still being debated. The similarity between the unit cells of α-UO_3, the U_3O_8 phases, and the compounds of intermediate composition, $UO_{2.9}$ and $UO_{2.83}$ (Table IX), is undoubtedly due to the uranium positions being identical, except for small movements from a hexagonal grouping. The oxygen atoms in α-UO_3 are grouped in rather deformed cubes around each uranium (*340*), and a structure was proposed for α-U_3O_8 where the

TABLE IX

STRUCTURALLY RELATED BINARY URANIUM OXIDES, UO_{3-x}

| Compound | Symmetry | Unit cell dimensions (Å) | | | Reference |
		a	b	c	
α-UO_3	Hexagonal[a]	6.87	3.97	4.17	(340)
$UO_{2.9}$	Orthorhombic	6.91	3.92	4.16	(51)
$UO_{2.83}$	Hexagonal[a]	6.68	3.86	4.17	(255)
α-U_3O_8	Orthorhombic	6.71	3×3.99	4.15	(21)
β-U_3O_8	Orthorhombic	7.05	3×3.91	2×4.15	(170)
U_3O_8 (high temperature form)	Trigonal[a]	6.82	$1/\sqrt{3} \times 3.94$	4.14	(287)
"U_2O_5"	Orthorhombic	6.73	8×3.96	2×4.14	(276)

[a] Dimensions transformed to orthohexagonal.

same positions are retained except for one missing oxygen, leaving the adjacent metal atom with a deformed octahedral environment (339). The existence of a solid solution between these two compounds, due to the removal of oxygens from some of the positions they adopt in UO_3, has frequently been suggested but never confirmed. Andresen (21) proposed an alternative structure derived by neutron diffraction, where the oxygen atoms in α-U_3O_8 are completely reshuffled. This is illustrated by Fig. 12.

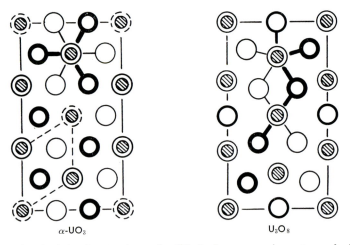

α-UO_3 U_3O_8

FIG. 12. On the left, the structure of α-UO_3 is drawn, uranium atoms shaded; the oxygens represented by dotted circles could be omitted to give a unit cell and formula characteristic of U_3O_8. The structure of U_3O_8 on the right was deduced from neutron diffraction data.

One uranium, having a distorted octahedral environment, is considered to be hexavalent, and two others that are probably pentavalent have seven oxygen neighbors grouped as a pentagonal bipyramid, the shorter distances between the metal and the two oxygens at the apexes forming a strongly bonded chain of the type U—O—U—O. It would be very instructive to examine the remaining phases in Table IX by neutron diffraction.

A large superlattice was reported for a compound believed at that time to be U_2O_5 (276), and preparations in the composition range $UO_{2.5}$–$UO_{2.67}$ proved that this region is one where many phases are perhaps present (170). A recent examination of U_3O_8 demonstrated that a variety of patterns could be obtained when the specimen is reduced *in situ* in an electron diffraction camera (278), and the formation of these reduced phases, $U_3O_{8-\delta}$, is due to blocks of the U_3O_8 structure becoming out of step with each other, leading to ordered as well as transient arrangements of atoms that are more or less stable. This study has undoubtedly revealed a series of structural homologues for which Andresen's structure of U_3O_8 could serve as the basic, or type, structure, and additional work may succeed in defining the chemical composition of each member.

E. Oxides Derived from the DO_9 (ReO$_3$-Type) Structure

1. BINARY OR PSEUDOBINARY OXYGEN DEFICIENT PHASES BO$_{3-x}$

ReO_3 and δ-UO_3, together with certain fluorides and oxyfluorides BX_3 of Ti, Nb, Mo, and Ta (116), have a simple cubic structure, DO_9, where regular metal-oxygen (and/or fluorine) octahedra share all six corners with one another. δ-UO_3 appears to have a deficit of oxygen (323) but its region of homogeneity is unknown. WO_3 can exist in several forms, and while most of them have structures similar in principle to the DO_9 type, the tungsten lattice is irregular and the exact nature of the distortion is a function of temperature. α-WO_x has only a narrow composition range, but tungsten as well as related molybdenum oxides in lower oxidation states are reported to have ranges of composition at elevated temperatures (Table X).

The phase $W_{20}O_{58}$ forming the upper composition limit of β-WO_x, $2.83 < x < 2.90$, appears to be strictly stoichiometric, and the diffraction data of this compound are dominated by a cubic DO_9-type subcell. The determination of the crystal structure (227) disclosed that the superlattice is due not as might be supposed to the loss of oxygen with the concomitant ordering of vacant sites, but to the regular interruption of the DO_9 struc-

TABLE X

TUNGSTEN AND MOLYBDENUM OXIDES AND ORDERED PHASES OF RELATED COMPOSITION

Compound	Composition range	Stoichiometric oxides of related formula
α-WO$_x$	$2.98 < x < 3.0$ (73, 126)	
β-WO$_x$	$2.83 < x < 2.90$ (73, 126)	W$_{20}$O$_{58}$; homologues of Table XI.
γ-WO$_x$	$2.66 < x < 2.72$ (73, 126)	W$_{18}$O$_{49}$ = WO$_{2.72}$
MoO$_x$	$2.65 < x < 2.75$ (124)	Mo$_{17}$O$_{47}$ = MoO$_{2.763}$
		Mo$_{10}$O$_{28}$ = MoO$_{2.800}$

ture by planes of discontinuity where octahedra share edges rather than corners. Like the reduced Ti$_n$O$_{2n-1}$ phases discussed earlier, some of the metal atoms at the edges of one of the WO$_3$ blocks are in interstitial positions of the adjacent block, and in this way the tungsten-to-oxygen ratio is reduced while the packing of the oxygen atoms remains virtually undisturbed. Additional ordered tungsten oxides in this composition region have not been reported, but part of the range is covered by a series of mixed tungsten and molybdenum oxides (Table XI), all examined by Magnéli and his co-workers.

If we imagine that the DO_9 structure is submitted to a shearing stress, then one region of it can be moved to an alternative position where it is joined up once more by sharing edges rather than corners. These "shear" planes of discontinuity can be constituted in different ways which, by following the analogy, depend upon the direction of the hypothetical forces. For W$_{20}$O$_{58}$ six octahedra in a group share edges, and for the mixed tungsten-molybdenum oxides there are four; in both cases the discon-

TABLE XI

STRUCTURAL HOMOLOGUES (Mo, W)$_n$O$_{3n-1}$

Compound	BO$_x$	Approximate Mo/W ratio	Reference
WO$_3$	3.00	0	
(Mo, W)$_{14}$O$_{41}$	2.929	1:1	(232)
(Mo, W)$_{12}$O$_{35}$	2.917	1:2	(232)
(Mo, W)$_{11}$O$_{32}$	2.909	—	(48)
(Mo, W)$_{10}$O$_{29}$	2.900	1:4	(48)
Mo$_9$O$_{26}$	2.889	∞	(223)
Mo$_8$O$_{23}$	2.875	∞	(223)

tinuities continue in two dimensions throughout the structure where they separate blocks of the DO_9 type. The oxides listed in Table XI have many features in common, and since they are given a general formula B_nO_{3n-1} (n = 8, 9, 10, 11, 12, and 14), they are also called a homologous series of oxides (229). The shear planes of discontinuity, all of the one kind, appear throughout the whole series, and in any one phase they recur at regular intervals. One phase differs from any other only in terms of their periodicity, or in other words in the size of the regular DO_9 blocks, where the numerical value of n of the formula is also a measure. For example when n = 9, the homologue Mo_9O_{26} contains blocks with a characteristic extension of *nine* octahedra, joined together at parallel discontinuities where some of the octahedra at the borders share edges (Figs. 13 and 14). The region BO_x, $2.88 < x < 2.93$, therefore contains six ordered phases with a common structural principle, and all have a pronounced cubic sub-cell of the DO_9 type.

An unusual feature of this system is that these phases of intermediate composition are all ordered, and long range forces of some special kind evidently play an important role in the structural chemistry of the molybdenum and tungsten oxides. $W_{18}O_{49}$ is a stoichiometric phase representing the upper composition limit reported for γ-WO_x ($2.66 < x < 2.72$) (225),

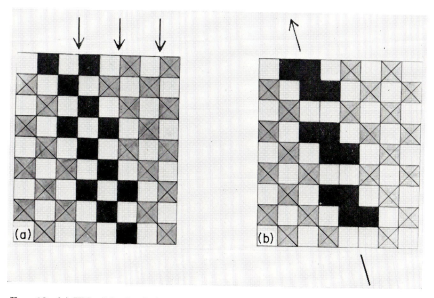

FIG. 13. (a) WO_3 (idealized) in projection down the octahedral corners. The black octahedra may adopt the configuration of (b) when blocks of structure are moved to adjacent positions where they share edges.

and is related by structural features it has in common with $Mo_{17}O_{47}(=$ $MoO_{2.763})$ (197) and also $Mo_{10}O_{28}(= MoO_{2.80})$ (198). Most of the metal atoms for all three are octahedrally coordinated to oxygen, and some of these octahedra are joined up in rings of five, a characteristic feature of this group found also in ternary oxides with the tetragonal tungsten bronze structure.

In these molybdenum oxides the rings are the projections of pentagonal tunnels containing oxygen atoms as well as additional metal ions which consequently have sevenfold coordination. The way in which these com-

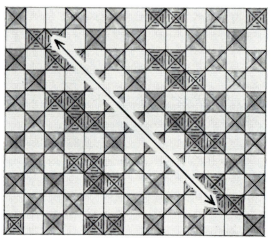

FIG. 14. Structure of Mo_9O_{26}, the homologue $n = 9$ of the series B_nO_{3n-1}. The arrow shows the extension characteristic of this particular member. The octahedra which are hatched are the "shear planes" of Fig. 13(b).

pacted groups of six metals and their associated oxygens are joined together leads to the formation of additional fragments, recognizable as empty pentagons (very distorted hexagons in $Mo_{17}O_{47}$), and also squares and triangles of octahedra (Figs. 15 and 16). The oxygen atoms in all of these phases are not in any simple form of regular packing, but resemble a series of random groups of elastic spheres of the kind found in dynamical representations of a dense liquid, or of a solid adopting a transient sequence of patterns when some spheres are extracted. Needless to say these are not chance arrangements, but are crystalline solids ordered at certain temperatures, bearing little relationship however, either to the DO_9 structure or to the shear structures derived from it, where in both cases the anion packing is regular.

The limiting B_nO_{3n-1} homologue appears to be the member $n = 8$ (i.e., $MoO_{2.875}$), and beyond this point the principle leading to a change of

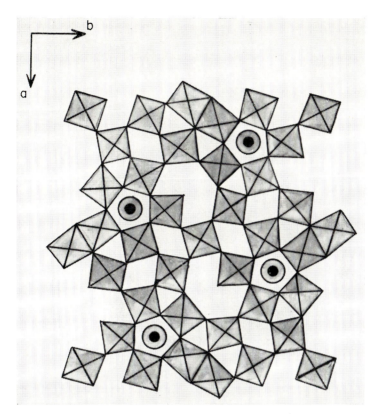

FIG. 15. Structure of $Mo_{17}O_{47}$. The octahedra are grouped into rings of five (and six), some containing additional metal and oxygen atoms, drawn as smaller and larger overlapping circles.

composition no longer can be recognized in stable or ordered phases, but might be the principle of a disordered non-stoichiometric region. The two molybdenum and one tungsten oxides we have been discussing, appear to be formed by the extraction of oxygen atoms from a close packed group, and the subsequent and extensive rearrangement of those remaining is influenced by the metal atoms, some being forced to adopt an unusual coordination.

2. TERNARY OXIDES A_xBO_3, ABO_{3-x} BASED UPON $E2_1$ (PEROVSKITE-TYPE) STRUCTURE

An ion A present at the centre of one of the spaces or *cages* present in the DO_9 structure is in twelvefold coordination, having as equidistant

FIG. 16. Structure of $Mo_{10}O_{28}$, see FIG. 15.

neighbors the eight atoms forming the corners of a cube (which is seen projected as a square in Fig. 17) together with four additional oxygens situated beyond the centers of four cube faces. A compound with the DO_9 framework in which all of the cages are filled has the formula ABO_3 and the perovskite structure, $E2_1$.

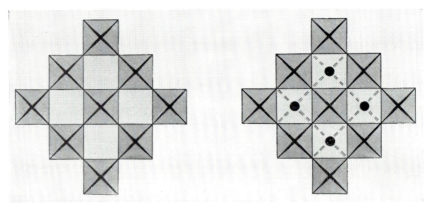

FIG. 17. The DO_9 (ReO$_3$-type) structure on the left, and the $E2_1$ (perovskite) on the right.

A wealth of experimental study has centered around this phase, but perovskites that are strictly cubic are remarkably few. The symmetry, which reflects the regular displacement of atoms from ideal cubic positions, may be rhombohedral, tetragonal, orthorhombic or perhaps monoclinic, and depends upon the relative sizes of the three ions, the valencies of A and B which are interdependent, and also upon their polarizabilities. Various views on these matters have recently been summarized by Ward (324). Perovskites are technically important materials, and their ferroelectric, magnetic, and semiconducting properties, which depend upon chemical composition, are influenced by the partial ionic substitution of other elements, and this, like temperature, can also affect the crystal symmetry. Phases with perovskite-like diffraction patterns may not always be perovskite-like in structure, however, and additional reflections may be due to ordering of substituent atoms or to lattice defects, which may be of several kinds. Non-stoichiometric perovskites can either be deficient in A, A_xBO_3, or in oxygen ABO_{3-x}. These are dealt with in turn.

a. *Compounds A_xBO_3 Intermediate between DO_9 and $E2_1$; Cubic Tungsten Bronzes and Related Phases.* The principal group of compounds in this category are the ternary oxides of tungsten A_xWO_3. These cubic and pseudocubic non-stoichiometric phases, together with the tetragonal and hexagonal tungsten oxides having the same generalized formula and discussed in Section II,F, are usually grouped together as the tungsten *bronzes*, an old term derived from their metallic appearance and properties.

For many years the tungsten bronzes were thought to be unique in chemistry, but many compounds related to them can be recognized, the resemblance taking three forms. Firstly, they may have the same structure and properties, but contain elements other than tungsten. Secondly, compounds of different composition and crystal structure may also have the properties of bronzes. Thirdly, there are several compounds crystallizing with tungsten bronze structures, but in all other respects are dissimilar. The name "bronze," which is not specific to tungsten oxides, is undoubtedly convenient and should be retained in the chemical literature to describe a series of *properties* of ternary metal oxides, and should not be used for phases assuming specific structures. These properties have recently been tentatively defined (20); and include:

(1) intense color and luster, ranging from yellow through to black;
(2) metallic conduction of electricity; semiconductivity;
(3) wide range of homogeneity due to a stable host lattice; and
(4) resistance to chemical attack by nonoxidizing acids.

The nature of the tungsten bronzes, which had defied chemists since their discovery by Wöhler in 1823, was elucidated by the classic studies of Hagg (142), who demonstrated that the sodium bronzes could be given the formula Na_xWO_3, with x varying continuously from nearly 1 to about 0.3. The composition $x = 1$ is never reached, but if it were, the structure would be a perovskite; the reason for this failure to achieve a full complement of atoms is not at all clear. The bronzes are therefore intermediate in structure between $E2_1$ and DO_9 and at low values of x appear to reflect the symmetry of the parent oxide WO_3. Sodium tungsten bronze is readily prepared by the interaction of WO_3 and sodium vapor, and the two phases, recognizable at the microscopical level, may coexist as characteristic domains in a single crystal (173).

In the interval Na_xWO_3, $0.32 < x < 0.93$, the x-ray evidence appeared to establish cubic symmetry over the entire range (62, 142), which, as the unit cell is small, imposes the condition that variability of composition is achieved without ordering of any kind. A good deal of additional attention has recently been given to this phase, and it is becoming increasingly clear that the simple mechanism is not altogether correct.

Irrespective of composition, the coefficient of thermal expansion of cubic sodium tungsten bronze shows an abrupt transition in the temperature interval 200°–300°C, found also in WO_3 where it corresponds to a change of symmetry (265). Optical evidence has now established that bronzes are cubic only outside certain temperatures, the values of which are a function of composition (180), and the change of symmetry at either boundary is similar to the cubic-tetragonal inversion of $BaTiO_3$, or to the low temperature transition of WO_3 (303), and is accompanied by twinning. All of this suggests that the cubic diffraction symmetry of the ordered bronze may not be real, but arises from the cubic sublattice of tungsten dominating the scattering by x-rays, and the light atoms sodium and oxygen, if they are in less symmetrical positions, will contribute evidence which is readily observable only by other means.

A single crystal neutron diffraction study of a bronze of the composition $Na_{0.75}WO_3$ has been reported (27), and even although the crystal contained domains of the tetragonal phase, the diffraction symmetry was cubic. The unit cell, however, was doubled, and the structure was shown to be one where sodium was ordered in six out of eight of the cubic A sites. The oxygens occupied only one in four of the positions imposed by the crystallographic space group, and for this reason it appeared likely that the twinning arose from local ordering of these atoms, which could be achieved only by a reduction of symmetry. Order of sodium and vacancies in the A positions persisted at low temperatures where cubic symmetry was real. It may be pertinent to ask whether sodium is ordered at different concentration levels, and if such ordered phases can be cubic.

The tetragonal Li and Na bronzes in Table XII are also related in structure to perovskite, but the tungsten atoms are displaced from certain planes. It is possible that the low symmetry shown by the two copper bronzes enables the copper to adopt a square coordination. La_xTiO_3 and Sr_xNbO_3 are typical cubic bronzes with intense color and wide composition ranges, but they are, of course, tungsten free.

In all compounds covered by the definition of a bronze, the metal ions of the host lattice must be capable of dual valency. A guest ion in an interlattice position liberates free electrons, which are not captured by individual host ions but are distributed instead over the whole structure; alternatively it may be that a fraction of the valency electrons are raised in energy to an impurity level, very close to or actually within the conduction band. This is dealt with in detail in Chapter 5.

Non-stoichiometric perovskites can also be prepared by ionic substitution in either the A or the B position without introducing valency anom-

TABLE XII

TUNGSTEN BRONZES A_xBO_3 CUBIC AND PSEUDOCUBIC, TOGETHER WITH RELATED BRONZES OF OTHER ELEMENTS

Compound	Composition	Symmetry	Unit cell dimensions	References
Li_xWO_3	$0.31 < x < 0.57$	Cubic	a variable, approx. 3.7 Å	(231, 296)
Li_xWO_3	$x = 0.3$ to 0.4	Tetragonal	$a = 5.14$, $c = 3.80$ Å	(231)
Na_xWO_3	$0.26 < x < 0.93$	Cubic	a variable, approx. 3.8 Å	(62, 142)
Na_xWO_3	$x = 0.10$	Tetragonal	$a = 5.25$, $c = 3.90$ Å	(228)
Cu_xWO_3	$0.26 < x < 0.77$	Orthorhombic at $x = 0.26$	$a = 3.88$, $b = 3.73$, $c = 7.74$ Å	(77)
		Triclinic at $x = 0.77$	$a = 5.85$, $b = 6.65$, $c = 4.88$ Å $\alpha = 135.7°$, $\beta = 91.7°$, $\gamma = 93.6°$	
Ag_xWO_3	$x = 0.01$		$a = 7.35$, $b = 3.73$, $c = 3.85$ Å	(289)
La_xTiO_3	$0.67 < x < 1.0$	Cubic[a]	a variable, approx. 3.9 Å	(195)
Sr_xNbO_3	$0.7 < x < 0.95$	Cubic	a variable, approx. 4.0 Å	(260)

[a] Johnston and Sestrich report that $LaTiO_3$ is orthorhombic (188a).

alies, but in these cases (Table XIII) metallic properties are absent. The substitution of the divalent ions Cd^{2+} or Pb^{2+} for Na in $NaNbO_3$, or Ta^{5+} for Ti^{4+} in $BaTiO_3$ or $PbTiO_3$, causes a departure from the ideal formula ABO_3 by the omission of A ions from the twelvefold interstitial positions, which in turn influences the Curie temperature if the material is a ferroelectric (see Chapter 5, Section IV,B).

b. *Oxygen Deficient Compounds* ABO_{3-x} *Based upon* $E2_1$ *(Perovskite) Structure.* Ternary oxides with anion deficiencies ABO_x, $2.5 < x < 3.0$, have been reported. $SrTiO_{2.5}$ and $SrVO_{2.5}$ both give simple x-ray powder patterns, the qualitative interpretation being in good agreement with the

TABLE XIII

Ferroelectric Perovskites, $A_{1-x}BO_3$

Compound	Composition range	Reference
$(Na_{1-x}Cd_{x/2})NbO_3$	$0 < x < 0.4$	(214)
$(Na_{1-x}Pb_{x/2})NbO_3$	$0 < x < 0.4$	(113)
$Ba_{1-x/2}(Ti_{1-x}Ta_x)O_3$	$0 < x < 0.14$	(292, 300)
$Pb_{1-x/2}(Ti_{1-x}Ta_x)O_3$	$0 < x < 0.5$	(301)

assumption of a perovskite-like structure where one-sixth of the oxygens are missing at random. The homogeneity range of $SrTiO_{2.5}$ extends to $SrTiO_3$ without change of lattice parameter. $SrVO_x$ has the limits $2.5 < x < 2.7$ (194) and it has been suggested that vanadium occupies some of the strontium positions in SrV_2O_4 [$= (Sr_{0.66}V_{0.33})VO_{2.66}$] which also gives perovskite-like diffraction data (275). The range of composition of these two oxygen deficient phases is also extended by the formation of solid solutions with $LaTiO_3$ (cubic) and with $LaVO_3$ (tetragonal?), [e.g., $La_xSr_{1-x}TiO_{2.5+x/2}$] both being perovskites (194). Anion vacancies can be induced by substitution in the B position, $BaFe^{3+}O_{2.5}$–$BaFe^{3+}_{0.5}Ta^{5+}_{0.5}O_3$ (120) and the corresponding niobium system (119) and Ward (324) gives references to $SrFeO_{3-x}$, $CaMnO_{3-x}$, and $SrCoO_{3-x}$ which do not have such wide homogeneity limits. Oxygen deficient tetragonal perovskites $(Ba_xBi_{1-x})BiO_{3-x/2}$, $0.44 < x < 1.0$, retain an octahedral grouping for Bi in the B sites, but the Ba and Bi which statistically occupy the A positions have six oxygens, two of each at 2.7, 3.1, and 3.6 Å, the latter doubtless unbonded (28).

If an oxygen is removed from a close-packed structure, the metal atom to which it was formerly bonded will have a highly unsymmetrical grouping, and some local rearrangement can be expected. The metal atom B must also be capable of existing in two different kinds of coordination with oxygen, octahedral as well as a five-, four-, three-, or twofold group in the oxygen deficient phase, and pentavalent vanadium is known to form octahedral, trigonal bipyramidal, or tetrahedral bonds to oxygen. Gorter (131) pointed out that changes of coordination of this kind would be difficult to detect in close-packed oxide systems unless they are ordered throughout the entire structure. This is found in the case of $CaFeO_{2.5}$(= $Ca_2Fe_2O_5$) (44), where complete rows of oxygens are regularly missing, and the accompanying movements of atoms remaining in the same planes, impose tetrahedral coordination upon the iron atoms, while calcium has an eight- or ninefold grouping (Fig. 18), not twelvefold as in perovskite itself. $KTiO_{2.5}$ (= $K_2Ti_2O_5$) could be expected to form an oxygen-deficient perovskite structure, but is also completely ordered, each titanium having five oxygen ligands grouped into a trigonal bipyramid (Fig. 19), and potassium an unsymmetrical environment of eight oxygens (17). The strong resemblance of the diffraction patterns of $K_2Ti_2O_5$ to a perovskite, a feature common to all of the alkali titanates, $Na_2Ti_3O_7$ (18), $Na_2Ti_6O_{13}$ (19), as well as $Na_{0.8}Ti_4O_8$ (20), is due to the atoms of all four phases forming an approximately cubic array which might be misinterpreted as belonging to an $E2_1$ structure deficient in both A and oxygen, $A_{1-x}BO_{3-y}$.

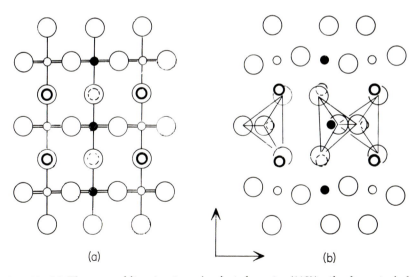

(a)   (b)

FIG. 18. (a) The perovskite structure (projected on to (110)): the largest circles oxygen, intermediate ones A ions, and smallest the B ions. (b) In $Ca_2Fe_2O_5$, oxygens are missing from the central row of octahedra, the remainder regrouped into tetrahedra which are outlined.

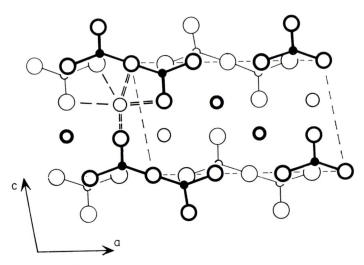

FIG. 19. Projected structure of $K_2Ti_2O_5$; the titanium atoms are in fivefold coordination.

These substances, discussed in Section II,L in somewhat more detail, have little or no real similarity to perovskite.

F. Oxides A_xBO_3 with Tetragonal and Hexagonal Structures

It was clear from Hägg's studies on sodium tungsten bronze (*142*) that one additional phase could be identified at the composition $Na_{0.3}WO_3$. Magnéli (*224*) showed that potassium tungsten bronzes, known since 1836 (*211*), are virtually isomorphous with it, and the two have the structure illustrated by Fig. 20. The tungsten-oxygen octahedra are joined together by corners in a framework with the formula WO_3 containing square and pentagonal empty spaces, the respective projections of cubic positions of the perovskite type, and five-sided *tunnels*, both running right through the structure. The octahedra appear to have been rearranged to provide some larger interstitial positions for the alkali metals than those present in the cubic bronze, but residual fragments of it are nevertheless present in the new one.

In terms of structure the formula of the tetragonal bronze is $A_{0.2}^{1}A_{0.4}^{11}$-WO_3, where A^1 is the fraction of cubic (or twelve-coordinated) sites and A^{11} the pentagonal prism (or fifteen-coordinated) tunnel positions, and evidently these two are only partly occupied by the alkali metals. A superlattice of the tetragonal sodium bronze could perhaps be caused by the preference of sodium for the A^1 positions (*226*), and the interstitial ions

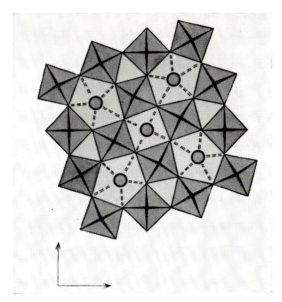

FIG. 20. Tetragonal tungsten bronze structure, the A ions drawn as circles.

in the mixed sodium potassium phase might be sorted out according to size. It is difficult to obtain direct evidence of this by x-ray methods, and it would be more profitable to study these phases by neutron diffraction or by exchange experiments. The tetragonal ammonium bronze (Table XIV) requires further examination.

Goodman (*128*) drew attention to the ferroelectric properties of $PbNb_2O_6$ (see Chapter 5, Section VI), and several subsequent studies of the phase relations on this and on compounds related to it have been made. Fran-

TABLE XIV

TETRAGONAL TUNGSTEN BRONZES

Compound	Composition range	Unit cell dimensions (Å)		References
		a	c	
Na_xWO_3	$0.28 < x < 0.38$	12.1	3.75	(*226*)
K_xWO_3	$0.48 < x < 0.54$	12.30	3.84	(*224*)
$(Na, K)_xWO_3$	$0.21 < x < 0.56$	—	—	(*60*)
Pb_xWO_3	$0.17 < x < 0.35$	12.20	3.78	(*42*)
$(NH_4)_xWO_3$	$x = 0.06$	7.60	6.36	(*235*)

combe and Lewis (114) showed that the large orthorhombic unit cell is transformed at elevated temperatures into a simpler, but closely related one, similar to that of tetragonal tungsten bronze. Many of the ferro-electric phases which can be prepared by substituting Ba for Pb, Ta for Nb, and by more subtle ionic replacements, have orthorhombic symmetry where the a and b axes, which are almost identical, correspond to the $(1\bar{1}0)$ and (110) axes of the tetragonal bronze, and c is doubled. In view of the undoubted importance of ferroelectrics in electrical technology, it is surprising that a detailed crystal structure analysis of at least one of the niobium phases has not yet been made. This would not only give unequivocal reasons for the lower symmetry, but would also establish the oxygen positions with some degree of accuracy in the isomorphous bronze where, owing to the presence of tungsten atoms with a high atomic number, they have only been deduced indirectly (226).

Lead metaniobate has the formula $Pb_{0.5}NbO_3$; one-sixth of the A sties are empty and composition variation can be induced by ionic substitution in two ways. Firstly, the proportion of A atoms is increased with the partial substitution by a group 4 element (Ti, Zr, Sn) for B, $A^{2+}_{(1+x)/2}[B^{5+}_{1-x}C^{4+}_{x}]O_3$. Where A, B, and C are Ba, Nb, and Zr, respectively, the limits appear to be $0.5 < x < 0.6$, the A sites being saturated (129) at the upper limit*; in the case of $K_x(W_{1-x}Ta_x)O_3$, $0.3 < x < 0.5$, the substitution of tungsten for tantalum reduces the number of occupied A positions (120). Secondly, the alkali metals Li, Na, K, and Rb will replace Pb^{2+} in $Pb_{0.5}NbO_3$ according to the generalized scheme $[A^{2+}_{(1-x)/2}C^{+}_{x}]B^{5+}O_3$, and once again the occupancy of the A sites may be close to the theoretical limit $0.5 < x < 0.6$ (129). Cs^+ is undoubtedly too large for the tunnels or holes, but Li^+ appears to substitute for Pb^{2+} even although it is considerably smaller; possibly it enters the small and normally empty trigonal pyramidal holes formed by the junction of three octahedra, but this would be difficult to prove by x-ray methods.

The system $PbO-Nb_2O_5$ contains another non-stoichiometric compound with the range $2PbO \cdot 3Nb_2O_5$ to $PbO \cdot 3Nb_2O_5$, separated from $Pb_{0.5}NbO_3$ by a two phase region (112). Similar compounds with Ba and with Sr in place of Pb and with Ta replacing Nb are also known (120, 270). All of these have unit cell dimensions relating them to the niobates with the tetragonal tungsten bronze structure, but the formulas in Table XV make it clear that the numbers of oxygen atoms are reduced. No single crystal data has yet been obtained which would show whether the oxygen defects are ordered in the crystal structure, either as vacancies or as dis-

---

* The formulas given in reference 129 imply that oxygen vacancies are formed. This was shown to be incorrect (302)

TABLE XV

TERNARY OXYGEN-DEFICIENT NIOBIUM AND TANTALUM OXIDES RELATED IN STRUCTURE
TO TETRAGONAL TUNGSTEN BRONZE

Compound	Composition range	Symmetry	Reference
$Pb_xNbO_{2.5+x}$	$0.17 < x < 0.33$	Tetragonal to orthorhombic	(114)
$Ba_xNbO_{2.5+x}$	$x = 0.25$	Tetragonal (doubtful)	(112)
$Sr_xNbO_{2.5+x}$	$x = 0.20$	Tetragonal	(112)
$(Ba, or Sr)_{0.5}TaO_{2.5+x}$	$0 < x < 0.5(?)$	Tetragonal	(120)

ordered crystallographic shears. They might perhaps be ordered in a much larger unit cell, leaving little evidence in the powder photographs.

A third class of tungsten bronze A_xWO_3, $0 < x < 0.33$, is made from K, Rb, or Cs polytungstates, either by reduction with hydrogen or by solid state reaction with WO_2 (231) (Fig. 21). It has a hexagonal host structure which can also occur in an alkali-free form (Table XVI), prepared readily enough as whiskers by heating commercial tungsten trioxide containing molybdenum as an impurity element.

The tungsten-oxygen octahedra of the host framework share all six corners with similar octahedra, and are grouped into six-membered rings,

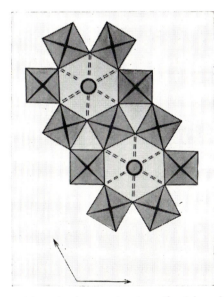

FIG. 21. Hexagonal tungsten bronze structure, the A ions drawn as circles.

TABLE XVI

HEXAGONAL TUNGSTEN BRONZES AND RELATED COMPOUNDS

Compound	Composition	Unit cell[a]	Reference
$Na_xK_yWO_3$	$x = 0.08, y = 0.13$	$a, 3c$	(60)
K_xWO_3	$x = 0.27$	a, c	(231)
Rb_xWO_3	$x = 0.29$	a, c	(230)
Cs_xWO_3	$x = 0.32$	a, c	(230)
Tl_xWO_3	$0.19 < x < 0.36$	$2a, c$	(288)[b]
$(MoW_{11})O_{36}$	BO_3	$a, b = 2a\sqrt{3}, \frac{1}{2}c$	(133)
$(MoW_{14})O_{45}$	BO_3	$a, b = 5a\sqrt{3}, \frac{1}{2}c$	(133)

[a] Approximate lattice dimensions $a = 7.4$ Å; $c = 7.6$ Å.
[b] Re-examination of Tl_xWO_3 by M. J. Sienko and A. D. Wadsley (unpublished) established hexagonal symmetry, not tetragonal as originally reported (288).

the projections of tunnels running through the crystal in one direction. The whiskers of alkali-free tungsten trioxide all have this structure, but molybdenum, present as an impurity, is sorted out in the host structure of different crystals in different ways to form individual ordered phases of a related series $(Mo, W_{3n-1})O_{9n}$, the members $n = 4$ and 5 having been specifically identified (133). The tungsten bronzes which are free of molybdenum are characterized by the subcell of the whisker phases; the c axis is doubled for reasons not altogether clear. The alkali metals K, Rb, or Cs, are located at positions within the tunnels where they are each coordinated to twelve (or perhaps eighteen) oxygen atoms from the framework, and with all possible sites filled, the formula is $A_{0.33}WO_3$. The range of composition for any one phase has not been reported.

There do not appear to be any compounds of Nb and Ta having the hexagonal bronze structure. Hexagonal and orthorhombic phases $Ba_{0.5}NbO_3$ with somewhat similar unit cell dimensions are known (112), and an oxygen-deficient barium-tantalum oxide was reported (118) (Table XVII). Attempts to solve this structure, evidently a new one, have not been altogether successful (117).

G. Multiple Oxides of Mixed Structure with Perovskite-Like Fragments

The diffraction patterns of compositions intermediate between $ATiO_3$ and $3ATiO_3 \cdot AO$, when A is an alkali earth metal, are very similar to one another, and it was widely believed that this is a region of solid solution containing defects, the weak reflections corresponding to distortions of the kind found in $CaTiO_3$ itself. It is now known that this region contains several phases probably of fixed composition, all the structures being related together in an extremely simple way. For clarity, in the case of the strontium compounds the formulas can be written $(SrTiO_3)_n \cdot SrO$, and when $n = 1$, for Sr_2TiO_4, the structure consists of single perovskite-like sheets interleaved with SrO(NaCl-type) sheets. $Sr_3Ti_2O_7$($n = 2$) and $Sr_4Ti_3O_{10}$($n = 3$) respectively contain double and treble perovskite sheets

TABLE XVII

HEXAGONAL A_xBO_3 OR A_xBO_{3-y} PHASES OF UNKNOWN STRUCTURE

Compound	Unit cell dimensions	Reference
$Ba_{0.5}NbO_3{}^a$	$a = 12.05, c = 3.94$ Å	(112)
$Ba_{0.5}NbO_3$	$a = 12.17, b = 10.25, c = 3.94$ Å (orthorhombic)	(112)
$Ba_xTaO_{2.5+x}$ $x = 0.44$	$a = 8.96, c = 7.79$ Å	(118)
$Ba_xTaO_{3.0-x}$ $x = 0.44$	$a = 8.96, c = 7.79$ Å	(117)

^{a} The hexagonal phase is obtained by quenching; the orthorhombic by annealing. The two structures appear to be related.

joined by SrO layers, and are therefore ordered members of an infinite series of potential compounds intermediate in structure between Sr_2TiO_4-($n = 1$) and $SrTiO_3$($n = \infty$). However, $Sr_4Ti_3O_{10}$ and also $Ca_4Ti_3O_{10}$ have never been prepared free from other phases, and additional compounds $n \geq 4$ may well contain stacking disorders difficult to detect by simple techniques.

The $BaO-TiO_2$ system has received a great deal of attention; it contains a large number of finite compounds (259), and the list can be supplemented by additional phases, stabilized by the substitution of small quantities of Sn or Zr for Ti, in closely related ternary systems (191). Isolated fragments of the perovskite structure have been identified in $BaTi_2O_5$ (160), and are believed also to be present in some of the other compounds, which offer a challenging problem to the crystallographer; $BaTi_4O_9$ (215) and $Ba_xTi_8O_{16}$ (89), on the other hand, are known to have tunnel structures.

TABLE XVIII

Ternary Oxides Containing Perovskite Domains

Compound[a]	Symmetry	Unit cell dimensions (Å)		Reference
		a	c	
$SrTiO_3$	Cubic	3.90		
$Sr_4Ti_3O_{10}$	B.C. tetragonal	3.90	28.1	(274)
$Sr_3Ti_2O_7$	B.C. tetragonal	3.90	20.40	(216, 274)
Sr_2TiO_4	B.C. tetragonal	3.88	12.60	(216, 273)

[a] Isomorphous calcium titanium oxides are also reported (78, 267).

The regular intergrowth of the perovskite structure with layers of another kind was reported earlier by Aurivillius (29–32a), in a notable study of the quaternary oxides $(Bi_2O_2)^{2+}(A_{n-1}B_nO_{3n+1})^{2-}$, where A = Ca, Sr, Ba, Pb, K, Na, or Bi and B = Ti, Nb, or Ta. The compounds $n = 2, 3, 4$, and 5 contain two, three, four, and five sheets of BO_6 octahedra sharing corners, and

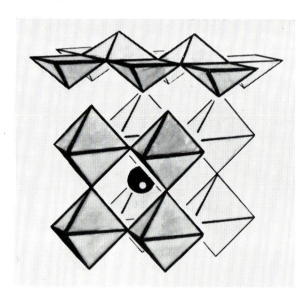

Fig. 22. Perspective drawing of $Bi_2AB_2O_9$, showing the perovskite layers of octahedra (with the A ion drawn as a black sphere) alternating with $(Bi_2O_2)^{2+}$ sheets of square pyramids.

the A ions are in twelve coordinated interstitial positions. For any one phase, these multiple perovskite layers of the one kind are separated by a $(Bi_2O_2)^{2+}$ sheet, consisting of BiO_4 square pyramids sharing edges (Fig. 22). When $n = 1$, the pyramidal sheets alternate with single octahedral sheets with no sites available for A ions; this particular phase has been prepared only as an oxyfluoride (Table XIX). Ferroelectricity is associated with perovskite structures, and is now reported in compounds with $n = 2$ (293), $n = 3$ (299c), $n = 4$ (299) and $n = 5$ (299a,b).

An interesting comparison is afforded by the substituted bismuth oxyhalides formed by fusing together Bi_2O_3 and Cd, Sr, Ba, Li, Na or Pb halides. Although these compounds do not contain structural elements relating them to perovskite, a discussion of them is included to show how layers of different kinds can build into stable phases containing various stacking sequences. If we denote the halogen sheets by H, and $(Bi_2O_2)^{2+}$ layers of square pyramids by Bi, three basic structures emerge which Sillén called the X_1, X_2, and X_3 types (290).

$$X_1 \quad —H—Bi—H—Bi—$$

$$X_2 \quad —H—H—Bi—H—H—Bi—$$

$$X_3 \quad —H—H—H—Bi—H—H—H—Bi—$$

The $(Bi_2O_2)^{2+}$ layers in X_2 are balanced by the two chloride layers forming the stoichiometric compound BiOCl. The net charge of the pyramidal layer in the X_1 phase, balanced by a single chloride layer, must be reduced by the substitution of lower valency ions for Bi^{3+}, while for X_3 it must be increased. This is achieved in the latter case, not by ionic substitution of higher valency ions for Bi^{3+}, but by the interpolation of additional metals into the octahedral spaces provided by the three chloride layers bracketed together in the symbolic formula above. This particular structure is illustrated by Fig. 23, and closely resembles the $n = 1$ structure of Aurivillius, but the octahedra share edges, not corners, and form a single NaCl-type (B1) sheet. Many substituted bismuth oxyhalides are mixtures of these three basic structures; the phases which may be designated X_1X_2, X_2X_3, $X_1X_1X_2$, and $X_1X_2X_3$ have layer sequences represented by adding together the structures of the X_1, X_2, and X_3 compounds successively in the particular order, where they pack together as layer components.

H. Hexagonal Oxides ABO_{3-x}

A group of hexagonal non-stoichiometric phases ABO_{3-x}, A = Ba and B = Fe, Co, or Ni, appear to be closely related to each other, and although

TABLE XIX

Quaternary Oxides with Perovskite Domains, $Bi_2O_2^{2+}(A_{n-1}B_nO_{3n+1})^{2-}$

Value of n	Compound	Composition	Symmetry	Unit cell dimensions (Å)			Reference
				a	b	c	
1	$Bi_2B(O, F)_6$	B = Ti, Nb, Ta. O:F ratio depends on valency of B	B.C. tetragonal	3.83		16.6	(32)
2	$Bi_2AB_2O_9$	A = Bi, Ca, Sr, Ba, Pb, K, or Na; B = Ti, Nb, Ta	F.C. orthorhombic (pseudotetragonal)	$\sqrt{2} \times 3.85$	$\sqrt{2} \times 3.85$ (Averaged for nine different compounds)	25.0	(29)
3	$Bi_4Ti_3O_{12}$		F.C. orthorhombic	$\sqrt{2} \times 3.88$	$\sqrt{2} \times 3.85$	32.8	(30)
4	$BiAB_4Ti_4O_{15}$	A = Ba, Pb, Sr, K, Na, Ca; B = Ti, Ge	F.C. orthorhombic (pseudotetragonal)	$\sqrt{2} \times 3.86$		41.8	(31, 299a, b)
5	$Bi_4A_2Ti_5O_{18}$	A = Pb, Sr	F.C. orthorhombic (pseudotetragonal)	$\sqrt{2} \times 3.86$		49.7	(32a, 299a, b)

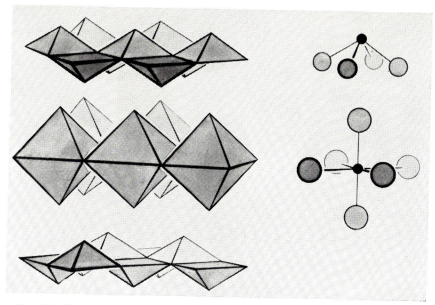

FIG. 23. Bismuth oxyhalide; the X_3 structure with $(Bi_2O_2)^{2+}$ sheets alternating with $B1$ (NaCl-type) sheets.

there is a considerable volume of literature about them, it is often conflict-ing and difficult to assess largely through the lack of sufficient and rigorous experimental detail.

In the interval $BaNiO_x$, $2 < x < 3$, Lander (209) showed that a number of phases exist, all with unit cell dimensions which could be expressed in general terms $n_1 \times a$, $n_2 \times b$, $n_3 \times c$, where a, b, and c are orthohexagonal axes, and n_1, n_2, and n_3 independent integers greater than or equal to unity. Hexagonal $BaNiO_3$, in certain ways related to perovskite, contains NiO_6 octahedra sharing faces which extend parallel to the c axis, and as a conse-quence the Ni atoms are brought close enough together to suggest that they are bonded, while the barium atoms are found in trigonal prismatic holes formed by adjacent octahedral strings. The same disposition of metal atoms was found in $BaNiO_2$, but these oxygens adopt other posi-tions to form a square coordination about nickel in an orthorhombic (nearly hexagonal) unit cell. These two end members represent the ex-tremes of structure in the composition interval; at the lower oxidation state there is fourfold coordination about nickel, at the upper it is sixfold, and in between both may presumably occur together. Lander also showed that the subcell of a phase of intermediate composition, $BaNiO_{2.67}$, con-tains an identical metal atom grouping, but the all-important oxygen positions, which represent the remaining feature of significance, could not be deduced. These undoubtedly are ordered, and a detailed examination of the phases giving the superlattice structures needs to be made in order to provide a mechanism for the composition variation, which we may guess to be due not simply to the removal of oxygen atoms from $BaNiO_3$, but to the rearrangement of those that are left into ordered metastable phases of intermediate compositions.

TABLE XX

HEXAGONAL OXYGEN-DEFICIENT PHASES ABO_{3-x} (A = Ba; B = Fe, Co, or Ni)

Compound	Unit cell dimensions	Reference
$BaFeO_3$ (?)	$a = 5.68, c = 13.86$ Å	(233)
$BaFeO_{2.74}$	$a = 5.76, c = 13.9$ Å	(139)
$BaFeO_{2.63}$	$a = 8.05$ Å (cubic)	(94)
$BaCoO_{2.85}$	$a = 5.59, c = 4.82$ Å	(139)
$BaCoO_{2.23}$	$a = 4.07$ Å (cubic)	(297)
$BaNiO_3$	$a = 5.58, c = 4.83$ Å	(209)
$BaNiO_{2.67}$	$a = 5.72, c = 4.3$ Å (subcell)	(209)
$BaNiO_2$	$a = 5.73, b = \sqrt{3} \times 5.32, c = 4.73$ Å (orthorhombic)	(209)

$BaCoO_3$ is unknown, but $BaCoO_{2.85}$ appears to be related to Lander's oxides (139), while a closely related phase was found at the composition $BaCoO_{2.31}$ (297). The powder pattern of $BaCoO_{2.23}$ can be indexed as cubic with a lattice constant of 4.07 Å (297), but $BaCoO_2$ has a structure related to that of quartz, Ba ions occupying interstices in a CoO_4 tetrahedral framework (294).

A mixed barium iron oxide was assigned the formula $BaFeO_3$, implying quadrivalent iron, because of similarity between its diffraction data and those of $BaTiO_3$ (233). Chemical analysis of a preparation which gave almost identical unit cell dimensions, resulted in the formula $BaFeO_{2.74}$ (139), and a cubic perovskite-like structure was suggested earlier for $BaFeO_{2.63}$ (94). Oxygen-deficient phases $Ba[B_{1/3}Ti_{2/3}]O_{3-x}$ having the hexagonal $BaTiO_3$ structure are obtained by substituting a variety of ions B for Ti (*85*), but ranges of homogeneity have not been explored.

J. Oxides Based upon the Spinel HI_1 Structure

The cubic spinel structure may be described in terms of nonmetal ions in cubic close packing, where one set of metal atoms A occupy one-eighth of the tetrahedral positions, and another set B one-half of the octahedral sites. It is doubtful if any one oxide structure has received more attention than this one; over thirty ions with radii between 0.5 and 1.0 Å of more than twenty-two elements in various combinations are known to be present in spinel-like phases (*130, 324*), which then have physical properties governed to a large degree by the crystallographic site into which they are assigned. Despite the wide diversity of chemical composition, spinels are usually stoichiometric, and only in special circumstances, usually involving out-of-equilibrium conditions, do they deviate from the ideal formula AB_2O_4.

1. METAL-DEFICIENT SPINELS

The existence of defect structures in metastable states is well supported by observations on γ-Fe_2O_3, prepared by the dehydration of γ-$FeOOH$ (lepidocrocite) or perhaps by the low temperature oxidation of Fe_3O_4. Hägg (*141*) and Verwey (*308*) independently showed that it should more properly have the formula $Fe_{2\frac{2}{3}}O_4$, and it appears to be non-stoichiometric over the entire range of composition $Fe_{2\frac{2}{3}}O_4$–Fe_3O_4, the vacancies being confined to the octahedral positions. Verwey noted that γ-Fe_2O_3 could not be dehydrated without destroying the structure, and Kordes (*205*) simultaneously reported that the isomorphous γ-Al_2O_3 gives a number of unexplained extra reflections on the x-ray powder patterns. More recent investigations have established a close similarity between these defective spinels and $LiFe_5O_8$ (*57, 84*), leading to a cubic structure where the octahedral positions vacated by a metal atom may or may not contain hydrogen ions; the composition range now appears limited to $Fe_8[H_4Fe_{12}]O_{32}$–$Fe_8[(Fe_{1\frac{1}{3}}vac._{2\frac{2}{3}})Fe_{12}]O_{32}$, the octahedrally coordinated ions bracketed. At the latter composition ordering may proceed still further, and the iron atoms and vacancies in one set of octahedral positions are segregated into sites of their own in a tetragonal superstructure formed by three spinel units (*246*).

Both γ-Mn_2O_3 and Mn_3O_4 have a tetragonally distorted spinel structure (*309*), but there appears to be no systematic study of the phase relations between them. Hydrogen ions possibly are present in γ-Mn_2O_3, and an appraisal of magnetic susceptibility measurements led to the conclusion that the vacant octahedral sites are disordered (*291*). Very long range ordering (*61*) and stacking faults in the oxygen lattice (*79*) of γ-Al_2O_3 were also reported. Ternary sulfides with the spinel structure are well-known, and β-In_2S_3 has a tetragonal superstructure formed by three spinel blocks joined together; in this case the cation vacancies are ordered in certain *tetrahedral* positions (*263*).

The ability to form solid solutions with B_2O_3 oxides was noted several years ago for the systems $MgAl_2O_4$–Al_2O_3 (*146*) and AFe_2O_4–Fe_2O_3 (*24*), where A is a divalent metal. The equilibrium phase diagram of the former (Fig. 24) shows that the solubility is negligible at 700°C, but increases

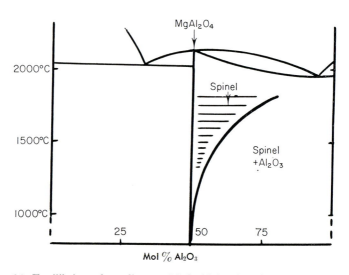

FIG. 24. Equilibrium phase diagram MgO–Al_2O_3, the spinel region hatched.

rapidly with temperature to reach a maximum at about 1800°C (*272*). The substitution of Al^{3+} in the solid is accompanied by vacancies in the metal positions, and the limiting compound has the formula $Mg_{0.21}Al_{2.53}O_4$ with 0.26 missing atoms per formula-unit, approximately one in twelve. The extension to the theoretical limit of the solid solution represented by the phase γ-Al_2O_3 (i.e., $Al_{2\frac{2}{3}}O_4$) has not been achieved. The non-stoichiometric spinel phase is retained by quenching from high temperature, but is resolved into $MgAl_2O_4$ and α-Al_2O_3 by thermal annealing. This exsolution process has been examined in some detail (*277*), and a metastable monoclinic phase close to the composition Al_2O_3, and related in structure to spinel, contains unoccupied octahedral positions that are ordered (*182*). The corresponding iron spinels, or ferrites, are also resolved into two phases by annealing (245). At high temperatures the ternary system $MgO-Fe_2O_3-Al_2O_3$ contains defective spinel with a very wide composition range (207), and this might prove to be a general feature for this class of compound.

2. HEXAGONAL FERRIMAGNETIC OXIDES

The ternary systems $BaO-Fe_2O_3-BO$ (B = Mg, Fe^{2+}, Co, Ni, or Zn) contain a large number of ferrimagnetic oxides related in structure to spinel, but with hexagonal symmetry. The chemical formulas are complex, and the principles upon which the structures are based are not unlike those of the several series of oxides and oxyhalides discussed in Section II,G. The preparation of pure phases proved to be a matter of great difficulty as the similarities between them often resulted in the parallel intergrowth of several compounds in one crystal, and regions of solid solution, or averaged structures, were not retained at room temperature. The proof that each compound is strictly stoichiometric is a tribute to the Dutch workers who succeeded in unraveling the chemical, structural, and magnetic characteristics of the whole system, which, for want of modern diffraction equipment and high resolution, might well have been dismissed as a single phase region with a wide composition range as it could well be at high temperatures.

The compounds are listed in Table XXI, taken from a review by Jonker (190). Phase M, together with $BaFe_2O_4$, is found in the binary system $BaO-Fe_2O_3$, and has the same structure as that of the mineral magnetoplumbite deduced by Adelsköld (2); the others were worked out by Braun

TABLE XXI

HEXAGONAL FERRIMAGNETIC OXIDES CONTAINING ELEMENTS OF THE SPINEL STRUCTURE (190)

Symbol of Compound	Composition	Unit cell dimensions (Å)		Cipher
		a	c	
M	$BaFe_{12}O_{19}$	5.88	$23.3 = 2 \times (5 \times 2.33)$	M_5
X	$Ba_2B_2Fe_{28}O_{46}$	5.88	$84.1 = 3 \times (12 \times 2.33)$	X_{12}
W	$BaB_2Fe_{16}O_{27}$	5.88	$32.8 = 2 \times (7 \times 2.34)$	W_7
Y	$Ba_2B_2Fe_{12}O_{22}$	5.88	$43.5 = 3 \times (6 \times 2.42)$	Y_6
Z	$Ba_3B_2Fe_{24}O_{41}$	5.88	$52.3 = 2 \times (11 \times 2.38)$	Z_{11}
U	$Ba_4B_2Fe_{36}O_{60}$	5.88	$113.1 = 3 \times (16 \times 2.36)$	U_{16}

(*58*). The lengths of the *c* axes can be broken up into double or triple multiples of about 2.35 Å, the distance between oxygen layers, and the bracketed numerals in the fourth column of Table XXI (*n* × 2.3 Å) are the number *n* of oxygen layers present in blocks of structure characteristic of each phase, while the other factor is the number of these blocks in the unit cell. The right-hand column of the table contains the ciphers M_5, X_{12}, etc., a shorthand method of representing both the phase and the size of the block within it. M_5, W_7, and Y_6 are "primary" blocks that are present in all phases. The positions of the atoms in these units (Fig. 25) are closely related to the spinel structure (represented by S), a principal

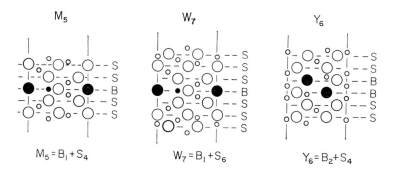

Fig. 25. Ferrimagnetic spinel blocks, M_5, W_7, Y_6 in projection, showing the atoms in a mirror plane containing the *c* axis (vertical). Small open circles, Fe in tetrahedral and octahedral coordination; small filled circles, Fe in fivefold coordination; large black circles, Ba; large open circles, oxygen.

difference being the substitution of a barium atom for an *oxygen*. The iron atoms are in three kinds of position, tetrahedral and octahedral in the spinel parts of a block, and in fivefold coordination, a trigonal bipyramid, in the layers containing barium ions (represented by B).

In M_5 there are therefore four layers of oxygens as in spinel, and one of oxygen plus Ba. A new shorthand notation is now introduced, and the M_5 layer becomes a hybrid of the two components, S_4 (spinel oxygen, 4 layers) and B_1 (barium oxygen, 1 layer). The structure of the block M_5 can therefore be represented by the juxtaposition of these two units, S_4 plus B_1, and that of the complete phase M by the sequence:

$$—S_4—B_1—S_4—B_1—\text{etc.}$$

$$\underbrace{}_{M_5} \quad \underbrace{}_{M_5}$$

W_7 contains six spinel-oxygen layers alternating with a B_1 layer (S_6 plus B_1), and the structure of phase W has the sequence:

$$-S_6-B_1-S_6-B_1-etc.$$
$$W_7 \qquad W_7$$

Y_6 has an S_4 block adjacent to two barium-oxygen layers, B_2, (S_4 plus B_2), and phase Y consists of:

$$-S_4-B_2-S_4-B_2-etc.$$
$$Y_6 \qquad Y_6$$

The three remaining phases X, Z, and U contain the blocks X_{12}, Z_{11}, and U_{16}, each of which can be broken up into the smaller units of the other phases. Jonker also pointed out that these additivity rules may be used to determine the exact chemical formula of each compound.

The $CaO-Fe_2O_3$ equilibrium phase diagram (257) contains evidence of three compounds of intermediate composition $CaFe_4O_7$, $CaFe_2O_4$, and $Ca_2Fe_2O_5$, but the extension to ternary systems has resulted in the preparation of three additional hexagonal phases, related to one another, and stabilized by a small amounts of the third element Mg or Y (59); the structures of these ferrimagnetics, $Ca_4Fe_{14}O_{25}$ (occurring in two forms) and $Ca_4Fe_{20}O_{33}$ have not yet been reported.

K. Ternary "Bronzes" $A_xB_3O_4$

The non-stoichiometric ternary oxide $Na_xPt_3O_4$ has a simple cubic host structure of formula B_3O_4 where each face of a cube of oxygens is joined to a face of another cube through platinum atoms, which join up to form non-intersecting linear chains in the directions of the cube axes (326) (Fig. 26). Sodium ions occupy the centers of the cubes, but the compound is stable whether they are present or not (327), having a theoretical composition range $0 < x < 1$. This explanation satisfies some early observations (335) that different preparations contained different amounts of sodium; "combined water," invariably present, could perhaps compete with it for the cubic sites. An isomorphous compound of palladium has been reported (279) and both substances, having a pronounced resistance to attack by strong acids as well as being conductors of electricity, should perhaps be classified as bronzes with a crystal structure of a new kind.

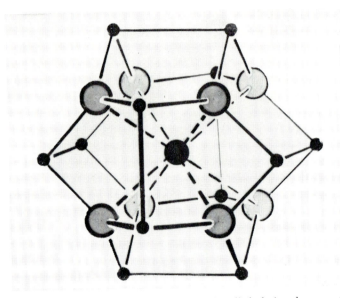

Fig. 26. The structure of $Na_xPt_3O_4$, a cage of Pt (small circles) and oxygen (large open circles). The large black circle at the centre is Na.

L. Ternary Alkali Titanates

1. Sodium Titanium Bronze Na_xTiO_2

The reduction in hydrogen of $Na_2Ti_3O_7$ yields the oxide bronze Na_xTiO_2, $0 < x < 0.25$, having an octahedrally coordinated host structure, TiO_2, of a kind previously unknown but having prominent features identifiable as scraps of other oxide types (20). In the simplest sense it contains fragments of perovskite $E2_1$, but the oxygen content of the host is reduced from TiO_3 to TiO_2 by extensive edge sharing of octahedra, the fragments joining up into unidirectional tunnels enclosing sodium ions (Fig. 27). Owing to the shapes of the TiO_6 octahedra, a single perovskite-like A position is grossly distorted and the sodium within it has only four close bonds to oxygen. The crystal on which this study was made had a composition $Na_{0.2}TiO_2$, and its appearance and its marked resistance to chemical attack are both characteristic of metal oxide bronzes.

The host structure bears a simple relationship to both V_6O_{13} and V_2O_5, and all three are members of a possible series of structural homologues $B_{2n}O_{5n-2}$, where disorder or solid solution formation is likely, but has not yet been studied.

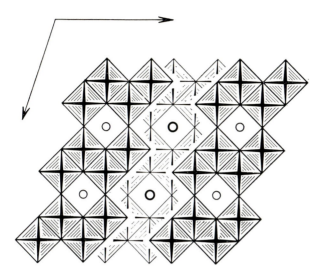

FIG. 27. Na_xTiO_2 projected as idealized regular octahedra. Na drawn as circles.

2. MIXED LAYER ALKALI TITANATES

Several of the anhydrous sodium titanates forming a sequence of structures can be grouped together under a common formula $A_nTi_6O_{10+n}$ ($n = 0$, 3, and 4), A representing the pseudocubic positions available to the alkali metal ions and not necessarily the number occupied. The Ti—O host lattices of all three phases are constructed from identical zig-zag ribbons of trebled octahedra sharing edges. These are joined corner-to-corner in puckered sheets present in each member, as isolated layers in $Na_2Ti_3O_7$ ($n = 4$) when all sodium positions are filled (18), joined by corners in the tunnel structure $Na_2Ti_6O_{13}$ ($n = 3$) where only two out of three positions are occupied by sodium (19), and having all available edges in common in the closed packed compound Ti_3O_5 ($n = 0$) (26) where there are no positions for the ions A (Fig. 28).

Fibrous substances of indefinite composition intermediate between the members $n = 3$ and 4 have been prepared both hydrothermally and from the melt (45), and a study of various alkali metal titanates appears to represent extensive solid solution in this region (281). Since both the trititanate ($n = 4$) and the hexatitanate ($n = 3$) host structures contain identical sheets, intergrowth at the unit cell level of one upon the other can be expected, i.e., the random insertion of discrete sheets of the $n = 4$

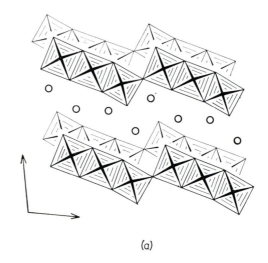

(a)

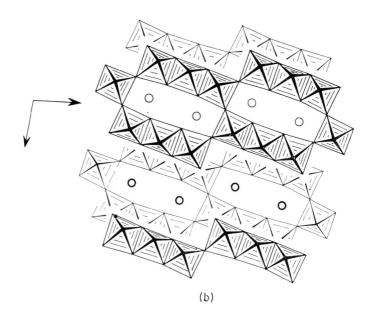

(b)

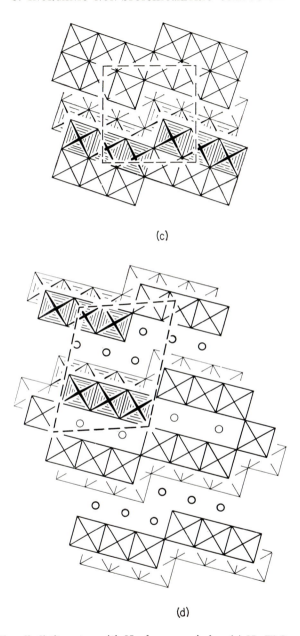

(c)

(d)

FIG. 28. The alkali titanates, with Na drawn as circles. (a) $Na_2Ti_3O_7$; (b) $Na_2Ti_6O_{13}$; (c) Ti_3O_5. Each contains structural elements of the same kind. In (d) the intergrowth of structural features of (a) and (b) is seen.

member into the structure of the $n = 3$ phase, bonded through the sodium ions and having none of the terminal oxygens in common, giving a simple mechanism whereby both Na and O are made to vary over a considerable composition range. Ordering is likely to occur only at intermediate points where the ratio of the two kinds of structural unit are simple whole numbers, but this may lead to substances with irrational formulas. $Na_{10}Ti_{18}O_{41}$ (i.e., $Na_{2.2}Ti_4O_{9.1}$) is the simplest ordered "phase" intermediate in structure between $Na_2Ti_3O_7$ and $Na_2Ti_6O_{13}$, the end members.

M. Oxides with the Approximate Formula B_2O_5

1. TERNARY ALKALI METAL VANADIUM "BRONZES"

The "spitting" or ejection of oxygen during the crystallization of melts in the systems of vanadium pentoxide with univalent metal (Li, Na, Ag) oxides has been known for many years, and in a series of phase studies Flood, Krog, and Sørum (108, 109, 110) demonstrated that two non-stoichiometric phases of intermediate composition, β and γ, are present in each system (Table XXII). In addition to defining composition limits, establishing isomorphous relationships and determining the unit cell sizes, they demonstrated that these reduced "vanadyl vanadates" are formed when oxygen is lost. Because of their metallic characteristics they can be classed as vanadium bronzes related to the tungsten bronzes. The chemical for-

TABLE XXII

COMPOSITION LIMITS OF VANADIUM OXIDE BRONZES

Nomenclature	Compound	A	Composition	Reference
β	$A_xV_2O_5$	Li	$0.2 < x < 0.33^a$	(109)
		Na	$0.13 < x < 0.31$	(110)
		Ag	$x \cong 0.33$	(108)
γ	$A_xV_3O_8$	Li	$1.13 < x < 1.33$	(109)
		Na	$x \cong 0.9$	(110)
		Ag	$x \cong 1.2$	(108)

^{a} A composition $Li_{0.62}V_2O_5$ was reported by Ozerov (248).

mulas of the two phases, $A_xV_2O_5$ and $A_xV_3O_8$, were determined only when the complete crystal structures were elucidated (313, 315) and are appropriately represented in terms of the number of crystallographic point positions occupied by atoms unrelated in space to one another; these then become $A_{2-x}V_6O_{15}$ and $A_{1+x}V_3O_8$.

These vanadium oxides contain structural elements of the same kind, a double zig-zag string of octahedra sharing edges, as well as a single zig-zag string where the octahedra may be distorted to such an extent that they should be regarded as trigonal bipyramids, the particular metal then being in fivefold coordination. The structure of $Na_{2-x}V_6O_{15}$, illustrated by Fig. 29 consists of numbers of these two units joined together through common oxygen atoms and forming an open framework, the irregular open spaces being the projections of tunnels persisting throughout the structure in one particular direction. The formula at the upper composition limit is $Na_{1.0}V_6O_{15}$, and the alkali metals occupy only one-half of the sevenfold positions in the tunnels. By analogy with other tunnel compounds derived from the $C4$ structure, a sodium ion can adopt one of two positions of equal energy which can then be expected to influence the remainder of the sites within the same tunnel to form a locally-ordered zig-zag sequence. On the other hand the diffraction evidence is satisfied only if these sequences of interstitial ions lack order in the structure as a whole (313). At the lower limit $Na_{0.5}V_6O_{15}$ some tunnels may contain ordered sequences while others are empty. It was suggested by Ozerov (247) that the alkali metals in this and the isomorphous bronze $K_{2-x}V_6O_{15}$ (249) are in the metallic state, the arguments being based upon measurements of electrical resistivity at various temperatures, and supported by a proposal for an alternative but improbable redistribution of alkali metal atoms. In view of the manifold changes to a distorted structure which can occur as the result of heating it up to its melting point, this model is not a likely one. A copper analogue, $Cu_{1.8}V_6O_{15}$, has also been prepared (248).

$Li_{1+x}V_3O_8$ contains the same double and the distorted single units joined into layers separated by lithium (Fig. 30). At the composition $Li_{1.0}V_3O_8$ these ions are present in octahedral positions formed by oxygen atoms from neighboring layers, and any excess lithium can find three additional tetrahedral sites (for each formula unit) into which they can fit. In view of the possible random occupancy by these ions of low atomic number, no direct evidence can be expected (315).

Flood and his co-workers showed that the Li, Na, and Ag metavanadates A_xVO_3, with the diopside structure (256), also have a range of composition $0.9 < x < 1.0$, and the way in which the single trigonal bipyramidal (or very distorted octahedral) string may be split into the tetrahedral chains of this particular structure has been pointed out (313). In all three of

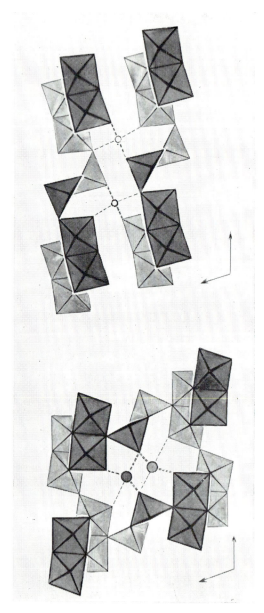

FIG. 30. (Right) Layer structure of $Li_{1+x}V_3O_8$.

FIG. 29. (Left) Tunnel structure of $Na_{2-x}V_6O_{15}$.

these non-stoichiometric phases the stability of the framework, whether it forms open tunnels, layers, or linear strings unconnected except through the univalent ion A, allows it to remain undisturbed. The dual valency which can be assumed by the vanadium ion offsets any absences from or additions to the interstitial positions in the different structures.

2. OXYGEN-DEFICIENT OXIDES Nb_2O_{5-x} AND RELATED PHASES

Despite the simple formula of niobium pentoxide, the structures of the various polymorphs are complex. The high temperature phase α-Nb_2O_5 had been reported by Brauer (52) to have a composition range NbO_x, $2.4 < x < 2.5$, due to the loss of oxygen close to the melting point, but it was shown more recently that two previously unknown compounds, $NbO_{2.46}$ and $NbO_{2.40}$, could be identified in this region (238). Their crystal structures have not yet been published, but Magnéli pointed out in a private communication that $NbO_{2.40}$ is isomorphous with orthorhombic $Ti_2Nb_{10}O_{29}$, and this mixed oxide together with the closely related phase $TiNb_2O_7$ are the two known members of an homologous series of oxides that might perhaps include one form of Nb_2O_5 as a terminal member (318, 319). Titanium and niobium are not segregated into special positions of their own, the one substituting isomorphously for the other in these compounds that can be regarded as stabilized, reduced niobium oxides with the general formula $B_{3n}O_{8n-3}$; $TiNb_2O_7$ is $B_3O_7(BO_{2.333})$ corresponding to $n = 3$, and $Ti_2Nb_{10}O_{29}$ or $B_{12}O_{29}(= BO_{2.417})$ to $n = 4$. The unit cells of these homologues are large but readily derived from the DO_9 type and can be described more succinctly in terms of two fragments of structure, a D (double) row of closely bonded octahedra and an S (single) row appearing in both compounds (Fig. 31). The D and S units may be joined by having octahedral corners in common, and the structure of the B_3O_7 phase ($n = 3$), represented by a shorthand notation is:

$$-D-S-D-S-$$

while $B_{12}O_{29}(n = 4)$ is written

$$-D-S-S-D-S-S-D-$$

The D units may be regarded as the *shear* planes of a hypothetical structure B_3O_8 formed solely by the S units, the parent for this series as TiO_2 is for the reduced phases Ti_nO_{2n-1}. $Ti_2Nb_{10}O_{29}(n = 4)$ exists in two forms with the same sequence of D and S units: orthorhombic where each alternate D sheet is the mirror image of the next one, and monoclinic where the sense of successive D's is the same. The homologue $n = 5$, $B_{15}O_{37}(= BO_{2.467})$, could not be prepared but the reduced oxide $NbO_{2.46}$ has a formula consistent with it. It might, however, be closely related to the high tempera-

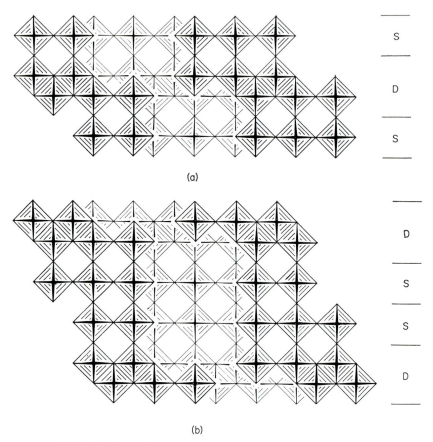

(a)

(b)

Fig. 31. (a) TiNb$_2$O$_7$ consisting of alternating D and S units. (b) Monoclinic Ti$_2$Nb$_{10}$O$_{29}$, where D alternates with $2S$. Random intergrowths of D and S are possible at intermediate compositions.

ture form of Nb$_2$O$_5$, which contains S units of finite size condensed in a different way, but nevertheless consisting of DO_9-type blocks ($120a$).

A feature of any series of metal oxides is the regularity of the structural features, or size of the blocks, present in any one phase. Compounds in between adjacent members, containing fragments of both in a mixed sequence, do not appear to have been reported. The complete structure of such a mixed phase in the TiO$_2$–Nb$_2$O$_5$ system can be predicted with relative ease, and attempts were made by the writer to prepare Ti$_5$Nb$_{16}$O$_{50}$ which might be expected to have an ordered sequence,

$$\begin{array}{ccc} n=3 & n=4 & n=3 \end{array}$$

$$-D-S-D-S-S-D-S-D$$

containing parts of the members $n = 3$ and 4, ordered in a phase of a new kind. The fusion of a mixture of oxides of this composition gave crystals containing D and S units alternating without any regularity, the diffraction data arising mainly from the DO_9-type subcell (322). This composition corresponds to a eutectic in the phase diagram (269), and when the two congruently melting phases $n = 3$ and 4 containing identical fragments of structure in different amounts are crystallized simultaneously, they disorder and form a metastable "phase," much as if they were shuffled like a deck of cards. In other systems as well, such as mixed calcium and potassium nitrates and even alloys, the formation of disorder or even of glasses is achieved at the eutectic composition (74, 199).

In this particular case the region between $TiNb_2O_7$ and $Ti_2Nb_{10}O_{29}$ ($BO_{2.33}$–$BO_{2.42}$) can be interpreted in two ways depending upon the experimental conditions. Reaction of the component oxides below the solidus gives a mixture of the two phases, but preparations quenched from the liquidus appear to represent a non-stoichiometric single phase region of solid solution, ordered at each end and disordered in between. The variation of oxygen content is due to a partly randomized change in the numbers of D and S units and not to holes in the framework of oxygen atoms.

N. Hydrous Oxides

1. HYDRATED VANADIUM OXIDE MINERALS

A commonly postulated mechanism for variability of composition in wet way preparations is the introduction of hydrogen as an additional element. A specific example is the reduction of orthorhombic MnO_2 by hydrazine (102),

$$MnO_2 + xe^- + xH^+ = MnO_{2-x}(OH)_x$$

where the unit cell volume of the product is a linear function of the proton concentration, and its limiting composition is $HMnO_2$ at $x = 1$.

A study of HVO_2, the mineral montroseite, showed that two phases coexisted with it in a particular single crystal, VO_2 (paramontroseite) with the same structure as orthorhombic MnO_2, and a phase of intermediate composition, HV_2O_4, both giving diffuse x-ray reflections. Evans and Mrose (99) who discuss this in some detail make it clear that these two minerals were formed by the loss of hydrogen ions from HVO_2, and exist as scattered domains in the more stable HVO_2 structure. The end members HVO_2 and VO_2 are identical except for hydrogen, which bonds oxygen atoms at the edges of interstitial tunnels formed by vanadium-oxygen octahedra. When hydrogen is present these atoms are 2.6 Å apart, and when absent the distance is 3.9 Å. The *random* removal of hydrogen would undoubtedly have resulted in serious structural damage, giving what would appear to be a homogeneous phase with diffuse x-ray reflections.

The most recent laboratory examination of the hydrous vanadium oxides revealed only three phases (*127*), but many additional ones are described in the mineralogical literature (Table XXIII). Evans and Mrose (*100*, *101*) also examined a number of these, $H_6V_4O_{10}$ (häggite), $H_{10}V_6O_{16}$ ("phase B" or protodoloresite) and $H_4V_2O_6$ (duttonite) are the respective members $n = 4$, 6, and ∞ of a structural series $H_{2n-2}V_nO_{3n-2}$, additional phases being considered likely. The structures of the members $n = 4$ and 6 leave no doubt that an apparent single crystal, which contributed diffraction data for both, contains these two substances alternating as blocks of random thickness, and not forming a homogeneous solid solution (Fig. 32). The two lie adjacent to each other on the ε_h–pH equilibrium diagram and evidently are formed by slight periodic alterations of hydrogen ion concentration during crystallization. $H_{10}V_6O_{16}$ ("phase B"), which is closely related in structure to $H_8V_6O_{16}$ (doloresite) can also intergrow with HVO_2 (montroseite) as well as VO_2 (paramontroseite) (Fig. 33).

These complex relationships indicate quite clearly that localized ordering is not confined to anhydrous materials prepared by fusion. The structure determinations of an analogous series of molybdenum oxyhydroxides $MoO_x(OH)_{3-x}$ related to MoO_3, identified by Glemser et al. (*125*), will be awaited with considerable interest.

TABLE XXIII

HYDRATED VANADIUM OXIDE MINERALS OF RELATED STRUCTURE

Ideal formula	Name	Symmetry	Lattice parameters (Å)				Reference
			a	b	c	β	
VO_2	Paramontroseite	Orthorhombic	4.89	9.39	2.93		(*99*)
HV_2O_4		Orthorhombic	4.80	9.63	2.93		(*99*)
HVO_2	Montroseite	Orthorhombic	4.54	9.97	3.03		(*98*)
$H_6V_4O_{10}$	Häggite	Monoclinic	12.17	2.99	4.83	98°15′	(*101*)
$H_{10}V_6O_{16}$	"Phase B"	Monoclinic	19.64	2.99	4.83	103°55′	(*101*)
$H_8V_6O_{16}$	Doloresite	Monoclinic	19.03	2.99	4.83	90°18′	(*101*)
$H_4V_2O_6$	Duttonite	Monoclinic	8.80	3.95	5.96	90°40′	(*100*)
$H_4V_4O_{12}$	Paraduttonite	Unknown					(*97*)

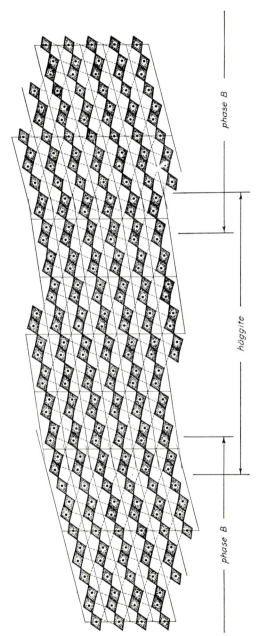

FIG. 32. Intergrowth of two hydrated vanadium minerals, phase B and häggite viewed as octahedra projected down their edges; the dotted lines are hydrogen bridges (courtesy H. T. Evans, Jr. and *American Mineralogist*).

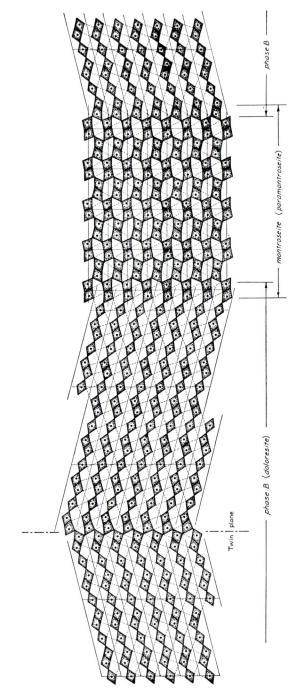

Fig. 33. Intergrowth of phase B, or doloresite, with montroseite, or paramontroseite; a twin plane is included (courtesy H. T. Evans, Jr. and *American Mineralogist*).

2. HYDRATED OXIDE LAYER STRUCTURES

Layer compounds consist of infinite two-dimensional sheets of closely-bonded ions or molecules held together largely by residual forces, and as a consequence there is a single cleavage by which the crystal may be split, as a book into its component leaves. A very large number of inorganic compounds belong to this class. Metal hydroxy salts after extensive ionic substitution are usually stoichiometric. Layer silicates, clay minerals, and lamellar graphite complexes, well known to be variable in composition, are treated in Chapter 6, Section V.

The mineral chalcophanite, an example of an oxide hydrate with a range of homogeneity $Zn_{1+x}Mn_3O_7 \cdot 3H_2O$, $0 < x < 0.25$, has a layer structure with the sequence:

$$-O-Mn-O-Zn-H_2O-Zn-O-Mn-O$$

the brackets enclosing double sheets of oxygens in hexagonal packing forming octahedral positions for manganese. In the related mineral lithiophorite, $(Al, Li)MnO_2 \cdot (OH)_2$, these are all filled (310), but in chalcophanite one manganese atom in every seven is systematically absent. Successive sheets of these are separated by a layer of water, and the zinc ions are located in the octahedral positions between the water and oxygen layers directly above and below the manganese vacancies. The structure is bound together by the zinc ions with some help from hydrogen bonds directed from the water layer. The composition range is caused by the fractional occupancy of another of these interlayer positions by Zn or Mn^{2+}, the valency anomaly being compensated by the reduction in the net valency of manganese in its octahedral layer; this was proved by direct evidence (312). Mackay (222) pointed out that this structure is only one of many to be expected in hydrous oxides of this kind, where a hexagonal distribution of vacancies of different kinds, together with variations in the stacking sequences of the layers themselves (83), affords an interesting comparison with the metal sulfides intermediate between the B8 and C6 types discussed in Section III,A.

III. CHALCOGENIDES (SULFIDES, SELENIDES, TELLURIDES)

A. Chalcogenides BX-BX₂ Intermediate between B8 and C6

A great many transition metal sulfides, selenides, and tellurides, where the non-metal atoms are in hexagonal close packing, tend to form the B8

(NiAs-type) structure at the composition BX, and the $C6$ (Cd(OH)$_2$-type) structure at BX$_2$. These two have many features in common.

The metal atoms in the $B8$ arrangement occupy the octahedral interstices of the sulfur lattice, which, when viewed in a direction perpendicular to the c axis, forms a sequence of "layers" of atoms of the same kind

$$—X—B—X—B—X \text{ etc.,}$$

B and X being metal and non-metal respectively (Fig. 34a). If the metal atoms from every second layer are completely removed without disturbing the sulfurs, the layer sequence becomes

$$...X—B—X...X—B—X...X—B—X...$$

This is the $C6$ structure (Fig. 34b), the remaining metals are in the octahedral positions formed by two layers of sulfur atoms, and these strongly bonded sheets are then merely packed together.

A large number of studies have been made of the transition metal chalcogenides falling into this group, one of the principle objectives being to show that the two types represent the end structures of a berthollide with a very wide composition range. If this were true, the mechanism would be simply due to the random insertion of additional metal atoms into the interlayer octahedral positions of the $C6$ structure until they are all filled, or conversely to the removal of metal atoms randomly from alternate layers in the $B8$ structure, implying differences of some kind in the bonding of different metal atoms in both sheets.

Tengnér (*304*) showed that the complete transition from the one structure to the other occurs for Co–Te and Ni–Te, and Ehrlich for Ti–Se and Ti–Te (*93*). In most other cases, the evidence, largely gathered by Debye-Scherrer x-ray photographs, demonstrated that the change is not altogether a simple one, as additional diffraction lines were usually found which could not be explained in terms of the simple hexagonal unit cells characteristic of the end members. Earlier than this, however, Haraldsen and his co-workers proved that the extra lines found in certain regions of the Cr–Se, Cr–Te, and Fe–S systems belong to superlattices and not to impurity phases. Recent studies, in which more modern x-ray diffraction techniques were available, revealed a remarkably complex series of phe-

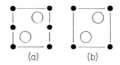

(a)   (b)

FIG. 34. (*a*) A unit cell of the $B8$ (NiAs) structure [(110) projection]. (*b*) A unit cell of the $C6$ [Cd(OH)$_2$] structure [(110) projection].

nomena occurring in this structural system, now known to be a simple one only in two or three of the cases already mentioned. Undoubtedly the complete $B8-C6$ transition can occur in many instances as a high temperature sequence, but the whole picture is still confused by conflicting evidence often arising from the arbitrary selection of the temperatures at which preparations were made or annealed; a detailed study of any one chemical system where temperature as well as composition are treated as variables would be arduous but undoubtedly rewarding.

The systems where the $B8-C6$ transition has been examined are now considered in a little more detail. In their study of the V-S system, Biltz and Köcher (47) noted a discrepancy between the observed and calculated densities at the composition $VS_{1.0}$ which can be explained only by assuming that the unit cell contains two formula units $V_{6/7}S_{6/7}$, implying that one atom in every seven of each kind is missing from the structure, and evidently in no kind of order. Discrepancies were also noted for ZrTe (153), TiSe and TiTe (220), CoTe (157) [a revision of Tengnér's earlier work where it is also noted that $CoTe_2$ has the $C18$ (marcasite) structure and not the $C6$], and CoSe and VSe (175).

Compounds containing a substantial percentage of a chemical anomaly often show a marked tendency to order. Neither $V_{6/7}S_{6/7}$ nor $Zr_{4/5}Te_{4/5}$, however, could be expected to have a simple unit cell with one vacancy of both B and X atoms appearing regularly in every seventh position and fifth position, respectively. Superlattices of both substances would therefor be large and difficult to detect except by single crystal x-ray techniques. For TiSe and TiTe on the other hand, the formula unit is $B_{7/8}X_{7/8}$, with one vacancy in eight, and a hexagonal superlattice found for each has axes that are simply twice those of the $B8$ subcell. An ordered structure fitting these data could certainly be devised, and it would be instructive to learn whether the nonmetals are rearranged to permit a more equitable distribution of chemical bonds than that resulting from the omission of atoms from a regular grouping.

The simultaneous absence of B and X atoms in equal amounts appears almost to be the rule and not the exception for chalcogenides $BX_{1.0}$, and it is possible that the ordered phases bear only a limited or residual resemblance to the $B8$ structure. Alternatively the $B8$ structure could be an unstable arrangement, and the limit of homogeneity, which for sulfides and selenides with this structure extends only to the composition $BX_{1.1}$ (i.e., B_7X_8), is reached when the anion positions are all occupied. At this composition, the systems Co–Se and Ni–Se exhibit changes of symmetry in an otherwise smooth $B8-C6$ transition.

In 1953 Bertaut (43) determined the crystal structure of Fe_7S_8 (pyrrhotite) which essentially is the $B8$ type with a complete sulfur lattice.

One iron atom in every four is removed from every second metal layer and these are ordered, giving the crystal monoclinic symmetry (Fig. 35). Shortly afterwards Jellinek (185) examined the phases in the Cr–S system, Cr_7S_8, Cr_5S_6, Cr_3S_4 and Cr_2S_3, all with little or no ranges of homogeneity, and these followed the pattern established for Fe_7S_8. For Cr_5S_6 there is one metal vacancy in every three positions for each alternate layer; for Cr_3S_4 one vacancy for two positions; and for Cr_2S_3 two in every three. These are all illustrated in Fig. 36, where it will be noted in the case of Cr_3S_4 that the symmetry of a single defective sheet must be at least orthorhombic. The selenides and tellurides of Cr, the selenides of iron and nickel, and possibly also the sulfides of dysprosium and ytterbium as well as tantalum telluride follow this pattern to a marked degree (Table XXIV), with some variations in the degree of order and in the sizes of the superlattices for each composition.

The triclinic form of Fe_7Se_8, like Fe_7S_8, contains one vacancy in every four metal positions confined to every second layer, but here the different superlattice reflects the way in which these "defective" layers are stacked one above the other. If Fe_7Se_8 is heat-treated at different temperatures, the superlattice c axis changes (Table XXV). This corresponds to different methods of stacking the defective sheets (243) and at a sufficiently high temperature the B8 structure, the subcell, is all that can be identified (242). At higher temperatures, therefore, the structure appears to become progressively more simple, reflecting the degree of organization of these sheets relative to one another; but the vacant positions still appear in alter-

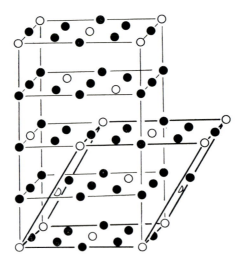

Fig. 35. The defective metal sheets in Fe_7S_8, the missing atoms drawn as open circles. The unit cell is shown in heavier outline.

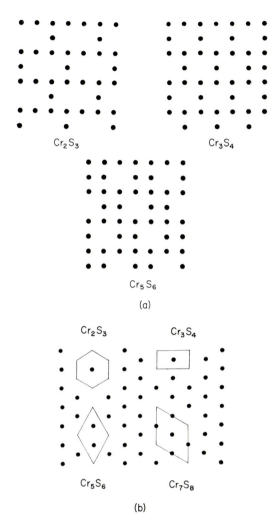

FIG. 36. (a) The structures of Cr_2S_3, Cr_3S_4, and Cr_5S_6 drawn in projection, the sulfur atoms being omitted for clarity. In each case the vacancies are confined to alternate metal atom layers and form a regular sequence, both in each sheet and between "defective" sheets. (b) A single sheet of metal atoms. The geometrical figures show how the vacancies form regular patterns of different kinds. For a particular phase, the appropriate pattern is regularly distributed over the whole of each defective sheet. "Cr_7S_8" is modelled upon Fe_7S_8 (Fig. 35).

nate sheets, and in any one sheet their regularity does not appear to be affected by temperature. This might mean that the composition B_7X_8 is the stable limit of the BS structure, the degree to which ordering occurs being an intrinsic property of a particular chemical system as well as being related to its thermal history.

TABLE XXIV

Binary Chalcogenides: Ordered Intermediates in the $B8$–$C6$ Interval with Normal Sulfur Lattices

[The compound and its range of composition (if any) is given first. The unit cell dimensions are expressed as multiples of the $B8$ structure with the hexagonal dimensions a and c or the orthohexagonal cell $a\sqrt{3}$, b, c. This is followed by the crystallographic spacegroup and the literature reference in parentheses.]

BX	B_7X_8	B_5X_6	B_3X_4	B_2X_3	BX_2
CrS $a, b\sqrt{3}, c, \beta = 101.6°$ Monoclinic, $C2/c$ Ordered (185)	Cr_7S_8 a, c Hexagonal, $P\bar{3}m1$ Disordered (185)	Cr_5S_6 $a\sqrt{3}, c$ Hexagonal, $P\bar{3}m1$ Ordered (185)	Cr_3S_4 $a\sqrt{3}, b, 2c, \beta = 91.5°$ Monoclinic, $I2/m$ Ordered (185)	Cr_2S_3 $a\sqrt{3}, 3c$ Hexagonal, $P\bar{3}1c$ Ordered (185)	
$CrSe_x$ $1 < x < 1.15$ a, c Hexagonal $B8$ Disordered (158)			$CrSe_x$ $1.17 < x < 1.34$ $a\sqrt{3}, b, c, \beta = 91.5°$ Monoclinic Partly ordered (158)	$CrSe_x$ $1.47 < x < 1.48$ a, c Hexagonal $B8$ Disordered (158)	
$CrTe_x$ Narrow range a, c Hexagonal $B8$ Disordered (159)			$CrTe_x$ $1.2 < x < 1.4$ $a\sqrt{3}, b, c, \beta = 90.3°$ Monoclinic Partly ordered (159)	$CrTe_x$ $1.5 < x < 1.7$ a, c Hexagonal $B8$ Disordered (159)	
FeS Narrow range[a] $a\sqrt{3}, 2c$ Hexagonal Ordered (156)	Fe_7S_8 $2a\sqrt{3}, 2b, 2c,$ $\beta = 118°$ Monoclinic, $C2/c$ Ordered (43)		Fe_3S_4 (smythite) $a, 6c$ Rhombohedral $R\bar{3}m$ Ordered (95)		FeS_2 $C2$ (pyrite) $C18$ (marcasite)

FeSe$_x$ 1.0 < x < 1.13	Fe$_7$Se$_8$	Fe$_5$Se$_6$	Fe$_3$Se$_4$	FeSe$_2$
a, c	2a√3, 2b, 4c,	a√3, b, c,	a√3, b, 2c,	C18 (marcasite)
	α = 89.8°	β = 90.2°	β = 92°	
	β = 89.4°,			
	γ = 90.0°			
Hexagonal B8	Triclinic P1̄	Monoclinic	Monoclinic	
Disordered (144)	Ordered (242)	Ordered (244)	Ordered (244)	
	(See Table XXV)			
				FeTe$_x$ 1.4 < x < 1.5
				a, b√3, c, β = 90°
				Monoclinic
				Partly ordered (136)
				FeTe$_x$ 1.95 < x < 2.1
				C18 (marcasite)
				(136)

NiSe$_x$ 1.0 < x < 1.1	Ni$_7$Se$_8$		NiSe$_x$ 1.23 < x < 1.40	NiSe$_x$ 1.97 < x < 2.0
a, c	a√3, 3b, 3c		a√3, b, 2c, β = 90.8°	C2 (pyrite) (187)
Hexagonal B8	Orthorhombic		Monoclinic	
Disordered (187)	Ordered (187)		Ordered (187)	

DyS$_x$ 1.4 < x < 1.5
(Also Er, Y)
2a√3, b, 2c, β = 106°
Partly ordered (106)

YbS$_x$ 1.5 < x < 1.57
a√3, 3c
Rhombohedral
Partly ordered (104)

[a] Two additional phases also reported, α''-FeS$_x$, 1.02 < x < 1.10, and ferromagnetic β-FeS$_x$, 1.11 < x < 1.14, both with disordered B8 structures (156).

VSe$_x$ (1.2 < x < 1.6) exhibits superlattices which have not been interpreted (175).

TABLE XXV

Temperature Dependence of Fe_7Se_8 Superlattice (242)

[Lattice constants expressed in terms of the hexagonal subcell ($B8$) axes a and c]

Temperature	Unit cell
290°C	$2a\sqrt{3}$, $2b$, $4c$ $\alpha = 89.8°$, $\beta = 89.4°$, $\gamma = 90.0°$ (Triclinic)
300°–350°C	$2a\sqrt{3}$, $2b$, $3c^a$ $\alpha = \beta = \gamma = 90°$ (Orthorhombic)
350°–450°C	$2a\sqrt{3}$, $2b$, $2c$ $\alpha = = \beta = \gamma = 90°$ (Hexagonal)
450°C	$a\sqrt{3}$, b, c $\alpha = \beta = \gamma = 90°$ (Hexagonal $B8$)

[a] Subsequently modified to hexagonal, $2a$ and $3c$ (243).

A good deal of additional detailed information is required before any single scheme encompassing all the phases in Table XXIV can be stated. Fe_3S_4, found as the mineral *smythite*, offers a somewhat different aspect: its structure is essentially a defective $B8$ one, but one layer of iron atoms in every four is completely empty (95). In other words, finite blocks of the $B8$ structure are separated from each other as they are in the $C6$ structure and there are no vacancies in any other metal sheet.

Within the composition limits BX–B_2X_3, there are several ways in which the metal atom vacancies could be distributed in the $B8$ structure:

(a) randomly distributed over all the positions and not confined to every second layer;
(b) randomly distributed in every second (or third etc.) layer;
(c) ordered in these layers but with no three-dimensional ordering;
(d) confined to layers, either ordered or disordered, with no regular sequence;
(e) ordered layers of two or more kinds.

As the composition approaches BX_2 from B_2X_3, the concentration of vacancies becomes large, and it is preferable to consider the mechanism of variability in composition as one where additional metal atoms are inserted into the $C6$ structure (Table XXVI).

TABLE XXVI

NON-STOICHIOMETRIC COMPOUNDS WITH THE $C6$ STRUCTURE

[The figures give ranges of x in BX_x. References in parentheses.]

	Ti	V	Co	Ni	Zr	Rh	Hf	Ta
S	1.8–2.0 (184)				1.7–2.0 (220)		1.5–2.0 (220)	
Se	1.2–2.0 (220)	1.6–2.0 (175)			1.7–2.0 (220)			
Te	1.0–2.0 (93)	1.13–1.85[a] (134)	1.0–1.9[b] (157)	1.0–2.0 (304)	0.8–2.0 (220)	1.0–2.0? (122)	1.5–? (220)	1.5–2.0 (307)

[a] VTe_2 with the $C6$ structure is prepared only with difficulty (134). VTe_x ($1.13 < x < 1.85$) varies from monoclinic ($a\sqrt{3}, b, 2c, \beta \cong 90°$) to orthorhombic. At $VTe_{1.82}$ an additional superlattice ($a\sqrt{3}, 3b, 2c$) is found.

[b] $CoTe_x$ ($1.9 < x < 2.1$) has the $C18$ (Marcasite) structure (157).

The tellurides and selenides alone have a very wide composition range and exhibit an anomaly between measured densities and those calculated from the x-ray data. This anomaly can be reconciled only by assuming that cation substitution in the $C6$ structure is accompanied by the simultaneous removal of some of the nonmetal atoms in preparations of intermediate composition. A similar effect was noted for the non-stoichiometric oxides and sulfides with the $B1$ structure where the anion lattice is complete only at about the point $BX_{1.1}$. Compounds nearing the composition BX_2 do not readily order, due probably to mechanical defects that arise from the strong cleavage characteristic of all layer structures, as well as to the limited occupancy of the positions in the defective layers by the metal atoms, where short-range interactions alone may be expected. The V–Te system is an exception, a superlattice of unknown origin where anion anomalies might be revealed appearing at the composition $VTe_{1.82}$ (*134*). Stoichiometric $VTe_{2.0}$ with the $C6$ structure is prepared only with difficulty.

Additional complications in the $B8$–$C6$ transition also arise from stacking anomalies in the metal or nonmetal sub lattices. If the hexagonal grouping of either atom is regularly interrupted by packing of another kind, a superlattice will result, the titanium, niobium, and tantalum sulfides in the interval BX–BX_2 providing examples (Table XXVII).

Sulfur, in all of the titanium sulfides, is in hexagonal close packing. The high temperature form of TiS has the $B8$ arrangement and can lose some of the metal atoms from alternate sheets. A second form has a different grouping of titanium—three in the usual $B8$ positions (viewed perpendicular to the c axis), the next three moved to an alternative set of octahedral positions, the sequence continuing regularly (Fig. 37*b*). As the ratio of titanium to sulfur decreases, the metal atoms are lost from the sheets bordering the junctions of the $B8$ blocks (*36, 148*). An anomaly of a similar kind was found for TiS_x (1.3 < x < 1.6) (*316*), illustrated by Fig. 37c. This shows another grouping of titanium in a hexagonal sulfur lattice, the disordered and defective layers alternating with filled layers. Ordering in these two different ways is possible at the composition Ti_2S_3, and one of these is known.

The niobium sulfides do not strictly belong to the $C6$–$B8$ transition, the sulfur atom positions in all five phases recently reported by Jellinek, Brauer, and Müller (*187*) being characteristic of the $C7$ (MoS_2) structure. Nevertheless they can be represented as a regular stacking disorder of $C6$. The two stoichiometric phases NbS_2 are isomorphous with the corresponding MoS_2 dimorphs and differ from one another only in the distribution of the metal atoms. In both cases these occupy trigonal prismatic holes which are formed by two adjacent sulfur layers lying directly one above

TABLE XXVII

BINARY CHALCOGENIDES: PHASES WITH REGULAR STACKING DISORDERS IN THE
SULFUR LATTICE

Ti	Nb
TiS_x $1.0 < x < 1.1$ Lattice dimensions $a = 3.43$, $c = 26.4$ Å Rhombohedral $R\bar{3}m$ (148)—Fig. 37b	NbS_x $1.0 < x < 1.18$ Lattice dimensions $a = 3.32$, $c = 12.92$ Å Hexagonal $P6_3$ mmc. (187)—Fig. 38f
TiS_x $1.3 < x < 1.6$ Lattice dimensions $a = 3.41$, $c = 11.46$ Å Hexagonal $P6_3mc$ (316)—Fig. 37c	NbS_x $1.4 < x < 1.5$ Lattice dimensions $a = 3.31$, $c = 12.60$ Å Hexagonal $P6_3/mmc$ (187)—Fig. 38e
Ti_2S_3 (Stoichiometric?) Lattice dimensions $a = 3.43$, $c = 3 \times 11.43$ Å Hexagonal (Rhombohedral?)—(183)	NbS_x $1.60 < x < 1.78$[a] Lattice dimensions $a = 3.33$, $c = 17.82$ Å Rhombohedral $R3m$ (187)—Fig. 38c
Ti_2S_3 (Stoichiometric?) Lattice dimensions $a = \sqrt{3} \times 3.43$, $c = 2 \times 11.43$ Å Monoclinic (Pseudohexagonal; $C62c$) (36)	NbS_2 (Stoichiometric?) Lattice dimensions $a = 3.31$, $c = 11.89$ Å Hexagonal $P6_3/mmc$ $C7$ structure type (187)—Fig. 38d
	NbS_2 (Stoichiometric?) Lattice dimensions $a = 3.33$, $c = 17.81$ Å Rhombohedral $R3m$ (187)—Fig. 38b

[a] Zr_2Se_3, $a = 3.76$, $c = 18.6$ Å (220) probably has the same structure as rhombohedral NbS_x.

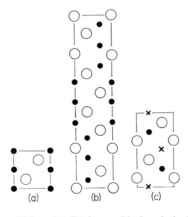

FIG. 37. The titanium sulfides. (a) $B8$ form; (b) rhombohedral TiS; (c) TiS_x, $1.3 < x < 1.6$.

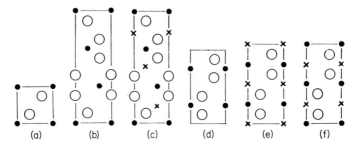

FIG. 38. The niobium sulfides compared with *C6*. (*a*) The *C6* structure; (*b*) rhombohedral NbS_2; (*c*) rhombohedral NbS_x, $1.6 < x < 1.78$; (*d*) hexagonal NbS_2; (*e*) hexagonal NbS_x, $1.4 < x < 1.5$; (*f*) hexagonal NbS_x, $1.0 < x < 1.18$. The partly filled positions are indicated by crosses.

the other. These S—Nb—S sheets are close packed together in one of two ways (Fig. 38b,d),

$$—S—Nb—S...S—Nb—S...S—Nb—S$$

the interlayer positions being octahedral in both. These positions may be partly occupied by additional niobium atoms in the two phases of NbS_x, $1.6 < x < 1.78$ and $1.4 < x < 1.5$ (Fig. 38c,e). The other compound NbS_x, $1.0 < x < 1.18$, closely resembles NbS_x, $1.4 < x < 1.5$; however, the octahedral sheets are completely filled, and the trigonal prismatic sheets are the defective ones (Fig. 38f). The interval $TaS–TaS_2$ also has a detailed series of layer sequences (*186*).

Despite the complexity of this one system, it should be noted that in the change from the layer structure to the more closely coordinated one, the sheets with the full complements of metal atoms and the defective sheets alternate regularly.

Three simple hexagonal structures, *A3*, anti-*C6* and anti-*B8* are illustrated in Fig. 39, the *anti* forms being simply those where metal and nonmetal interchange positions. The metals in all three are in hexagonal close packing, and the structures differ from one another only in terms of the nonmetals which occupy some or all of the octahedral interstitial positions.

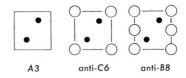

A3   anti-C6   anti-B8

FIG. 39. The *A3*, anti-*C6*, and anti-*B8* structures [(110) projection].

The anti-*B8* structure has been reported for the platinum and rhodium borides (*25*), but not for any of the transition metal chalcogenides. The interval BX_x, $0.5 < x < 1.0$, might contain an anti-*C6* anti-*B8* transition analogous to the *B8*–*C6* interval,

...B—X—B...B—X—B...   Anti-*C6*

—B—X—B—X—B—X—B—   Anti-*B8*

Tl$_2$S, the only sulfide structure in this group (Table XXVIII) which has been examined in any detail has the anti-*C6* structure and minor shifts of atoms from ideal positions are responsible for the large unit cell. CrTe$_{0.5}$ is probably related to it, and VTe$_x$, $0.7 < x < 0.8$, as well as Ni$_6$S$_5$ (i.e., NiS$_{0.83}$), both of intermediate composition, have superlattices which might reveal some kind of order in the defective anion lattice.

This speculation is based upon assumptions that may eventually prove to be false. Hahn and Ness (*151*) showed that a density discrepancy exists for TiSe$_x$, $0.6 < x < 0.7$, and this, like the case of the subchalcogenides with the B_h structure noted in Section III,B, may be resolved by considering the substitution of Ti for Se in the anion positions. Over the small composition range of this phase the titanium positions, assuming a *B8* structure, are filled, and nine-tenths of the anion sites are occupied. The variability of composition is then due not to the creation of additional vacancies but to the relative amounts of Ti or Se present in the one complete set of atomic positions. The structure of a tetragonal phase Ti$_5$Te$_4$, first recognized as a berthollide TiTe$_x$, $0.25 < x < 0.70$ (*151*), has now been reported by Grønvold *et al.* (*138*) who showed it to be derived from *B8* by the regular substitution of Ti for certain Te atoms accompanied by slight alterations of position.

B. Chalcogenides with B_h (Tungsten Carbide) Structure

The sub-chalcogenides crystallizing with the B_h structure (Table XXIX) have extremely simple structures where the unit cell contains only one atom of each kind (Fig. 40). ZrSe$_x$, $0.66 < x < 0.75$, and Zr$_3$S$_2$ (which may perhaps have a composition range) have a filled metal lattice, and some of the sulfur or selenium atoms are absent at random. Discrepancies between the x-ray and the observed densities found for TiS$_x$, $0.5 < x < 0.75$, and ZrTe$_x$, $0.5 < x < 0.75$, may be explained by the substitution of metal for nonmetal as in the case of TiSe$_x$, $0.6 < x < 0.7$. This is illustrated by Table XXX, where a revised structural formula Ti(Ti, S)$_{0.9}$, indicating substitutional solid solution, appears to be constant. The com-

TABLE XXVIII

SUB-CHALCOGENIDES: PHASES WITH NON-METAL DEFICIENT $B8$ STRUCTURES

Ti	V	Cr	Ni	Tl
$TiSe_x$ $0.58 < x < 0.66$	VTe_x $0.7 < x < 0.8$	$CrTe_x$ $x \cong 0.5$	NiS_x $x \cong 0.83$ (i.e., Ni_6S_5)	TlS_x $0.66 < x < 0.75$
a, c	$2a\sqrt3, b, 2c, \beta = 93.6°$	a, c (subcell alone has been indexed)	$2a\sqrt3, b, 3c$ (rearranged)	(Unit cell unknown) (150) See also Tl_2S $2a\sqrt3, 3c$
Hexagonal	Monoclinic (134)	Hexagonal (159)	Orthorhombic (217)	Rhombohedral
Disordered (151)	Ordered	Unknown order	Also "Ni_7S_6" of unknown symmetry	Ordered; Anti-$C6$ (196)

TABLE XXIX

SUB-CHALCOGENIDES WITH THE B_h (TUNGSTEN CARBIDE) STRUCTURE

TiS$_x$ $0.50 < x < 0.75$ Lattice dimensions $a = 3.27$, $c = 3.21$ Å Hexagonal (151)	ZrS$_x$ x approx. 0.66 Lattice dimensions $a = 3.43$, $c = 3.43$ Å Hexagonal (149) Homogeneity range not examined
	ZrSe$_x$ $0.66 < x < 0.75$ Lattice dimensions $a = 3.55$, $c = 3.61$ Å Hexagonal (152)
	ZrTe$_x$ $0.50 < x < 0.75$ Lattice dimensions $a = 3.76$, $c = 3.86$ Å Hexagonal (153)

position range is achieved by the relative numbers of Ti and S atoms that occupy the nonmetal positions.

The similarity between the B_h and the $B8$ structures can be seen from Fig. 40. The claim that NbS$_{1-\delta}$ has the former structure, and NbS$_{1+\delta}$ the latter (145), has not been verified by more recent work (187).

C. Copper Chalcogenides BX$_x$, $0.5 < x < 1$, Related to the Anti-C1 Structure

A non-stoichiometric phase of the approximate composition Cu$_9$S$_5$ (= CuS$_{0.56}$), existing as the mineral digenite, is found in the subsolidus region of the system CuS$_{0.5}$–CuS; above 70°C it forms solid solutions with

TABLE XXX

SUBSTITUTION OF METAL FOR NON-METAL IN TiS$_x$, $0.5 < x < 0.75$ (151)

Empirical formula	D, calculated for empirical formula (gm·cm^{-3})	D, observed (gm·cm^{-3})	Revised formula
TiS$_{0.75}$	3.96	4.31	Ti(Ti$_{0.09}$S$_{0.82}$) = Ti(Ti, S)$_{0.91}$
TiS$_{0.66}$	3.81	4.39	Ti(Ti$_{0.15}$S$_{0.71}$) = Ti(Ti, S)$_{0.86}$
TiS$_{0.50}$	3.51	4.46	Ti(Ti$_{0.27}$S$_{0.64}$) = Ti(Ti, S)$_{0.91}$

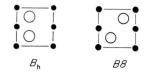

B_h $B8$

FIG. 40. The B_h and $B8$ structures [(110) projection].

Cu_2S and with CuS, or can, more specifically, gain or lose copper from a simple disordered cubic structure which is regarded as anti-$C1$ (i.e., CaF_2, where Cu and S occupy the F and Ca positions respectively). The mechanism of this effect has been greatly clarified by the work of Morimoto and Kullerud (234), who extended the homogeneity range to include Cu_2S and Cu_5FeS_4 (bornite) in a region of the Cu–Fe–S system.

Between the limits $BS_{0.56}$ and $BS_{0.67}$ several metastable cubic phases can be prepared by quenching, each having a different superlattice of the simple subcell whose size depends upon composition (Tables XXXI and XXXII). The structures, described only in a preliminary report (234), are illustrated schematically in Fig. 41 which gives the stacking order of the atoms along the threefold axes of the various unit cells. The sulfur lattice is complete, and defines the subcell for all members. However, the positions of the metals are not equivalent to each other, and some layers are filled while others have vacant positions which are disordered. The transition from one phase to the next one richer in copper is achieved by fitting the additional atoms into some but not all of these layers, until a point is reached where the whole copper sublattice is regrouped into a new sequence of

TABLE XXXI

PHASES IN THE Cu_5FeS_4–Cu_9S_5 SYSTEM (234)

	High temperature form	Metastable form (rapid cooling)	Low temperature form	Mineral
Cu_5FeS_4	⌐——→	$2a$ ——→	Modified $2a$	identical with *Bornite*
	⌐- - -→	$3a$		
$1a$–	——→	$4a$ ——→	Modified $4a$	
	——→	$5a$ ——→	Modified $5a$	identical with *Digenite*
Cu_9S_5	⌐——→	$6a$ ——→	Modified $6a$	

TABLE XXXII

Composition of Phases in Cu_5FeS_4–Cu_9S_5 System; Metastable Forms (234)

Composition range	Cell edge of unit cube (Å)	Cell edge in terms of subcell (Å)	Structure type
$B_{1.5}S^a$	10.94	5.47×2	$2a$
$\begin{cases} B_{1.51}S \\ \text{to } B_{1.69}S \end{cases}$	$\begin{cases} 21.92 \\ \text{to } 22.12 \end{cases}$	$\begin{cases} 5.48 \times 4 \\ \text{to } 5.53 \times 4 \end{cases}$	$4a$, possibly $3a$
$\begin{cases} B_{1.71}S \\ \text{to } B_{1.78}S \end{cases}$	$\begin{cases} 27.70 \\ \text{to } 27.80 \end{cases}$	$\begin{cases} 5.54 \times 5 \\ \text{to } 5.56 \times 5 \end{cases}$	$5a$
$B_{1.8}S$	33.42^b	5.57×6	$6a$

[a] Cu and Fe considered together as B.
[b] Also reported in an electron diffraction study of the growth of sulfide films on metallic copper (306)

filled and partly occupied layers forming a different superlattice. It seems likely that the vacancies are ordered in any one layer but have no three-dimensional order. Several of the metastable phases invert to low tem-

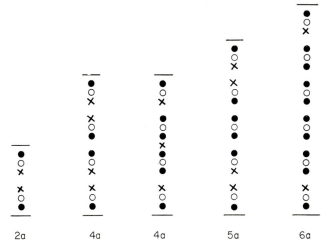

FIG. 41. The copper sulfides; the positions of metal (black circles) partly occupied metal (crosses) and sulfur (open circles) along the threefold axes of the unit cells.

perature stable forms in a few days at room temperature, and this could correspond to an alignment of the defective layers. This rearrangement is accompanied by twinning.

In CuS the unit cell contains six copper atoms, two in triangular coordination and four tetrahedral, grouped in layers. Cu_2S occurs in three temperature dependent forms (64), the high temperature cubic modification having the anti-$C1$ structure with all copper tetrahedrally bonded to sulfur. Changes of structure in the preparations which are intermediate in composition between these two undoubtedly occur in steps, each representing a metastable phase where the ordering corresponds to transient arrangements of atoms which are more or less stable. The low temperature form of digenite, Cu_9S_5, contains copper in three different kinds of coordination, including octahedral (87). The metastable substances that were examined were quenched from well above the disordering temperatures. Therefore, variations of composition in the high temperature solid solution region may be accompanied by structural alterations of the kind restricted to localized domains in metastable forms.

Much the same relations occur in the copper-rich region of the Cu–Se system, but the superlattice sequence has not yet been noticed. Cu_2Se, which is difficult to prepare with the exact stoichiometric formula, has the anti-$C1$ structure at high temperatures, and progressively loses copper from certain planes in a complicated way (49). But on re-examination this might prove to be like the Cu–S system. The limiting composition is Cu_9Se_5, the mineral berzelianite, the selenium analogue of digenite. Some copper selenides have structures unrelated to anti-$C1$, and one such phase is discussed in Section III,D.

D. Compounds in the Range $BX_{0.5}$–$BX_{1.0}$ Intermediate in Structure between $C38$ and Anti-$B10$

A group of sub-chalcogenides in Table XXXIII contains an interesting transition between two layer structures which may be referred to Fig. 42. The upper half is the sheet found for FeSe by Hägg and Kindström (144), consisting of square pyramids where the four edges containing the metal atoms are all shared with other pyramids, the nonmetals being at the apexes. In the $B10$ (PbO) structural type, metal and nonmetal occupy interchanged positions and FeSe, therefore, has the anti-$B10$ structure. Additional metal atoms may be added to a pyramid of this kind to form an unsymmetrical octahedron as in the lower part of Fig. 42, and a complete sheet of octahedra sharing edges, together with the way they are packed together, is characteristic of the $C38$ (Cu_2Sb) structure. The iron selenide and telluride as well as rickardite, $CuTe_x$, $0.72 < x < 0.78$, listed

TABLE XXXIII

SUB-CHALCOGENIDES WHICH MAY BE INTERMEDIATE BETWEEN THE $C38$ AND THE
ANTI-$B10$ STRUCTURE TYPES

$FeSe_x\ 0.8 < x < 1.0$	Cu_3Se_2 (Umangite)	$ZrS_x\ x \cong 0.75$
Tetragonal; $a = 3.77$,	Orthorhombic; $a = 4.28$,	Tetragonal; $a = 3.54$,
$c = 5.52$ Å	$b = 6.40$, $c = 12.46$ Å	$c = 8.05$ Å
$P4/nmm$ (144)	$P22_12_1$ (90)	$P4/mmm$ (149)
$FeTe_x\ 0.8 < x < 0.9$	$CuTe_x\ 0.5 < x < 0.6$	$ZrSe_x\ 0.7 < x < 0.8$
Tetragonal; $a = 3.82$,	Hexagonal; $a = 4.15$,	Tetragonal; $a = 3.63$,
$c = 6.28$ Å	$c = 7.19$ Å	$c = 8.36$ Å
$P4/nmm$ (136)	$P6/mmm$ (252)	$P4/mmm$ (152)
	$CuTe_x\ 0.72 < x < 0.78$	$ZrTe_x\ 0.7 < x < 0.8$
	Tetragonal; $a = 3.95$,	Tetragonal; $a = 3.69$,
	$c = 6.06$ Å	$c = 9.55$ Å
	$P4/nmm$ (111)	$P4/mmm$ (153)
	$CuTe_x\ 0.93 < x < 1.00$	
	Orthorhombic; $a = 3.15$,	
	$b = 4.07$, $c = 6.92$ Å	
	$Pmmn$ (4)	

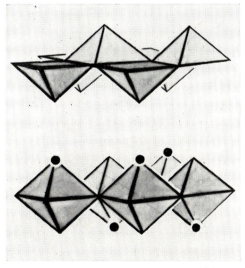

FIG. 42. The upper half contains square pyramids which are transformed with octahedra (lower half) by the interpolation of additional atoms drawn as circles.

in Table XXXIII are intermediate between $BX_{0.5}$ and $BX_{1.0}$ in structure as well as in composition. The variation is achieved by metals being inserted into a sheet where they change some of the square pyramids into octahedra.

Some other copper tellurides have been included in this group. CuTe with a small composition range has the anti-*B10* structure, but the copper atom positions are puckered, so that the pyramid is distorted. The arrangement of atoms in $CuTe_x$, $0.5 < x < 0.6$, is unknown, but the hexagonal unit cell bears a simple geometrical relationship to the tetragonal unit cell characteristic of the *C38* structure, and a detailed study of this phase including the relations with the other copper tellurides would undoubtedly be profitable.

It may be instructive to speculate on the possible crystal structures of the other substances included in this group, none having been examined in any detail except to establish the unit cell constants. Cu_3Se_2 found as the mineral umangite could have the structure in Fig. 42, where half of the pyramids are *regularly* changed into octahedra, each sheet containing regular rows of these two units alternating with one another, to become exactly intermediate between anti-*B10* and *C38*. A B_5X_4 structure consisting of an ordered alternating sequence of sheets of pyramids and octahedra could be expected as a low temperature phase. In this case stacking disorders might also be found.

The non-stoichiometric zirconium chalcogenides have a longer c axis than the other compounds in Table XXXIII. This could arise from a basic BX structure with pyramidal sheets of the anti-*B10* arrangement packed in a different way. Intermediate compositions could then be due to the formation of an asymmetrical octahedron from a square pyramid. A phase $TlTe_x$, $0.58 < x < 0.60$, with a tetragonal unit cell was reported (*258*). A good deal of additional study in this system is clearly desirable.

E. Chalcogenides BX_x, $1.0 < x < 1.5$, with the *B3* (Zinc Blende) Structure

Considerable interest is at present being shown in the semiconducting compounds BX with the *B3* structure, B and X being elements from Groups 2 and 6 or from Groups 3 and 5 of the periodic table. Grossly defective compounds which appear to be isomorphous are also formed by Group 3 and 5 combinations, i.e., Ga_2Se_3, Ga_2Te_3 and In_2Te_3 (*150*), and attention has been drawn to the solid solutions they form with cadmium, zinc, or mercury telluride, all of which have the non defective *B3* structure (*147*).

It might be expected that the mechanism in the interval BX_x, $1.0 < x < 1.5$, is due to the continuous and random creation of vacant metal positions in the monotellurides by the substitution of Group 3 ions. However, in a more recent study (337) it was shown that, in any such system, two regions of solid solution are separated by a two-phase region. The x-ray diffraction data for ordered In_2Te_3 prepared by annealing is recognizable superficially as a B3 superlattice, but two simultaneous attempts to determine the crystal structure gave different results, each equally plausible but neither definitive (336).

According to the first it was claimed that the metal vacancies in the defective B3 structure in In_2Te_3 are ordered into complete layers regularly repeated. In the other analysis, similarities between the C1 (CaF_2) and the B3 structures were recognized, and an anti-C1 arrangement was proposed, with indium atoms ordered in one-third of the fluorine positions and tellurium occupying the calcium sites. Random arrangements of finite domains in this second proposal were considered to be possible even in a carefully prepared single crystal, and this would be expected to give diffraction evidence indistinguishable from that of a B3 arrangement. In still another study the segregation of the vacant tetrahedra into groups of four was proposed from space group data, but was found difficult to prove (343).

Specimens of intermediate composition, $1.0 < x < 1.5$, give additional superlattices of unknown structure (336), and the mechanism of transition is therefore completely unknown. It is clear, however, that ZnTe, for example, remains a homogeneous phase up to the composition $BX_{1.15}$ ($= B_7X_8$) presumably by the creation of metal vacancies. The non-stoichiometric chalcogenides with the B1 and B8 structures also have this composition limit.

F. Compounds BX_x, $1.33 < x < 1.50$, with the $D7_3$ (Th_3P_4) Structure

The crystal structure of non-stoichiometric cerium sulfide CeS_x, $1.33 < x < 1.50$, is based upon the cubic $D7_3$ (Th_3P_4) type. At one composition limit, Ce_3S_4, the positions are all filled, and at the other one-ninth of the cerium atoms are extracted at random. This defective structure was also found for the sesquisulfides of La, Ac, Pu, and Am prepared at high temperatures (341) and a continuous transition between the above limits was established for the sulfides of the additional rare earth metals Nd, Sm, Gd, and Eu (41), as well as for Ce. Preparations at lower temperatures of the composition B_2S_3 give complex x-ray powder patterns (203), and while this may correspond to an ordered structure of a defective $D7_3$ kind, it is also possible that oxysulfides are present (35).

U_3Se_4 has the $D7_3$ structure without a composition range. U_2Se_3, in common with several uranium and thorium chalcogenides, is isostructural with Sb_2S_3 ($D5_8$).

G. Compounds BX_x, 1.0 $< x <$ 1.8, Related to the $C33$ (Bi_2Te_2S) Structure

$BiTe_x$, 1.1 $< x <$ 1.8, (155), a technically important semiconductor, crystallizes with the rhombohedral $C33$ structure which in some ways resembles an intermediate phase in the $B8$–$C6$ transition with a stacking fault. Bi_2Te_3 contains sheets consisting of double octahedral layers, the nonmetals of adjacent sheets providing octahedral spaces as in the $C6$ grouping (Fig. 43), which, as the composition becomes richer in metal, may undoubtedly be occupied in part by addition of bismuth atoms. When they are completely filled the formula is $BiTe$, and the structure, still with the same unit cell and space group as Bi_2Te_3, will be isomorphous with rhombohedral TiS noted in Fig. 37b; but this has not yet been proved.

Examination of the densities reveals an anomaly at the composition $BiTe_{1.0}$, that is satisfied only by omitting one atom of each kind in every seven, presumably at random. This is a feature of monochalcogenides with the $B8$ and $B1$ structures, and a satisfactory explanation of this

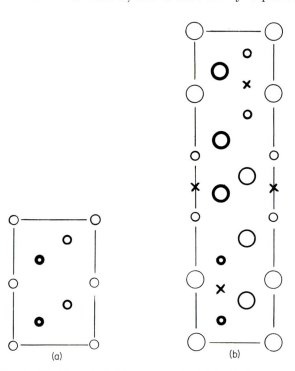

Fig. 43. (a) Metallic bismuth (with change of origin). (b) Structure of Bi_2Te_3, Bi small, Te large. The crosses are positions where additional Bi atoms can be accommodated.

phenomenon is still required. The extension of the composition range from $BiTe_{1.5}$ to $BiTe_{1.8}$ could be due to the exclusion of some of the bismuth atoms from the octahedral positions in the double sheets. The unit cells of metallic bismuth and Bi_7Te_3 (hedleyite) as well as $BiTe_x$, above, are rhombohedral, all with a common subcell, but the three phases have different superlattices. The structure of bismuth metal is identical with that of $BiTe_x$ except that the *tellurium* positions of the latter are all occupied by *bismuth* atoms; Bi_7Te_3 undoubtedly corresponds

TABLE XXXIV

SUPERLATTICE FORMATION BY THE BISMUTH TELLURIDES AND SELENIDES

[The unit cells are given as multiples of the hexagonal subcells which, for the tellurides, have the approximate dimensions $a = 4.4$, $c = 6.0$ Å.]

Compound[a]	Unit cell	Mineral name	Range of composition	Reference
Bi	$a, 2 \times c$		—	(305)
Bi_7Te_3[b]	$a, 20 \times c$	Hedleyite	—	(325)
$BiTe_x$	$a, 5 \times c$	Wehrlite	$1.1 < x < 1.8$	(325)
$BiTe_x$	$a, 5 \times c$	Tellurobismuth		(325)
BiSe	a, c			(286)
Bi_3Se_4	$a, 7 \times c$		Unknown	(286)
Bi_2Se_3	$a, 5 \times c$		Unknown	(286)

[a] Bi_2Se is also reported (1); no lattice parameters given.
[b] Two distinct minerals $Bi_{4+x}Te_{1-x}S_2$ (joseite A) and $Bi_{4+x}Te_{2-x}S$ (joseite B), each with the superlattice $a, 7 \times c$ are reported (305). The composition range is unknown.

to a structure of intermediate composition where the replacement is ordered but only partly achieved. A detailed study of it would provide information of value in this kind of replacement mechanism, proposed elsewhere for $TiSe_x$ (B8) and for TiS_x and $ZrTe_x$ (B_h).

Bi_2Te_2S (tetradymite) has the same arrangement of atoms as Bi_2Te_3, but the sulfur atoms are ordered into complete layers (210). This compound could be expected to have a composition range.

Although the phase diagram Bi–Se contains only two compounds of intermediate composition (154), electron diffraction examination of evaporated films suggests that Bi_2Se_3, isomorphous with Bi_2Te_3, as well as the additional phase, Bi_3Se_4, are berthollides (285, 286). BiSe was given a cubic unit cell, but by a simple transformation of the crystallographic axes it can be shown to have the same hexagonal subcell as BiTe. The metal atoms of the compound Bi_3Se_4 are aggregated into continuous layers resulting in triple octahedral sheets which are then simply packed together, suggesting that the change in composition $BX-BX_{1.5}$ in this system might proceed in steps where sheet sequences of different kinds are formed.

Sb_2Te_3 is isomorphous with Bi_2Te_3. Bi_2S_3 and the antimony compounds Sb_2S_3 and Sb_2Se_3 crystallize in a hexagonal or closely related orthorhombic structure which is given the symbol $D5_8$. The thorium chalcogenides Th_2X_3 are classified with these, and the sulfide, originally given wide composition limits (298), is now thought to be of fixed composition (132).

H. Compounds Based upon the $D5_8$ (Bi_2S_3) Structure: Copper in Interstitial Tetrahedral Positions

The complex Pb, Bi, Sb, and Ag sulfide minerals having a coordination of six or higher often contain copper as an accessory element. The role it plays may be illustrated by considering the minerals listed in Table XXXV ranging in composition from Bi_2S_3 (bismuthinite) to $CuPbBiS_3$ (aikinite) both of which have a $D5_8$ host structure.

The alternative formula in the table is used to represent each of them as a member of a sequence,

$$B_2S_3 - Cu_xB_2S_3 - CuB_2S_3$$

the introduction of copper being accompanied by the substitution of Pb for Bi to compensate for the valency anomaly which would otherwise

TABLE XXXV

Copper Substitution in Minerals with the $D5_8$ Structure

Mineral	Formula	Alternative formula[a]
Bismuthinite	Bi_2S_3	Bi_2S_3
Gladite	$Cu_2Pb_2Bi_{10}S_{18}$	$Cu_{1/3}(Pb, Bi)_2S_3$
Lindstromite	$Cu_2Pb_2Bi_6S_{12}$	$Cu_{1/2}(Pb, Bi)_2S_3$
Hammarite	$Cu_2Pb_2Bi_4S_9$	$Cu_{2/3}(Pb, Bi)_2S_3$
Aikinite	$CuPbBiS_3$	$Cu_1(Pb, Bi)_2S_3$

[a] The Pb and Bi atoms are grouped together as the metal ions of the host lattice B_2S_3.

arise. The x-ray powder patterns of all five minerals are very much alike (*250*) and the three compounds of intermediate composition appear to be transitional in structure between the end members, which are virtually identical except for the copper occupying tetrahedral holes in the Bi_2S_3 lattice (*334*) (Fig. 44). The exact formulas found for these three compounds are likely to be reflected in their structures, and further examination of them might be expected to show that the copper preferentially enters

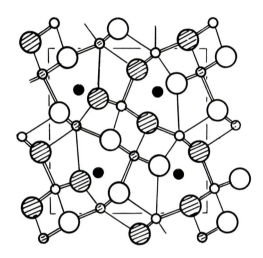

FIG. 44. Structure of Bi_2S_3. Black circles are tetrahedral positions all occupied in the related substance $CuPbBiS_3$.

some of the tetrahedral positions of the host lattice, which, however, remains virtually unaltered. A high temperature study of this system might well be interpreted as a solid solution with a *B1*-like structure. Preparations of $CuPbAsS_3$ have been reported as cubic (*331*), but the mineral seligmannite of the same composition has the aikinite structure (*213*).

Copper appears to be tetrahedrally bonded in most sulfide minerals where the metal-to-sulfur ratio is less than one, and tetrahedral positions occur in many of their structures. Cosalite $Pb_2Bi_2S_5$ (*329*) has one such position for each formula unit, and the mineral benjaminite of uncertain formula having a similar powder photograph (*251*) could be intermediate in composition between $Pb_2Bi_2S_5$ and an unknown substance $CuPbBi_3S_5$. Meneghinite $Pb_{13}Sb_7S_{23}$ invariably contains copper in varying proportions which could fill some or all of the four tetrahedral positions present in the structure (*96*).

J. Phases Which May Represent Structures Intermediate between the $B1(BX)$ and the $D5_8$ (B_2X_3) Types: The Mineral Sulfosalts

The ternary and quarternary sulfides of lead and the group 5 elements arsenic, antimony, and bismuth form a bewildering array of stable phases well known to the geologist and mineralogist but seldom considered by the chemist. These minerals which contain silver and copper as well as iron, manganese, mercury, and other elements, can be considered as ordered phases occurring in the composition region $BX-B_2X_3$, and it may be profitable to examine briefly what is known about them.

Classical methods of phase analysis in any one system tend to be over-simplified by the formation of large regions of solid solution representing unavoidable out-of-equilibrium conditions. On the other hand, when large ore bodies are cooled very slowly, the solid solutions tend to a so-called reconstructive transformation (63) into new phases which in turn undergo additional segregation, the sequence depending upon the concentration of the various metals in the solution, the rate of cooling, and the temperature of the order-disorder transformations (91).

The crystallographic constants of the chemically related phases that have been recorded leave little doubt on several points. Firstly, the unit cells are large, and the phases are ordered to a greater or lesser degree. Secondly, the unit cell constants of adjacent phases are often alike, and this could mean they contain structural elements of the same kind. Thirdly, they usually have a simple subcell. Considered together, these three features make it seem likely that intergrowth of one compound with another can occur, and solid solutions of varying composition, characterized by the subcell, will be found in certain regions if these solutions are highly disordered.

This can occur by a simple substitution mechanism without involving gross lattice anomalies. The minerals diaphorite $Pb_2Ag_3Sb_3S_8$ ($= B_8S_8$) (165), freieslebenite $PbAgSbS_3$ ($= B_3S_3$) (163), miargyrite $AgSbS_2$, and possibly matildite $AgBiS_2$ ($= B_2S_2$) (171) all have crystal structures isomorphous with PbS (Table XXXVI) which has the $B1$ structure. The large unit cells correspond to the ordering of the metal atoms of the various kinds into unique positions. Laboratory preparations of these substances, on the other hand, simply give the diffraction data of $B1$ compounds, proving that the metals are disordered in the positions they adopt in the cubic sulfur lattice, and the exact compositions of these minerals appear only as points on a normal solid solution phase (330).

The chemical reason for this is not difficult to see. If the charge of the lead ion in PbS is exactly balanced by Ag^+ and Sb^{3+} in equal amounts,

TABLE XXXVI

LEAD–SILVER–ANTIMONY SULFIDE MINERALS

Structural formulas	Mineral name	Unit cell dimensions (Å)				Space group	Reference
		a	b	c	β		
PbS	Galena	5.93				$Fm3m$	
$PbAgSbS_3$? ⎫	Freieslebenite	7.53	12.29	5.88	92°14'	$P2_1/n$	(163)
$Pb_2Ag_3Sb_3S_8$ ⎬ BX	Diaphorite	15.85	32.09	5.90	90°10'	$C2_1/a$	(165)
$AgSbS_2$ ⎭	Miargyrite	13.17	4.39	12.83	98°37'	$C2/c$	(171)
$PbAgSb_3S_6$ ⎫	Andorite	13.03	19.15	4 × 4.29 or 12 × 4.27		$P*ca$	(88, 241)
$Pb_4AgSb_5S_{12}$ ⎬ B_5X_6	Fizelyite	13.19	19.27	2 × 4.37		$Pnm*$	(241)
$Pb_3Ag_2Sb_5S_{12}$ ⎭	Ramdohrite	13.03	19.15	6 × 4.29		$Pn*a$	(88, 241)
$Pb_5Ag_2Sb_6S_{15}/B_{13}X_{15}$	Owyheeite	22.82	27.20	2 × 4.095		$Pnam$ (subcell)	(262)

the lattice has little inducement to alter, and any change will be due to the atoms of various kinds finding preferred positions by a slow process of diffusion in the solid state below the order-disorder transformation temperature. There can be little doubt, however, that a disordered crystal of any one compound will consist of domains of the ordered form in random orientation, but it can be assumed that Ag^+ and Sb^{3+} substitute for Pb^{2+} isomorphously. Unlike the other chalcogenides with the $B1$ structure, there are no vacant positions at the composition BX.

If these two ions, either alone or in unequal amounts, replace some of the lead ions in PbS, anomalies of a different kind which involve major structural changes of one kind or another can, and do, arise. The second group of quaternary sulfides in Table XXXVI, $PbAgSb_3S_6$, $Pb_4AgSb_5S_{12}$, and $Pb_3Ag_2Sb_5S_{12}$ (?), the *andorite* group of minerals, all have simplified formulas B_5X_6, where $B = Pb + Ag + Sb$. All are obviously isomorphous if the subcell alone is considered, and appear to differ only in the ordering of the metal ions into layers in the larger unit cells. The subcell for this group contains blocks of a rather distorted $B1$ structure, infinite in two dimensions but only two octahedra in thickness (Fig. 45) (*166*). These are joined at the edges by additional metal atoms having a coordination number of eight, instead of six. The substitution of Sb and Ag for Pb does not simply create a "cation vacancy" as might be supposed by analogy with the binary chalcogenides with the $B1$ structure, but forces a rearrangement of structure where the essential character of the host is not completely lost.

A detailed examination of $Pb_5Ag_2Sb_6S_{15}$ (owyheeite, Table XXXVI) has not yet been made, but it is possible to construct an atomic model fitting the unit cell in which blocks of a related kind are present. The blocks are three octahedra thick instead of two and are again joined together by atoms in an eightfold grouping. While this does not constitute a proof, it nevertheless appears likely that a series of phases could exist with structures characterized by different block widths, bearing a strong resemblance to the "series" of metallic oxides of intermediate composition noted in Section II,E,1. Disorder involving either the positions of the blocks or, possibly, of sequences of blocks of different thickness would give a solid having a simple PbS-like diffraction pattern. It would be reasonable to assume at first sight that such a solid contains metal vacancies.

This particular system is made difficult by the presence of three different metal ions, and a more systematic study should start with simpler chemical systems. Table XXXVII lists the minerals occurring in the binary systems of PbS with Sb_2S_3, Bi_2S_3, and As_2S_3, respectively. These are considered in turn.

The equilibrium fusion diagram $PbS–Sb_2S_3$ was constructed by Robinson (*261*) from earlier data with which his own experiments substantially

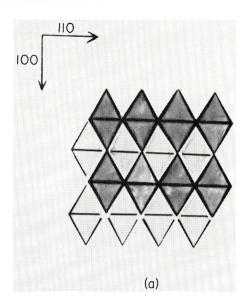

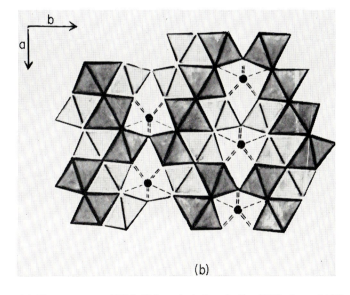

FIG. 45. (a) The structure of PbS (B1) projected on to the (110) plane. (b) The structure of the andorite minerals, B_5X_6. Blocks of distorted PbS-like groups (as in 45a) are joined by metals in eightfold coordination.

TABLE XXXVII

Minerals Occurring in the Composition Region $PbS-B_2S_3$ (B = As, Sb, or Bi)

Arsenic		Antimony		Bismuth	
Formula	Name	Formula	Name	Formula	Name
$Pb_{14}As_7S_{24}$	Jordanite	$Pb_6Sb_2S_9$	—	$Pb_6Bi_2S_9$	Beegerite
$Pb_9As_4S_{15}$	Gratonite	$(Cu)Pb_{13}Sb_7S_{23}$	Meneghinite	$Pb_3Bi_2S_6?$	Lillianite? (doubtful)
$Pb_{10}As_6S_{19}$	Guitermanite	$Pb_5Sb_2S_8$	Geochronite	$Pb_2Bi_2S_5$	Cosalite
$(Ag, Cu)_2Pb_6As_4S_{13}$	Lengenbachite	$Pb_3Sb_2S_6$	Falkmanite	$Pb_5Bi_6S_{14}$	Wittite
$Pb_2As_2S_5$	Dufrenoysite	$Pb_5Sb_4S_{11}$	Boulangerite	$Pb_6Bi_{10}S_{21}?$	Cannizarite
$Pb_6As_{10}S_{21}(?)^a$	Rathite	$Pb_9Sb_8S_{21}$	Semseyite	$PbBi_2S_4$	Galenobismutite
$Pb_4As_6S_{13}(?)^a$	Baumhauerite	$Pb_7Sb_8S_{19}$	Heteromorphite	$Pb_3Bi_8S_{15}$	Chivitite
$Pb_5As_8S_{17}$	Liveingite	$(Fe)Pb_4Sb_6S_{11}$	Jamesonite	$PbBi_4S_7$	Bonchevite
$PbAs_2S_4$	Sartorite	$Pb_5Sb_8S_{17}$	Plagionite	$PbBi_6S_{10}$	Ustarasite
	(or sceroclase)	$Pb_7Sb_{12}S_{25}$	Robinsonite		
		$Pb_6Sb_{14}S_{27}$	Zincenite		
		$Pb_3Sb_8S_{15}$	Fullopite		
		$Pb_2Sb_6S_{11}$	Keelyite		

[a] See text for note added in proof.

agreed, and the only phases of intermediate composition that could be prepared by him were $Pb_5Sb_4S_{11}$ and $Pb_7Sb_{12}S_{25}$, although several others were made hydrothermally as growths on PbS itself. The crystal structures of $CuPb_{13}Sb_7S_{23}$ *(96)* and $FePb_4Sb_6S_{11}$ *(237)* (stabilized by the "foreign" atoms Cu and Fe), as well as $Pb_5Sb_4S_{11}$ *(50)* have been determined. The first contains blocks of the PbS-type joined together by antimony atoms in sevenfold coordination of two different kinds bearing a resemblance to the andorite structures (Fig. 46a). $PbSb_2S_4$ is now reported as well *(48a)*.

The list of lead bismuth sulfides is not particularly well defined, and some of the phases are doubtful. Equilibrium diagrams for the system Pb–Ag–Bi–S were prepared by van Hook *(172)*, and the structures of $Pb_2Bi_2S_5$ *(166)* and $PbBi_2S_4$ *(334)* are known. The first of these is particularly relevant (Fig. 46b), as it contains domains of the PbS structure two octahedra wide, infinite in one dimension but *finite* in depth. The junction between them is effected by the change of coordination number of certain terminal metal atoms from six to *eight*. Once again it can be readily seen that if the domain size is increased either in width or depth, a new metal-to-sulfur ratio is possible and this could be represented as the structure of a closely related phase, possibly a homologue.

Although a good deal of doubt about the formulas and, indeed, the identity of the lead arsenic sulfide minerals still remains, there is nevertheless a rich list of phases between the limits $PbS–As_2S_3$, most of which have been synthesized hydrothermally *(264)*. Some of the difficulties confronting the mineralogist seeking chemical formulas are expressed in recent studies in this system *(240)*, where a single needle crystal contained three distinct phases distributed evenly in zones all over it, each having unit cell dimensions like the other two. These phases appeared to be $Pb_6As_{10}S_{21}$ (rathite), $Pb_8As_8S_{20}$ (dufrenoysite), and possibly $Pb_4As_6S_{13}$ (baumhauerite). This intergrowth could be achieved only if the three components are closely related to one another.*

Hellner devised a scheme where a formula factor, the ratio of the numbers of metal atoms to sulfur atoms, is related to the percentage of PbS-like components in the unit cell, and he applied this to all the sulfide minerals except those with tetrahedral coordination *(164)*. Where PbS domains are present in a structure this has much to commend it, but it is difficult to extend the idea to the sulfosalts where the octahedron is not the dominant structure polyhedron. The interrelationships between atomic arrangement and chemical constitution must nevertheless have a simplifying scheme,

---

* *Note added in proof*: Since this was written a long paper by Le Bihan *(212)* has appeared. Rathite exists in three forms: (I) $Pb_7As_9S_{20}$, (II) $Pb_9As_{13}S_{28}$, and (III) $Pb_6As_{10}S_{20}$. Baumhauerite proved to have the formula $Pb_5As_9S_{18}$, and the four structures are compared with that of sartorite, $PbAs_2S_4$, reported earlier *(240)*.

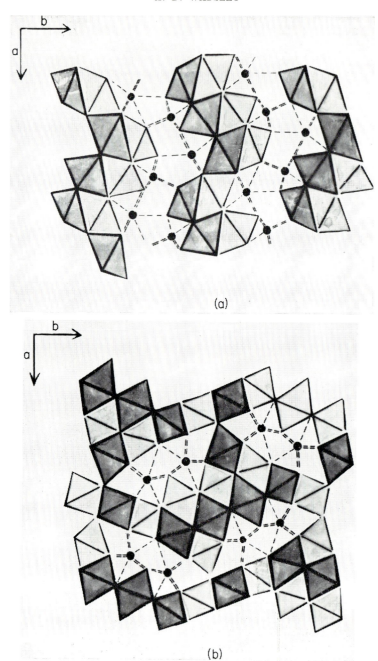

Fig. 46. (a) Projected structure of $(Cu)Pb_{13}Sb_7S_{23}$ (meneghinite). (b) Projected structure of $Pb_2Bi_2S_5$ (cosalite). In both cases distorted PbS-like groups are joined by metal atoms, in sevenfold grouping in (a), and eightfold in (b).

and there is real need for a systematic study as detailed accounts of structure determinations are available for only a very few phases selected more or less at random. One group of compounds, however, bears a strong resemblance to the As_2S_3 structure. This contains a double chain B_2S_4 (B a group 5 element), the B atoms having three sulfur neighbors at the corners of a triangular pyramid. This structure is very closely related to $HgSb_4S_8$ (236) and the B_2S_4 unit occurs also in $FeSb_2S_4$ (65), $PbAs_2S_4$ (240), modified and extended to B_3S_7 in $FePb_4Sb_6S_{14}$ (237), and as still larger B_6S_8 units in $Pb_5Sb_4S_{11}$ (50). It is not difficult to see from the examples that this building principle is capable of considerable extension.

IV. CLASSIFICATION ACCORDING TO STRUCTURE

It is clear that order-disorder plays a particularly significant role in solid state chemistry. We have stressed the evidence that a non-stoichiometric phase may be metastable, and may conceal one or more discrete compounds where an anomaly of structure is ordered and identifiable by x-ray diffraction methods. Where such stable phases are found, it is reasonable to assume that the anomaly persists as domains with short-range order in the related high temperature berthollide, where it cannot be readily deduced *ab initio*.

The examples from the oxide and chalcogenide literature show a great wealth of detail, converging upon several kinds of mechanism briefly outlined in Section I,E of this chapter. Some of these were discussed by Anderson (5) and amplified by Schlenk (280) in a general review of occlusion compounds and were used by the writer (314) as the basis of an assessment of the inorganic literature on non-stoichiometric systems.

A. Substitution

As a method of changing the composition of a berthollide, the substitution of one element, B, in the lattice positions of the other, X, although commonly found in intermetallic compounds, is confined to the binary chalcogenides having the *B8*, *B*$_h$, and *C33* structures (Sections III,A, III,B, and III,G), where the atomic arrangements are typical of the metallic state, ordering being recognizable in certain compounds of fixed and sometimes complex formulas. The replacement of oxygen by barium in the ordered ferrimagnetic spinels (Section II,J,2) is an isolated case in the oxide literature; and here an adjacent metal ion of the host lattice adopts a lower coordination number.

B. Interpolation

The introduction of an excess of one component, B or X, in a binary compound BX_x, or the incorporation of a third element A leading to a ternary berthollide, is commonly referred to as an interstitial solid solution. Here we classify in terms of the gross structural features of the host lattice.

1. CAGES

The simplest examples of cages are the interstitial compounds of the metals, which are predominantly metallic in character. The evidence for these has not been discussed in this chapter.

The interpolation of excess anions into the fluorite structure (discussed in Section II,C,2), the formation of cubic or pseudocubic tungsten bronzes (in Section II,E,2,a), and the inclusion of copper in the $D5_8$ and other sulfosalt minerals are all examples of systems where potential sites in the host structures may be occupied by ions of one kind or another, and ordering is again a feature. The presence of a third ion may also induce the formation of a new kind of phase with appropriate sites, as in the case of the platinum bronze (Section II,K).

2. TUNNELS

Tunnels, or interstitial cages linked unidimensionally which may be partly occupied by metal or nonmetal ions, or by molecules, are present in a wide variety of structures discussed in Sections II,B,2, II,F, II,L,1, and II,M,1, and it is notable that these can all occur as ternary oxide bronzes. Most tunnel compounds can only be prepared in the presence of the guest ions, and the available evidence favors the occurrence of order within any one tunnel.

3. LAYERS

The interpolation of additional metal ions between adjacent sheets of a layer structure was noted for the defective $C6$ phases formed by many chalcogenides BX_2 (Section III,A), as well as in the copper sulfides and selenides with the anti-$C1$ (Section III,C) and the anti-$B10$ (Section III,D) structures. Ordering of these interpolated atoms appears to be possible when the compounds are metal-like, and has not been observed in the defective $C6$ substances or in the hydrated oxide mineral chalcophanite (Section II,N,2).

C. Subtraction

Metal, nonmetal, or both ions simultaneously, may be absent from the structure.

1. Subtraction of Both Ions B and X from BX_x

A composition range was noted for certain oxides and chalcogenides with the *B1* and *B8* structures (Sections II,A, III,A, and also possibly Section III,G). Homogeneous berthollides are formed by quenching from high temperatures, the composition limits in the *B1* oxides corresponding to filled metal positions and nonmetal absences at the one end, and vacant metal positions in a complete anion lattice at the other. The chalcogenides present a different picture at the metal-rich end where the substitution of metal for nonmetal is likely.

In this category, phases at the composition BX contain equal numbers of vacancies of both kinds of atom which can order into superlattices when annealed, perhaps involving a change of composition. Different kinds of coordination, the clustering of crystalline defects and the ordering of substituent atoms can all be recognized in studies of these compounds which may, in fact, bear only a statistical resemblance to the simpler structure types with which they are usually classified.

2. Subtraction of Metal Ions B from BX_x

The transition from *B8* to *C6* (Section III,A) takes place by the removal of metal atoms from *B8*, but a continuous transition appears not to be the rule, the ordering of the defective metal lattice at certain fixed points representing the formation of stable structures closely related to each other as well as to the end members. The same may well be true of the related chalcogenides with stacking disorders which are so difficult to crystallize, as well as the anti-*C1* (Section III,C) and also possibly the *B3* (Section III,E) and $D7_3$ (Section III,F) structures.

Vacancies in the metal positions of spinel appear only at high temperatures, and the system γ-Fe_2O_3–Fe_3O_4, so frequently quoted as an example of a berthollide, should be re-examined over the entire range in view of the recent evidence cited in Section II,J,1.

3. Subtraction of Non-Metal Ions X from BX_x or ABX_x

The loss of nonmetal from close-packed oxide systems can involve two distinct mechanisms—the first treated above, and the other discussed in Section IV,D. Even though the $C1$ and $D5_3$ structures are closely related (Section II,C,1), the transition between them is not necessarily a smooth one, ordered intermediates being found in regions where the closely related pyrochlore structure, itself a berthollide, is found. The uranium oxides intermediate between α-UO_3 and U_3O_8 (Section II,D), the oxygen-deficient perovskites (Section II,E,2,b), and the ternary hexagonal compounds related to $BaNiO_3$ (Section II,H), all give evidence of a similar kind, none of it exhaustively explored. It appears likely that if oxygen is extracted, the remaining anions regroup symmetrically around the metals which suffer changes of coordination, and anion vacancies, as such, may not exist.

D. Shear

The removal of oxygen from certain kinds of compound, TiO_2 (Section II,B,1), U_3O_8 (Section II,D), WO_3 (Section III,E,1) and Nb_2O_5 (Section M,2) does not involve changes of coordination, but leads to the compression of the structure along certain planes by what may be called crystallographic shear, the polyhedra (octahedra in all known cases) being condensed upon each other. When these shear planes are ordered, an homologous series of related oxides can be recognized, and when they are not, there is good reason to believe they are retained, but in a disordered form difficult to recognize except as a berthollide.

The possible occurrence of modified forms of shear in the sulfosalt minerals has been examined (Section III,J), where the domains of the host structure are joined by metal ions with changed coordination numbers.

E. Intergrowth

The ordered intergrowth of two distinct kinds of structure is a feature of certain oxides and oxyhalides (Section II,G), the hexagonal barium-substituted spinels (Section II,J,2), and the mixed-layer alkali titanates (Section II,L,2), and the possible formation of berthollides at high temperatures by these systems could be examined experimentally. The segregation of structural components into two or more distinct phases, coexisting at random in the one crystal, is a logical extension in the reverse direction, and the hydrated vanadium minerals (Section II,N,1) and certain sulfosalt minerals provide well-documented examples.

REFERENCES

1. Abrikosov, N. Kh., Bankina, V. F., and Kharitonovich, K. F., *Russ. J. Inorg. Chem. (Transl.)* **5,** 978 (1960).

2. Adelsköld, V., *Arkiv Kemi, Mineral. Geol.* **A12**, No. 29 (1938).
3. Alberman, K. B., Blakey, R. C., and Anderson, J. S., *J. Chem. Soc.* p. 1352 (1951).
4. Anderko, K., and Schubert, K., *Z. Metallk.* **45**, 371 (1954).
5. Anderson, J. S., *Ann. Repts. on Progr. Chem.* (*Chem. Soc. London*) **43**, 104 (1946).
6. Anderson, J. S., *Bull. soc. chim. France* p. 781 (1953).
7. Anderson, J. S., and Johnson, K. D. B., *J. Chem. Soc.* p. 1731 (1953).
8. Anderson, J. S., and Sterns, M., *J. Inorg. & Nuclear Chem.* **11**, 272 (1959).
9. Andersson, G., *Acta Chem. Scand.* **8**, 1599 (1954).
10. Andersson, G., and Magnéli, A., *Acta Chem. Scand.* **11**, 1065 (1957).
11. Andersson, S., *Acta Chem. Scand.* **14**, 1161 (1960).
12. Andersson, S., Private communication (1961).
13. Andersson, S., Collén, B., Kuylenstierna, U., and Magnéli, A., *Acta Chem. Scand.* **11**, 1641 (1957).
14. Andersson, S., and Jahnberg, L., *Acta Chem. Scand.* (in press).
15. Andersson, S., and Magnéli, A., Final Tech. Rept. No. 1, p. 21 (1958). Dept. of Army Contract No. DA-91-508-EUC-245.
16. Andersson, S., Sundholm, A., and Magnéli, A., *Acta Chem. Scand.* **13**, 989 (1959).
17. Andersson, S., and Wadsley, A. D., *Nature* **187**, 499 (1960).
18. Andersson, S., and Wadsley, A. D., *Acta Cryst.* **14**, 1245 (1961).
19. Andersson, S., and Wadsley, A. D., *Acta Cryst.* **15**, 194 (1962).
20. Andersson, S., and Wadsley, A. D., *Acta Cryst.* **15**, 201 (1962).
21. Andresen, A., *Acta Cryst.* **11**, 612 (1958).
22. Aronson, S., and Belle, J., *J. Chem. Phys.* **29**, 151 (1958).
23. Aronsson, B., *Arkiv Kemi* **16**, 379 (1960).
24. van Arkel, A. E., Verwey, E. J. W., and van Bruggen, M. G., *Rec. trav. chim.* **55**, 331 (1936).
25. Aronsson, B., Stenberg, E., and Åselius, J., *Acta Chem. Scand.* **14**, 733 (1960).
26. Åsbrink, S., and Magnéli, A., *Acta Cryst.* **12**, 575 (1959).
27. Atoji, M., and Rundle, R. E., *J. Chem. Phys.* **32**, 627 (1960).
28. Aurivillius, B., *Arkiv Kemi, Mineral. Geol.* **A16**, No. 17 (1943).
29. Aurivillius, B., *Arkiv Kemi* **1**, 463 (1949).
30. Aurivillius, B., *Arkiv Kemi* **1**, 499 (1949).
31. Aurivillius, B., *Arkiv Kemi* **2**, 519 (1950).
32. Aurivillius, B., *Arkiv Kemi* **5**, 39 (1952).
32a. Aurivillius, B., and Fang, P. H., *Phys. Rev.* **126**, 893 (1962).
33. Aurivillius, B., and Lundqvist, T., *Acta Chem. Scand.* **9**, 1209 (1955).
34. Baenziger, N. C., Eick, H. A., Schuldt, H. S., and Eyring, L., *J. Am. Chem. Soc.* **83**, 2219 (1961).
35. Banks, E., Stripp, K., Newkirk, H. W., and Ward, R., *J. Am. Chem. Soc.* **74**, 2450 (1952).
36. Bartram, S. F., *Dissertation Abstr.* **19**, 1216 (1958).
37. Belbeoch, B., Piekarski, C., and Perio, P., *Bull. soc. franç. minéral. et. crist.* **83**, 206 (1960).

38. Bénard, J., *Bull. soc. chim. France* p. 109 (1949).
39. Bénard, J., *Inst. intern. chim. Solvay Counseil chim., Brussels, 1956* p. 83 (1956).
40. Bénard, J., *Inst. intern. chim. Solvay Counseil chim., Brussels, 1956* p. 109 (1956).
41. Bennaceraff, A., and Guittard, M., *Compt. rend. acad. sci.* 248, 2012 (1959).
42. Bernoff, R. A., and Conroy, L. E., *J. Am. Chem. Soc.* 82, 6261 (1960).
43. Bertaut, E. F., *Acta Cryst.* 6, 557 (1953).
44. Bertaut, E. F., Blum, P., and Sagnières, A., *Acta Cryst.* 12, 149 (1959).
45. Berry, K. L., Aftandilian, V. O., Gilbert, W. W., Meibohm, E. P. H., and Young, H. S., *J. Inorg. & Nuclear Chem.* 14, 231 (1960).
46. Bevan, D. J. M., *J. Inorg. & Nuclear Chem.* 1, 49 (1955).
47. Biltz, W., and Köcher, A., *Z. anorg. u. allgem. Chem.* 241, 324 (1939).
48. Blomberg, B., Kihlborg, L., and Magnéli, A., *Arkiv Kemi* 6, 133 (1953).
48a. Bokii, G. B., and Romanova, E. M., *Soviet Physics Cryst. (Transl.)* 6, 701 (1962).
49. Borchert, W., *Z. Krist.* 106, 5 (1945).
50. Born, L., and Hellner, E., *Am. Mineralogist* 45, 1266 (1960).
51. Boullé, A., and Dominé-Bergès, M., *Compt. rend. acad. sci.* 227, 1365 (1948); 228, 72 (1949).
52. Brauer, G., *Z. anorg. u. allgem. Chem.* 248, 1 (1941).
53. Brauer, G., and Gingerich, K. A., *J. Inorg. & Nuclear Chem.* 16, 87 (1960).
54. Brauer, G., and Gradinger, H., *Naturwissenschaften* 24, 559 (1951).
55. Brauer, G., and Littke, W., *J. Inorg. & Nuclear Chem.* 16, 67 (1960).
56. Brauer, G., and Müller, O., *Z. anorg. u. allgem. Chem.* 295, 218 (1958).
57. Braun, P. B., *Nature* 170, 1123 (1952).
58. Braun, P. B., Thesis, University of Amsterdam, 1956.
59. Braun, P. B., and Kwestroo, W., *Philips Research Repts.* 15, 394 (1960).
60. Brimm, E. O., Brantley, J. C., Lorenz, J. H., and Jellinek, M. H., *J. Am. Chem. Soc.* 73, 5427 (1951).
61. Brindley, G. W., and Nakahira, M., *Nature* 183, 1620 (1959).
62. Brown, B. W., and Banks, E., *J. Am. Chem. Soc.* 76, 963 (1954).
63. Buerger, M. J., *Am. Mineralogist* 33, 101 (1948).
64. Buerger, M. J., and Buerger, N. W., *Am. Mineralogist* 29, 55 (1944).
65. Buerger, M. J., and Hahn, T., *Am. Mineralogist* 40, 226 (1955).
66. Buser, W., Graf, P., and Feitknecht, W., *Helv. Chim. Acta* 37, 2322 (1954).
67. Butler, G., and Copp, J. L., *J. Chem. Soc.* p. 725 (1956).
68. Butler, G., and Thirsk, H. R., *Acta Cryst.* 5, 288 (1952).
69. Byström, A., *Arkiv Kemi, Mineral. Geol.* A20, No. 11 (1945).
70. Byström, A., and Byström, A. M., *Acta Cryst.* 3, 146 (1950).
71. Cameron, A., Harbard, E. H., and King, A., *J. Chem. Soc.* p. 55 (1939).
72. Casey, J. J., Katz, L., and Orr, W. C., *J. Am. Chem. Soc.* 77, 2187 (1955).
73. Choain, C., and Marion, F., *Compt. rend. acad. sci.* 252, 3258 (1961).
74. Cohen, M. H., and Turnbull, D., *Nature* 187, 131 (1961).
75. Cole, W. F., Wadsley, A. D., and Walkley, A., *Trans. Electrochem. Soc.* 92, 133 (1947).
76. Collongues, R., Perez y Jorba, M., and Lefèvre, J., *Bull. soc. chim. France* p. 70 (1961).

77. Conroy, L. E., and Sienko, M. J., *J. Am. Chem. Soc.* **79**, 4048 (1957).
78. Coughanour, L. W., Roth, R. S., and Deprosse, V. A., *J. Research Natl. Bur. Standards* **52**, 37 (1954).
79. Cowley, J. M., *Acta Cryst.* **6**, 53 (1953).
80. Croatto, U., *Gazz. chim. ital.* **74**, 20 (1944).
81. Cromer, D. T., *J. Phys. Chem.* **61**, 753 (1957).
82. Dachs, H., *Z. Krist.* **107**, 370 (1956).
83. Dasgupta, D. R., and Mackay, A. L., *J. Phys. Soc. Japan* **14**, 932 (1959).
84. David, I., and Welch, A. J. E., *Trans. Faraday Soc.* **52**, 1642 (1956).
85. Dickson, J. G., Katz, L., and Ward, R., *J. Am. Chem. Soc.* **83**, 3026 (1961).
86. Dietzel, A., and Tober, H., *Ber. deut. keram. Ges.* **30**, 71 (1953).
87. Donnay, G., Donnay, J. D. H., and Kullerud, G., *Am. Mineralogist* **43**, 230 (1958).
88. Donnay, J. D. H., and Donnay, G., *Am. Mineralogist* **39**, 161 (1954).
89. Dryden, J. S., and Wadsley, A. D., *Trans. Faraday Soc.* **54**, 1574 (1958).
90. Earley, J. W., *Am. Mineralogist* **35**, 338 (1950).
91. Edwards, A. B., "Textures of the Ore Minerals," p. 137. Australian Inst. Mining Met., Melbourne, 1954.
92. Ehrlich, P., *Z. Elektrochem.* **45**, 362 (1939).
93. Ehrlich, P., *Angew. Chem.* **A60**, 68 (1948).
94. Erchak, M., Fankuchen, I., and Ward, R., *J. Am. Chem. Soc.* **68**, 2085 (1946).
95. Erd, R. C., Evans, H. T., and Richter, D. H., *Am. Mineralogist* **42**, 309 (1957).
96. Euler, R., and Hellner, E., *Z. Krist,* **113**, 345 (1960).
97. Evans, H. T., *U.S. Geol. Survey, Profess. Papers* **No. 400-B**, (1960).
98. Evans, H. T., and Block, S., *Am. Mineralogist* **38**, 1242 (1953).
99. Evans, H. T., and Mrose, M. E., *Am. Mineralogist* **40**, 861 (1955).
100. Evans, H. T., and Mrose, M. E., *Acta Cryst.* **11**, 56 (1958).
101. Evans, H. T., and Mrose, M. E., *Am. Mineralogist* **45**, 1144 (1960).
102. Feitknecht, W., Oswald, H. R., and Feitknecht-Steinmann, V., *Helv. Chim. Acta* **43**, 1947 (1960).
103. Ferguson, R. E., Guth, E. D., and Eyring, L., *J. Am. Chem. Soc.* **76**, 3890 (1954).
104. Flahaut, J., Domange, L., Guittard, M., and Loriers, J., *Bull. soc. chim. France* p. 102 (1961).
105. Flahaut, J., and Guittard, M., *Compt. rend. acad. sci.* **242**, 1318 (1956).
106. Flahaut, J., Loriers, J., and Patrie, M., *Compt. rend. acad. sci.* **245**, 2291 (1957).
107. Fleischer, M., *Am. Mineralogist* **45**, 176 (1960).
108. Flood, H., Krog, Th., and Sørum, H., *Tiddskr. Kjemi Bergvesen Met.* **3**, 32 (1943).
109. Flood, H., Krog, Th., and Sørum, H., *Tiddskr. Kjemi Bergvesen Met.* **6**, 59 (1946).
110. Flood, H., and Sørum, H., *Tiddskr. Kjemi Bergvesen Met.* **6**, 55 (1946).
111. Forman, S. A., and Peacock, M. A., *Am. Mineralogist* **34**, 441 (1949).
112. Francombe, M. H., *Acta Cryst.* **13**, 131 (1960).

113. Francombe, M. H., and Lewis, B., *J. Electronics* **2**, 387 (1957).
114. Francombe, M. H., and Lewis, B., *Acta Cryst.* **11**, 696 (1958).
115. Frenkel Ya. I., *Z. physik* **35**, 652 (1926).
116. Frevel, L. K., and Rinn, H. W., *Acta Cryst.* **9**, 626 (1956).
117. Galasso, F., and Katz, L., *Nature* **188**, 1099 (1960).
118. Galasso, F., Katz, L., and Ward, R., *J. Am. Chem. Soc.* **80**, 1262 (1958).
119. Galasso, F., Katz, L., and Ward, R., *J. Am. Chem. Soc.* **81**, 820 (1959).
120. Galasso, F., Katz, L., and Ward, R., *J. Am. Chem. Soc.* **81**, 5898 (1959).
120a. Gatehouse, B. M., and Wadsley, A. D., Unpublished data (1963).
121. Gattow, G., and Glemser, O., *Z. anorg. u. allgem. Chem.* **309**, 121 (1961).
122. Geller, S., *J. Am. Chem. Soc.* **77**, 2641 (1955).
123. Glemser, O., Gattow, G., and Meisiek, H., *Z. anorg. u. allgem. Chem.* **309**, 1 (1961).
124. Glemser, O., and Lutz, G., *Naturwissenschaften* **34**, 215 (1947).
125. Glemser, O., Lutz, G., and Meyer, G., *Z. anorg. u. allgem. Chem.* **285**, 173 (1956).
126. Glemser, O., and Sauer, H., *Z. anorg. u. allgem. Chem.* **252**, 144 (1943).
127. Glemser, O., and Schwarzmann, E., *Z. anorg. u. allgem. Chem.* **278**, 249 (1955).
128. Goodman, G., *J. Am. Ceram. Soc.* **36**, 369 (1953).
129. Goodman, G., *J. Am. Ceram. Soc.* **43**, 105 (1960).
130. Gorter, E. W., *Phil. Mag. Suppl.* **6**, No. 23, 336 (1957).
131. Gorter, E. W., *Proc. Intern. Congr. Pure and Appl. Chem., 17th Congr.* Vol. 1, p. 303 (1959).
132. Graham, J., and McTaggart, F. K., *Australian J. Chem.* **13**, 67 (1960).
133. Graham, J., and Wadsley, A. D., *Acta Cryst.* **14**, 379 (1961).
134. Grønvold, F., Hagberg, O., and Haraldsen, H., *Acta Chem. Scand.* **12**, 971 (1958).
135. Grønvold, F., and Haraldsen, H., *Nature* **162**, 69 (1948).
136. Grønvold, F., Haraldsen, H., and Vidhovde, J., *Acta Chem. Scand.* **8**, 1927 (1954).
137. Grønvold, F., and Jacobsen, E., *Acta Chem. Scand.* **10**, 1440 (1956).
138. Grønvold, F., Kjekshus, A., and Raaum, F., *Acta Cryst.* **14**, 930 (1961).
139. Gushee, B. E., Katz, L., and Ward, R., *J. Am. Chem. Soc.* **79**, 5601 (1957).
140. Guth, E. D., Holden, J. R., Baenziger, N. C., and Eyring, L., *J. Am. Chem. Soc.* **76**, 5239 (1954).
141. Hägg, G., *Z. physik. Chem. (Leipzig)* **B29**, 95 (1935).
142. Hägg, G., *Z. physik. Chem. (Leipzig)* **B29**, 192 (1935).
143. Hägg, G., *Acta Chem. Scand.* **4**, 88 (1950).
144. Hägg, G., and Kindström, A. L., *Z. physik. Chem. (Leipzig)* **B22**, 453 (1933).
145. Hägg, G., and Schönberg, N., *Arkiv Kemi* **7**, 371 (1954).
146. Hägg, G., and Söderholm, G., *Z. physik. Chem. (Leipzig)* **B29**, 88 (1935).
147. Hahn, H., Frank, G., Klingler, W., Störger, A. D., and Störger, G., *Z. anorg. u. allgem. Chem.* **279**, 241 (1955).
148. Hahn, H., and Harder, B., *Z. anorg. u. allgem. Chem.* **288**, 241 (1956).
149. Hahn, H., Harder, B., Mutschke, U., Ness, P., *Z. anorg. u. allgem. Chem.* **292**, 82 (1957).

150. Hahn, H., and Klingler, W., *Z. anorg. u. allgem. Chem.* **259**, 135 (1949); **260**, 97, 111 (1949).
151. Hahn, H., and Ness, P., *Z. anorg. u. allgem. Chem.* **302**, 17 (1959).
152. Hahn, H., and Ness, P., *Z. anorg. u. allgem. Chem.* **302**, 37 (1959).
153. Hahn, H., and Ness, P., *Z. anorg. u. allgem. Chem.* **302**, 136 (1959).
154. Hansen, M., "Constitution of Binary Alloys," p. 335, Fig. 193. McGraw-Hill, New York, 1958.
155. Hansen, M., "Constitution of Binary Alloys," p. 340, Fig. 196. McGraw-Hill, New York, 1958.
156. Haraldsen, H., *Z. anorg. u. allgem. Chem.* **246**, 169 (1941).
157. Haraldsen, H., Grønvold, F., and Hurlen, T., *Z. anorg. u. allgem. Chem.* **283**, 143 (1956).
158. Haraldsen, H., and Mehmed, F., *Z. anorg. u. allgem. Chem.* **239**, 369 (1938).
159. Haraldsen, H., and Neuber, A., *Z. anorg. u. allgem. Chem.* **234**, 353 (1937).
160. Harrison, F. W., *Acta Cryst.* **9**, 495 (1956).
161. Hassel, O., and Nilssen, S., *Z. anorg. u. allgem. Chem.* **181**, 172 (1929).
162. Hauffe, K., "Reaktionen in und an Festen Stoffe." Springer, Berlin, 1955.
163. Hellner, E., *Z. Krist.* **109**, 284 (1957).
164. Hellner, E., *Naturwissenschaften* **45**, 38 (1958).
165. Hellner, E., *Z. Krist.* **110**, 169 (1958).
166. Hellner, E., *J. Geol.* **66**, 503 (1958).
167. Hoekstra, H. R., and Katz, J. J., *J. Am. Chem. Soc.* **74**, 1683 (1952).
168. Hoekstra, H. R., Santoro, A., and Siegel, S., *J. Inorg. & Nuclear Chem.* **18**, 166 (1961).
169. Hoekstra, H. R., and Siegel, S., *J. Inorg. & Nuclear Chem.* **18**, 154 (1961).
170. Hoekstra, H. R., Siegel, S., Fuchs, L. H., and Katz, J. J., *J. Phys. Chem.* **59**, 136 (1955).
171. Hoffman, W., *Sitzber. preuss. Akad. Wiss. Physik. math. Kl.* p. 111 (1938).
172. van Hook, H. J., *Econ. Geol.* **55**, 759 (1960).
173. Horie, T., and Iwai, T., *J. Phys. Soc. Japan* **16**, 424 (1961).
174. Hoschek, E., and Klemm, W., *Z. anorg. u. allgem. Chem.* **242**, 63 (1939).
175. Hoschek, E., and Klemm, W., *Z. anorg. u. allgem. Chem.* **242**, 49 (1939).
176. Hund, F., and Fricke, R., *Z. anorg. u. allgem. Chem.* **258**, 198 (1949).
177. Hund, F., and Niessen, G., *Z. Elektrochem.* **56**, 972 (1952).
178. Hund, F., and Peetz, U., *Z. anorg. u. allgem. Chem.* **271**, 6 (1952).
179. Hurlen, T., *Acta Chem. Scand.* **13**, 365 (1959).
180. Ingold, J. H., and De Vries, R. C., *Acta Met.* **6**, 736 (1958).
181. Isupov, V. A., *Soviet Physics Cryst.* (*Transl.*) **3**, 96 (1958).
182. Jagodzinski, H., *Z. Krist.* **109**, 388 (1957).
183. Jeannin, Y., *Compt. rend. acad. sci.* **251**, 246 (1960).
184. Jeannin, Y., and Bénard, J., *Compt. rend. acad. sci.* **248**, 2875 (1959).
185. Jellinek, F., *Acta Cryst.* **10**, 620 (1957).
186. Jellinek, F., *J. Less-Common Metals* **4**, 9 (1962).
187. Jellinek, F., Brauer, G., and Müller, H., *Nature* **185**, 376 (1960).
188. Jette, E. R., and Foote, F., *J. Chem. Phys.* **1**, 29 (1933).
188a. Johnston, W. D., and Sestrich, D., *J. Inorg. & Nuclear Chem.* **20**, 32 (1961).
189. Jona, F., Shirane, G., and Pepinsky, R., *Phys. Rev.* **98**, 903 (1955).

190. Jonker, G. H., *Proc. Intern. Congr. Pure and Appl. Chem, 16th Congr.*, *Sect. chim. min.* p. 117 (1958).

191. Jonker, G. H., and Kwestroo, W., *J. Am. Ceram. Soc.* **41**, 390 (1958).

192. Kaspar, J. S., and Prener, J., *Acta Cryst.* **7**, 246 (1954).

193. Katz, T., *Ann. chim.* (*Paris*) **12**, 5 (1950).

194. Kestigian, M., Dickinson, J. G., and Ward, R., *J. Am. Chem. Soc.* **79**, 5598 (1957).

195. Kestigian, M., and Ward, R., *J. Am. Chem. Soc.* **77**, 6199 (1955).

196. Ketelaar, J. A. A., and Gorter, E. W., *Z. Krist.* **101**, 367 (1939).

197. Kihlborg, L., *Acta Chem. Scand.* **14**, 1612 (1960).

198. Kihlborg, L., Final Tech. Rept. No. 1, p. 24 (1960). Dept. of Army Contract No. DA-91-591-EUC-1319.

199. Klement, W., Willens, R. H., and Duwez, P., *Nature* **187**, 869 (1960).

200. Klemm, W., *Chemie* **56**, 6 (1943).

201. Klemm, W., and Grimm, L., *Z. anorg. u. allgem. Chem.* **250**, 42 (1942).

202. Klemm, W., and Klein, H. A., *Z. anorg. u. allgem. Chem.* **248**, 167 (1941).

203. Klemm, W., Meisel, K., and von Vogel, H., *Z. anorg. u. allgem. Chem.* **190**, 123 (1930).

204. Koehler, W. C., Wollan, E. O., and Wilkinson, M. K., *Phys. Rev.* **110**, 37 (1958).

205. Kordes, E., *Z. Krist.* **92**, 139 (1935).

206. Kurnakow, N. S., *Z. anorg. u. allgem. Chem.* **88**, 109 (1914).

207. Kwestroo, W., *J. Inorg. & Nuclear Chem.* **9**, 65 (1959).

208. Kwestroo, W., and Roos, A., *J. Inorg. & Nuclear Chem.* **13**, 325 (1960).

209. Lander, J. J., *Acta Cryst.* **4**, 148 (1951).

210. Lange, P. W., *Naturwissenschaften* **27**, 133 (1939).

211. Laurent, A., *Ann. chim. et phys.* **67**, 215 (1838).

212. Le Bihan, M. T., *Bull. soc. franç. minéral et crist.* **85**, 15 (1962).

213. Leineweber, G., *Z. Krist.* **108**, 161 (1956).

214. Lewis, B., and White, E. A. D., *J. Electronics* **1**, 646 (1956).

215. Lukaszewicz, K., *Roczniki Chem.* **31**, 1111 (1957).

216. Lukaszewicz, K., *Roczniki Chem.* **33**, 239 (1959)

217. Lundqvist, D., *Arkiv Kemi, Mineral. Geol.* A24, No. 21 (1947).

218. McCullough, J. D., and Britton, J. D., *J. Am. Chem. Soc.* **74**, 5225 (1952).

219. McCullough, J. D., and Trueblood, K. N., *Acta Cryst.* **12**, 507 (1959).

220. McTaggart, F. K., and Wadsley, A. D., *Australian J. Chem.* **11**, 445 (1958).

221. Mackay, A. L., *Mineral. Mag.* **32**, 545 (1960).

222. Mackay, A. L., Private communication (1961).

223. Magnéli, A., *Acta Chem. Scand.* **2**, 501 (1948).

224. Magnéli, A., *Arkiv Kemi.* **1**, 213 (1949).

225. Magnéli, A., *Arkiv Kemi.* **1**, 223 (1949).

226. Magnéli, A., *Arkiv Kemi.* **1**, 269 (1949).

227. Magnéli, A., *Arkiv Kemi.* **1**, 513 (1950).

228. Magnéli, A., *Acta Chem. Scand.* **5**, 670 (1951).

229. Magnéli, A., *Acta Cryst.* **6**, 495 (1953).

230. Magnéli, A., *Acta Chem. Scand.* **7**, 315 (1953).

231. Magnéli, A., and Blomberg, B., *Acta Chem. Scand.* **5**, 372 (1951).

232. Magnéli, A., and Blomberg-Hansson, B., Kihlborg, L., and Sundkvist, G., *Acta Chem. Scand.* **9**, 1382 (1955).

233. Malinofsky, W. W., and Kedesdy, H., *J. Am. Chem. Soc.* **76**, 3090 (1954).
234. Morimoto, N., and Kullerud, G., *Carnegie Inst. Wash. Publ. Geophys. Lab.* p. 116 (1960).
235. Neugebauer, J., Hegedüs, A. J., and Millner, T., *Z. anorg. u. allgem. Chem.* **302**, 50 (1959).
236. Niizeki, N., and Buerger, M. J., *Z. Krist.* **109**, 129 (1957).
237. Niizeki, N., and Buerger, M. J., *Z. Krist.* **109**, 161 (1957).
238. Norin, R., and Magnéli, A., *Naturwissenschaften* **47**, 354 (1960).
239. Norrish, K., *Mineral Mag.* **29**, 496 (1951).
240. Nowacki, W., Bürki, H., Iitaka, V., and Kunz, V., *Schweiz. mineral. petrog. Mitt.* **41**, 103 (1961).
241. Nuffield, E. W., *Trans. Roy. Soc. Can.*, Sect. IV [3] **39**, 41 (1945).
242. Okazaki, A., *J. Phys. Soc. Japan* **14**, 112 (1959).
243. Okazaki, A., *J. Phys. Soc. Japan* **16**, 1162 (1961).
244. Okazaki, A., and Hirakawa, K., *J. Phys. Soc. Japan* **11**, 930 (1958).
245. Okazaki, C., *J. Phys. Soc. Japan* **15**, 2013 (1960).
246. Van Oosterhout, G. W., and Rooijmans, C. J. M., *Nature* **181**, 44 (1958).
247. Ozerov, R. P., *Soviet Physics Cryst.* (*Transl.*) **2**, 219 (1957).
248. Ozerov, R. P., *Russ. J. Inorg. Chem.* (*Transl.*) **4**, 476 (1959).
249. Ozerov, R. P., Gol'der, G. A., and Zhdanov, G. S., *Soviet Physics Cryst.* (*Transl.*) **2**, 211 (1957).
250. Padĕra, K., *Chem. Erde* **18**, 14 (1956).
251. Palache, C., Berman, H., and Frondel, C., *in* "The System of Mineralogy" (J. D. Dana, ed.), Vol. 1, p. 441. Wiley, New York, 1944.
252. Patzak, I., *Z. Metallk.* **47**, 418 (1956).
253. Pauling, L., and Shappell, M. D., *Z. Krist.* **75**, 128 (1930).
254. Perez y Jorba, M., Collongues, R., and Lefèvre, J., *Compt. rend. acad. sci.* **249**, 1237 (1959).
255. Perio, P., *Bull. soc. chim. France.* p. 776 (1953).
256. Petrásová, M., Madar, J., and Hanic, F., *Chem. zvesti.* **12**, 410 (1958).
257. Phillips, B., and Muan, A., *J. Am. Ceram. Soc.* **41**, 445 (1958).
258. Rabenau, A., Stegherr, A., and Eckerlin, P., *Z. Metallk.* **51**, 295 (1960).
259. Rase, D. E., and Roy, R., *J. Am. Ceram. Soc.* **38**, 102 (1955).
260. Ridgley, D., and Ward, R., *J. Am. Chem. Soc.* **77**, 6132 (1955).
261. Robinson, S. C., *Econ. Geol.* **43**, 293 (1948).
262. Robinson, S. C., *Am. Mineralogist* **34**, 398 (1949).
263. Rooijmans, C. J. M., *J. Inorg. & Nuclear Chem.* **11**, 78 (1959).
264. Rösch, H., and Hellner, E., *Naturwissenschaften* **46**, 72 (1959).
265. Rosen, C., Banks, E., and Post, B., *Acta Cryst.* **9**, 475 (1956); **9**, 477 (1956).
266. Roth, R. S., *J. Am. Ceram. Soc.* **39**, 196 (1956).
267. Roth, R. S., *J. Research Natl. Bur. Standards* **61**, 437 (1958).
268. Roth, R. S., *J. Research Natl. Bur. Standards* **62**, 27 (1959).
269. Roth, R. S., and Coughanour, L. W., *J. Research Natl. Bur. Standards* **55**, 209 (1955).
270. Roth, R. S., and Waring, J. L., *J. Research Natl. Bur. Standards* **65**, 337 (1961).
271. Roth, W. L., *Acta Cryst.* **13**, 140 (1960).
272. Roy, D. M., Roy, R., and Osborn, E. F., *Am. J. Sci.* **251**, 337 (1953).

273. Ruddlesden, S. R., and Popper, P., *Acta Cryst.* **10**, 538 (1957).
274. Ruddlesden, S. R., and Popper, P., *Acta Cryst.* **11**, 54 (1958).
275. Rudörff, W., and Reuter, B., *Z. anorg. u. allgem. Chem.* **253**, 177 (1947).
276. Rundle, R. E., Baenziger, N. C., Wilson, A. S., and McDonald, R. A., *J. Am. Chem. Soc.* **70**, 99 (1948).
277. Saalfeld, H., and Jagodzinski, H., *Z. Krist.* **109**, 87 (1957).
278. Sato, R., Doi, H., Ishii, D., and Uchikoshi, H., *Acta Cryst.* **14**, 763 (1961).
279. Scheer, J. J., van Arkel, A. E., and Heyding, R. D., *Can. J. Chem.* **33**, 683 (1955).
280. Schlenk, W., *Fortschr. chem. Forsch.* **2**, 92 (1951).
281. Schmitz-Dumont, O., and Reckhard, H., *Monatsh. Chem.* **90**, 134 (1959).
282. Schottky, W., *Z. physik. Chem. (Leipzig)* **B29**, 335 (1935).
283. Schottky, W., and Wagner, C., *Z. physik. Chem. (Leipzig)* **B11**, 163 (1930).
284. Schwartz, R. S., Fankuchen, I., and Ward, R., *J. Am. Chem. Soc.* **74**, 1676 (1952).
285. Semilitov, S. A., *Trudy Inst. Krist. Akad. Nauk S.S.S.R.* **10**, 76 (1954).
286. Semilitov, S. A., and Pinsker, Z. G., *Doklady Akad. Nauk S.S.S.R.* **100**, 1079 (1955).
287. Siegel, S., *Acta Cryst.* **8**, 617 (1955).
288. Sienko, M. J., *J. Am. Chem. Soc.* **81**, 5556 (1959).
289. Sienko, M. J., and Mazumder, B. R., *J. Am. Chem. Soc.* **82**, 3508 (1960).
290. Sillén, L. G., Dissertation, University of Stockholm, p. 67 (1940).
291. Sinha, K. P., and Sinha, A. P. B., *J. Phys. Chem.* **61**, 758 (1957).
292. Smolenskii, G. A., Isupov, V. A., and Agranovskaya, A. I., *Doklady Akad. Nauk S.S.S.R.* **113**, 1053 (1957).
293. Smolenskii, G. A., Isupov, V. A., and Agranovskaya, A. I., *Soviet Phys. Solid State (Transl.)* **1**, 149 (1959).
294. Spitzbergen, U., *Acta Cryst.* **13**, 197 (1960).
295. Straumanis, M. E., Ejima, T., and James, W. J., *Acta Cryst.* **14**, 493 (1961).
296. Straumanis, M. E., and Hsu, S. S., *J. Am. Chem. Soc.* **72**, 4027 (1950).
297. Strauss, S. W., Fankuchen, I., and Ward, R., *J. Am. Chem. Soc.* **73**, 5084 (1951).
298. Strotzer, E. F., and Zumbusch, M., *Z. anorg. u. allgem. Chem.* **247**, 415 (1941).
299. Subbarao, E. C., *J. Chem. Phys.* **34**, 695 (1961).
299a. Subbarao, E. C., *Phys. and Chem. Solids*, **23**, 665 (1962).
299b. Subbarao, E. C., *J. Am. Ceram. Soc.* **45**, 165 (1962).
299c. Subbarao, E. C., *Phys. Rev.* **122**, 804 (1961).
300. Subbarao, E. C., and Shirane, G., *J. Am. Ceram. Soc.* **42**, 279 (1959).
301. Subbarao, E. C., and Shirane, G., *J. Am. Ceram. Soc.* **43**, 119 (1960).
302. Subbarao, E. C., and Shirane, G., *J. Chem. Phys.* **32**, 1846 (1960).
303. Tanisaki, S., *J. Phys. Soc. Japan* **15**, 566 (1960).
304. Tengnér, S., *Z. anorg. u. allgem. Chem.* **239**, 126 (1938).
305. Thompson, R. M., *Am. Mineralogist* **34**, 342 (1949).
306. Trehan, Y. N., and Goswami, A., *Trans. Faraday Soc.* **55**, 2162 (1959).
307. Ukrainskii, Yu. M., Kovba, L. M., Simanov, Yu. P., and Novoselova, A. V., *Russ. J. Inorg. Chem. (Transl.)* **4**, 1305 (1959).

308. Verwey, E. J. W., Z. Krist. 91, 65 (1935).
309. Verwey, E. J. W., and de Boer, J. H., Rec. trav. chim. 55, 531 (1936).
310. Wadsley, A. D., Acta Cryst. 5, 676 (1952).
311. Wadsley, A. D., Acta Cryst. 6, 433 (1953).
312. Wadsley, A. D., Acta Cryst. 8, 165 (1955).
313. Wadsley, A. D., Acta Cryst. 8, 695 (1955).
314. Wadsley, A. D., Revs. Pure and Appl. Chem. (Australia) 5, 165 (1955).
315. Wadsley, A. D., Acta Cryst. 10, 261 (1957).
316. Wadsley, A. D., Acta Cryst. 10, 715 (1957).
317. Wadsley, A. D., J. Proc. Roy. Soc. N. S. Wales 92, 25 (1958).
318. Wadsley, A. D., Acta Cryst. 14, 660 (1961).
319. Wadsley, A. D., Acta Cryst. 14, 664 (1961).
320. Wadsley, A. D., and Andersson, S., Nature 192, 551 (1961).
321. Wadsley, A. D., and Walkley, A., Revs. Pure and Appl. Chem. (Australia)
     1, 203 (1951).
322. Wadsley, A. D., Unpublished data (1963).
323. Wait, E., J. Inorg. & Nuclear Chem. 1, 309 (1955).
324. Ward, R., in "Progress in Inorganic Chemistry" (F. A. Cotton, ed.),
     Vol. 1, p. 465. Interscience, New York, 1959.
325. Warren, H. V., and Peacock, M. A., Univ. Toronto Studies Geol. Ser. 49,
     55 (1945).
326. Waser, J., and McClanahan, E. D., J. Chem. Phys. 19, 413 (1951).
327. Waser, J., and McClanahan, E. D., J. Chem. Phys. 20, 199 (1952).
328. Weiser, H. B., and Milligan, W. O., J. Phys. Chem. 39, 25 (1935).
329. Weitz, G., and Hellner, E., Z. Krist. 113, 385 (1960).
330. Wernick, J. H., Am. Mineralogist 45, 591 (1960).
331. Wernick, J. H., Geller, S., and Benson, E., Phys. and Chem. Solids 4, 154
     (1958).
332. Westman, S., Final Tech. Rept. No. 1, p. 8 (1960). Dept. of Army Contract
     No. DA-91-591-EUC-1319.
333. Westman, S., and Nordmark, C., Acta Chem. Scand. 14, 465 (1960).
334. Wickman, F. E., Arkiv Mineral. Geol. 1, 219 (1951).
335. Wöhler, L., Z. anorg. u. allgem. Chem. 40, 450 (1904).
336. Woolley, J. C., Pamplin, B. R., and Holmes, P. J., J. Less-Common Metals
     1, 362 (1959).
337. Woolley, J. C., and Ray, B., Phys. and Chem. Solids 15, 27 (1960); 16,
     102 (1960).
338. Yakel, H. L., Banks, E., and Ward, R., J. Electrochem. Soc. 96, 304
     (1949).
339. Zachariasen, W. H., Manhattan Progr. Rept. No. CK 2667 (1945).
340. Zachariasen, W. H., Acta Cryst. 1, 265 (1948).
341. Zachariasen, W. H., Acta Cryst. 2, 57 (1949).
342. Zachariasen, W. H., Acta Cryst. 2, 388 (1949).
343. Zaslavskii, A. I., and Sergeeva, V. M., Soviet Phys. Solid State (Transl.)
     2, 2556 (1961).
344. Zintl, E., and Croatto, U., Z. anorg. u. allgem. Chem. 242, 79 (1939).
345. Zintl, E., and Udgård, A., Z. anorg. u. allgem. Chem. 240, 150 (1939).

CHAPTER 4

O. M. Katz* and E. A. Gulbransen

Westinghouse Research Laboratories,
Pittsburgh, Pennsylvania

Occluded Gases in Transition Metals

I. Introduction... 211
II. Crystal Structures of the Interstitial Compounds............... 211
  A. Normal Structures....................................... 212
  B. X_2 Structures.. 214
III. Materials... 214
  A. Purity... 214
  B. Metallurgical Features.................................. 215
  C. Sample Preparation..................................... 216
IV. Adsorption, Hydride Formation, and Hydrogen Solution Processes... 216
  A. Nature of Adsorption................................... 216
  B. Formation of Thin Hydride Films and Solution of Hydrogen Atoms... 218
V. Diffusion of Hydrogen...................................... 218
  A. Diffusion Kinetics...................................... 218
  B. Experimental Results.................................... 222
VI. Effect of Oxide Films and Pretreatments on the Occlusion of Hydrogen... 225
  A. In Zirconium... 225
  B. In Group V Alloys...................................... 233
VII. Thermodynamic Analyses................................... 233
  A. Free Energy Expression................................. 234
  B. Effect of Temperature and Pressure on Solubility of Hydrogen in α-Zr.. 235
  C. Terminal Solubility of Hydrogen......................... 236
  D. Decomposition Pressures and Removal of Hydrogen from the Metal.. 236
  E. Method.. 237
  F. Characteristics of Occluded Hydrogen.................... 240
VIII. Crystal Structure and Phase Diagram Studies of Zr–H.......... 250
  A. Early Absorption Studies................................ 252
  B. Early Crystal Structure Studies......................... 252
  C. Experimental Studies................................... 253
  Text References... 258
  Additional Bibliography on Hydrogen in Metals............. 261

* *Present address*: Westinghouse Bettis Atomic Power Laboratory, Pittsburgh
Pennsylvania.

210

I. INTRODUCTION

The occlusion of gases in metals is an important subject in the new science of materials. Occluded gases can greatly affect the metal's mechanical, physical, and corrosion properties. In the last 15 years it has become obvious that ductile refractory alloys of Nb, Cr, Mo, Ti, and W for example could only be produced with low residual gas contents. High gas contents in these and the other Group IV, V, and VI elements alter such physical properties as magnetic susceptibility, electrical resistivity, specific heat, and superconductivity. For Zr alloys, the corrosion resistance in water at elevated temperatures is a function of the occlusion of small quantities of hydrogen resulting from the oxidation of the metal. The presence of occluded gases in metals can have a quite different effect if one wishes to use the metal in electronic tubes or in high vacuum equipment. A clear understanding of the occlusion process is necessary if metals are to be used correctly in our rapidly developing technology.

From the viewpoint of this book the occlusion of gases in certain metals is of interest. Some of the interstitial structures formed between the transition metals and the non-metals hydrogen, boron, carbon and nitrogen are excellent examples of non-stoichiometric compounds. The large amount of work done on the interstitial solution of carbon in iron (38, 43, 70) has laid a good foundation for understanding gas-metal structures.

We will not attempt a complete review of the work in this field since several reviews (11, 12, 14, 85) have been made in recent years. However, a section appended to the bibliography lists some of the more recent studies of hydrogen in metals. Instead, we will consider some of the principles involved in the occlusion process. Hydrogen in zirconium is used as the main example. This system has been studied extensively by us (27–30) and by other workers (17, 57, 59, 64).

Before looking into details of the occlusion process, let us first consider the crystal structure or atomic geometry of the interstitial compounds of the transition metals.

II. CRYSTAL STRUCTURES OF THE INTERSTITIAL COMPOUNDS

Interstitial compounds are formed when the transition metals react with hydrogen, boron, carbon and nitrogen. These compounds are metallic in their physical properties, have metallic luster, and are generally opaque. The compounds show a sequence of phases and a range of homogeneity in the individual compounds. Non-stoichiometric compositions are found in many cases.

Technically these compounds have many valuable properties due to their high melting points, extreme hardness, and—with the exception of the hydrides—high stability.

The interstitial compounds differ greatly from the compounds formed when hydrogen, boron, carbon, and nitrogen react with non-transition metals. For these compounds the physical properties differ widely from that of the metal. The compounds behave as true chemical compounds of essentially definite chemical composition.

The crystal structures and the physical properties of the interstitial compounds are related to the small size of the non-metallic atom. The important factor characterizing the structures is the ratio of the radius of the non-metallic atom, X, to that of the metal atom, B.

Two basic types of structures have been found by Hägg (32–35), who has done much of the early work in this field: (a) normal structures and (b) X_2 structures.

A. Normal Structures

Normal structures are formed if the radius ratio r_X/r_B is less than about 0.59. Here, the metal atoms are in contact and the non-metallic atoms are arranged in the interstices of the structure. The metal atoms are usually arranged as in the pure element. Cubic or hexagonal close-packed structures with a coordination number of 12 or a cubic body-centered structure with a coordination number of 8 are found. Simple hexagonal lattices are sometimes observed.

The non-metallic elements occupy the largest spaces in the structure in which contact is maintained with their metal neighbors and in which maximum coordination is achieved. In the cubic close-packed structure the non-metal atoms, if large enough, occupy the sixfold coordinated interstices at the center of the unit cell and at the centers of cell edges. Since there are four octahedral holes per unit cell, the occupation of all the octahedral sites results in a formula of BX and the NaCl-type structure. The maximum hydride composition in the Pd–H system approaches PdH, and recent neutron diffraction studies (94) showed the H in octahedral holes.

If the non-metal atoms are relatively too small to form the sodium chloride structure, the fluorite structure having the composition BX_2 is formed. Here, the non-metal atom resides in smaller fourfold or tetra-hedrally coordinated sites in the centers of the eight small cubes into which the cubic close-packed unit cell can be divided. This type is formed in the

Ti, Zr, and Hf–H systems, being a distorted face-centered cubic structure. This phase region embraces a large range of metal excess compositions whose c/a axial ratios change continuously from above to below 1 (*86*). The Group V metals also contain hydrogen in tetrahedral sites (*54*). Although here the structure is body-centered cubic with six such sites per metal atom, the maximum composition attained below 1 atm of H_2 is only BH. Some recent experiments with Nb (*8*) and V (*66*) at elevated pressures reported the additional formation of a cubic close-packed, nonstoichiometric region which supposedly corresponds to the Group IV hydrides. If only one-half of the sites are symmetrically filled in the BX_2 structure, a zinc blende type is formed. (See Chapter 3, Section III, E.)

It is now known that both the octahedral and tetrahedral sites can be occupied in the same structure. Evidence for this comes from the lanthanide-type hydrides of the rare earth elements. Thus dihydrides of La and Ce (*13, 79*) showed both metal excess and hydrogen excess compositions in the same phase region. Since the hydrides had a cubic close packed structure, the excess hydrogen must reside in other than tetrahedral sites. Octahedral sites were also occupied by H in $CeH_{2.7}$ as shown by neutron diffraction studies (*42*).

However, as a reasonable guide to those normal structures where only one type of interstitial site is occupied, the classification by Hägg is useful (*20*). Table I designates the interstitial structures in terms of (*a*) the nature of the metal lattice and (*b*) the coordination number of the non-metal atom. The radius ratio of interstitial X to metal B is a helpful criterion for assaying the appearance of a particular structure type.

TABLE I

CLASSIFICATION OF NORMAL INTERSTITIAL STRUCTURES (*20*).

C. N. of metal	Type of metal lattice	C. N. of non-metal	Type symbol	Radius ratio r_X/r_B
12	12a Cubic close-packed	6	12a, 6[a]	>0.41
		4	12a, 4[b]	>0.23
	12b Hexagonal close-packed	6	12b, 6	>0.41
		4	12b, 4[c]	>0.23
8	8a Cubic body-centered	4	8a, 4	>0.29
	8b Simple hexagonal ($c/a=1$)	6	8b, 6	>0.53

[a]Cf. NaCl.   [b]Cf. Fluorite and Zinc blende.   [c]Wurzite.

B. X_2 Structures

If the ratio r_X/r_B is very small, interstitial structures of the composition BX_2 occur. The two types are described in terms of a distorted cubic, close-packed structure. In the first type shown in Fig. 1a the X_2 groups are arranged parallel to one edge of the cube which is extended so that the cell is tetragonal. Here the X_2 groups, e.g., C—C, are arranged in the six-fold coordinated interstices of the metal lattice. Axial ratios greater than unity occur. In the carbides LaC_2, CeC_2, PrC_2, NdC_2, UC_2, and VC_2 axial ratios of 1.15 to 1.20 are found. The second type in Fig. 1b has the X_2 groups lying parallel to a cube face with their axes in two mutually perpendicular directions. The same interstices are occupied as in the first

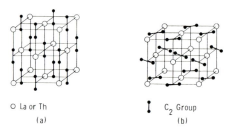

○ La or Th   ❘ C_2 Group
(a)   (b)

Fig. 1. Two types of interstitial X_2 structures [after Evans (20)]: (a) LaC_2; (b)ThC_2.

type. This structure is found in ThC_2 and ZrC_2. There is some thought that hydrides of the ZrH_2 type might have the H atoms coordinated in an H—H group and belong to this structure category also. In the group shown in Fig. 1b, a tetragonal cell with an axial ratio of less than unity is formed.

III. MATERIALS

A. Purity

The purest metals and alloys which can be obtained should be used in the study of gas-metal reactions. All too often the H, B, N, O, and C impurities are ignored in the preparation of pure metals. These levels in particular should be at an absolute minimum. Before 1940 little attention was given to the reduction of gaseous contaminants.

To obtain gas-free materials it is necessary to utilize gettered, inert atmospheres or high vacuum melting conditions. Many laboratory methods have been scaled up to meet the commercial demand for high quality metals. Some of these methods are zone refining (71), levitation melting (68), electron beam melting (83), vacuum arc-cold hearth, and vacuum induction melting (*19*). Many high purity reactive metals are now being produced by the hot-wire decomposition of volatile halides of the metal (*61*); Zr and Hf crystal bars are produced by the decomposition of the tetraiodides at 1200°–1500°C in a pre-evacuated chamber. Hf crystal bar of the following analyses in ppm has been attained: H 4, O 13, N 13, Al <35, B <0.5, C—12, Ca <25, Cd <2.5, Co <5, Cr <10, Cu <25, Fe <100, Mg <10, Mn <10, Mo <10, Na <10, Ni <15, Pb <10, Si <20, Sn <15, Ti <15, U 0.4, V <10, W <20, Hf + Zr 99.8$^+$ wt%.

The analyses of small gaseous impurities has presented many problems. Vacuum fusion methods have been used with some success (*39, 77*). More recently a combination of chemical reaction and light spectroscopy (*21, 22*), and the point to plane solid state mass spectrometer have been used for analyses (*41*). For hydrogen, perhaps the simplest method of analysis is hot vacuum extraction from the solid (*15*). With the transition metals of concern in this chapter this means pressures less than 10^{-4} mm of Hg between 600° and 1000°C.

The melting cycle is not the only source of gaseous contaminants. Moderate machining rates in air have been found to raise the oxygen level from less than 100 ppm to 500 ppm in Zr and Hf base alloys. Exposure to reducing atmospheres at elevated temperatures must be followed by vacuum annealing to remove the hydrogen, and even this is not too practical for large pieces (*81*). Hydrogen can also be introduced during abrading where water vapor is present (*82*), during etching or pickling (*3*), or while plating metals or alloys (*46*). Hydrogen is a particularly bad actor due to its great ability to diffuse far into the metal interior and adversely affect its mechanical properties (*38, 75*). Unfortunately, the hydrogen cannot be readily removed from the metal or alloy in all cases and may reside in preferential sites as dislocation and imperfection centers (*45*), trapped as CH_4 (*72*), or held in carbide phases (*5*)—particularly at temperatures below 200°C.

B. Metallurgical Features

In addition to purity the metallurgical nature of the alloys must be considered. Of utmost importance is the stressed condition brought about by prior plastic deformation. Since gaseous atoms in metallic solution strain the lattice appreciably and cause deformation, it is reasonable to suppose that the presence of deformation in the lattice will affect the occlusion process. A 50% reduction in area by cold rolling increased the occlusive capacity of Fe–C alloys two to three times (*56, 90*). In addition, cold rolling introduced a predominantly exothermic occlusion process below 300°C when only the normal endothermic process existed in annealed alloys. The interaction of occluded nitrogen with dislocations during plastic deformation has been shown to have an effect on the tensile yield point and strain aging phenomena (10). Hence, fully annealed materials are probably the best for studying gas-metal reactions. However, the time, temperature, and percentage of prior deformation still affect the grain size, orientation, and hardness of the annealed sample.

Another metallurgical feature which must be considered when selecting materials is the microstructural arrangement of phases. Although it would be best to study the thermodynamically stable phase structure, it is not always possible or desirable (84). In such cases it is necessary to know the time-temperature-transformation characteristics of the alloy so that no precipitation occurs during reaction with the gas. Studies of Fe–C alloys in particular have shown that the occlusion of hydrogen is a function of the amount and dispersion of Fe_3C (90).

C. Sample Preparation

Finally, we must consider the type of samples introduced into the gas reaction apparatus. In later sections, we will discuss the effects of some preparation variables. However, much of the work in our laboratories involves sheet specimens, with surface areas from 5 to 20 cm^2, so that the times are not prohibitively long. For high temperature reactions it is possible to lower the surface area by utilizing cylinders or spheres. Spheres tend to be advantageous in cases where the edges of rectangular specimens promote non-uniform reaction.

Samples are metallographically polished through 4/0 paper under a purified form of kerosene, washed in benzene, acetone, and absolute alcohol, and stored temporarily in a vacuum desiccator. As shown later, a 1-hour vacuum anneal at 700°C is necessary to dissolve the room-temperature oxide film. Where the oxide can neither be dissolved nor reduced, abrasion should be done in an inert-gas, dry box and the sample transferred directly to the reaction apparatus (24). Mechanical abrasion of samples is well suited for the study of hydrogen reactions since chemical removal of films may leave other highly impervious and unpredictable deposits on the surface (27, 31). Some additional considerations in the preparation of single crystal and evaporated metal samples are presented in the literature (73).

IV. ADSORPTION, HYDRIDE FORMATION, AND HYDROGEN SOLUTION PROCESSES

A. Nature of Adsorption

Due to their molecular motion all gases collide with surfaces. These collisions with metals result in a wide variety of physical and chemical phenomena depending upon the pressure, temperature, adsorption energy, stability of compounds of the metal and gas, solubility limit of the gas in the metal, and diffusion coefficients of the gases and metal ions in the reaction products on the surface.

Adsorption is the preliminary process for all surface reactions including the occlusion of gases. The fundamental cause of adsorption is the temporary stay of molecules at the surface (7). The basic equation is

$$\sigma = n\tau \tag{1}$$

where σ is the number of molecules per unit area of the surface, and n is the number of molecular collisions per second with a unit area of surface; τ is the average time a molecule resides on the surface.

The number n is given by

$$n = 3.52 \times 10^{22} P/(MT)^{1/2} \tag{2}$$

where P is the pressure in millimeters of Hg, M is the molecular weight of the gas, and T is the absolute temperature. For hydrogen at 20°C and a pressure of 760 mm of Hg, $n = 1.10 \times 10^{24}$ molecules/cm^2-sec. This result tells us that nearly 2 moles of hydrogen collide each second with a cm^2 of surface. At a pressure of 10^{-5} mm of Hg several monolayers of hydrogen collide with a surface each second.

Of equal importance in Eq. (1) is the value of τ; here τ is a strong function of temperature. Frenkel (7) has given the following equation for τ

$$\tau = \tau_0 \exp (Q/RT) \tag{3}$$

Here τ_0 is the time of oscillation of molecules in the adsorbed state, Q is the heat of adsorption, R is the gas constant, and T is the absolute temperature; τ_0 has a value of 10^{-13} to 10^{-14} sec; τ may be called the time of adsorption and represents the length of time an adsorbed molecule stays on the surface before evaporating; Q is the major factor in determining the value of τ. For a surface containing 3.5×10^{15} atoms per cm^2 calculations show that Q must be greater than 1500 cal/mole to get appreciable adsorption. These considerations show that hydrogen and other gases which are occluded in metals have appreciable heats of adsorption.

If the heat of adsorption is large (5–10 kcal/mole) the bond is either covalent, ionic, or most probably both. If the bond is ionic the hydrogen might be in the state H_2^-. Here, a high surface dipole would be produced. More likely the bond is partially or predominately covalent with the hydrogen being dissociated and producing a lower surface dipole. Once a monolayer is formed a slower reaction follows. The total amount of hydrogen taken up by adsorption is between 1 and 2 monolayers. The rate of uptake of hydrogen is found to be proportional to $P^{1/2}$ or to $n^{1/2}$. The factor $P^{1/2}$ suggests dissociation of hydrogen in the first layer. The rate of uptake of hydrogen is related to τ, the time of adsorption, by Eq. (3).

B. Formation of Thin Hydride Films and Solution of Hydrogen Atoms

If the pressure of hydrogen is higher than the equilibrium pressure for the hydrogen-metal-hydride equilibrium, the chemisorbed layer of hydrogen is not stable. A tendency exists for further hydriding. Hydride forms or hydrogen atoms or ions diffuse into the metal.

The formation of hydride films on the surface should follow the pattern of all nucleation processes. First, there is the activation energy of nucleation itself, which decreases as the pressure of hydrogen is increased. Second, there is the activation energy associated with the elementary atomic processes such as the surface diffusion of hydrogen or metal ions. If the activation energy for nucleation is small and the hydrogen pressure high, nucleation can start in a nearly uniform manner. However, if the nucleation energy is high, nuclei of hydride will appear at the most favorable imperfect points on the crystal face, such as imperfections, dislocations, etc. It is not clear how the adsorbed layer of hydrogen begins to transform into a thin hydride layer.

The formation of hydride nuclei has not been studied experimentally. However, much can be learned from experimental studies on the nucleation of oxide and sulfide crystals (4). Even for the latter systems the sites for nucleation and the mechanism of nucleation are not well established.

Solution of hydrogen atoms in the metal lattice occurs simultaneously or under certain conditions preferentially to the formation of a hydride surface phase. Many factors affect the kinetics of these processes including the presence of other gases in the metal structure, the presence of imperfect points for nucleation on the surface, and the magnitude of the heats and entropies of activation for the several processes. Hydrogen solution can occur by interstitial diffusion in the metal lattice, by grain boundary diffusion, and by diffusion along certain imperfections in the metal structure.

In most systems both a hydride phase and solution of hydrogen occur simultaneously after the initial stage of adsorption. The diffusion of hydrogen gas through a hydride phase into the metal will be considered next.

V. DIFFUSION OF HYDROGEN

A. Diffusion Kinetics

Diffusion of non-metal atoms such as hydrogen, carbon, boron, or nitrogen occurs with widely different rates, depending upon the metal, the temperature, the condition of the metal surface, and the presence or absence of surface oxide or other films. In this section we present an analysis of the diffusion of hydrogen gas in pure zirconium (*29*).

Wagner (*87*) discussed the general problem of diffusion in binary systems of more than one phase. From a mathematical point of view this problem is similar to that of melting or solidification in which one substance changes into another with emission or absorption of heat. The common feature of these problems is the existence of a moving surface of separation between two phases, at which material or heat is being transferred. The original solution of the heat problem is due to Neuman and was presented in a book by Carslaw and Jaeger (*9*).

1. GENERAL PICTURE

Figure 2 shows the analysis given by Wagner (*87*) for diffusion from a surface into a heterogeneous system for a flat plate. C_s is the surface concentration at $x = 0$, C_0 is the concentration at time $t = 0$, and $C_{\mathrm{II,I}}$ is the concentration in phase II at the interface ξ with phase I. Diffusion proceeds from the surface in the homogeneous phase II. At time t the region of phase II extends from $x = 0$ to $x = \xi$.

Since hydrogen reacts with zirconium to form two hydride phases in addition to dissolving in α-zirconium, the validity of the diffusion picture shown in Fig. 2 may be questioned. However, the ϵ and δ hydride phases for most purposes can be considered as one phase, since their ranges of homogeneity are nearly continuous and since their crystal structures are similar.

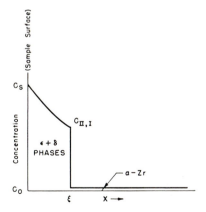

FIG. 2. Diffusion picture, hydrogen into zirconium [after Wagner (*87*)]: $t > 0$; $C_s = \mathrm{ZrH}_{1.965}$; $C_{\mathrm{II,I}} = \mathrm{ZrH}_{1.40}$; $C_0 = \mathrm{ZrH}_{0.001}$ at 250° C.

The effect of solution of hydrogen in the metal is negligible since the solubility at 250°C is of the order of $ZrH_{0.001}$ (28).

2. GENERAL SOLUTION

The following equation governs the diffusion process:

$$\partial C/\partial t = D(\partial^2 C/\partial x^2) \tag{4}$$

Here the diffusion coefficient, D, is assumed to be independent of concentration. The boundary condition is

$$C = C_s \qquad \text{at } x = 0 \text{ and } t > 0 \tag{5}$$

At the interface $x = \xi$ thie concentration of diffusing species in phase II is that relating to the equilbrium value between phases I and II:

$$C = C_{II,I} \qquad \text{at } x = \xi \tag{6}$$

When the interface is displaced by $d\xi$ for a time dt, the quantity

$$(C_{II,I} - C_0) \, d\xi$$

of hydrogen must be supplied from the region $x < \xi$. Thus,

$$(C_{II,I} - C_0) \, d\xi = D \, dt (\partial C/\partial x)_{\xi \to 0} \tag{7}$$

A particular solution of equation (I) for boundary condition (II) is

$$C = C_s - B \operatorname{erf} (x/2\sqrt{Dt}), \qquad \text{for } 0 < x < \xi \tag{8}$$

Here, B is a constant and erf is the error function.

Wagner (87) assumed, as did Neuman (9), that the plane of discontinuity is shifted proportional to $t^{1/2}$. Thus,

$$\xi = \gamma 2\sqrt{Dt} \tag{9}$$

Here γ is a dimensionless parameter.

Substituting, one obtains

$$C_s - C_{II,I} = B \operatorname{erf} (\gamma) \tag{10}$$

$$C_{II,I} - C_0 = (B/\sqrt{\pi}) \exp (-\gamma^2) \tag{11}$$

Eliminating B, one has

$$\frac{C_s - C_{II,I}}{C_{II,I} - C_0} = \sqrt{\pi} \gamma \exp (\gamma^2) \operatorname{erf} \gamma \tag{12}$$

γ can be found from Eq. (12) and B from Eqs. (10) and (11).

D is usually found by observing the displacement ξ and by the use of Eq. (9). However, if the reaction is followed by a weight gain method, D

must be obtained from the average concentration in the sample as a function of time.

3. Solution for Weight Gain Mehtod

Let $\bar{C}$ be the average concentration in phase II, $0 < x < \xi$. Then,

$$\bar{C} = \xi^{-1} \int_0^\xi C(x, t) \, dx$$

$$= \xi^{-1} \int_0^\xi \left(C_s - B \, \text{erf} \, \frac{x}{2\sqrt{Dt}} \right) dx \tag{13}$$

$$= \xi^{-1} \left[C_s \xi - B \int_0^\xi \text{erf} \frac{\gamma x}{\xi} \right] dx \tag{14}$$

Integrating,

$$\bar{C} = C_s - B \, \text{erf} \, \gamma + (B/\gamma\sqrt{\pi})[1 - \exp(-\gamma^2)] \tag{15}$$

This shows that $\bar{C}$ is independent of t.

Substituting Eq. (10) and rearranging,

$$\frac{\bar{C} - C_{\text{II,I}}}{C_s - C_{\text{II,I}}} = \frac{1 - \exp(\gamma^2)}{\gamma\sqrt{\pi} \, \text{erf} \, (\gamma^2)} \tag{16}$$

Using this analysis, Eqs. (12) and (16) are plotted as a function of γ. From the plot of Eq. (12) a value for γ is obtained and from a plot of Eq. (16) and this value of γ, a value for

$$\frac{(\bar{C} - C_{\text{II,I}})}{(C_s - C_{\text{II,I}})}$$

can be obtained.

From these plots $\gamma = 0.425$ and

$$\frac{\bar{C} - C_{\text{II,I}}}{C_s - C_{\text{II,I}}} = 0.485$$

Now an expression can be written for the average concentration $\bar{C}_A$ over the whole specimen:

$$\bar{C}_A(d/2) = \bar{C}\xi + C_0[(d/2) - \xi] \tag{17}$$

Here $d/2$ is the half thickness and C_0 the solubility of hydrogen in α-Zr. For temperatures of 250°C and lower, C_0 has a value of 0.001 or less in terms of the ratio H/Zr and is, therefore, negligible.

Substituting Eqs. (9) and (17) and the values for γ and $\bar{C}$,

$$\bar{C}_A = 2.845(D^{1/2}t^{1/2}/d) \tag{18}$$

For 0.0127-cm specimens, this equation becomes

$$\bar{C}_A = 224D^{1/2}t^{1/2} \tag{19}$$

and for 0.0508-cm specimens,

$$\bar{C}_A = 56D^{1/2}t^{1/2} \tag{20}$$

In deriving Eqs. (18) and (17) it is assumed that C_s is constant and independent of pressure. Phase diagram studies by Gulbransen and Andrew (27) showed that C_s had a value of 1.965 in terms of the ratio H/Zr, and for temperatures of 250°C and lower, C_s is independent of pressures of the order of 1 cm Hg and higher.

4. Testing of the Mechanism of the Reaction

The reaction mechanism upon which Eq. (18) is based can be tested experimentally. First, plots of $\bar{C}_A$ versus $t^{1/2}$ can be used to test the square root of time relationship. Second, use of different thicknesses of samples tests the validity of Eq. (18). Third, use of both hydrogen and deuterium having different diffusion coefficients gives an additional way of testing Eq. (18). Fourth, the analysis assumes a constant value for C_s. The effect of pressure, therefore, should be negligible. Fifth, a plot of log D versus $1/T$ should give a straight line and a reasonable heat of activation.

B. Experimental Results

To study the diffusion of hydrogen into zirconium we used a sensitive vacuum microbalance apparatus (27). Kinetic studies were made for the temperature range of 60° to 250°C at a hydrogen pressure of 50 mm of Hg. Oxide films were removed by heating to 700°C in high vacuum. Oxide films dissolve in the metal under these conditions leaving an oxide-free metal surface.

To test the diffusion picture developed in this section the average concentration $\bar{C}_A$ of hydrogen was plotted against $t^{1/2}$. At 250°C a straight line was found up to a concentration H/Zr of 1.60 or the limit of the two phase region. Similar results were found at other temperatures. We conclude that Eq. (18) describes the time behavior of the hydriding process, including the assumption made by Wagner (87) concerning the movement of the interface between phases.

If the hydride $ZrH_{1.965}$ is formed on the surface, then the surface concentration C_s should be independent of pressure if the pressure is greater than the equilibrium pressure of $ZrH_{1.965}$. This is true for all of the experimental conditions considered here. Studies on the effect of hydrogen pressure on the kinetics of solution showed the effect is negligible.

Equation (18) also relates the average concentration $\bar{C}_A$ versus $t^{1/2}$ curve to the sample thickness by the factor $1/d$ where d is the thickness. This relationship was confirmed experimentally by change of sample thickness.

1. CALCULATION OF DIFFUSION COEFFICIENTS

Equation (18) is used to calculate diffusion coefficients from $\bar{C}_A$ versus $t^{1/2}$ plots. These are summarized in Table II. Figure 3 shows these data on a log D versus $1/T$ plot, and from the slope a heat of activation of 11,400 cal/mole was calculated. Data for samples of different thicknesses are included.

D_0 is calculated from the equation

$$D = D_0 \exp\left(-\Delta H^*/RT\right) \tag{21}$$

TABLE II

DIFFUSION DATA FOR HYDROGEN (10).

$t°C$	$1/T \times 10^3$	D_{avg} (cm²/sec)	D_0 (cm²/sec)
60	3.0021	4.60×10^{-11}	1.341×10^{-3}
80	2.832	7.09×10^{-11}	0.784×10^{-3}
100	2.680	2.54×10^{-10}	1.178×10^{-3}
120	2.544	3.25×10^{-10}	0.705×10^{-3}
125	2.512	6.43×10^{-10}	1.144×10^{-3}
150	2.360	1.625×10^{-9}	1.26×10^{-3}
175	2.232	2.470×10^{-9}	0.876×10^{-3}
200	2.114	6.02×10^{-9}	1.099×10^{-3}
225	2.008	1.33×10^{-8}	1.33×10^{-3}
250	1.912	2.215×10^{-8}	1.217×10^{-3}
			avg 1.09×10^{-3}

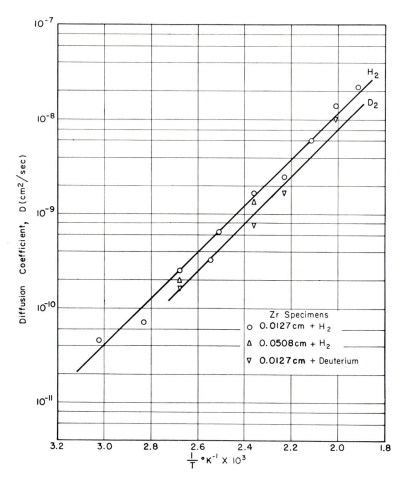

FIG. 3. D versus $1/T$ log plot for $60°$–$250°$C; $\Delta H = 11{,}400$ cal/mole of H; $P = 1.1$ to 5.0 cm of H_2 gas.

Here, D_0 is the extrapolated value of D at infinite temperature, and ΔH^* is the heat of activation of diffusion. The values of D_0 are tabulated and an average value of 1.09×10^{-3} is calculated. The data could be represented by

$$D = 1.09 \times 10^{-3} \times \exp\,(-11{,}400/RT)\ \text{cm}^2/\text{sec} \qquad (22)$$

The value of 11,400 cal/mole for the heat of activation of diffusion for hydrogen (Table II) appears to be reasonable since heats of activation of 5740–10,100 cal/mole have been observed (2) for the diffusion of hydrogen in palladium. The most reliable work on diffusion of hydrogen in palladium gave a value of 5740 cal/mole (47, 48).

Our analysis is actually for the diffusion of hydrogen through the hydride layer and, therefore, does not yield the same D_0 and activation energy as a later work (*62*). This later work obtained a

$$D = 4.74 \times 10^{-4} \exp(-5940/RT) \text{ cm}^2 \text{ sec}$$

by the gradient and degassing technique in the α range. Values from both equations for D do still fall close to each other and within the predicted range for hydrogen diffusion in metals.

Figure 3 also shows data on the diffusion of deuterium in zirconium. Although the data are somewhat scattered, the temperature dependence is the same as that found for the diffusion of hydrogen, so the heat of activation for the diffusion process is the same for both gases. Calculated D_0 values for hydrogen and for deuterium are 1.09×10^{-3} and 7.3×10^{-4}, respectively. The ratio of D_{H_2}/D_{D_2} is independent of temperature and approximately equal to 1.5.

Jost and Widman (*47*, *48*) observed a ratio of 1.3 for D_{H_2}/D_{D_2}. Using the transition state theory of diffusion, they showed that the effect of the mass of the diffusion species is in the frequency term in the expression for the diffusion coefficient, the frequency of vibration being proportional to $1/\sqrt{m}$ or $1/\sqrt{2}$. Thus, the simple theory gives a ratio of D_{H_2}/D_{D_2} of 1.41. This compares with the experimental value of about 1.5.

A similar analysis could be made using the classical theory of diffusion as expressed in Eq. (22). The major effect appears to be that of mass on frequency of vibration along the path for reaction. Considering the scattering of experimental results, the diffusion of deuterium in zirconium is adequately explained by Eq. (18) with the effect of mass on the frequency of vibration of the particular diffusing species explaining the ratio of D_{H_2}/D_{D_2}.

VI. EFFECT OF OXIDE FILMS AND PRETREATMENTS ON THE OCCLUSION OF HYDROGEN

A. In Zirconium

Although the reaction of hydrogen with metals has been studied extensively, only minor attention has been given to the kinetics of the reaction. The experimental problem of preparing reproducibly clean metal surfaces is basic to kinetic studies. Many of the early studies were made on impure metals using poor experimental conditions. As a consequence conclusions have been drawn from inadequate data. The mechanism of occlusion has been found to be extremely complex. Some of the important factors which affect the kinetics of the occlusion process are: (i) surface preparation; (ii) cold working of the metal; (iii) occluded gases; (iv) pretreatment with hydrogen; (v) oxide films; and (vi) impurities in the gas atmosphere.

This section is concerned with the influence of some of these factors on the kinetics of occlusion. A simple picture of the occlusion processes was given in Section IV. These processes are: (i) chemisorption; (ii) diffusion of hydrogen through surface films; (iii) transfer of hydrogen from the film to the metal; (iv) diffusion into metal; and (v) formation of one or more hydride phases.

From an experimental point of view, it is difficult to separate the rate-controlling process from the other rate processes. This is especially true of zirconium where metal and hydride phases may exist. In addition, stable oxide films and other contaminating films form readily on the metal surface, and these may retard reaction with hydrogen. These films may dissolve in the metal at higher temperatures under vacuum or inert gas atmospheres and reappear if the rate of film formation is greater than the rate of solution of the oxide into the metal. Therefore, it has been difficult to study the relative influence of oxide films and the physical structure of the metal, and many unusual physical effects have been noticed for this reaction.

1. Theories on the Variable Rate of Reaction

An analysis of the literature on the occlusion process for exothermic occluders such as zirconium indicates that two theories exist for the variable rate of reaction observed when zirconium is exposed to hydrogen. The first is the "rift theory" of occlusion developed by Smith (78). In this theory an expanding and contracting series of rifts are used to explain active and passive states of the metal. The second is the oxide film theory in which a coherent thin oxide film prevents access of hydrogen to the metal. However, this oxide dissolves in the metal at high temperature under high vacuum conditions. Clean metal is then exposed for reaction. Recent work supporting this point of view is that of Hall and co-workers (37).

Before presenting our interpretation, it is of interest to indicate the main experimental characteristics of the occlusion process upon which Smith has developed the rift theory of occlusion. It should be noted that much of the work was made on specimens probably contaminated with oxide and other films.

The characteristics are as follows. (i) Metal is inert to gaseous hydrogen at room temperature and normal pressure in its ordinary form. (ii) If gradually heated the metal begins to react at an indefinite opening temperature. (iii) The rate of reaction is self-accelerating in its early stages.

(iv) At high pressures the metal in its ordinary state reacts and is permeable at lower pressures. (v) Metal in its ordinary state reacts with hydrogen liberated upon it by chemical displacement or by electrolysis. (vi) Permeability of metal to hydrogen may be increased or decreased by repeated absorption and evolution of hydrogen, apparently depending upon the rate with which the gas is expelled. (vii) Metal heated to high temperatures in vacuo is inert to gaseous hydrogen and may be impervious to cathodic hydrogen. (viii) Permeability is increased by plastic deformation, in some cases manyfold. This increase is accompanied by an increase in occlusive capacity.

In addition to these general characteristics Smith gives five additional characteristics of exothermic occluders such as zirconium. (ix) After a metal is heated to an activation temperature above that described in (ii), the metal possesses for some time an induced high permeability at ordinary temperatures and pressures. This is known as thermal activation. (x) This high permeability declines gradually at a rate which differs from one lot of metal to another. (xi) Metal having high permeability and charged with hydrogen loses its permeability slower than if uncharged. (xii) If heated and cooled while charged with hydrogen, the metal shows decreased permeability and does not give up its hydrogen to vacuum until heated to above its opening temperature. (xiii) In the composition range of two solid phases, exothermic occluders show smaller permeability and occlusion capacity during adsorption than during evolution of hydrogen. This phenomena is called *hysteresis*.

Smith's rift theory has certainly introduced a great deal of controversy as to where the hydrogen atom resides in metal lattices and how it diffuses. Although a simple explanation based on lattice solution and diffusion appears adequate in most cases, defects which have been enlarged beyond their normal size are proposed as necessary for hydrogen solution and mobility. Exothermic occlusion is said to occur first by rift occlusion, followed by true interstitial solution. However, the process of single phase exothermic occlusion does not seem too different from the endothermic occlusion process which is said to be all rift controlled. Even though the rift hypothesis seems to be in general disfavor as an all inclusive mechanism, the basic premise of lattice defects and imperfections affecting hydrogen occlusion and mobility cannot be dismissed (*5*, *45*, *53*, *72*).

2. EXPERIMENTAL STUDY

A vacuum microbalance apparatus was used (*29*) for the study of the kinetics of hydrogen occlusion. The reaction system was of all glass construction and could be evacuated readily to pressures of 10^{-6} mm of Hg, or lower. Pure hydrogen was prepared by diffusing purified electrolytic hydrogen through a palladium tube.

To study the rate of hydriding of zirconium it was necessary to devise a test procedure which gives a reaction rate characteristic of an oxide-free metal and a reaction rate which is reproducible. Since the oxide film normally present on the surface cannot be reduced in the case of zirconium oxides, it was necessary to remove the oxide by heating in high vacuum. It was found that heating the specimen to 700°C in a vacuum of 10^{-6} mm Hg or less for one hour gave a reproducible reaction rate with hydrogen. For convenience, the conditions of 150°C and a pressure of 2.4 cm of Hg were chosen. The reaction showed no evidence of an induction period.

Results are given in terms of weight gain in micrograms/cm² and plots are made of weight versus time in minutes.

a. Effect of Temperature of Vacuum Heating. To show the effect of vacuum heating procedures on rate of hydriding at test conditions, specimens were heated for 1 hour at a series of temperatures in high vacuo before cooling to 150°C to determine the rate of hydriding. If it is assumed that the rate of reaction with hydrogen at low temperatures was limited by the presence of oxide films, vacuum heating at higher temperatures, which tends to dissolve the oxide, should increase the rate of reaction. In experiments presented here vacuum heating was made in the same apparatus as the rate study and without intermediate exposure to a gas atmosphere of any kind.

Figures 4 and 5 show the results. A new specimen was used for each experiment. Curve A in Fig. 4 represents the reaction of a specimen having the room temperature equilibrium film, while curve B shows the rate of attack after a preheat of one hour at 150°C. Curves A, B, and C of Fig. 5 show the rate of attack with hydrogen after preheats of one hour at 300°, 500°, and 700°C. It was found that the 500° and 700°C experiments gave similar rates of attack. Curves B and C are typical of many tests for these conditions of pressure and temperature. Results were reproducible within the limits of experimental error.

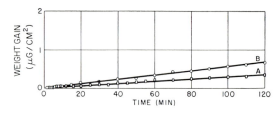

Fig. 4. Effect of time and temperature of annealing on hydriding of Zr at 150°C and 2.4 cm of H₂ gas: (A) room temperature equilibrium film; (B) anneal 150°C for 1 hour.

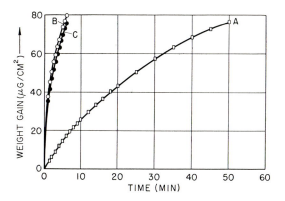

FIG. 5. Effect of temperature of annealing on hydriding of Zr at 150°C and 2.4 cm of H₂ gas: (A) annealed 300°C for 1 hour; (B) annealed 500°C for 1 hour; (C) annealed 700°C for 1 hour.

The rate of reaction for curve A of Fig. 4 was zero for the first 5 minutes and averages 0.473×10^{-4} $\mu g/cm^2$-sec for the first 2 hours. Curve C of Fig. 5 shows a rate of reaction of 0.365 $\mu g/cm^2$-sec for the first 2 minutes. The ratio of the rate of reaction of specimens having the room temperature oxide present to the specimen annealed at 700°C was 1/7700. An even greater ratio would be found if the rates were calculated for the 1-minute time interval.

Results can be interpreted readily by the oxide film theory. Thus, the inert character of the metal in its ordinary state can be attributed to the normal room temperature oxide film having a thickness of the order of 10 to 50 Å. This film is transparent and is an effective barrier to diffusion of gaseous hydrogen. It dissolved gradually into the zirconium as the temperature of heating was raised and the rate of reaction, therefore, was greatly increased. There appears to be no evidence that high heating of a metal such as zirconium renders it inert as interpreted by Smith (78).

b. *Effect of Thickness and Character of Oxide Films on Rate of Reaction.* Figure 6a shows weight gain versus time curves for a series of oxide pretreatments in which the thickness and character of the oxide was studied. Curve A shows the weight gain curve for the specimen containing the room temperature equilibrium oxide. Curve B shows the rate of reaction for a specimen having been preheated under high vacuum to 700°C for 1 hour and then exposed to 0.1 atm pressure of oxygen at 25°C for 20 hours. Curve C shows the rate of reaction for a specimen which had been annealed at 700°C and then oxidized at 150°C at an oxygen pressure of 7.6 cm Hg for 5 minutes to form an oxide film 63 Å thick. Curves D and E show the effect of oxide film of 500 Å thickness formed at 250° and 275°C, while curve F shows the rate of reaction of a film-free specimen. These results again may be explained on the basis of a coherent oxide film which dissolves slowly in the metal at temperatures of 250°C and higher. In general, oxides formed at room temperature have the greatest effect on rate of hydriding. The thicker films formed at temperatures of 250° and 275°C are less resistant to hydriding for two reasons. First, solution of the film occurs, which diminishes the film thickness. Second, the oxides formed at higher temperatures have a larger crystallite size. Thus, the fitting of the grains of oxide would be less perfect, and a greater porosity would be noted.

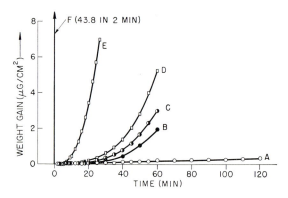

FIG. 6a. Effect of oxide on hydriding of Zr at 150°C and 2.4 cm of H_2 gas: (A) room temperature equilibrium film; (B) annealed + 20-hour exposure to O_2 at room temperature; (C) annealed + 63A film; (D) annealed + 500A film at 250°C; (E) annealed + 500A film at 275°C; (F) annealed—no film.

The fact that rate of reaction increases with time can be attributed to gradual breakdown of the oxide film physically by passage of hydrogen as well as to the gradual solution of the oxide into the metal.

Again the oxide film theory appears to explain observed facts better than the rift theory.

c. *Effect of Successive Hydrogen Treatments and Exposure to Oxygen.* Smith (78) has stated that successive hydrogen treatments affect permeability and occlusive capacity of the metal. In early stages of the reaction up to a H/Zr ratio of 0.2, no such evidence is observed, providing one is working with an oxide-free zirconium surface.

Three rates of hydriding experiments are compared in Fig. 6b. Curve A shows the control experiment with the rate of hydriding determined after the 700°C vacuum anneal. Curve B shows a rate of hydriding experiment for a sample which was given a high vacuo anneal at 700°C, hydrided at

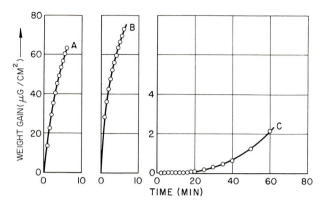

FIG. 6b. Effect of pretreatment on hydriding Zr at 150°C and 2.4 cm of H_2 gas: (A) annealed 700°C for 1 hour; (B) annealed—hydrided 150°C—dehydrided 700°C; (C) annealed—hydrided 150°C—dehydrided 700°C—oxidized room temperature.

150°C to 100 $\mu g/cm^2$ or to $ZrH_{0.2}$, the hydrogen removed by heating to 700°C, and then cooled to 150° for the second hydriding. Curve A shows a total reaction of 57 $\mu g/cm^2$ for 5 minutes, while Curve B shows a total reaction of 66.5 $\mu g/cm^2$ for 5 minutes. A small change appears in the rate of reaction due to previous adsorption and desorption of hydrogen in the lattice. However, the effect is a minor one when compared to the effect of oxide films. This is shown in curve C of Fig. 6b. In this experiment the sample was heated, hydrided at 150°C, heated to 700°C, exposed to room temperature oxygen, and then hydrided at 150°C. The effect of room temperature oxidation was great.

More experiments will have to be made to determine effect of the reaction of large quantities of hydrogen and subsequent removal on the rate of hydriding. Small quantities adsorbed and removed have only minor effects on the rate of hydriding.

d. Effect of Oxygen in Solid Solution. Samples of zirconium were heated to 700°C to dissolve the oxide film, then dosed with oxygen to give samples having 0.016, 0.027, 0.064, and 0.068 wt % of oxygen above the oxygen content of the original metal. Specimens were then heated in vacuo for 1 hour at 700°C to homogenize the oxygen before cooling to 150°C where further reaction with hydrogen occurred. Rapid homogenization was assumed to occur in the 1-hour vacuum anneal at 700°C for the following reasons: (*a*) thickness of the specimens was only 0.0127 cm with both sides of the specimen exposed to the original oxygen treatment; (*b*) the small amounts of oxygen that had to be homogenized; (*c*) the high rate of attack of zirconium with oxygen at 700°C.

The weight gain curves showed total weight gain values varying from

55 $\mu g/cm^2$ to 63 $\mu g/cm^2$ after 5 minutes of reaction. Within experimental error, oxygen in solid solution in small amounts exerts only minor effects on the rate of hydriding at 150°C.

e. *Effect of Nitrogen in Solid Solution.* Samples of zirconium were prepared as described above except that reagent grade nitrogen gas was used to dose the samples with given amounts of nitrogen. Thus, samples having 0.0095, 0.0196, 0.0491, and 0.096 wt % of nitrogen above the original nitrogen content were prepared. Again homogenization was assumed to occur in a 1-hour vacuum treatment at 700°C for the reasons given above. As in the case of oxygen in solid solution, the results showed that small amounts of nitrogen have only minor effects on the rate of reaction.

3. SUMMARY

High purity zirconium containing the room temperature equilibrium oxide film reacts very slowly with hydrogen at 150°C and 2.4 cm of Hg pressure, and in a self-accelerating manner. Similar specimens preheated in high vacuo at temperatures above 500°C for 1 hour react very rapidly with hydrogen at 150°C and 2.4 cm of Hg pressure without an induction period. The ratio of the rate of reaction for the preheated specimens relative to those not preheated was 7700 or greater. Results are interpreted in terms of an oxide film limiting the rate of reaction, this film dissolving in the metal as the temperature of annealing was raised. Thus the oxide film present on the unannealed specimen limits the rate of reaction and imposes an induction period on the reaction. Previous work summarized by Smith, showing that vacuum heating the metal decreases the rate of reaction of hydrogen, may be interpreted now as due to formation of an oxide or other contaminating film.

Further experiments show that the nature of the oxide film is very important in its resistance to hydrogen. Thus, room temperature equilibrium oxide films are more resistant to hydrogen than thicker oxide films formed at higher temperatures. This is explained in part by a partial solution of the oxide and to the presence of larger oxide crystallites in the films formed at higher temperatures.

Small amounts of dissolved oxygen and nitrogen up to 0.1 wt% have only a minor effect on the rate of hydriding for hydrogen adsorptions up to 0.2 atom of H per atom of Zr. Many of the unusual occlusive characteristics given by Smith may be interpreted on the basis of the oxide film theory which offers an effective resistance to the reaction with hydrogen at low temperatures.

B. In Group V Alloys

The effect of an oxide film on hydrogen occlusion is not unique to Zr. All group IV and V transition metals have room temperature oxide films which cannot be reduced by hydrogen below the metal melting point (65). Hence, they also must be heated in high vacuum to dissolve the film. A recent study (52) with a Nb + 10 wt% U solid solution alloy showed that a thin high temperature oxide could greatly reduce the hydriding rate at 297°C. An oxide of 39 $\mu g/cm^2$ was added to the sample by reaction at 1000°C. Although solution of oxide occurred at 1000°C, an appreciable oxide film remained on the surface since the rate of hydriding was greatly reduced at 297°C. Thus, reactions occurring in 1–3 hours at 297°C on oxide free samples required 16 hours at 297°C with an oxide present. Above a concentration $n_H/(n_U + n_{Nb})$ of 0.30 in solid solution in the alloy, there was no effect of the oxide on the rate of hydriding. The greater lattice expansion due to concentrations >0.30 would be expected to provide a greater stress for cracking the surface oxide barrier. In all cases the equilibrium concentration at a given H_2 pressure was the same with or without a surface film. For situations where a localized second phase hydride of greatly different lattice parameters is formed, the effect of a surface oxide is expected to be negligible. Such was the case for U + 10 wt% Nb alloys in the same study.

VII. THERMODYNAMIC ANALYSES

Thermodynamic and statistical mechanics concepts can be applied to the solution of hydrogen, carbon, boron, and nitrogen in the transition metals. Experimentally the hydrogen systems are easier to study. In the first part of this section we will treat the problem of hydrogen solution in zirconium. We will present our own analyses (27–30), although other workers have also treated the problem (17, 57, 59, 64). The object of the treatment is to express the normal solubility of hydrogen in zirconium, the terminal or maximum solubility in zirconium, and the decomposition pressures of hydrogen over the metal and hydride phases in terms of fundamental quantities such as free energy, heat, and entropy of solution of hydrogen in the metal and hydride phases. Zirconium reacts with hydrogen at temperatures below 550°C to form a solid solution of hydrogen in α-Zr and two hydride phases $ZrH_{1.4}(\delta)$ and $ZrH_2(\epsilon)$.

The following assumptions will be made: (i) gas goes into solution as atoms; (ii) Henry's law holds for the complete solid solution range; (iii) activity of α-Zr solid solution is that of the pure metal; (iv) the composition of hydride phase $ZrH_{1.4}$ is constant; and (v) the partial molal heat of solution of hydrogen in α-Zr and the standard heat of formation of the hydride phase are invariant over the temperature range of interest.

Equations will be developed for the equilibrium between hydrogen gas, α-Zr, and the δ-ZrH$_{1.4}$ phases. Similar equations can be derived for the equilibrium of hydrogen gas with ϵ-ZrH$_{1.965}$ and the equilibrium between ϵ-ZrH$_{1.965}$ and δ-ZrH$_{1.4}$ phases.

A. Free Energy Expression

The following equations represent the dissolution of hydrogen in the α- and δ-hydride phases:

$$\tfrac{1}{2}H_2(g) = H \text{ (dissolved in } \alpha\text{-Zr)} \tag{23}$$

and

$$\tfrac{1}{2}H_2(g) = H \text{ (dissolved in } \delta\text{-phase)} \tag{24}$$

At equilibrium we have

$$\tfrac{1}{2}G_{H_2(g)} = \bar{G}_{H(\alpha)} \tag{25}$$

and

$$\tfrac{1}{2}G_{H_2(g)} = \bar{G}_{H(\delta)} \tag{26}$$

where $G_{H_2(g)}$ refers to the free energy of hydrogen gas and $\bar{G}_{H(\alpha)}$ and $\bar{C}_{H(\delta)}$ refer to the partial molal free energy in the α- and δ-phases.

Since the gas phase is ideal,

$$\tfrac{1}{2}G_{H_2(g)} = \tfrac{1}{2}G^{\circ}_{H_2(g)} + \tfrac{1}{2}RT \ln P_{H_2} \tag{27}$$

where $G^{\circ}_{H_2(g)}$ refers to the molal free energy at unit pressure and P_{H_2} is the pressure of hydrogen.

Next we consider the effect of hydrogen concentration in the metal or hydride on the partial molal free energy. We set

$$\bar{G}_H = \bar{G}^{\circ}_H - T\bar{S}_p \tag{28}$$

where $\bar{S}_p$ is the partial molal entropy of number and position, $\bar{G}_H$ is the standard partial molal free energy when $\bar{S}_p = 0$. Here we assume $\bar{H}_H$ is invariant with composition and the change in $\bar{S}_p$ is solely due to the entropy of number and position.

$\bar{S}_p$ is derived from statistical considerations involving the number and location of hydrogen atom sites. For both α-Zr and the hydride phases the hydrogen atoms occupy tetrahedral interstices of which there are two for each Zr atom.

We now express the entropy of number and position of N_H hydrogen atoms arranged in N_s sites. For random distribution

$$S_p = R \ln \frac{N_s!}{N_H!(N_s - N_H)!} \tag{29}$$

The corresponding partial molal entropy term is

$$\bar{S}_p = \partial S_p / \partial N_H = -R \ln \left(\frac{N_H}{N_s - N_H} \right) \tag{30}$$

substituting in Eq. (28) gives the equation

$$\bar{G}_H = \bar{G}_H^\circ + RT \ln \left(\frac{N_H}{N_s - N_H} \right) \tag{31}$$

If we substitute $\bar{G}_H^\circ = \bar{H}_H^\circ - T\bar{S}_H^\circ$, we obtain

$$\bar{G}_H = \bar{H}_H^\circ - T\bar{S}_H^\circ + RT \ln \left(\frac{N_H}{N_s - N_H} \right) \tag{32}$$

Here $\bar{H}_H^\circ$ and $\bar{S}_H^\circ$ are the standard partial molal heat and entropy of formation. This equation corresponds to the more familiar free energy equation if the term $N_H/(N_s - N_H)$ were replaced by the mole fraction or composition. The standard reference state corresponds to a Zr/H ratio of unity.

B. Effect of Temperature and Pressure on Solubility of Hydrogen in α-Zr

Equations 25 (or 26), 27, and 32 are combined to give

$$\tfrac{1}{2}G_{H_2(g)}^\circ + \tfrac{1}{2}RT \ln P_{H_2} = \bar{H}_H^\circ - T\bar{S}_H^\circ + RT \ln \left(\frac{N_H}{N_s - N_H} \right) \tag{33}$$

Rearranging and applying to the α-phase

$$\frac{N_{H(\alpha)}}{N_s - N_{H(\alpha)}} = P_{H_2}^{\frac{1}{2}} \exp \left[\frac{\tfrac{1}{2}G_{H_2(g)}^\circ - (H_{H(\alpha)}^\circ - T\bar{S}_{H(\alpha)}^\circ)}{RT} \right] \tag{34}$$

since $\bar{G}_{H_2(g)}^\circ = \bar{H}_{H_2(g)}^\circ - T\bar{S}_{H_2(g)}^\circ$, then

$$\frac{N_{H(\alpha)}}{N_s - N_{H(\alpha)}} = P_{H_2}^{\frac{1}{2}} \exp - \left[\frac{(\bar{H}_{H(\alpha)-1/2}H_{H_2(g)}^\circ) - T(\bar{S}_{H(\alpha)-1/2}^\circ S_{H_2(g)}^\circ)}{RT} \right] \tag{35}$$

Equation (35) includes Sieverts' law which states that the solubility of hydrogen is proportional to $P^{1/2}$. Since entropy is lost on condensing the gas into the metal, the term $(\bar{S}_{H(\alpha)}^\circ - \tfrac{1}{2}S_{H_2(g)}^\circ)$ is negative and when multiplied by $-T$ gives a positive contribution in the exponential term of Eq. (35). For the solubility $N_H/(N_s - N_H)$ to decrease with increase in temperature requires that the term $(\bar{H}^{\circ}_{H(\alpha)} - \frac{1}{2}H^{\circ}_{H_2(g)})$ must be negative and larger than $T(\bar{S}^{\circ}_{H(\alpha)} - \frac{1}{2}S^{\circ}_{H_2(g)})$. If $(\bar{H}^{\circ}_{H(\alpha)} - \frac{1}{2}H^{\circ}_{H_2(g)})$ is positive, the solubility will increase with increase of temperature since the entropy term is positive.

C. Terminal Solubility of Hydrogen.

For equilibrium we have

$$\bar{G}_{H(\alpha)} = \bar{G}_{H(\delta)} \qquad (36)$$

and substituting Eq. (32) for each phase and rearranging we have

$$\frac{N_{H(\alpha)}}{N_s - N_{H(\alpha)}} \Big/ \frac{N_{H(\delta)}}{N_s - N_{H(\delta)}}$$

$$= \exp - \left[\frac{(\bar{H}^{\circ}_{H(\alpha)} - \bar{H}^{\circ}_{H(\delta)}) - T(\bar{S}^{\circ}_{H(\alpha)} - \bar{S}^{\circ}_{H(\delta)})}{RT} \right] \quad (37)$$

This equation can be used in two ways. First, if the solubilities of hydrogen in the two phases were known, the term

$$(\bar{H}^{\circ}_{H(\alpha)} - \bar{H}^{\circ}_{H(\delta)}) - T(\bar{S}^{\circ}_{H(\alpha)} - \bar{S}^{\circ}_{H(\delta)})$$

could be evaluated. Second, if this term were known the ratio of solubilities could be calculated.

Equation (37) could be used to predict the effect of temperature on the terminal solubility of $N_{H(\alpha)}$ if $N_{H(\delta)}$ is invariant with temperature. This is approximately true although recent work (18) would introduce a small correction for $N_{H(\delta)} = f$ (temperature). Equation (37) suggests that if $\bar{H}^{\circ}_{H(\delta)} > \bar{H}^{\circ}_{H(\alpha)}$ and negative then $N_{H(\alpha)}$ increases with temperature. If $H^{\circ}_{H(\alpha)} > H^{\circ}_{H(\delta)}$ and negative the $N_{H(\alpha)}$ decreases with temperature. These equations show that the terminal solubility $N_{H(\alpha)}$ can show an endothermic behavior while the over-all solubility is exothermic in nature.

D. Decomposition Pressures and Removal of Hydrogen from the Metal.

Equation (35) can be arranged to give

$$P_{H_2} = \left(\frac{N_{H(\alpha)}}{N_s - N_{H(\alpha)}} \right)^2$$

$$\times \exp \left[\frac{2(\bar{H}_{H(\alpha)-1/2}H^{\circ}_{H_2(g)}) - 2T(\bar{S}^{\circ}_{H(\alpha)-1/2}S^{\circ}_{H_2(g)})}{RT} \right] \quad (38)$$

We are also interested in the derivative of Eq. (38) with respect to $1/T$

$$\frac{1}{2}\frac{d \ln P_{H_2}}{d(1/T)} = \frac{\bar{H}^{\circ}_{H(\alpha)} - \frac{1}{2}H^{\circ}_{H_2(g)}}{R} \tag{39}$$

This equation gives an additional method of obtaining $(\bar{H}^{\circ}_{H(\alpha)} - \frac{1}{2}H^{\circ}_{H_2(g)})$ for the α-phase and a similar function for the δ-phase.

E. Method

Equations (32), (35), (37), (38), and (39) form the basis of our thermodynamic description of the zirconium-hydrogen system. Values of

$$(\bar{H}^{\circ}_{H(\alpha)} - \frac{1}{2}H^{\circ}_{H_2(g)}) \quad \text{and} \quad (\bar{H}^{\circ}_{H(\delta)} - \frac{1}{2}H^{\circ}_{H_2(g)})$$

can be determined experimentally from the slope of logarithmic plots of the decomposition pressures of hydrogen versus $1/T$. The values of $\bar{S}^{\circ}_{H(\alpha)}$ and $\bar{S}^{\circ}_{H(\delta)}$ can be determined from Eq. (35) and from the values of the solubility at a given temperature and the values of $\bar{H}^{\circ}_{H(\alpha)} - \frac{1}{2}H^{\circ}_{H_2(g)}$ and $\bar{H}^{\circ}_{H(\delta)} - \frac{1}{2}H^{\circ}_{H_2(g)}$. Thus, a series of measurements of the decomposition pressures as a function of temperatures give both the partial molal free energy and the partial molal heat of formation of the given hydrogen alloy from the gas and metal. Since these quantities differ for the several phases, a study over a broad concentration and temperature range enables all of the necessary thermodynamic quantities to describe the Zr–H alloy system to be determined.

A static method was chosen to measure the decomposition pressures. The temperature range was selected so that the pressures were in the range of 1×10^{-4} to 1×10^{-1} mm of Hg. For the volume of the system and the size of the specimens used, appreciable composition changes were observed only for pressures above 10^{-2} mm of Hg.

The hydrogen alloys were in the composition range of $ZrH_{0.015}$ to $ZrH_{0.079}$. They were prepared by direct reaction with hydrogen and the weight increase determined by a sensitive vacuum microbalance. Without removing the specimen from the apparatus, the equilibrium decomposition pressures were measured in the temperature range of $425°$ to $600°C$ using a calibrated McLeod gage.

The normal solubility in the α-zirconium phase was determined by direct measurement of the weight gain for a given temperature and pressure. The terminal solubilities of hydrogen in α-zirconium in equilibrium with the δ-hydride phase were evaluated in two ways, as shown in Fig. 7. Figure $7a$ shows the log P versus $1/T$ method. Figure $7a(1)$ shows a typical plot for a mixture of α- and δ-phases when both phases were present for all temperatures. Figure $7a(2)$ shows a typical plot when the two-phase region BC goes over into a single-phase region AB. The temperature at which the two phases were in equilibrium was that given by the point B. The slopes of the two parts of the plot gave the values of

$$(\bar{H}^{\circ}_{H(\alpha)} - \tfrac{1}{2}H^{\circ}_{H_2(g)}) \quad \text{and} \quad (\bar{H}^{\circ}_{H(\delta)} - \tfrac{1}{2}H^{\circ}_{H_2(g)})$$

The intersection of CB with BA gave the temperature at which the given hydrogen alloy composition represented the terminal solubility.

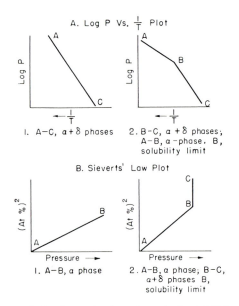

A. Log P Vs. $\frac{1}{T}$ Plot

1. A−C, $\alpha + \delta$ phases

2. B−C, $\alpha + \delta$ phases; A−B, α -phase. B, solubility limit

B. Sieverts' Law Plot

1. A−B, α phase

2. A−B, α phase; B−C, $\alpha + \delta$ phases B, solubility limit

Fig. 7. Methods for determination of terminal solubilities in α-Zr.

The second method shown in Fig. $7b$ was based on Sieverts' law. Here, the decomposition pressures at a given temperature were plotted as a function of the square of the concentration. A straight-line relationship was found which confirms Sieverts' law. Figure $7b(1)$ shows a typical plot for compositions within the α-zirconium solid solution phase. Figure $7b(2)$ shows a similar plot for the case where the solubility limit was reached at point B. The line BC indicated that the decomposition pressure was constant over the two-phase region. The intercept of AB and BC gave the terminal solubility.

Table III gives a summary of the thermodynamic functions obtained in an experimental study by Gulbransen and Andrew (28). From these quantities and Eqs. 32, 35, 37, 38, and 39 the solubility of hydrogen, terminal solubility, and equilibrium pressures can be evaluated for temperatures below 550°C and for the α- and δ-phases.

TABLE III

THERMODYNAMIC DESCRIPTION OF HYDROGEN IN ZIRCONIUM (28)

1. Standard partial molal heats of formation:

α-Phase $\bar{H}^{\circ}_{H(\alpha)} - \frac{1}{2}H^{\circ}_{H_2(g)} = -14{,}250$ cal/gm-atom of H

δ-Phase $\bar{H}^{\circ}_{H(\delta)} - \frac{1}{2}H^{\circ}_{H_2(g)} = -22{,}875$ cal/gm-atom of H

2. Standard partial molal entropies of formation:

α-Phase $\bar{S}^{\circ}_{H(\alpha)} - \frac{1}{2}\bar{S}^{\circ}_{H_2(g)} = -15$ cal/gm-atom of H (°C)

δ-Phase $\bar{S}^{\circ}_{H(\delta)} - \frac{1}{2}\bar{S}^{\circ}_{H_2(g)} = -17.05$ cal/gm-atom of H (°C)

α-Phase $\bar{S}^{\circ}_{H(\alpha)} = 3.9$ cal/gm-atom of H (°C)

δ-Phase $\bar{S}^{\circ}_{H(\delta)} = 1.83$ cal/gm-atom of H (°C)

3. Standard partial molal free energies of formation:

α-Phase $\bar{G}^{\circ}_{H(\alpha)} - \frac{1}{2}G^{\circ}_{H_2(g)} = -2605$ cal/gm-atom of H

δ-Phase $\bar{G}^{\circ}_{H(\delta)} - \frac{1}{2}G^{\circ}_{H_2(g)} = -9734$ cal/gm-atom of H

4. Partial molal free energies of solution (by two methods):

α-Phase equil with δ-phase at 500°C, $N_H = 0.0452$

$\bar{G}_{H(\alpha)} = \bar{G}_{H(\delta)} = -8390$ cal/gm-atom of H

δ-Phase at $N_{H(\delta)}$ of 1.4 and 500°C

$\bar{G}_{H(\delta)} = -8430$ cal/gm-atom of H

5. Difference in partial molal free energies at 500°C:

$\bar{G}^{\circ}_{H(\alpha)} - \bar{G}^{\circ}_{H(\delta)} = 7130$ cal/gm-atom of H

6. Solubility of hydrogen in α-phase at 500°C:

$N_{H(\alpha)} = 0.0452$ H/Zr

F. Characteristics of Occluded Hydrogen

1. Zr ALLOYS

A consideration of the reaction of ternary alloys with hydrogen led us to a study of the Zr–Hf–H system. Very few systematic studies of alloy-hydrogen systems have been conducted. Those studies of value for computing thermodynamic functions involved: Zr–Ti + H_2 *(69)*; U–Zr + H_2 *(57)*; U–Nb + H_2 *(52)*; Zr–Ni + H_2 *(60)*; Ti–O + H_2 *(40)*; and Zr–O + H_2 *(16)*. The characteristics of hydrogen in terminal solid solutions and in non-stoichiometric intermediate phases can be determined from the variation of thermodynamic functions with hydrogen content.

Utilizing an analysis similar to that of the previous section, relative partial molal free energies were computed and plotted in Fig. 8 for two solid solution Zr–Hf alloys, B–6 and B–8 *(49)*. Further computations produced Figs. 9 and 10 which show the more fundamental quantities of enthalpy and entropy. Solution of hydrogen in the α-phase is controlled by the binding energy of hydrogen in the lattice as exemplified by behavior of the $\Delta \bar{H}$ plot. At very low hydrogen contents the protons are retained very strongly; but as the hydrogen content increases, the heat of vaporization, which is $-\Delta \bar{H}$, $(\frac{1}{2} H_{H_2}^{\circ} - \bar{H}_{H_i})$, decreases markedly. H_i is hydrogen in solid solution i. In contrast with the Zr–H system it is no longer possible to consider $\Delta \bar{H}$ as invariant with composition in the α-phase. Henry's law does not apply to the entire α-region, but this should not be interpreted

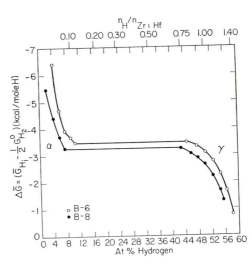

FIG. 8. Relative partial molal free energy of hydrogen versus percentage of hydrogen at 752°C in two Zr–Hf alloys.

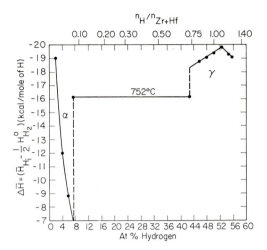

FIG. 9. Relative partial molal enthalpy versus percentage of hydrogen for B–8 alloy of Zr–Hf.

as failure of the hydrogen to dissolve as atoms. The true reason probably lies in the large deviations from noninteracting idealized solutions.

In the γ-phase, H is bound more tightly than it was in the phase from which it formed at the plateau pressure. This may be due to the somewhat

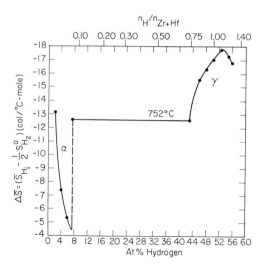

FIG. 10. Relative partial molal entropy versus percentage of hydrogen for B–8 alloy of Zr–Hf.

different binding in the hydride (23) as compared to the metal, even though the hydride probably still has metallic characteristics (6). Hydrogen solution in γ is entropy controlled, at least up to 52 atom % H. This implies that at high hydrogen contents the hydrogen atoms and their surrounding stress fields interact appreciably. Continued solution in the non-stoichiometric γ-region is then limited by the number of low energy lattice voids still available. The reversal in the thermodynamic functions above 52 atom% H could be attributed to a phase transformation, ordering, or a change in type of site occupied by the proton. Only the first seems applicable judging from recent work (80) which showed a random arrangement of protons in tetrahedral sites up to high hydrogen content in Group IV hydrides.

Our results on the Zr–Hf–H system indicated that the plateaus shown in Figs. 8, 9, and 10 corresponded to three phase regions as predicted by the Gibbs phase rule. This means that the areas immediately adjacent to the plateau should correspond to two phase regions. In the α-region, some indication was given in Henry's law plots for the presence of another phase boundary. In the γ-region, both the face-centered cubic and face-centered tetragonal phases were found at all temperatures.

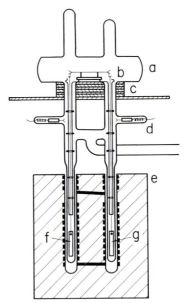

Fɪɢ. 11. Microbalance reaction chamber. a. rectangular balance tube, b. radiation shields, c. vibrationless support, d. grounding device, e. furnace, f. sample, g. non-reacting counterweight.

2. Group V Alloys

Using the same apparatus as for the Zr–Hf–H study, an investigation was conducted into the nature of the Nb + H_2 (50) and Nb–10 wt% U + H_2 (52) systems. Although employing a gravity type microbalance similar to that used previously (11, 26), the apparatus is worthy of mention since it is unique and particularly applicable to the study of hydrogen reaction (51). A schematic drawing is shown in Fig. 11. Spurious weight changes occur just from the changes in H_2 pressure. Therefore, it was necessary to build the reaction chamber as symmetrical as possible and to utilize a nonreacting counterweight (g) which experienced the same thermal gradients as the sample (f). Radiation shields (b) limited convection currents. Since this effect could not be eliminated completely, calibration curves shown in Fig. 12 were also used.

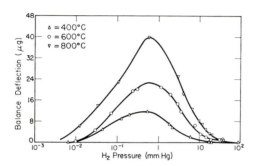

Fig. 12. Pressure correction.

The Group V metals are particularly interesting from the viewpoint of non-stoichiometric research since they form complete solid solutions with hydrogen above approximately 150°C with no evidence of a stoichiometric hydride. These transition metal-hydrogen systems are similar to the fairly well characterized Pd–H system (25, 58, 67). For the Pd–H system, shown in Fig. 13, if the temperature exceeds 295°C or the pressure exceeds 19.8 atm, only a single face-centered cubic solid solution is possible. The thermodynamic functions are known to vary continuously over the entire range of hydrogen composition at temperatures above the two-phase region.

Tables IV and V summarize the thermodynamic functions for the Nb–H system. Values were based on a mole of hydrogen (H) in solution, a mole of niobium in solution, and a mole of alloy formed, respectively. A mole of alloy corresponded to one gram formula weight of the given solution (i) under discussion. Three types of least squares error calculations were performed for comparison with the literature since the errors previously

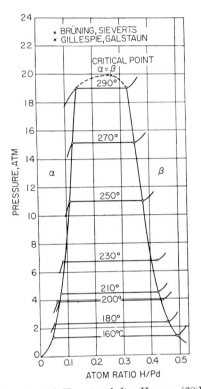

FIG. 13. Pd–H system [after Hansen (38)].

reported were not always adequately defined. It was felt that high percentage confidence limits, i.e., the standard deviation times a factor which depended on the sample size, were the appropriate type of errors to report with the thermodynamic data. The values given are the most probable ones, and with 90% confidence the intervals in the tables contain the absolute true values.

The values presented in Table V were obtained through the use of the Gibbs-Duhem equation, which, in terms of partial functions for the Nb–H system, becomes for the total free energy of formation for solution i:

$$\Delta G_{f_i} = N_{H_i}(\bar{G}_{H_i} - \tfrac{1}{2}G_{H_2}^\circ) + N_{Nb_i}(\bar{G}_{Nb_i} - G_{Nb}^\circ) \tag{40}$$

Since, as given previously, from Eqs. 25 and 27

$$\bar{G}_{H_i} - \tfrac{1}{2}G_{H_2}^\circ = RT \ln P_{H_2}^{\frac{1}{2}}$$

then

$$\bar{G}_{Nb_i} - G_{Nb}^\circ = -RT \int_{N_H=0}^{N_{H_i}} (N_{H_i}/N_{Nb_i}) \, d \ln P_{H_2}^{\frac{1}{2}} \tag{41}$$

TABLE IV

Relative Partial Molal Enthalpies[a] and Entropies[b] of H in Nb (50)

N_H, $\bar{H}_H - \frac{1}{2}H^\circ_{H_2}$	Standard deviation	90% confidence limits	50% confidence limits	$\bar{S}_H - \frac{1}{2}S^\circ_{H_2}$	Standard deviation	90% confidence limits	50% confidence limits
0.035– 7.59	0.35	±0.66	±0.25	− 5.54	0.48	±0.91	±0.35
0.050– 8.20	0.37	±0.71	±0.27	− 7.59	0.52	±0.98	±0.37
0.075– 9.14	0.33	±0.60	±0.23	− 9.46	0.50	±0.90	±0.35
0.100– 9.32	0.18	±0.32	±0.13	−10.17	0.28	±0.50	±0.19
0.125– 9.45	0.14	±0.24	±0.10	−10.66	0.22	±0.39	±0.15
0.150– 9.63	0.12	±0.21	±0.08	−11.17	0.18	±0.32	±0.12
0.175– 9.74	0.09	±0.16	±0.06	−11.53	0.14	±0.25	±0.10
0.200– 9.88	0.08	±0.14	±0.06	−11.93	0.12	±0.21	±0.08
0.225–10.05	0.11	±0.19	±0.08	−12.32	0.17	±0.30	±0.12
0.250–10.27	0.12	±0.22	±0.08	−12.81	0.19	±0.33	±0.13
0.275–10.49	0.19	±0.33	±0.13	−13.29	0.29	±0.52	±0.20
0.300–10.70	0.21	±0.36	±0.14	−13.81	0.32	±0.57	±0.22
0.325–10.88	0.29	±0.52	±0.20	−14.26	0.46	±0.82	±0.32
0.350–10.91	0.20	±0.37	±0.14	−14.67	0.32	±0.59	±0.22
0.375–10.90	0.18	±0.33	±0.13	−15.22	0.29	±0.55	±0.21
0.400–10.65	0.20	±0.60	±0.17	−15.63	0.32	±0.95	±0.26
0.405–10.40	1.06	—[c]	—[c]	−15.78	1.78	—[c]	—[c]

[a] In kcal/mole of H.
[b] In cal/°C-mole of H.
[c] The sample size was too small to allow a useful confidence statement.

TABLE V
Total Enthalpies[a] and Entropies[b] of Formation in Nb–H System (50)

N_{H_i}	ΔH_{f_i}	Standard deviation	90% confidence limits	50% confidence limits	ΔS_{f_i}	Standard deviation	90% confidence limits	50% confidence limits
0.035	−0.21	0.02	±0.03	±0.01	−0.08	0.02	±0.04	±0.02
0.050	−0.34	0.01	±0.02	±0.01	−0.19	0.02	±0.03	±0.01
0.075	−0.56	0.02	±0.03	±0.01	−0.41	0.02	±0.05	±0.02
0.100	−0.78	0.03	±0.05	±0.02	−0.65	0.04	±0.07	±0.03
0.125	−1.02	0.03	±0.05	±0.02	−0.93	0.04	±0.07	±0.03
0.150	−1.26	0.03	±0.05	±0.02	−1.20	0.04	±0.08	±0.03
0.175	−1.51	0.03	±0.06	±0.02	−1.50	0.05	±0.08	±0.03
0.200	−1.76	0.02	±0.04	±0.02	−1.81	0.03	±0.06	±0.02
0.225	−2.01	0.02	±0.04	±0.02	−2.13	0.03	±0.06	±0.02
0.250	−2.29	0.04	±0.07	±0.03	−2.49	0.05	±0.10	±0.04
0.275	−2.56	0.04	±0.08	±0.03	−2.84	0.06	±0.12	±0.04
0.300	−2.84	0.04	±0.08	±0.03	−3.22	0.07	±0.12	±0.05
0.325	−3.09	0.04	±0.07	±0.03	−3.55	0.06	±0.11	±0.04
0.350	−3.41	0.06	±0.10	±0.04	−4.01	0.09	±0.16	±0.06
0.375	−3.71	0.06	±0.11	±0.04	−4.44	0.11	±0.22	±0.08
0.400	−4.03	0.03	±0.07	±0.02	−4.94	0.04	±0.12	±0.03
0.405	−4.09	—	—c	—c	−5.04	—	—c	—c

[a] In kcal/mole of alloy.
[b] In cal/°C-mole of alloy.
c The sample size was too small to allow a useful confidence statement.

Noting that $\ln P_{H_2}^{\frac{1}{2}}$ approaches $-\infty$ as N_H approaches 0, it is convenient in a binary system to incorporate $N_H + N_{Nb} = 1$. This makes the final usable form of

$$\bar{G}_{Nb_i} - G_{Nb}^\circ = RT\left[\ln N_{Nb_i} - \int_{N_H=0}^{N_{H_i}} (N_{H_i}/N_{Nb_i})\, d\ln(P_{H_2}^{\frac{1}{2}}/N_H)\right] \quad (42)$$

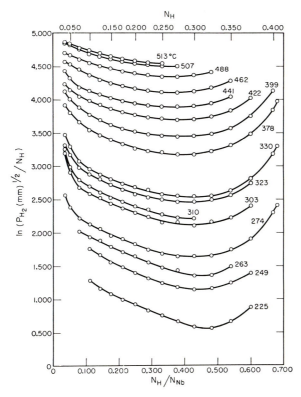

FIG. 14. Equilibrium isotherms for the Nb–H system.

Figure 14 is a plot of the data. All curves were extrapolated to $N_H = 0$, utilizing the slope at the last experimental point, in order to evaluate the integral in the preceding equation. At no place did the curves become horizontal, as they must if Henry's law was obeyed. However, as the temperature rose, the leveling of the curves indicated that a more ideal type of solution was occurring. At higher temperatures the ability of the lattice to relax should help to compensate for the stresses set up on expansive entry of hydrogen. This is not inconsistent with the general attainment of a looser or freer molecular configuration due to chemical reaction at elevated temperatures. It must also be noted in Fig. 14 that the dilute portions of the isotherms slope less steeply as the temperature rises. Possibly this is due to the decreasing importance of any low energy atypical sites above approximately 450°C.

Table VI is a listing of literature values for the Nb–H (*1*), Ta–H (*54*), and V–H (*53*) systems. These values compare closely with those given in our Tables IV and V. The trends are the same in all three systems. More recent confirming studies (*55*, *63*) have also been made.

The interpretation of hydrogen behavior in the Group V transition metals

TABLE VI

LITERATURE VALUES FOR THE Nb–H, Ta–H, AND V–H SYSTEMS[a]

N_H	0.05	0.10	0.20	0.30	0.333
Nb–H					
$\bar{H}_{H_i} - \frac{1}{2}H_{H_2}^\circ$	−8.21	−8.51	−9.28	−9.92	−10.10
$\bar{S}_{H_i} - \frac{1}{2}S_{H_2}^\circ$	−7.63	−9.20	−11.28	−12.87	−13.47
Ta–H					
$\bar{H}_{H_i} - \frac{1}{2}H_{H_2}^\circ$	−9.50	−9.40	−9.50	−9.70	−9.30
$\bar{S}_{H_i} - \frac{1}{2}S_{H_2}^\circ$	−9.9	−11.1	−12.7	−14.8	−14.9
ΔH_{f_i}	−0.48	−0.94	−1.86	−2.86	−3.18
ΔS_{f_i}	−0.40	−0.92	−2.1	−3.6	−4.08
V–H					
$\bar{H}_{H_i} - \frac{1}{2}H_{H_2}^\circ$	−7.79	−7.89	−8.28	−8.68	−8.69
$\bar{S}_{H_i} - \frac{1}{2}S_{H_2}^\circ$	−8.75	−10.12	−11.85	−13.74	−14.59
$\bar{H}_V - H_V^\circ$	+0.002	+0.019	+0.088	+0.196	+0.202
$\bar{S}_V - S_V^\circ$	+0.11	+0.22	+0.53	+1.11	+1.51
ΔH_{f_i}	−0.387	−0.772	−1.585	−2.470	−2.760
ΔS_{f_i}	−0.34	−0.81	−1.95	−3.34	3.85

[a] Enthalpies in kcal/mole of H, metal, or alloy; entropies in cal/°C-mole of H, metal, or alloy.

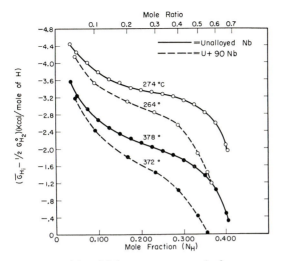

FIG. 15. Relative partial molal free energy versus hydrogen composition.

follows the same outline as in the Zr–Hf system except that here there are no discontinuities at plateaus. Hence, all data apply to a continuous body-centered cubic phase region. Figures 15 and 16 show the variation of partial molal functions with hydrogen content for the Nb and Nb + 10 wt% U

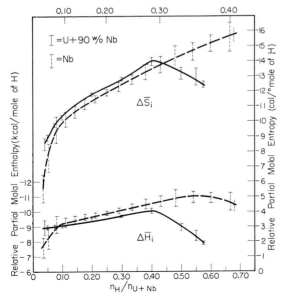

FIG. 16. Enthalpy and entropy functions for the U + 90 wt% Nb–H and Nb–H systems.

alloys. The trend is similar to that observed in the γ-phase of the Zr–Hf–H alloys. In essence, the entropy factor is controlling at all hydrogen contents up to the inversion point in the curves. Even though hydrogen binding became stronger as gas was added up to the inversion point of the $\Delta \bar{H}_i$ curve, the interaction of protons in interstitial voids caused the $\Delta \bar{S}_i$ values to rise sharply. Inversion in the Nb + 10 wt% U alloy, at least, may be due to formation of a new hydride phase which could be the well-characterized UH_3. In all of our studies of Group IV and V elements and alloys, the enthalpy and entropy functions are invariant with temperature.

VIII. CRYSTAL STRUCTURE AND PHASE DIAGRAM STUDIES OF Zr–H

One of the difficult problems in the study of occlusion of gases by the transition metals is the construction of a phase diagram. The construction of a phase diagram requires a great deal of information about the system. First, the several phases must be identified, their crystal structures determined, and their range of homogeneity evaluated. Second, the effect of temperature and pressure on the existence of the several phases must be determined. Third, a temperature-composition phase diagram must be built up.

Various experimental methods are used to construct a phase diagram. X-ray diffraction analyses, micrographic analyses, and chemical analyses can be used to study all of the systems. In addition, electrical resistivity and microhardness changes can be used to pinpoint phase boundaries. But

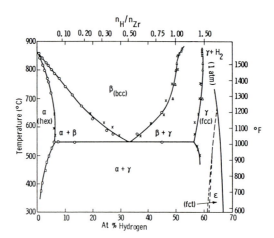

Fig. 17. Zr–H system representation.

perhaps the most common is the thermochemical method. A complete
Zr–H diagram (57, 59), as determined by this latter method, is given in
Fig. 17. The points represented by the squares have been obtained by us
by the methods discussed above. It is always worthy of mentioning that

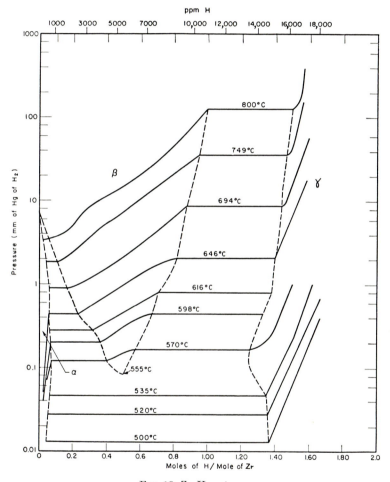

FIG. 18. Zr–H system.

Fig. 17 is not an isobaric section but is obtained from isotherms as shown
in Fig. 18. Where appropriate, small plateaus would also appear in the
isotherms in the γ-region corresponding to the γ + ε two-phase region.

This section will present an analysis of the data we contributed to Fig.
17. Equilibrium decomposition pressure versus $1/T$ curves and x-ray
diffraction analyses will be discussed. Before presenting our own studies

it is essential to look into the early absorption and x-ray diffraction studies on this system.

A. Early Absorption Studies

It has been known for a long time that zirconium can absorb considerable quantities of hydrogen and still show a metallic appearance. Winkler (*92*, *93*) first observed the large capacity of zirconium for absorption of hydrogen and proposed that definite gaseous and solid hydrides were formed. Gaseous hydrides were not confirmed by Wedekind (*89*), nor by Schwarz and Konrad (*74*). The formation of the hydride ZrH_2 was suggested by Weiss and Neumann (*91*) and Wedekind (*88*) from studies of the absorption of hydrogen by zirconium.

Smith (*78*) has designated zirconium as belonging to the class of exothermic occluders. These metals absorb hydrogen in large quantities, form alloys of greater complexity, exhibit solid solution phenomena, and form one or more secondary phases.

1. ABSORPTION ISOTHERMS

Sieverts and Roell (*76*) first studied absorption isotherms on samples of metal powders containing 91% zirconium at 800° and 1100°C and an absorption isobar at 760 mm of Hg hydrogen pressure. Consistent results were difficult to attain by their methods.

Hall *et al.* (*37*) recognized the role of surface contamination and eliminated surface oxide by heating to high temperature in vacuo before studying the absorption of hydrogen. Absorption isotherms show strong "kinks" for compositions between $ZrH_{1.0}$ and $ZrH_{1.4}$ and the shapes of the curves show a resemblance to those found for the palladium-hydrogen system where a two-phase region has been noted. Hall *et al.* interpreted the shape of the curves in terms of two solution processes occurring together, only one of which is rate-determining.

B. Early Crystal Structure Studies

Hägg (*36*) studied the zirconium-hydrogen phases on specimens prepared at high temperature and cooled to room temperature. Five phases were noted by Hägg: (i) α-Zr + solid solution of hydrogen, having the hexagonal close-packed structure; (ii) β-Zr$_4$H, stable only at high temperatures, having a face-centered cubic structure; (iii) γ-Zr$_2$H having the hexagonal close-packed structure; (iv) δ-ZrH phase having the face-centered cubic structure; and (v) ϵ-ZrH$_2$ having the face-centered tetragonal phase.

Although no details of Hägg's preparation procedures are given, many of the samples were prepared above the α–β transformation temperature for zirconium, the existence of which Hägg was probably unaware. Recent work which will be presented here has not confirmed the existence of β-Zr$_4$H and γ-Zr$_2$H. Also, the δ-phase has been found to have the composition ZrH$_{1.4-1.6}$. Considering the low purity of the zirconium available and the lack of information on the α–β transformation of zirconium, Hägg's work is highly enlightening.

C. Experimental Studies

1. DECOMPOSITION PRESSURE STUDIES

Part of the phase diagram Zr–H was determined by combining results of decomposition pressure studies and x-ray crystal structure analyses. Of particular interest to us was that portion of the diagram below 550°C. Twenty-one compositions were prepared in the vacuum microbalance in the composition range of ZrH$_{0.025}$ to ZrH$_{1.74}$. The number after hydrogen

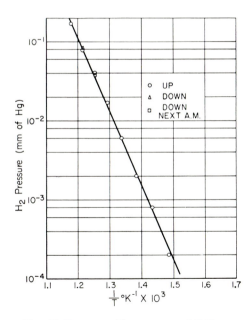

FIG. 19. Decomposition pressure of ZrH$_{1.36}$.

TABLE VII

SUMMARY OF X-RAY DATA (25°C) (27)

Temperature (°C)	Preparation time (minutes)	Composition	Treatment	Results[b]
100	10	$ZrH_{0.10}$	Hom.[a] 100°C, 21 hours	$\alpha + \delta + tr\ \gamma'$
125	10	$ZrH_{0.15}$	Hom. 125°C, 20.5 hours	$\alpha + \delta + tr\ \gamma'$
150	12	$ZrH_{0.246}$	Hom. 150°C, 20 hours	$\alpha + \delta + tr\ \gamma'$
150	45	$ZrH_{0.48}$	Hom. 150°C, 20 hours	$\alpha + \delta + s.a.\ \gamma'$
150	81	$ZrH_{0.52}$	Hom. 250°C, 19 hours	$\alpha + \delta + tr\ \gamma'$
250	—	$ZrH_{0.52}$	Prepared from ϵ-phase	$\alpha + \delta + s.a.\ \gamma'$
150	48	$ZrH_{0.53}$	Direct, not hom.	$\alpha + \delta + s.a.\ \gamma'$
200	13	$ZrH_{0.55}$	Hom. 200°C, 20 hours	$\alpha + \delta + tr\ \gamma'$
225	8	$ZrH_{0.755}$	Hom. 225°C, 20 hours	$\alpha + \delta + tr\ \gamma'$
225	15	$ZrH_{0.84}$	Hom. 225°C, 20.3 hours	$\alpha + \delta + tr\ \gamma'$
175	165	$ZrH_{1.105}$	Hom. 175°C, 15.5 hours	$\alpha + \delta + s.a.\ \gamma'$
225	38	$ZrH_{1.33}$	Hom. 225°C, 20.5 hours	$\alpha + \delta + tr\ \gamma'$
225	51	$ZrH_{1.44}$	Hom. 325°C, 18 hours	$\delta + tr\ \gamma'$
225	65	$ZrH_{1.44}$	Hom. 225°C, 19 hours	$\delta + tr\ \gamma'$
230	1	$ZrH_{1.51}$	Heated to 500°C, hom. 200°C, 63 hours	δ
250	27	$ZrH_{1.54}$	Heated to 375°C, hom. 325°C, 19 hours	δ

250	29	$ZrH_{1.56}$	Prepared from ε-phase (fast)	δ + tr ε
250	48	$ZrH_{1.60}$	Prepared from ε-phase (fast)	δ + ε
270	51	$ZrH_{1.64}$	Hom. 250°C, 18 hours	ε
275	23	$ZrH_{1.64}$	H₂ quenched	ε + tr δ
225	57	$ZrH_{1.647}$	Hom. 225°C, 19.5 hours	δᶜ
225	82	$ZrH_{1.77}$	Hom. 225°C, 19 hours	ε
150	5580	$ZrH_{1.84}$	H₂ cooled	ε
200	300	$ZrH_{1.87}$	Hom. 175°C, 15 hours	ε
225	180	$ZrH_{1.965}$	Hom. 200°C, 19 hours	ε

ᵃHomogenized.
ᵇtr—trace; s.a.—small amount.
ᶜNot in agreement with other observations of this study.

refers to the number of atoms of hydrogen for each atom of zirconium. Decomposition pressures are measured in the temperature range of 325° to 550°C directly after preparation to avoid contamination. Pressure measurements were made on both heating and cooling the sample to assure equilibrium values.

Logarithm pressure versus $1/T$ plots were made of the data. Figure 19 shows a typical plot for the composition $ZrH_{1.36}$. Straight lines of the same slope and absolute values were obtained for all compositions from $ZrH_{0.05}$

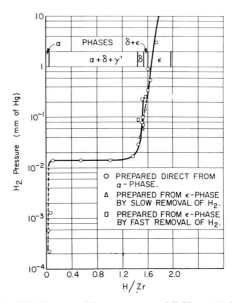

FIG. 20. Decomposition pressures of ZrH_x at 500°C.

to $ZrH_{1.36}$. Compositions above $ZrH_{1.36}$ no longer fit this family of curves. This suggests a change in the phases present in the samples.

Figure 20 shows a log pressure versus composition H/Zr plot for 500°C together with room temperature crystal structure studies of the phases. These will be discussed later. Figure 20 can be interpreted as follows. (i) Below a composition $ZrH_{0.045}$, a single phase region of α-Zr with hydrogen in solid solution exists. (ii) A two-phase region of α- and δ-phases was found between $ZrH_{0.04}$ to $ZrH_{1.40}$. (iii) A two-phase region of ϵ- and δ-phases probably exists between $ZrH_{1.56}$ and $ZrH_{1.64}$. (iv) The δ-phase has a range of homogeneity from about $ZrH_{1.4}$ to $ZrH_{1.56}$. (v) The ϵ-phase has a range of homogeneity of $ZrH_{1.64}$ to $ZrH_{1.965}$.

Figure 20 also shows that a γ'-phase is formed in the composition range of $ZrH_{0.05}$ to $ZrH_{1.36}$. This phase was always found in trace amounts. It is

TABLE VIII

COMPARISON LATTICE PARAMETERS ZIRCONIUM HYDRIDE PHASES

Phase	Composition (at 500°C)	Structure	Lattice parameters (Å)	
			Gulbransen and Andrew (27)	Hägg (36)
ϵ	$ZrH_{1.965}-ZrH_{1.64}$	Face-centered tetragonal	$a = 4.97 \pm 0.09$ $c = 4.48 \pm 0.01$ $a/c = 1.11 \pm 0.01$	$a = 4.974$ $c = 4.440$ $a/c = 1.118$
δ	$ZrH_{1.44}-ZrH_{1.56}$	Face-centered cubic	$a = 4.78 \pm 0.01$	$a = 4.778$
γ'	ZrH_x	Face-centered tetragonal	$a = 4.61 \pm 0.01$ $c = 4.975 \pm 0.01$ $a/c = 0.926 \pm 0.003$	

probably a transitional phase between the α-Zr structure and the δ-hydride structure.

2. Crystal Structure Studies

Twenty-five compositions were prepared in the vacuum microbalance. Table VII shows a summary of the x-ray diffraction data including the homogenization treatments. Four structures were found: α-Zr, δ- and ϵ-hydride phases and an intermediate γ'-phase. Figure 20 shows also the correlation of the x-ray crystal structure data with the equilibrium decomposition pressure data at 500°C, as noted above.

Thermodynamic studies at 500°C are in essential agreement with crystal structure studies made on specimens prepared at temperatures of 300°C and lower. One exception is to be noted. This is the presence in the crystal structure studies of a minor transitional phase. The existence of this phase now designated as the γ'-phase in the zirconium-hydrogen system was first recognized by Jack (44) in a preliminary x-ray study of our specimens. It was also suggested by Jack that this phase is a transition phase between the hexagonal α-Zr phase and Hägg's face-centered cubic δ-phase. It is present only in small or trace amounts together with the α- and δ-phases.

Thermal properties of this new phase have not been investigated. It appears to form by direct preparation in the $\alpha + \delta$ region of composition or by removal of hydrogen from the ϵ-phase. The composition of this phase has not been determined. However, a plot of the volume of the several hydride phases suggests a composition near $ZrH_{0.5}$ or the same composition as Hägg's hexagonal γ-phase which we have not observed in this study.

Table VIII shows a summary of crystal structure data on the several phases formed in the zirconium-hydrogen system with the alloys being formed at low temperatures. Averaged lattice parameters are also given. The δ-phase was studied by direct hydriding to the given composition and also by removal of hydrogen from ϵ-phase preparations until the proper composition was achieved. Results are internally consistent with one possible exception noted in Table VII.

Text References

1. Albrecht, W. M., Mallett, M. W., and Goode, W. D., *J. Electrochem. Soc.*, **106**, 981 (1959).
2. Barrer, R. M., "Diffusion in and through Solids," p. 221. Cambridge Univ. Press, London and New York, 1941.
3. Bastien, P., *Arch, Hutnictwa*, **4**, 93 (1959). *Material-pruefung* **1**, 3 (1959).
4. Benard, J., "Oxidation of Metals," Gauthier-Villars, Paris, 1962.
5. Berg, T. G. O., *Bull. Am. Ceramic Soc.* **40**, 78 (1961).
6. Bickel, R. W., USAEC Report NAA-SR-4173 (January 15, 1960).

7. de Boer, J. H., "The Dynamical Character of Adsorption," Oxford Univ. Press, London and New York, 1953.
8. Brauer, G., and Muller, H., *Angew. Chem.* **70**, 53 (1958). *J. Inorg. & Nuclear Chem.* **17**, 102 (1961).
9. Carslaw, H. S., and Jaeger, J. C., "Conduction of Heat in Solids," Oxford Univ. Press (Clarendon, London and New York, 1959.
10. Codd, I., and Petch, N. J., *Phil. Mag.* **5**, 30 (1960).
11. Cotterill, P., *Prog. in Mater. Sci.* **9**, 205 (1961).
12. Cupp, C. R., *Progr. in Metal Phys.* **4**, 105 (1952).
13. Dioler, K., and Rothe, W., *Z. Elektrochem.* **59**, 970 (1955).
14. Dushman, S., and Lafferty, J. M., "Scientific Foundations of Vacuum Technique," 2nd ed., Chapter 8. Wiley, New York, 1962.
15. Eborall, R., "Determination of Gases in Metals," p. 192. Iron and Steel Inst. London, 1960.
16. Edwards, R. K., and Levesque, P., *J. Am. Chem. Soc.* **77**, 1312 (1955).
17. Ells, C. E., and McQuillan, A. D., *J. Inst. Metals* **85**, 89 (1956).
18. Espogna, L., Azou, P., and Bastien, P., *Compt. rend. acad. sci.* **247**, 1199 (1958); **249**, 1105 (1959).
19. Evans, C. T., Jr., *Am. Inst. Mining Met. Engrs. Electric Furnace Conf., Pittsburgh, December, 1957.*
20. Evans, R. C., "An Introduction to Crystal Chemistry," 145. Cambridge Univ. Press, London and New York, 1952.
21. Fassel, V. A., Gordon, W. A., and Jasinski, R. J., *Proc. 2nd Intern. Conf. on Peaceful Uses of Atomic Energy, Geneva* Vol. 28, Paper 917, p. 583 (1958).
22. Gerasimova, N. G., Ivanova, T. F., Sventitskii, N. S., Startsev, G. P., Taganov, K. I., and Trantovius, M. E., *Bull. Acad. Sci. USSR, Phys. Ser. (Engl. Transl.)* **19**, No. 2, 136 (1955).
23. Gibb, T. R. P., Jr., and Schumaker, D. P., *J. Phys. Chem.* **64**, 1407 (1960).
24. Gibb, T. R. P., Jr., McSharrey, J. J., and Krushwitz, H. K., *J. Am. Chem. Soc.* **74**, 6203 (1952).
25. Gillespie, L. J., and Galstaun, L. S., *J. Am. Chem. Soc.* **58**, 2565 (1936).
26. Gulbransen, E. A., *Advances in Catalysis* **5**, 119 (1953).
27. Gulbransen, E. A., and Andrew, K. F., *J. Electrochem. Soc.* **101**, 474 (1954).
28. Gulbransen, E. A., and Andrew, K. F., *J. Metals* **7**, 136 (1955).
29. Gulbransen, E. A., and Andrew, K. F., *J. Electrochem. Soc.* **101**, 560 (1954).
30. Gulbransen, E. A., and Andrew, K. F., *J. Electrochem. Soc.* **101**, 348 (1954).
31. Gulbransen, E. A., and Andrew, K. F., *J. Electrochem. Soc.* **104**, 709 (1957).
32. Hägg, G., *Z. physik. Chem. (Leipzig)* **B6**, 221 (1929).
33. Hägg, G., *Z. physik. Chem. (Leipzig)* **7**, 339 (1930).
34. Hägg, G., *Z. physik Chem. (Leipzig)* **8**, 445 (1930).
35. Hägg, G., *Z. physik Chem. (Leipzig)* **12**, 33 (1931).
36. Hägg, G., *Z. physik Chem. (Leipzig)* **11**, 439 (1930).
37. Hall, M. N. A., Martin, S. L. H., and Rees, A. L. G., *Trans. Faraday Soc.* **41**, 306 (1945).
38. Hansen, M., "Constitution of Binary Alloys," p. 353. McGraw-Hill, New York, 1958.
39. Harris, W. F., "Technology of Columbium," p. 57. Electrochem. Soc., New York, 1958.
40. Hepworth, M. T., and Schuhmann, R., Jr., *Trans. Am. Inst. Mining Met. Engrs.* **224**, 875 (1962).

260   O. M. KATZ AND E. A. GULBRANSEN

41. Hickam, W. M., and Sweeney, G. G., Westinghouse Central Laboratory, private communication (May, 1962).
42. Holey, C. E., Jr., Mulford, R. N. R., and Ellinger, F. H., *J. Phys. Chem.* **59**, 1226 (1955).
43. Hume-Rothery, W., and Raynor, G. V., "The Structure of Metals and Alloys," p. 240. Inst. of Metals, London, 1956.
44. Jack, K., Westinghouse Central Laboratory, private communication (1962).
45. Johnson, E. W., and Hill, M. L., *Trans. Am. Inst. Mining Met. Engrs.* **128**, 1101 (1960).
46. Johnson, H. H., Schneider, E. J., and Troiano, A. R., *Iron Age* **182**, 47 (1958).
47. Jost, W., and Widman, A., *Z. physik. Chem. (Leipzig)* **B29**, 247 (1935).
48. Jost, W., and Widman, A., *Z. physik. Chem. (Leipzig)* **45**, 285 (1940).
49. Katz, O. M., Westinghouse Central Laboratory (December, 1962). To be published.
50. Katz, O. M., and Gulbransen, E. A., "Metallurgy of Columbium," p. 523. Publ. by Am. Inst. Mining Met. Engrs. and Wiley (Interscience), New York, 1961.
51. Katz, O. M., and Gulbransen, E. A., "Vacuum Microbalance Techniques," Vol. 1. Plenum Press, New York, 1961.
52. Katz, O. M., and Gulbransen, E. A., *J. Nuclear Mater.* **5**, 269 (1962).
53. Kofstad, P., and Wallace, W. E., *J. Am. Chem. Soc.* **81**, 5019 (1959).
54. Kofstad, P., Wallace, W. E., and Hyvonen, L. J., *J. Am. Chem. Soc.* **81**, 5015 (1959).
55. Komjathy, S., *J. Less-Common Metals* **2**, 466 (1960).
56. Kotyk, M., and Davis, H. M., *Trans. Am. Soc. Metals* **53**, 653 (1961).
57. LaGrange, L. D., Dykstra, L. J., Dixon, J. M., and Merten, V., *J. Phys. Chem.* **63**, 2035 (1959).
58. Lewis, F. A., *Platinum Metals Rev.* October, 1960, p. 132; January, 1961, p. 21.
59. Libowitz, G. G., *J. Nuclear Mater.* **2**, 1 (1960); **5**, 228 (1962).
60. Libowitz, G. G., Hayes, H. F., and Gibb, T. R. P., Jr., *J. Phys. Chem.* **62**, 76 (1958).
61. Lustman, B., and Kerze, F., Jr., "The Metallurgy of Zirconium," p. 135. McGraw-Hill, New York, 1955.
62. Mallett, M. W., and Albrecht, W. M., *J. Electrochem. Soc.* **104**, 142 (1957).
63. Mallett, M. W., and Koehl, B. G., *J. Electrochem. Soc.* **109**, 611 (1962).
64. Miller, G. L., "Zirconium" (Metallurgy of the Rarer Metals Series), p. 348, Academic Press, New York, 1958.
65. Miller, G. L., "Tantalum and Niobium" (Metallurgy of the Rarer Metals Series), p. 188. Academic Press, New York, 1959.
66. Maeland, A. J., Gibb, T. R. P., Jr., and Schumacher, D. P., *J. Am. Chem. Soc.* **83**, 3729 (1961).
67. Moon, K. A., *J. Phys. Chem.* **60**, 502 (1956).
68. Nisbett, J. D., "Vacuum Metallurgy Symposium," p. 1. Electrochem. Soc., New York, 1954.
69. Pessall, N., and McQuillan, A. D., *Trans. Am. Inst. Mining Met. Engrs.* **224**, 536 (1962).
70. Pearson, W. B., "Lattice Spacings and Structures of Metals and Alloys," p. 919. Pergamon Press, New York, 1958.
71. Pfann, W. G., "Zone Melting," Wiley, New York, 1958.
72. Podgurski, H. H., *Trans. Am. Inst. Mining Met. Engrs.* **221**, 389 (1961).
73. Rhodin, T. N., Jr., *Advances in Catalysis* **5**, 39 (1953).
74. Schwarz, R., and Konrad, E., *Ber. deut. chem. Ges.* **54**, 2122 (1921).
75. Scott, T. E., and Troiano, A. R., *J. Metals* **11**, 619 (1959).
76. Sieverts, A., and Roell, E., *Z. anorg. u. allgem. Chem.* **159**, 289 (1926).

77. Sloman, H. A., Harvey, C. A., and Kubaschewski, O., *J. Inst. Metals* **80**, 391 (1952).
78. Smith, D. P., *"Hydrogen in Metals,"* Univ. of Chicago Press, Chicago, Illinois, 1948.
79. Stalinski, B., *Bull. Acad. Sci. Poland* **3**, 613 (1955).
80. Stalinski, B., Coogan, C. E., and Gutowsky, H. S., *J. Chem. Phys.* **34**, 1191 (1961).
81. Steiner, J. E., *Metal Progr.* **76**, 72 (1959).
82. Swets, D. E., Frank, R. C., and Fry, D. L., *Trans. Am. Inst. Mining Met. Engrs.* **212**, 219 (1958).
83. Thomas, D. E., and Hayes, E. T., "The Metallurgy of Hafnium," p. 125. U. S. Atomic Energy Commission, Washington, 1961.
84. Thomas, D. E., Fillnow, R. H., Goldman, K. M., Hino, J., van Thyne, R. J., Holtz, F. C., and McPherson, D. J., *Intern. Conf. on Peaceful Uses of Atomic Energy* **5**, 610 (1958). Paper 1924-USA.
85. Turovtseva, Z. M., and Kunin, L. L., "Analysis of Gases in Metals," Chapter 1. Transl. and publ. by Consultants Bureau, New York, 1961.
86. Vaughan, D. A., and Bridge, J. R., *Trans. Am. Inst. Mining Met. Engrs.* **206**, 528 (1956).
87. Wagner, C., quoted by Jost, W., *in* "Diffusion in Solids, Liquids, and Gases," p. 68. Academic Press, New York, 1960.
88. Wedekind, E., *Ann. Chem. Liebigs*, **371**, 378 (1910).
89. Wedekind, E., *Ann. Chem. Liebigs* **395**, 149 (1913).
90. Weiner, J. E., and Davis, H. M., *Trans. Am. Soc. Metals* **53**, 853 (1961).
91. Weiss, L., and Neumann, E., *Z. anorg. u. allgem. Chem.* **65**, 248 (1910).
92. Winkler, A., *Ber. deut. chem. Ges.* **23**, 2642 (1890).
93. Winkler, A., *Ber. deut. chem. Ges.* **24**, 873 (1891).
94. Worsham, J. E., Wilkinson, M. K., and Shull, C. G., *J. Phys. Chem. Solids* **3**, 303 (1957).

ADDITIONAL BIBLIOGRAPHY ON HYDROGEN IN METALS

1. *Aluminum*
    a. Bergsma, J., and Goldkoop, J. A., *Acta Cryst.* **14**, 223 (1961).
    b. Cochran, C. N., *J. Electrochem. Soc.* **108**, 317 (1961).
    c. Draley, J. E., and Ruther, W. E., *J. Electrochem. Soc.* **104**, 329 (1957).
    d. Tragert, W. E., *J. Electrochem. Soc.* **106**, 903 (1959).
    e. van Vucht, J. H. N., *Philips Research Repts.* **16**, 245 (1961).

2. *Chromium*
    a. Espagno, L., Azou, P., and Bastien, P., *Compt. rend. acad. sci.* **248**, 2003 (1959).

3. *Cobalt*
    a. Korst, W. L., *J. Phys. Chem.* **66**, 370 (1962).

4. *Copper*
    a. de Jager, W. G. R., *Metalen* **14**, 34 (1959).
    b. Rudd, D. W., Yose, D. W., and Johnson, S., *J. Phys. Chem.* **65**, 1018 (1961).

5. *Hafnium*
    a. Goon, E. J., and Malgiolia, J., USAEC Rept. NYO-7547 (1958).
    b. Sherwood, E. M., *Ind. Eng. Chem.* **47**, 2044 (1955).
    c. Sidhu, S. S., Campos, F. P., and Zauberis, D. D., *Nuclear Sci. Eng.* **3**, 778 (1958).
    d. Sidhu, S. S., and McGuire, J. C., *J. Appl. Phys.* **23**, 1257 (1952).
    e. Veleckis, E., and Edwards, R. K., "Metallurgy of Hafnium," p. 194. Publ. by USAEC, 1961.

6. *Iron and Steel*
  a. Acosta, R. S., *Inst. hierro y acero* **13**, 778 (1960).
  b. Arkharov, V. I., and Kragina, A. A., *Phys. Metals Metallog.* **8**, 37 (1959).
  c. Bogotskaia, I. A., and Kovha, L. D., *Doklady Acad. Nauk USSR.* **133**, 862 (1960).
  d. Banege-Nia, A., *Compt. rend. acad. sci.* **250**, 524 (1960).
  e. Bastien, P., and Amiot, P., *Rev. mét.* **55**, 24 (1958).
  f. Blanchard, R., *Compt. rend. acad. sci.* **248**, 966 (1959).
  g. Blanchard, P. A., Quigg, R. J., Schaller, F. W., Steigerwald, E. A., and Troiano, A. R., USAEC Rept. WADC T. R. 59-172 (April, 1959).
  h. Carmichael, D. C., Hornaday, J. R., Morris, A. E., and Parlee, N. A., *Trans. Am. Inst. Mining Met. Engrs.* **218**, 826 (1960).
  i. Darken, L. S., *Phys. Chem. Metallic Sol. Intermetallic Comp* **2**, 88 (1959).
  j. Evans, U. R., "Corrosion and Oxidation of Metals," p. 393. St. Martins Press, New York, 1960.
  k. von der Forst, P., *Giesserei* **46**, 931 (1959).
  l. Foster, P. K., *Nature* **188**, 399, 1960.
  m. Frank, R. C., Swets, D. E., and Fry, D. L., *J. Appl. Phys.* **29**, 892, (1958).
  n. Heller, W. R., *Acta.* **9**, 600, 1961.
  o. Herzog, E., and Hugo, M., *Compt. rend. acad. sci.* **248**, 408 (1958).
  p. Hobson, J. D., *J. Iron Steel Inst.*, *(London)* **191**, 342 (1959).
  q. Hobson, J. D., *J. Iron Steel (London)* **32**, 240 (1959).
  r. Hudson, R. M., Riedy, K. J., Stragand, *Corrosion* **16**, 115, 123 (1960).
  s. Johnson, E. W., and Hill, M. L., *Trans. Am. Inst. Mining Met. Engrs.* **128**, 1101 (1960).
  t. Kolgatin, N. N., Glikman, L. A., Teodorovich, V. P., and Deryabina, V. I., *Metalloved. Term. Obrabotka Met.* **1959**, Brutcher 4654.
  u. Karpenko, G. V., *Proc. Acad. Sci. USSR* **113**, 850 (1957).
  v. de Kazincy, F., and Lindberg, O., *Jernkontorets Ann.* **144**, 288 (1960).
  w. Lee, R. W., Swets, D. E., and Frank, R. C., *Mem. Sci. Rev. Met.* **58**, 36 (1961).
  x. Onishi, I., and Kikuta, Y., *Osaka Univ. Technol. Repts.* **10**, 193 (1960).
  y. Plusquellec, J., *Mem. Sci. Rev. Met.* **57**, 265 (1960).
  z. Plusquellec, J., Azou, P., and Bastien, P., *Compt. rend. acad. sci.* **248**, 1816(1959).
  a'. Sacks, K., and Odgers, M., *J. Iron Steel Inst. (London)* **196**, 406 (1960).
  b'. Smialowski, A., *Neue Hütte* **2**, 621 (1957).
  c'. Steigerwald, E. A., Schaller, F. W., and Troiano, A. R., *Trans. Am. Inst. Mining Met. Engrs.* **218**, 832 (1960).
  d'. Tetelman, A. S., *Acta Met.* **9**, 205 (1961).
  e'. Wahlin, H. B., and Mack, D. J., *Acta Met.* **7**, 687 (1959).

7. *Lanthanum and the Rare Earths*
  a. Gibson, J. A., Miller, J. F., Kennedy, P. S., and Rengstorff, G. W. P., "Properties of Rare Earth Metals and Compounds," Battelle Mem. Inst., Columbus, 1959.
  b. Hoiley, C. E., Mulford, R. N. R., and Ellinger, F. H., *J. Phys. Chem.* **59**, 1226 (1955).
  c. Kubota, Y., and Wallace, W. E., Univ. of Pittsburgh (1961), private communication (Ho-H).
  d. Mikheeva, V. I., and Kost, M. E., *Russ. Chem. Rev. (English Transl.)* 283 (1960).
  e. Mulford, R. N. R., and Holley, C. E., *J. Phys. Chem.* **59**, 1222 (1955).
  f. Pebler, A., and Wallace, W. E., *J. Phys. Chem.* (1962), to be published.
  g. Stalinski, B., *Bull. Acad. Sci. Poland* **5**, 1001 (1957); **7**, 269 (1959).

h. Warf, J. C., and Hardcastle, K., *J. Am. Chem. Soc.* **83**, 2206 (1961).
i. Zanowick, R. L., and Wallace, W. E., Univ. of Pittsburgh (1961), private communication (Eu-H).

8. *Magnesium*
    a. Koeneman, J., and Metcalfe, A. G., *Trans. Am. Soc. Metals* **51**, 1072 (1959).
    b. Lelong, P., Dosdat, J., Boghen, J., and Herenguel, J., *J. Nuclear Mater.* **3**, 222 (1961).
    c. Mannchen, W., and Bornkessel, K., *Z. Metallk. N* **51**, 482 (1960).
    d. Sharov, M. V., and Serebryakov, V. V., *Zavodskoya Lab.* **24**, 1226 (1958).

9. Nickel
    a. Belyakov, Y. I., and Iovov, N. I., *Zhur. Tekh. Fiz.* **31**, 204 (1961).
    b. Grimes, H. H., *Acta Met.* **7**, 782 (1959).
    c. Harrison, E. R., and Hobbis, L. C. W., *Rev. Sci. Instr.* **26**, 305 (1955).
    d. Hill, M. L., and Johnson, E. W., *Acta Met.* **3**, 566 (1955).
    e. Hobbis, L. C. W., and Harrison, E. R., *Rev. Sci. Instr.* **27**, 238, 332 (1956).
    f. Janko, A., and Michel, P., *Compt. rend. acad. sci.* **251**, 1001 (1960).
    g. Kavtaradze, N. N., *Izvest. Akad. Nauk. USSR.* 822 (1957); 1045 (1958).
    h. Landecker, K., and Gray, A. J., *Rev. Sci. Instr.* **25**, 1151 (1954).
    i. Oda, Z., and Arata, H., *J. Phys. Chem.* **62**, 1471 (1958).
    j. Rudd, D. W., Vose, D. W., and Vetrano, J. B., USAEC Rept. NAA-SR-4898 (June, 1960).
    k. Snoek, J. L., and Haes, E. J., *Appl. Sci. Research* **A2**, 326 (1951).
    l. Wortman, R., Gomer, R., and Lundy, R., *J. Chem. Phys.* **27**, 1099 (1957).

10. *Niobium*
    a. Albrecht, W. M., Goode, W. D., and Mallett, M. W., *J. Electrochem. Soc.* **106**, 981 (1959).
    b. Klopp, W. D., and Barth, V. D., Defense Metals Inform. Center, Mem. No. 50 (April, 1960).
    c. Knowles, D. R., United Kingdom Atomic Energy Rept. IGR-R/C-190 (March, 1957).
    d. McKinley, T. D., *Am. Inst. Mining Met. Engrs. Annual Meeting*, (April, 1957).
    e. Paxton, H. W., *Trans. Am. Inst. Mining Met. Engrs.* **215**, 725 (1959).
    f. Rudd, D. W., *J. Phys. Chem.* **66**, 351 (1962).
    g. Wainwright, C., *Bull. Inst. Metals* **4**, 68 (1958).
    h. Wilcox, B. A., *J. Less-Common Metals* **2**, 292 (1960).

11. *Palladium*
    a. Ash, R., and Barrer, R. M., *J. Phys. Chem. Solids* **16**, 246 (1960).
    b. Beljakov, Y. I., and Iovov, N. I., *Zhur. Tekh. Fiz.* **30**, 216 (1960).
    c. Carson, A. W., Flanagan, T. B., and Lewis, F. A., *Trans. Faraday Soc.* **56**, 363, 371, 1332 (1960).
    d. Cochran, N., *Rev. Sci. Instr.* **29**, 69 (1958).
    e. Davis, W. D., USAEC Rept. KAPL-1227 (October, 1954) and KAPL-1375 (April, 1955).
    f. Darling, A. S., *Metallurgia* **60**, 137 (1959).
    g. Darling, A. S., *Platinum Metals Rev.* **2**, 16 (1958).
    h. Everett, D. H., and Nordon, P., *Proc. Roy. Soc.* **A259**, 341 (1960).
    i. Fallon, R. J., and Castellan, G. W., *J. Phys. Chem.* **63**, 160 (1959).
    j. Flanagan, T. B., and Lewis, F. A., *Trans. Faraday Soc.* **55**, 1400, 1959.
    k. Fritz, J. J., Maria, H. J., and Aston, J. G., *J. Chem. Phys.* **34**, 2185 (1961).

264 O. M. KATZ AND E. A. GULBRANSEN

l. Hoare, J. P., *J. Phys. Chem.* **64**, 1780 1960.

m. Hoare, J. P., *J. Electrochem. Soc.* **107**, 635 (1960).

n. Hurlbert, R. C., and Konecny, J. O., *J. Chem. Phys.* **34**, 655 (1961).

o. Juenker, D. W., van Swaay, M., and Birchevall, C. E., *Rev. Sci. Instr.* **26**, 888 (1955).

p. Katz, O. M., and Gulbransen, E. A., *Rev. Sci. Instr.* **31**, 615 (1960).

q. Levine, P. L., and Weale, K. E., *Trans. Faraday Soc.* **56**, 357 (1960).

r. Lewis, R., and Ubbelohde, A. R., *Proc. Roy. Soc.* **A220**, 279 (1953).

s. Lindsay, W. T., Jr., and Pement, F., USAEC Rept. WAPD-T-1267 and WAPD-T-1268 (October, 1960).

t. Maeland, A. J., and Gibb, T. R. P., Jr., *J. Phys. Chem.* **65**, 1270 (1961).

u. Moon, K. A., *J. Phys. Chem.* **60**, 502 (1956).

v. Mosevich, I. A., and Tverdovskii, I. P., *Zhur. L. Vert. Trudy GIPKH* **42**, 173 (1959).

w. Nace, D. M., and Aston, J. G., *J. Am. Chem. Soc.* **79**, 3619 (1957).

x. Nakhutin, I. Y., and Sutiagina, Y. I., *Fiz. Met. and Mellography* **7**, 137 (1959).

y. Ostrounov, V. V., *Zhur. Fiz. Khim.* **34**, 2571 (1960).

z. Ratchford, J., and Castellan, G. W., *J. Phys. Chem.* **62**, 1123 (1958).

a'. Schuldiner, S., and Hoare, J. P., *J. Electrochem. Soc.* **105**, 278 (1958).

b'. Silberg, P. A., and Bachman, C. H., *J. Chem. Phys.* **29**, 777 (1957).

c'. Singer, O. P., and Castellan, G. W., *J. Chem. Phys.* **33**, 633 (1960).

d'. van Swaay, M., and Birchenall, C. E., *Trans. Am. Inst. Mining Met. Engrs.* **218**, 285 (1960).

e'. Worsham, J. E., Jr., Wilkinson, M. K., and Shull, C. G., *J. Phys. Chem. Solids* **3**, 303 (1957).

12. *Platinum*
  a. Chapoorian, J. A., *Nature* **190**, 528 (1961).

13. *Plutonium*
  a. Mulford, R. N. R., and Sturdy, G. E., *J. Am. Chem. Soc.* **77**, 3449 (1955), **78**, 3897 (1956).

14. *Tantalum*
  a. Clauss, A., and Forestier, H., *Plansee Proc., Reutte/Tyrol, Austria*, 1958, p. 277.
  b. Gabrysh, A. F., Eyring, H., Wadsworth, M. E., Baker, G. S., and Ree, T., *J. Appl. Phys.* **31**, 1785 (1960).
  c. Hall, W. K., Wallace, W. E., and Cheselske, F. J., *J. Phys. Chem.* **65**, 128 (1961).
  d. Seraphim, D. P., Novick, D. T., and Budnik, J. L., *Acta Met.* **9**, 446 (1961).
  e. Waite, T. R., Wallace, W. E., and Craig, R. S., *J. Chem. Phys.* **24**, 634 (1956).

15. *Thorium*
  a. Mallett, M. W., and Campbell, I. E., *J. Am. Chem. Soc.* **73**, 4850 (1951).
  b. Mallett, M. W., and Sheipline, V. M., "Reactor Handbook," Vol. 1, p. 155. Publ. by USAEC, 1955.
  c. Peterson, D. T., and Westlake, D. G., *J. Phys. Chem.* **63**, 1514 (1959); *Trans. Am. Inst. Mining Met. Engrs.* **215**, 444 (1959); *J. Phys. Chem.* **64**, 649 (1960).
  d. Rundle, R. E., Shull, C. G., and Wollan, E. O., *Acta Cryst.* **5**, 22 (1952).
  e. van Vucht, J. H. N., *Vacuum* **10**, 170 (1960).
  f. Zachariasen, W. H., *Acta Cryst.* **6**, 393 (1953).

16. *Titanium*
  a. Albrecht, W. M., and Mallett, M. W., *Trans. Am. Inst. Mining Met. Engrs.* **212**, 204 (1958).

b. Burk, B. I., and Nikolaev, G. I., *Proc. Acad. Sci. U.S.S.R.* **116**, 825 (1957).

c. Coucoulas, A., and Margolin, H., *Trans. Am. Inst. Mining Met. Engrs.* **218**, 958 (1960).

d. Fleitman, A. H., *Trans. Am. Soc. Metals* **52**, 170 (1960).

e. Gibb, T. R. P., Jr., and Krushwitz, H. W., *J. Am. Chem. Soc.* **72**, 5365 (1950).

f. Glazunov, S. G., Kornilov, I. I., and Yakimova, A. M., *Izvest. Akad. Nauk SSSR* **9**, 17 (1958).

g. Haynes, R., *J. Inst. Metals* **88**, 509 (1960).

h. Hepworth, M. T., *Mines Mag.* **50**, 40 (1960).

i. Haag, R. M., and Shipko, F. J., *J. Am. Chem. Soc.* **78**, 5155 (1956).

j. Huber, O. J., Gates, J. E., Young, A. P., Pobereskin, M., and Frost, P. D., *Trans. Am. Inst. Mining Met. Engrs.* **209**, 918 (1957).

k. Hughes, P. C., and Lamborn, I. R., *J. Inst. Metals* **89**, 165 (1961).

l. Jones, D. W., Pessall, N., and McQuillan, A. D., *Phil. Mag.* **6**, 455 (1961).

m. Köster, W., Bangert, L., and Evers, M., *Z. Metallk.* **47**, 564 (1956).

n. Lenning, G. A., Craighead, C. M., and Jaffee, R. I., *Trans. Am. Inst. Mining Met. Engrs.* **200**, 367 (1954); **206**, 1235 (1956).

o. McQuillan, A. D., and McQuillan, M. K., "Titanium." Academic Press, New York, 1956.

p. Morton, J., and Stark, D. S., *Trans. Faraday Soc.* **56**, 351 (1960).

q. Nadler, R. A., and Day, D. L., *Trans. Am. Inst. Mining Met. Engrs.* **218**, 841 (1960).

r. Otake, Y., Sumitomo, *Light Metals* **A1**, 6 (1960).

s. Schwartzberg, F. R., Williams, D. N., and Jaffee, R. I., *J. Inst. Metals* **88**, 352 (1960).

t. Sidhu, S. S., Heaton, L., and Zauberis, D. D., *Acta Cryst.* **9**, 607 (1956).

u. Sofina, V. V., and Pavlovskoya, N. G., *Zhur. Fiz. Khim.* **34**, 525 (1960).

v. Stalinski, B., Coogan, C. K., and Gutowsky, H. S., *J. Chem. Phys.* **34**, 1191 (1961).

w. Williams, D. N., and Jaffee, R. I., *J. Less-Common Metals* **2**, 42 (1960).

x. Zhurenkova, A. A., *Izvest. Vuz-Cher. Metall.* p. 8 (September, 1960).

17. *Tungsten*

a. Brennan, D., and Fletcher, P. C., *Proc. Roy. Soc.* **A250**, 389 (1959).

b. Hickmott, T. W., *J. Chem. Phys.* **32**, 810 (1960).

18. *Uranium*

a. Abraham, B. M., and Flotow, H. E., *J. Am. Chem. Soc.* **77**, 1446 (1955).

b. Abraham, B. M., Osborne, D. W., Flotow, H. E., and Marcus, R. B., *J. Am. Chem. Soc.* **82**, 1064 (1960).

c. Albrecht, W. M., and Mallett, M. W., *J. Electrochem. Soc.* **103**, 404 (1956).

d. Burkart, M. W., ed., USAEC Rept. WAPD-127 in 3 parts, 400 pp. (1957–1959).

e. Davis, W. D., USAEC Rept. KAPL-1548 (August, 1956).

f. Farr, J. D., Giorgi, A. L., Bowman, M. G., and Money, R. K., *J. Inorg. Nuclear Chem.* **18**, 42 (1961).

g. Fergason, L. A., *Nuclear Sci. Engr.* **10**, 53 (1961).

h. Gardner, H. R., and Riches, J. W., USAEC Rept. HW-43428 (October, 1956).

i. Gibb, T. R. P., Jr., McSharry, J. J., and Krushwitz, H. W., Jr., *J. Am. Chem. Soc.* **74**, 6203 (1952).

j. Gulbransen, E. A., Andrew, K. F., and Ruka, R. J., Westinghouse Research Lab., Pittsburgh, Pennsylvania, unpublished work (October, 1956).

k. Hopkinson, B. E., *Corrosion Technol.* 337 (November, 1959).

l. Libowitz, G. G., *J. Chem. Phys.* **27**, 514 (1957).

m. Libowitz, G. G., and Gibb, T. R. P., Jr., *J. Phys. Chem.* **61**, 793 (1957).

n. Lin, S. T., and Kaufmann, A. R., *Phys. Rev.* **102**, 640 (1956).

o. Mallett, M. W., and Trzeciak, M. J., *Fir. Nuclear Eng. Sci. Congr.* **1**, 168 (1957).

p. Mattraw, H. C., *J. Phys. Chem.* **59**, 93 (1955).

q. Mogard, H., and Cabane, G., *Rev. Met.* **51**, 617 (1954).

r. Meredith, K. E., and Waldron, M. B., *J. Inst. Metals* **87**, 311 (1959).

s. Owen, B. G., and Gibson, R. A., *J. Nuclear Energy* **B1**, 92, 1959.

t. Rundle, R. E., *J. Am. Chem. Soc.* **73**, 4172 (1949).

u. Singleton, J. H., Ruka, R. J., and Gulbransen, E. A., Westinghouse Research Lab., Pittsburgh, Pennsylvania unpublished work (November, 1956).

v. Troutner, V. H., *Corrosion* **16**, 117 (1960).

w. Wilkinson, W. D., and Murphy, W. F., "Nuclear Reactor Metallurgy," p. 63. Van Nostrand, Princeton, New Jersey, 1958.

19. *Vanadium*

a. Eustice, A. L., and Carlson, O. N., *Trans. Am. Soc. Metals* **53**, 501 (1961).

b. Roberts, B. W., and Rogers, H. C., *Trans. Am. Inst. Mining Met. Engrs.* **206**, 1213 (1956).

c. Rostoker, W., "Metallurgy of Vandium," p. 76. Wiley, New York, 1958.

d. Veleckis, E., Ph.D. Thesis, Illinois Inst. of Technol., Chicago, 1960.

20. *Yttrium*

a. Funston, E. S., *J. Metals* **12**, 738 (1960).

b. Roach, J. D., *Trans. Am. Inst. Mining Met. Engrs.* **221**, 646 (1961).

21. *Zirconium*

a. Beck, R. L., *Trans. Am. Soc. Metals* **55**, 1962.

b. Belle, J., Cleland, B. B., and Mallett, M. W., *J. Electro-chem. Soc.* **101**, 211 (1954).

c. Bernstein, R. B., and Cubicciotti, D. D., *J. Phys. Colloid Chem.* **55**, 238 (1951).

d. Berry, W. E., Vaughn, D. A., and White, E. L., *Corrosion* **17**, 109 (1961).

e. Bokros, J. C., *J. Nuclear Mater.* **3**, 216, 320 (1961).

f. Boyle, R. F., and Kisiel, T. J., Bettis Tech. Rev., USAEC Document WAPD-BT-10, p. 31 (October, 1958).

g. Brown, A., and Hardie, D., *J. Nuclear Mater.* **4**, 110 (1961).

h. Chang, R., *J. Nuclear Mater.* **2**, 335 (1960).

i. Cox, B., *J. Electrochem Soc.* **109**, 6, 1962.

j. Dalgaard, S. B., Can. Atomic Energy Comm. Rep. CR Met-911 (1960).

k. Douglass, D. L., and Dearing, B. E., USAEC Rept. KAPL-2071 (January, 1960).

l. Douglas, T. B., *J. Am. Chem. Soc.* **80**, 5040 (1958).

m. Douglas, T. B., and Victor, A. C., *Nat. Bur. Standards (U. S.) J. Research* **61**, 13 (1958).

n. Espagno, L., Azou, P., and Bastien, P., *Mem. Sci. Rev. Met.* **57**, 254 (1960).

o. Forscher, F., *J. Metals* **8**, 536 (1956).

p. Hausner, H. H., Kalish, H. S., and Angier, R. P., *Trans. Am. Inst. Mining Met. Engrs.* **191**, 625 (1951); Discussion *ibid.* **194**, 510 (1952).

q. Johnston, W. V., USAEC Rept. KAPL 2000-5 (1959).

r. Kass, S., *J. Electrochem. Soc.* **107**, 594 (1960).

s. Katz, O. M., USAEC Rept. WAPD-AIW(M)-1137 (March 14, 1958).

t. Katz, O. M., and Gulbransen, E. A., *J. Chem. Educ.* **37**, 533 (1960).

u. Lamale, G. E., Hare, A. W., Krause, H. H., Hopkins, A. K., Stang, J. H., Simons, E. M., and Dickerson, R. F., USAEC Rept. BMI-1401 (December, 1959).

v. Langeron, J. P., and Lehr, P., *Rev. Met.* **55**, 901 (1958).

w. Markowitz, J. M., USAEC Rept. WAPD-TM-171 (January, 1959); *Proc. 2nd Intern. Conf. on Peaceful Uses of Atomic Energy, Geneva* Vol. 6, Paper 709, p. 235 (1958).

x. Martin, S. L. H., and Rees, A. L. G., *Trans. Faraday Soc.* **50**, 343, 1954.

y. McQuillan, A. D., and Pessall, N., *Acta Cryst.* **14**, 1287 (1961).

z. McGeary, R. K., *"Zirconium and Zirconium Alloys,"* p. 168. Am. Soc. Metals, 1953.

a'. Ostberg, G., *J. Nuclear Mat.* **5**, 208 (1962).

b'. Paprocki, S. J., and Hodge, E. S., *Nuclear Met.* **7**, 73 (1960).

c'. Sawatzky, A., *J. Nuclear Mat.* **2**, 62, 321 (1960).

d'. Someno, M., *Japan. J. Inst. Metals* **24**, 249 (1960).

e'. Spalaris, C. N., Pickett, A. E., and Gaul, G. G., *Nuclear Sci. Eng.* **8**, 83 (1960).

f'. Troutner, V. H., *Corrosion* **16**, 115 (1960).

g'. Wadsworth, G. B., Picklesimer, M. L., and Adamson, G. M., Jr., USAEC Rept. TID-7526 p. 186 (February, 1957).

h'. Wanklyn, J. N., and Hopkinson, B. E., *J. Appl. Chem.* **8**, 496 (1958).

i'. Whitwham, D., *Mem. Sci. Rev. Met.* **57**, 2 (1960).

j'. Whitwham, D., Huber, A., and Herenguel, J., *Acta Met.* **7**, 65 (1959).

k'. Yeniscavish, W., Wolfe, R. A., and Lieberman, R. M., *J. Nuclear Mater.* **1**, 271 (1959).

CHAPTER **5**

E. C. Subbarao
Westinghouse Research Laboratories,
Pittsburgh, Pennsylvania

Physical Properties of
Non-Stoichiometric Inorganic Compounds

I.	Introduction	268
II.	Ionic Conductivity	270
	A. Modified ZrO_2	271
	B. Modified ThO_2	278
III.	Electrical Conductivity	281
	A. Sodium Tungsten Bronzes	281
	B. $Fe_{1-x}O$	288
	C. Other Examples	292
IV.	Ferroelectricity	294
	A. $BaTiO_3$	294
	B. Other Examples	296
V.	Magnetic Properties	298
	A. Magnetic and Neutron Diffraction Studies on $Fe_{1-x}O$	298
	B. Mössbauer Study of $Fe_{1-x}O$	303
	C. Other Examples	304
VI.	Concluding Remarks	304
	References	305

I. INTRODUCTION

Consider an inorganic stoichiometric compound BX, composed of the metal B and nonmetal X. If B can exist in two valence states, then the compound may consist of both species and the electrical neutrality is preserved by introducing appropriate number of vacancies or interstitial atoms. The B atom, instead of being present in more than one valence state, may be replaced by another atom A of fixed valency different from

268

that of B, provided again the sizes of B and A are not greatly different. The charge balance is restored by creation of vacancies or interstitial atoms. The stability and the extent of non-stoichiometry achieved by mixed valency or isomorphous substitution is limited by considerations of size and energetics (95).

Some of the structural implications of variable composition discussed in Chapter 3 may be used as the basis for classification of these non-stoichiometric compounds, as follows:

A. Mixed valency
  (1) Missing cations from a normal lattice site, e.g., $Fe_{1-x}O$
  (2) Missing anions from a normal lattice site, e.g., $SrCoO_{3-x}$
  (3) Interstitial cations, e.g., TiO_{2-x}
  (4) Interstitial anions, e.g., UO_{2+x}

B. Isomorphous replacement
  (1) Missing anions from a normal lattice site, e.g., $Ca_xZr_{1-x}O_{2-x}$
  (2) Missing cations from a normal lattice site, e.g., $(Pb_{1-x}La_{2/3x})Nb_2O_6$

More than one type of defect may be present in a crystal. However, generally one kind predominates in a crystal at a given temperature and pressure. Thus non-stoichiometry exists mostly on one side of a binary compound in a phase diagram. The notable exceptions to this are found among the *B1* oxides and sulfides and the sulfides with structures intermediate between *B8* and *C6* (cf. Chapter 3).

In this chapter, we will be concerned only with compounds in which the defect concentration is much larger than that introduced by thermal energy. We will deal with instances in which the deviation from stoichiometry arises essentially from changes in composition and, therefore, the concentration of defects is to a large extent independent of temperature. The defect concentration may be large enough to be designated in the chemical formula, e.g., as in $Fe_{1-x}O$.

A direct correlation of non-stoichiometry to physical properties was convincingly provided by the work of Wagner and co-workers ($5, 129, 130$) in the early 1930's on the electrical properties of non-stoichiometric compounds (Chapter 2). Since then, much research has been done not only on the electrical properties but also on the importance of non-stoichiometry to catalysis ($42, 49$), oxidation of metals (95), and diffusion (Chapters 2 and 4).

No attempt has been made in this chapter to review the physical properties of all non-stoichiometric inorganic compounds studied. Instead, a few systems were chosen, admittedly arbitrarily, for detailed discussion. The systems chosen were ones in which rather systematic physical property measurements on more or less well-characterized specimens were made alongside of structural studies, so that a reasonable understanding of the physical behavior may be obtained. The examples selected involve the influence of non-stoichiometry on electrical conductivity, ionic conductivity, ferroelectricity, magnetism, and phase transitions. Additional non-stoichiometric systems in which the physical properties were studied are included in the list of references; however, this list is not claimed to be complete.

II. IONIC CONDUCTIVITY

Diffusion phenomena have an important bearing on rate processes such as sintering, solid-state reactions, oxidation, creep deformation and on electrical conductivity. In a perfect crystal lattice in which a proper atom is located on every lattice site, there would be no ionic conductivity. But in real crystals, there are always present, due to composition or thermal energy, vacant lattice sites or interstitial ions which contribute to ionic conductivity. The conductivity behavior of defect solids has found applications in galvanic cells (77), fuel cells (133), and oxygen gauges (134).

We will be concerned here with electrical conductivity and diffusion in non-stoichiometric oxides in which vacant lattice sites are present due to composition. For a general review of ionic conductivity, reference may be made to Dekker (22) and to the review by Lidiard (85). Some of the basic theory is discussed in Chapter 2, Section IV,C. In the temperature region where the defects due to composition are far in excess of the defects created by thermal energy (extrinsic region), the diffusion constant, D, associated with the migration of vacancies is

$$D = f\lambda^2 p \tag{1}$$

where λ is the lattice parameter, f is a geometrical factor of the lattice, and p is the jump probability of a vacancy per second; p may be written in the form

$$p = \nu \exp\left(-\epsilon/kT\right) \tag{2}$$

where ν is a frequency, ϵ is the activation energy associated with a jump, k is the Boltzmann constant, and T is absolute temperature (see Eq. 172 in Chapter 2). If migration of pairs and interaction effects of defects can be neglected, and the concentration of vacancies is constant or is known as a function of temperature, then the activation energy for diffusion of vacancies can be obtained from the temperature dependence of the diffusion coefficient.

The total conductivity of an isotropic crystal is given by the scalar relation

$$i = \sigma E \qquad (3)$$

where i is the current density, E is the field strength, and σ is the conductivity. The portion of the total current carried by one species whose conductivity is σ_i, is represented by the transference number, t_i, so that $t_i = \sigma_i/\sigma$. The transference numbers for the different species (cations, anions, and electrons), of course, add up to unity. In the oxides to be discussed here the transference number for one of the species generally far exceeds that of the others.

The conductivity, σ, in the extrinsic region is

$$\sigma \propto n \exp\left(-\epsilon/kT\right) \qquad (4)$$

where n is the number of vacancies per unit volume and ϵ is the activation energy for jump of a vacancy assuming that $t_{\text{vacancies}} = 1$. Einstein pointed out an important simple relation between electrical conductivity σ and the diffusion coefficient D as follows (Nernst-Einstein equation):

$$\sigma = Dnz^2e^2/kT \qquad (5)$$

where z = valence, e = electronic charge and the other symbols have the usual notation (see also Eqs. 166 and 173 in Chapter 2). It must be remembered that this relation is applicable only when the conductivity and self-diffusion are due to the same mechanism.

We will discuss in some detail the transport properties of "stabilized" zirconia, which has vacant anion sites. Brief reference will be made to other examples.

A. Modified ZrO₂

The room temperature monoclinic form of ZrO_2 (see Chapter 3, Section II,C,1) transforms to the tetragonal modification at about 1100°C, accompanied by a large volume change. It has long been known that the addition of oxides of divalent or trivalent metals to ZrO_2 results in a cubic form in which the disruptive monoclinic ⇌ tetragonal inversion is suppressed or eliminated. The following are among the oxides investigated for the "stabilization" of zirconia: CaO (27, 58, 101), MgO (27, 28), Y_2O_3 (26, 57, 97, 110), La_2O_3 (14, 124), Nd_2O_3 (14), and In_2O_3 (110). The phase diagram for the system ZrO_2–CaO is shown in Fig. 1 (27, 101). According to the phase diagram, in specimens rapidly cooled from 2000°C, the cubic ZrO_2 solid solution extends from 16 to 30 mole % CaO, with possibly a wider range at higher temperatures. However, other investi-

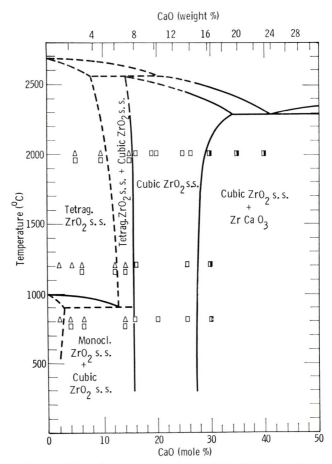

Fig. 1. Phase diagram for the system ZrO_2–CaO (27, 101).

gators obtained different results. For example, Hund (58), who prepared his samples at 1460°C, found a cubic phase from 10 to 20 mole % CaO. These variations may be due to differences in particle size and reactivity of the initial materials (24) and any dissociation of the cubic phase that may take place during slow cooling. Such phase separation is known to take place rather easily in zirconia stabilized by MgO (27). The cubic phase has a fluorite ($C1$) type structure in which Ca^{2+} and Zr^{4+} ions occupy the cation sites and oxygen ions some of the anion sites. Electrical neutrality is preserved by leaving other anion sites vacant. The lattice constant, according to Hund (58), increases from 5.1137 Å at 10% CaO to 5.1236 Å at 20 mole % CaO, since the Ca^{2+} ion is larger than the Zr^{4+} ion. The measured densities are compared with values computed for two models—one with anion vacancies, and the other with interstitial cations (Table I). These data support the model in which Ca^{2+} and Zr^{4+} completely fill the cation lattice, and vacant anion sites, equal in number to the number of Ca^{2+} ions, are introduced. The high concentration of anion vacancies leads to an observed high electrical conductivity, which has been attributed to oxygen ion mobility (58, 77).

The resistivity of the entire ZrO_2–CaO system at $1000°C$ was measured by Trombe and Foëx (125). The resistivity exhibits maxima at $2\ ZrO_2 \cdot CaO$ and at $ZrO_2 \cdot CaO$, and goes through minima corresponding to the eutectic compositions in the phase diagram (Fig. 2). An approximately flat curve

TABLE I

CALCULATED AND MEASURED DENSITIES OF SAMPLES IN THE SYSTEM ZrO_2–CaO (58)

Mole %		Density gm/cm³		
ZrO_2	CaO	Calculated		Observed
		Anion vacancies	Cation interstitials	
94.7	5.3	5.9_4	6.1_0	5.9_7
89.7	10.3	5.7_7	6.0_8	5.7_8
84.9	15.1	5.6_0	6.0_4	5.6_0
80.4	19.6	5.4_3	6.0_1	5.4_7

of high conductivity is observed in the cubic region of the system; however, the phase boundaries denoted by Trombe and Foëx do not exactly agree with the phase diagram (Fig. 1) of Duwez et al. (27). The resistivity maximum at $2\ ZrO_2 \cdot CaO$ appears to be anomalous since no compound is believed to exist at this composition. It would be interesting to examine the possible ordering of vacancies and/or Ca ions at this composition. Further, the data at high ZrO_2 content are complicated by phase transitions. It appears worthwhile to repeat the resistivity measurements. Trombe and Foëx (124) also measured the electrical resistivity at $1000°C$ of compositions in the system ZrO_2–La_2O_3 and found only one maximum, at $La_2Zr_2O_7$ ($2\ ZrO_2 \cdot La_2O_3$) which has a pyrochlore-type structure (97).

Measured electrical conductivity in oxide systems is the sum of ionic and electronic contributions. In the ZrO_2–CaO solid solutions the concentration of oxygen ion vacancies is fixed by the composition and is virtually independent of oxygen pressure and of temperature so that the

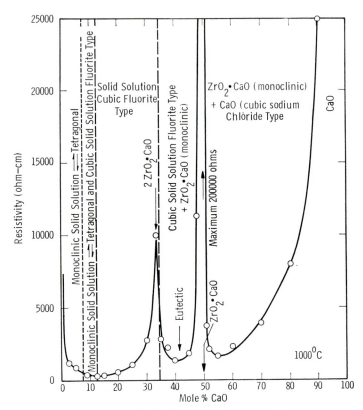

FIG. 2. Electrical resistivity in the system ZrO_2–CaO at 1000°C (125).

ionic contribution will not be pressure-dependent. However, at elevated temperatures, the concentration of excess electrons $\ominus$ and electron holes $\oplus$ are presumably determined by the oxygen partial pressure of the surrounding atmosphere by the reactions (see Chapter 2, Section V,B,1)

$$O^{2-}(\text{lattice}) = \square_{O}^{2-} + \tfrac{1}{2} O_2(g) + 2 \ominus \tag{6}$$

$$\tfrac{1}{2} O_2(g) + \square_{O}^{2-} = O^{2-}(\text{lattice}) + 2 \oplus \tag{7}$$

where $\square_{O}^{2-}$ denotes oxygen ion vacancy.

Assuming that association or interaction effects are small at the concentrations considered (though it is not certain if this assumption is reasonable), one can write a mass action law and obtain the following expressions for the pressure dependence of the concentration of electrons $C_{\ominus}$ and of electron holes $C_{\oplus}$:

$$C_{\ominus} = K_1 P_{O_2}^{-1/4} \tag{8}$$

$$C_{\oplus} = K_2 P_{O_2}^{+1/4} \tag{9}$$

where K_1 and K_2 are constants. Even if the concentration of electrons or electron holes is small, they make a substantial contribution to the total electrical conductivity since their mobility is high. The total conductivity is given by

$$\sigma = \sigma_{ionic} + \mathfrak{F}l_\ominus C_\ominus + \mathfrak{F}l_\oplus C_\oplus \qquad (10)$$

or, in terms of oxygen pressure, by

$$\sigma = \sigma_{ionic} + K_3 P_{O_2}^{-1/4} + K_4 P_{O_2}^{+1/4} \qquad (11)$$

Here $\mathfrak{F}$ is the Faraday constant (96,500 coulombs per equivalent), C is the concentration in moles per cm^3, and l is the mobility (cm sec^{-1} per volt cm^{-1}).

Experimentally, the total electrical conductivity of $Zr_{0.85}Ca_{0.15}O_{1.85}$ was found to be independent of oxygen pressure in the range 1 to 10^{-22} atm over a wide temperature interval, the maximum temperature employed being 1627°C (58, 75, 77). This indicates that the electrical conductivity is essentially entirely ionic, that is, there is no appreciable electronic contribution. This result is in agreement with the emf measurements of Kiukkola and Wagner (77) in a galvanic cell of the type

$$Fe, Fe_{1-x}O \mid (ZrO_2 + CaO) \mid Fe_{1-y}O, Fe_3O_4$$

where $Fe_{1-x}O$ and $Fe_{1-y}O$ denote wüstite coexisting with metallic iron and with magnetite, respectively. The observed emf values, $\mathcal{E}$, agree very satisfactorily with those computed from CO–CO_2 equilibrium calculations (20) according to the equation

$$\mathcal{E} = \frac{RT}{2\mathfrak{F}} \ln \frac{(P_{CO_2}/P_{CO})_{II}}{(P_{CO_2}/P_{CO})_{I}} \qquad (12)$$

where the subscripts I and II refer to the left-hand and right-hand electrodes of the cell, respectively (Table II). The ratios establish the oxygen partial pressure at the anode and cathode of the cell used.

Recently, Weissbart and Ruka (135), in an attempt to estimate the transference number for electrons, used a galvanic cell of the type

$$P_{O_2}^{anode}, Pt \mid Zr_{0.85}Ca_{0.15}O_{1.85} \mid Pt, P_{O_2}^{cathode}$$

at 1000°C. They measured the oxygen picked up by zirconium strips acting as getters in the hot zone of the anode chamber. These measurements were made on open circuit and also with a constant current drawn from the cell. Faraday's laws were found to be closely obeyed. These data indicate that the electronic contribution to the total conductivity has a maximum upper limit considerably less than 2%. In a second experiment, with the zirconium getter removed, the transference number for electrons, t_e, was determined from the relation, $t_e = 1 - \mathcal{E}/\mathcal{E}_0$, where $\mathcal{E}_0$ is the calculated emf for the ionic species and $\mathcal{E}$ is the measured open circuit voltage. For oxygen partial pressures of 0.2 and 10^{-17} atm at the anode and 1 atm at the cathode, t_e was found to be about 0.002 and 0.006, respectively. Furthermore, according to these investigators, extended electrolysis at 1100°C revealed no measurable change in resistance or apparent deterioration of the electrolyte, indicating very small transference number for cations, perhaps less than 10^{-2}. All these results point to the conclusion that in $Zr_{0.85}Ca_{0.15}O_{1.85}$, the transference number of anions is near unity, with that for cations and for electrons being less than 10^{-2}.

TABLE II

EMF of the Cell

Fe, $Fe_{1-x}O$ | $(ZrO_2 + CaO)$ | $Fe_{1-y}O$, Fe_3O_4 (77)

Temp. (°C)	Electrolyte						Calc.
	0.85 ZrO_2 + 0.15 CaO		0.60 ZrO_2 + 0.40 CaO				
	$\mathcal{E}$ (mv)		$\mathcal{E}$ (mv)				$\mathcal{E}$ (mv)
800	72	73	71	71	71	70	72.5
900	103	103	103	103	102	101	102.1
1000	134	133	136	134	132	134	134.8
1100	166	165	—	166	—	166	168.5

Kingery et al. (75) and others (58) have shown that the log conductivity varies linearly with reciprocal absolute temperature over a wide range (Fig. 3). Over the range 700° to 1725°C, these data can be represented by the relation

$$\sigma = 1.50 \times 10^3 \exp(-1.26/kT) \quad (\text{ohm-cm})^{-1} \quad (13)$$

The activation energy of 1.26 ev (29.1 kcal/mole) is in good agreement with the value of 1.21 ev (27.9 kcal/mole) of Hund (58). However, the absolute values of the conductivity (and the pre-exponential term) seem to vary over a wide range from one investigation to another. These differences may be traced to sample preparation and electrode conditions.

Direct measurements of the oxygen ion diffusion by isotopic exchange were carried out by Kingery et al. (75) over the temperature range 700 to 1100°C with the results shown in Fig. 4. These data can be represented by

$$D = 1.0 \times 10^{-2} \exp(-1.22/kT) \quad \text{cm}^2/\text{sec} \quad (14)$$

The diffusion is presumed to be due to vacancy migration: the large concentration of oxygen ion vacancies (about 7.5%) in the structure of $Zr_{0.85}Ca_{0.15}O_{1.85}$ due to its composition leads to a high value for the diffusion coefficient. Since the oxygen ion vacancies are not affected by temperature, the measured activation energy corresponds only to the energy required for movement of oxygen ions in the fluorite lattice by a vacancy mechanism.

One can calculate the electrical conductivity (σ) resulting from the ion mobility determined from the diffusion coefficient (D) by means of the Nernst-Einstein relation (Eq. 5) for the oxygen ions. The conductivity due to oxygen ion mobility calculated on this basis is essentially equal to the measured total conductivity at different temperatures (Fig. 4). Thus, within experimental error, the entire electrical conductivity can be attributed to oxygen ion mobility, i.e., the transference number for

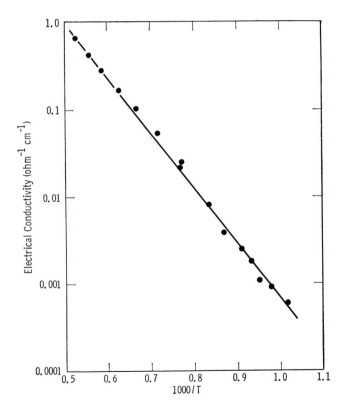

FIG. 3. Electrical conductivity of $Zr_{0.85}Ca_{0.15}O_{1.85}$ (75).

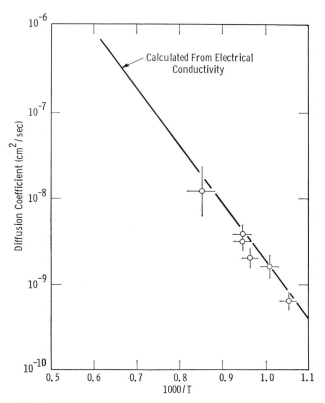

FIG. 4. Comparison of directly measured oxygen ion diffusion coefficients for $Zr_{0.85}Ca_{0.15}O_{1.85}$ with the line calculated from measured electrical conductivity data using the Nernst-Einstein relation (75).

oxygen ions in $Zr_{0.85}Ca_{0.15}O_{1.85}$ is near unity and is consistent with the estimated transference numbers for electrons and cations.

B. Modified ThO_2

The crystal structure of pure ThO_2 is cubic, fluorite type (C1) with four molecules in the unit cell (Chapter 3, Section II,C,1). Hund and co-workers (59–61) have found, by comparison of measured densities with computed values, that in the solid solutions of ThO_2 with La_2O_3 and Y_2O_3, the trivalent ion replaces Th^{4+} ions accompanied by an appropriate number of oxygen ion vacancies. The observed increase of electrical conductivity has been explained in terms of the migration of oxygen ions via a vacancy mechanism; however, a clear estimate of electronic contribution in thoria systems is not available (77). Johnson and Curtis (19, 67) have found that CaO, which is soluble in ThO$_2$ up to 12.5 mole %, improves the sintering rate of ThO$_2$. No change in lattice parameters were detected with the addition of CaO due to the similar sizes of Ca^{2+} and Th^{4+}. It is reasonable to assume that the introduction of CaO into ThO$_2$ also causes anion vacancies.

The ThO$_2$ systems are preferable to the ZrO$_2$ systems for a study of the transport properties of non-stoichiometric oxides with the fluorite lattice because ThO$_2$ itself has the cubic fluorite lattice (C1). The specific resistivity measurements of Hund in the systems ThO$_2$–Y$_2$O$_3$ and ThO$_2$–La$_2$O$_3$ indicate that the electrical conductivity is not linearly dependent on the concentration of anion vacancies when more than 8% of A$_2$O$_3$ is present (59–61). At these higher concentrations, a number of vacancies will have vacancies as nearest neighbors and the interaction of

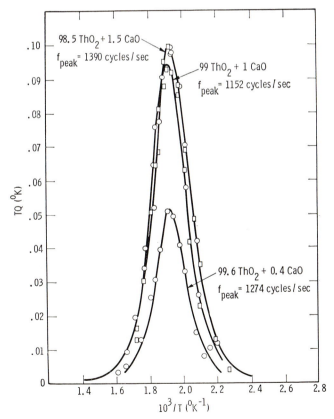

FIG. 5. Internal friction, Q, in ThO$_2$ specimens containing CaO (127).

defects becomes important. It should be interesting to make conductivity measurements at lower concentrations of the additive.

Consider a defect solid in which the vacancies are randomly distributed over the available sites. Now if an external electric or mechanical stress which varies sinusoidally with time is applied to this solid, the parameters specifying the distribution of vacancies will vary sinusoidally with time about their equilibrium values. Even after sufficient time has been allowed, there will be a lag between the driving force and the response, the phase angle of which will depend on the ratio of frequency of driving force to the jump frequency. The variation of this ratio with frequency or temperature gives rise to an internal friction peak or a dielectric loss peak. Dielectric loss peaks due to a vacancy-impurity pair in doped NaCl have been observed by Breckenridge (9) and others. An unambiguous discussion of the associated internal friction peaks in alkali halides does not

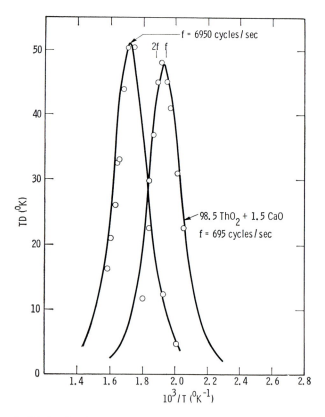

Fig. 6. Dissipation factor, D, in ThO₂ specimens containing CaO (127).

seem to be available (84). Wachtman (127) recently developed the theory of mechanical and dielectric relaxations arising from a single impurity-vacancy pair, without interaction between pairs, for the particular case of CaO in ThO_2. The theory predicts an internal friction peak and a dielectric loss peak to be absent in pure ThO_2 but present in CaO-containing samples, the height of the peaks increasing with CaO content. Experimental measurements of internal friction and dielectric relaxation were made on pure and doped ThO_2 (127). An internal friction peak was absent in pure ThO_2 but was present in CaO-containing samples, the peak height increasing with CaO-content at least up to 1 mole % CaO (Fig. 5). Defects, other than impurity-vacancy pairs, seem to be present in samples with larger CaO contents. The corresponding dissipation factor peaks are shown in Fig. 6. In agreement with theory, both the internal friction and dissipation factor curves have a single relaxation time and the dissipation factor peak has the predicted frequency dependence. Organic inclusion compounds, clathrates and urea adducts, have been studied similarly; see Chapter 10, Section II.

III. ELECTRICAL CONDUCTIVITY

The omission of some metal ions in the metal oxide BO may promote some of the metal ions to a higher valency (e.g., as in $Fe_{1-x}O$). The introduction of a lower fixed valent ion into the metal site of a metal oxide has the same effect (e.g., lithium substituted transition metal oxides). The presence of metal ions in sites normally vacant affects the behavior of the host lattice (e.g., alkali tungsten bronzes). The influence of defects of these kinds on electrical properties will be the topic of this section. The electrical behavior and related properties of sodium tungsten bronzes is discussed, followed by a review of the transport properties of $Fe_{1-x}O$, which has a metal-deficient lattice. Finally, brief reference will be made to the electrical properties of other non-stoichiometric compounds. In the examples cited in this section, the observed electrical conductivity is predominantly electronic in nature, whereas in the cases considered in Section II, the measured conductivity is mostly ionic.

A. Sodium Tungsten Bronzes

1. GENERAL CONSIDERATIONS

In tungsten bronzes, oxygen octahedra surrounding tungsten ions, are linked through corners. The interstices fromed by the WO_6 octahedra

282 E. C. SUBBARAO

may be occupied by alkali ions or by divalent ions like Cu etc., the resulting compounds being designated as A_xWO_3 with $0 < x < 1$. The size of
the A ion and the value of x determine the symmetry of the crystal, which
may be cubic, tetragonal, hexagonal, or monoclinic. The preparation,
crystal chemistry and structure of the tungsten bronzes are discussed in
detail in Chapter 3, Sections II,E and II,F and are also reviewed by Hägg
and Magneli (45).

Of the tungsten bronzes, cubic sodium tungsten bronzes were examined
most extensively and they will be discussed in this section. Sodium tungsten
bronzes were first reported by Wöhler (139) in 1824. X-ray diffraction
studies have shown the cubic perovskite structure for Na_xWO_3 with
$0.32 < x < 0.93$ (21). However, recent studies have cast doubt on the
true symmetry of these compounds. For example, an x-ray diffraction
study of cubic Na_xWO_3 specimens with $x = 0.3$ to 0.8 revealed an abrupt
change in linear expansion coefficient at a temperature, which varies with
the sodium content (96). Ingold and DeVries (63) observed birefringence
in electrolytically grown crystals of Na_xWO_3 ($x = 0.52$ to 0.93) when
examined under reflected plane polarized light. The birefringence and
twins, which appear as parallel bands alternately light and dark, disappear
outside a limited temperature range. This effect is reversible with temperature. These results are explained in terms of a tetragonal crystal
structure with c/a in the range 0.990 to 1.000 and with twinning on the
{101} plane, as in tetragonal $BaTiO_3$. The transition temperatures (63, 96)
are summarized in Fig. 7 for different sodium contents. The disagreement
between the two sets of data may be due to the different methods employed for crystal growth and to the uncertainties in the x values. These
data suggest tetragonal symmetry at some temperature for a wide range
of x values. However, neutron diffraction studies on twinned single crystals
did not detect tetragonal distortion, but showed a cubic lattice with
doubled lattice parameter (3).

2. ELECTRICAL PROPERTIES

The electrical resistivity of cubic sodium tungsten bronze was investigated in single crystal form (12, 36, 44, 56) and in sintered masses (116).
The crystals used were prepared by the reaction of Na_2WO_4, WO_3, and
W at elevated temperatures (10) or by diffusion of sodium into Na_xWO_3
with small values of x (13). The conclusions of these early measurements
are that: (i) the resistivity decreases linearly with decreasing temperature
from about 600° to 125°K; and (ii) a plot of the resistivity versus the
sodium concentration exhibits a minimum at about $x \simeq 0.7$ in Na_xWO_3.

The resistivity minimum has been the subject of much speculation. For example, Brown and Banks (12), who discovered the minimum, suggested a tentative hypothesis based upon an equilibrium between dissociated (sodium ions plus free electrons) and undissociated sodium atoms at $x = 0.70$. Thus, the resistivity would decrease up to $x = 0.70$ because of the increase in the number of charge carriers (free electrons), and would increase for $x > 0.70$ because of the increase in the number of scattering

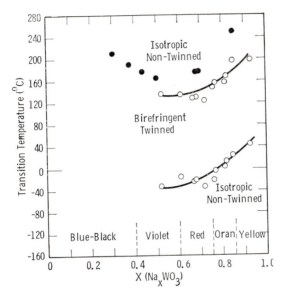

FIG. 7. Phase transitions in Na_xWO_3 as a function of x. Open circles represent optical observations (63) and solid circles represent thermal expansion measurements (96).

centers (sodium atoms) though the number of charge carriers remains constant. However, the Hall effect measurements of Gardner and Danielson (36) have shown that, within experimental error, the free-electron concentration is equal to the sodium concentration for bronzes with $0.58 < x < 0.90$. Hence no explanation involving an anomalous behavior in the total number of charge carriers appears to be tenable.

Juretschke (70) has proposed a correlation between a predicted minimum in the resistivity-pressure curve of pure sodium and the minimum in the resistivity-sodium concentration curve of Na_xWO_3. Although the change in resistivity with atomic volume of sodium in Na_xWO_3 is in the right direction to produce a minimum, the magnitude of the volume effect seems to be too small to account for the observed minimum. Gardner and Danielson (36) have suggested the ordering of sodium ions as a possible explanation. Atoji and Rundle (3) have since found that sodium ions are ordered in $Na_{0.75}WO_3$.

While the cause of the resistivity minimum was thus a matter of speculation, careful remeasurements by Ellerbeck et al. (29) of the electrical resistivity of Na_xWO_3 crystals grown by electrolysis have shown that serious errors are introduced by sample inhomogeneity. Resistivity measurements at a number of locations of the crystal at 25°C were used to test for sample homogeneity, the criterion being that the ratio of the average deviation to the average resistivity be less than 5%. Heat treatment of the crystals at 675°C for 24 hours generally improved the homogeneity and decreased the resistivity. Some of their results are plotted in Fig. 8 and these do not show a minimum.

The room temperature resistivities as a function of sodium concentration, taken from the data of various investigators, are also shown in Fig. 8. The agreement between the results of Brown and Banks (12) and those

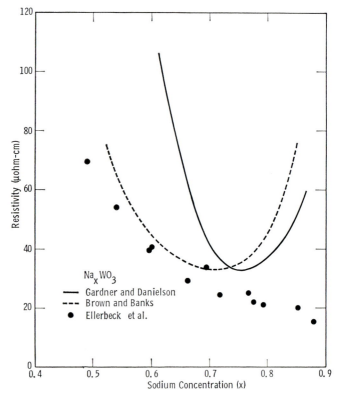

FIG. 8. Room temperature electrial resistivity versus sodium concentration of Na_xWO_3 (29).

of Ellerbeck *et al.* (*29*) is better at low x values than at higher x values. The absence of a minimum in resistivity near $x = 0.70$ for electrically homogeneous specimens is in striking contrast to the deep minimum reported by previous workers. A minimum is absent at 0°, 523°, and 773°K as well.

The minimum in resistivity observed in the crystals of Gardner and Danielson may be due to the fact that the amount of inhomogeneity was a minimum at $x = 0.75$ and was larger at larger and smaller values of x, where, they assumed, the stability of the cubic phase decreases. The inhomogeneities are generally found to be inclusions of high resistivity

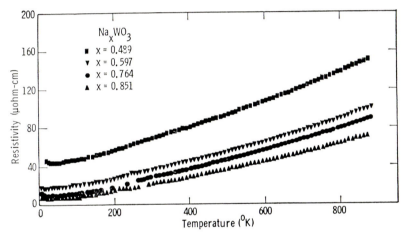

FIG. 9. Electrical resistivity versus temperature for four compositions of Na_xWO_3 (*29*).

material. Brown and Banks (*12*) observed the minimum in crystals for which high x values were attained by diffusing sodium into low x value crystals. The high activation energy for diffusion of sodium in $Na_{0.78}WO_3$ (over 50 kcal/mole) (*113*) seems to make it extremely difficult to prepare a large single crystal with a uniform sodium concentration by diffusion at relatively low temperatures.

Figure 9 shows the electrical resistivity as a function of temperature in the range from 4° to 873°K for four representative x values (*29*). The resistivity decreases nearly linearly with falling temperature. The residual resistivity, by extrapolation to 0°K, is quite large compared to that of pure metals. Also, the extrapolated conductivity of Na_xWO_3 increases approximately as x^4 in the range from $x = 0.48$ to 0.88. If the number of free electrons varies as x (*36*), then the mobility of the electrons at 0°K would vary approximately as x^3.

The dependence of conductivity (σ) upon sodium concentration (x) at high temperatures is approximately linear. At high temperatures, thermal scattering is dominant and the linear dependence of σ upon x would indicate that for thermal scattering the conductivity is proportional to the number of free electrons and the mobility of the electrons is independent of the sodium concentration. Ellerbeck et al. (29) have verified that the mobility of the electrons is independent of the electron concentration (which equals the sodium concentration) and therefore independent of the Fermi energy. This result is also in conformity with the slow increase in density of states obtained by Vest et al. (126) for $x = 0.56$ and $x = 0.70$. However, the anomalous increase in the density of states at $x = 0.81$ and 0.89 observed by Vest et al. is not confirmed by the resistivity or the magnetic susceptibility measurements (43).

The Hall coefficient, R_H, of Na_xWO_3 crystals was found to vary from -6.1×10^{-4} cm^3/coulomb at $x = 0.58$ to -4.0×10^{-4} cm^3/coulomb at $x = 0.90$. (36, 56). The electron density (n) corresponding to each value of Hall constant was calculated from the free-electron relation $R_H = 1/ne$ where e is the magnitude of the electronic charge. The electron density is plotted as a function of sodium concentration in Fig. 10. Within

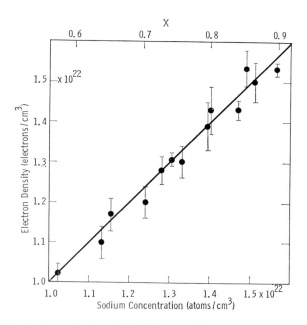

Fig. 10. The electron density of Na_xWO_3 as a function of sodium concentration. These two quantities are observed to be about equal in absolute magnitude from $x = 0.58$ to $x = 0.90$ (36).

experimental error, the computed points for all sodium concentrations fall on a line which has a slope of 45 degrees and which represents one free electron for each sodium atom in the crystal.

The model, presently favored, for the conductivity of Na_xWO_3 may be described as follows. The crystal structure of Na_xWO_3 consists of a WO_3 lattice with sodium in interstitial sites. Hall data show that each sodium atom ionizes completely to contribute one (nearly) free electron to a conduction band. The temperature dependence of conductivity is in conformity with the metallic nature of the bronze. At high temperatures conductivity varies linearly with sodium concentration, while the mobility remains independent of sodium content. Thermal scattering is suggested as the dominant factor at these temperatures. The behavior at $0°K$ is not well understood.

3. OTHER PROPERTIES

The magnetic susceptibility of the bronzes has been examined by several authors (82, 117), the most complete investigation being the one recently made by Greiner et al. (43). These workers measured the room temperature susceptibility of single crystals of Na_xWO_3 with $x = 0.49$ to 0.89 and of WO_3 powder. Selected values are given in Table III. The values obtained by various investigators are in good agreement, except the values of Stubbin and Mellor (117), which are greater by a factor of ten. The susceptibility, measured on samples with $x = 0.85, 0.76$, and 0.49, showed that the paramagnetism of each sample remained essentially constant over a wide temperature range ($100°$ to $300°K$). The diamagnetism of WO_3 was also found to be invariant with temperature from $300°$ to $107°K$. The molar susceptibility was independent of temperature as would be expected for the proposed model. The molar susceptibility is given by

$$\chi_M = \chi_{(WO_3)} + x\chi_{(Na^+)} + \chi_e(x) \tag{15}$$

Here $\chi_{(WO_3)} = 13.9 \pm 1.2$ (10^{-6} emu/mole) (43), $\chi_{(Na^+)} = -6.1$ (10^{-6} emu/mole) (11). χ_e was computed for two cases: (i) for a nearly-free electron with the effective mass $m^* = 1.6\ m$; and (ii) for the density of states obtained from the low temperature electronic specific heat data of Vest et al. (126). The measured and computed values of room temperature susceptibility, shown in Fig. 11, show good quantitative agreement as regards both the x and temperature dependence. These data seem to favor the computation based on density of states from electronic specific heat rather than the one based on the nearly-free electron model with $m^* = 1.6\ m$.

On the basis of the metallic nature of sodium tungsten bronzes, a strong
paramagnetic (positive) shift of the nuclear magnetic resonance of sodium
may be expected. NMR studies on crushed crystals of Na_xWO_3 (x =
0.56 to 0.89) by Jones et al. (68) showed an extremely small, essentially
zero, shift of the Na^{23} resonance. This indicates that the conduction

TABLE III

ROOM TEMPERATURE MAGNETIC SUSCEPTIBILITY OF Na_xWO_3 AND WO_3

Specimen	Mass Susceptibility χ (emu $\times$ 10^{-6})	Reference
WO_3	-0.060	Tilk and Klemm (123)
WO_3	-0.090	Conroy and Sienko (18)
WO_3	-0.059	Greiner et al. (43)
$Na_{0.489}WO_3$	0.007	Greiner et al. (43)
$Na_{0.596}WO_3$	0.014	Greiner et al. (43)
$Na_{0.694}WO_3$	0.033	Greiner et al. (43)
$Na_{0.793}WO_3$	0.047	Greiner et al. (43)
$Na_{0.85}WO_3$	0.053	Greiner et al. (43)
$Na_{0.554}WO_3$	0.013	Kupka and Sienko (82)
$Na_{0.956}WO_3$	0.057	Kupka and Sienko (82)
$Na_{0.6-0.7}WO_3$	0.20	Stubbin and Mellor (117)
$Na_{0.92}WO_3$	0.43	Stubbin and Mellor (117)
$Na_{0.9}WO_3$	0.42	Stubbin and Mellor (117)

electron probability density at the nuclei of Na atoms is zero. Several
models have been proposed to account for this fact (74, 111) but no
clear-cut interpretation seems to be available at present.

B. $Fe_{1-x}O$

Ferrous oxide, or wüstite, has rock-salt-type crystal structure (B1, see
Chapter 3, Section II,A, classified as BO_x). The non-stoichiometry of
FeO has been examined by several workers (20, 33, 66). By careful comparison of x-ray and pycnometric densities, Jette and Foote (66) have
shown that the structure consists of a filled anion lattice with some vacant

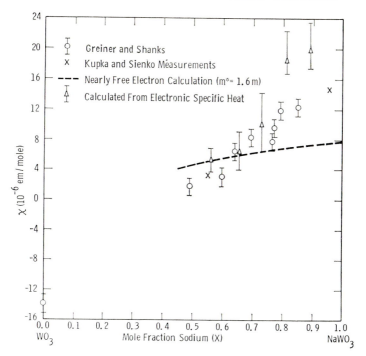

Fig. 11. Comparison between the results of the theoretical calculations and the measured room temperature magnetic susceptibilities for sodium tungsten bronzes of different sodium contents (43).

metal sites. The extent of non-stoichiometry, or x, in $Fe_{1-x}O$, is dependent upon the conditions of preparation. The phase field of the non-stoichiometric iron oxide widens with increasing temperature (20), due to the increasing importance of the entropy of vacancy formation (37, 137). The maximum iron content corresponds to about $Fe_{0.95}O$. The vacancies in the metal sites are accompanied by the formation of some Fe^{3+} ions to achieve electrical neutrality. The stoichiometric compound FeO itself does not seem to be thermodynamically stable.

1. SELF-DIFFUSION OF IRON

The rate of self-diffusion of iron in wüstite was measured by Himmel et al. (51) at 983°, 897°, and 800°C. Over the range of compositions investigated, the self-diffusion coefficient increases essentially linearly with the concentration of cation vacancies at each temperature (Fig. 12). The effect is noticeably greater at 983° than at 897°C. At 983°C, the self-diffusion coefficient increases almost by a factor of four between the iron-rich and oxygen-rich boundaries of the wüstite phase field. This is consistent with the notion that the diffusion coefficient, D, is proportional to the number of vacancies per unit volume.

The self-diffusion coefficient being rather sensitive to changes in composition, the data collected at different temperatures are best compared at a given vacancy concentration. The log D for $Fe_{0.907}O$ was found to vary linearly with the reciprocal of absolute temperature. These data are well approximated by the equation

$$D_{FeO} = 0.118 \exp \left(-1.29/kT \right) \text{ cm}^2/\text{sec} \tag{16}$$

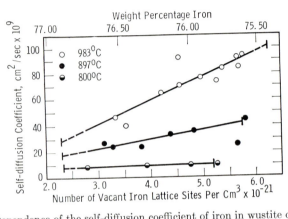

FIG. 12. Dependence of the self-diffusion coefficient of iron in wustite on composition. The short vertical lines represent the limits of the wustite phase field at each temperature (51).

between 700° and 1000°C. The activation energy of 1.29 ev (29.8 kcal/mole) is about the same as for oxygen ion diffusion in $Ca_{0.15}Zr_{0.85}O_{1.85}$, about 1.22 ev (27.1 kcal/mole) (75). It may be noted that the self-diffusion of iron in $Fe_{1-x}S$ (B8; cf. Chapter 3, Section III,A) also increases with increasing non-stoichiometry but at different rates in the a and c directions of the hexagonal crystal. Here, the average diffusion coefficient between 350°C and the melting point may be represented by $D_{FeS} = 1.6 \times 10^{-3} \exp \left(-0.91/kT \right) \text{ cm}^2/\text{sec}$ (17).

2. ELECTRICAL PROPERTIES

Wagner showed that for FeO in equilibrium with the ambient atmosphere at 800°–1000°C, the following reaction may be written (see Chapter 2, Section V,B):

$$2 \text{ Fe}^{2+} + \tfrac{1}{2} O_2(g) \rightleftharpoons 2 \text{ Fe}^{3+} + \square_{Fe^{2+}} + O^{2-} \tag{17}$$

where $\square_{Fe^{2+}}$ are the cation vacancies. For each cation vacancy created, two Fe^{3+} ions are formed. Applying the law of mass action, one obtains the equilibrium constant, K, as

$$K = \frac{[Fe^{3+}]^2 [\square_{Fe^{2+}}]}{P_{O_2}^{1/2}} \tag{18}$$

where the brackets represent the concentrations. Since there are two Fe^{3+} ions for each cation vacancy, i.e., $[\square_{Fe^{2+}}] = 2[Fe^{3+}]$,

$$[Fe^{3+}] \propto P_{O_2}^{1/6}. \tag{19}$$

Wagner assumed that the electrical conductivity is proportional to the number of Fe^{3+} ions. The conductivity may then be expected to increase as the one-sixth power of the oxygen partial pressure. Experimentally, Wagner and Koch (130) found the electrical conductivity of wüstite to be roughly proportional to the eighth root of the oxygen pressure in the temperature range 800° to 1000°C. The sign of the observed dependence confirms that $Fe_{1-x}O$ is a metal-deficient compound. The lack of precise quantitative agreement between the calculated and observed pressure dependence may be due to lack of complete equilibrium between the surrounding atmosphere and the bulk of the solid sample or due to variation of activation energy with defect concentration, as was noted in transition metal oxide systems, doped with lithium (50).

The transference number for cations in wüstite can be calculated at least approximately if the Nernst-Einstein relation can be assumed to be valid here. At 1000°C and $P_{O_2} \simeq 4 \times 10^{-15}$ atm Wagner and Koch's experimental value for the conductivity is 107 ohm^{-1} cm^{-1}. Under the same conditions, the number of cations, n, $\simeq 4.88 \times 10^{22}$ per cc, while the self-diffusion coefficient, found by Himmel et al. is roughly 6.4×10^{-7} cm^2/sec. These values lead to a transference number of about 2×10^{-4} for Fe^{2+} ions in wüstite. Therefore, most of the current in $Fe_{1-x}O$ is carried by electrons. This analysis assumes the association and interaction effects to be negligible. This assumption is not true, however, at least in highly iron-deficient wüstites as will be shown in a later section. In that case, there is a coalescence of defects leading to the formation of magnetite-like, Fe_3O_4, clusters (see Chapter 3, Section II,A). If these clusters are mobile to any extent, their motion would contribute to the measured self-diffusion coefficient but not to the electrical conductivity, since the clusters are electrically neutral. If this takes place, the Nernst-Einstein relationship would be inapplicable. However, it must be noted that the Nernst-Einstein relationship leads to a reasonable value for the transference number of Fe^{2+} ions in wüstite, suggesting that both diffusion and ionic conductivity in this oxide are indeed due to the same mechanism, i.e., the migration of free or dissociated vacancies, which are in effect, negatively charged. It may be noted that, if association effects are taken into account, the transference number for Fe^{2+} ions would be smaller than the value given above.

C. Other Examples

Cerium sulfide, Ce_3S_4, has cubic structure, $D7_3$ of Th_3P_4 type (space group $I\,\bar{4}\,3d–T_d^6$) (141); cf. Chapter 3, Section III,F. Vacancies in the metal sites can arise so that in the end member $Ce_{2.67}S_4$ (Ce_2S_3), $10\frac{2}{3}$ metal atoms are randomly distributed over the twelve equivalent positions in the unit cell with vacancies at every ninth site on the average. This metal atom subtraction is consistent with a decrease of density from 5.675 gm cm^{-3} for Ce_3S_4 to 5.186 gm cm^{-3} for $Ce_{2.67}S_4$ (141). However, there is a slight expansion of the lattice constant (from 8.6076 Å for Ce_3S_4 to 8.6173 Å for $Ce_{2.67}S_4$ (16). The system $Ce_{2.67}S_4$ to Ce_3S_4 covers a large range of electrical conductivity. At room temperature, a sample of $Ce_{2.67}S_4$ was found to be an insulator with a resistivity greater than 10^9 ohm-cm. As cerium was added, the resistivity dropped to about 10^{-3} ohm-cm for Ce_3S_4 at room temperature. All the samples showed small positive temperature coefficients of resistivity between room temperature and 1000°C (2, 102). Seebeck coefficient measurements showed all the samples studied were of the n-type. The mode of electrical conduction in cerium sulfides is not yet well understood.

The samarium-sulfur system, also with the $D7_3$ structure, is similar in many ways to cerium-sulfur system (55, 94), particularly, in the region $Sm_{2.67}S_4$ to Sm_3S_4. In this region, the electrical behavior of the two systems is quite comparable.

The praseodymium oxide compounds with their varying solubility limits between $PrO_{1.5}$ (Pr_2O_3) and PrO_2 were recently summarized by Eyring and co-workers (4) and are dealt with in Chapter 3, Section II,C,1. All these compounds may be considered to be derived from the fluorite lattice, exhibited by PrO_2, by ordered omission of the oxygen ions. The anion vacancies lead to slight distortions and some of the phases have rhombohedral symmetry. Foëx (31) measured the electrical resistivity of sintered pellets of $PrO_{1.5}$ in hydrogen between 600 and 1200°C and of $PrO_{1.833}$ (Pr_6O_{11}) in oxygen between 300 and 700°C (Fig. 13). At 600°C, the resistivity of $PrO_{1.5}$ is seven orders of magnitude larger than that of $PrO_{1.833}$. Thermal emf data on $PrO_{1.833}$ was obtained by Martin (88) from 200 to 1100°C when $PrO_{1.833}$ is progressively denuded of oxygen as the temperature increases (Fig. 14). The Seebeck coefficient is negative and the numerical value decreases with increasing temperature up to 780°C.

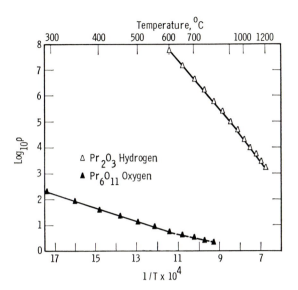

FIG. 13. Electrical resistivity (ohm-cm) of $PrO_{1.5}$ in hydrogen and of $PrO_{1.833}$ in oxygen (31).

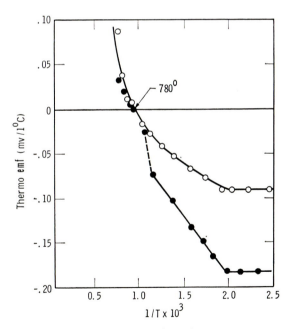

FIG. 14. Thermo emf of $PrO_{1.833}$ versus reciprocal of absolute temperature for two specimens (88).

However, p-type conduction is exhibited by $PrO_{1.833}$ at temperatures above 780°C, and also by compositions PrO_x with $x \leq 0.75$.

IV. FERROELECTRICITY

Many oxide ferroelectrics crystallize with perovskite (e.g., $BaTiO_3$; cf. Chapter 3, Section II,H), pyrochlore (e.g., $Cd_2Nb_2O_7$, $E8_1$; cf. Chapter 3, Section II,C,1) and tungsten-bronze (e.g., $PbNb_2O_6$; cf. Chapter 3, Section II,F) type structures. Linkages through corners of oxygen octahedra surrounding Ti or Nb ions, forming O-metal-O chains, is a common feature of these structure types. The large cations occupy the interstices in the framework formed by the TiO_6 or NbO_6 octahedra.

Internal field calculations on the perovskite lattice (e.g., $BaTiO_3$) by Slater (112) and others have shown that the interaction between Ti and O_1 ions (where O_1 are the oxygen ions on lines passing through Ti ions in the z direction) is especially strong, enhancing the effect of the polarizability of the Ti ion significantly. According to this analysis, the O_1–Ti–O_1 interactions are very important for the occurrence of ferroelectricity in $BaTiO_3$ with only a minor role being played by the Ba ions. However, the significant influence of replacing Ba^{2+} by other divalent cations suggests that the A ions in ABO_3 compounds are also a factor in determining the ferroelectric properties and Curie temperatures. For details, reference may be made to reviews of ferroelectricity (32, 73, 76).

A. $BaTiO_3$

Barium titanate, $BaTiO_3$, has tetragonal symmetry at room temperature and becomes cubic at the Curie temperature, 120°C. At the phase transition, dielectric constant, spontaneous polarization, lattice constants and other parameters change discontinuously. From the foregoing discussion of the origin of ferroelectricity in $BaTiO_3$, it may be expected that non-stoichiometry introduces a disturbing effect on the local fields responsible for polarization catastrophe and consequently on the Curie temperature. We will discuss the influence of vacancies in oxygen and Ba sites on the Curie temperature of $BaTiO_3$. No examples of vacancies in B site of ABO_3 perovskite-type compounds are reported (132).

Non-stoichiometry can be achieved by reducing a $BaTiO_3$ crystal in a hydrogen atmosphere at an elevated temperature so that oxygen ion vacancies are formed. Electrical neutrality is preserved presumably by the conversion of some Ti^{4+} ions into Ti^{3+} ions. The formula may then be written as $BaTi^{3+}_{2x}Ti^{4+}_{1-2x}O_{3-x}$. It has been shown that reduced barium titanate is cubic at room temperature and exhibits a dielectric constant maximum at a temperature corresponding to Curie temperature, which is well below room temperature (6, 92). DeVries (23) has observed the disappearance of ferroelectric domain structure on reduction of barium titanate ceramics. It would be interesting to determine if the missing oxygen ions are the ones in the z direction, which are believed to have an important role in O_1–Ti–O_1 interactions. On reoxidation of the reduced samples, the Curie temperature was found to move up to the usual 120°C.

When an ion of valency higher than four (e.g., Nb^{5+}; Chapter 3, Section II,H) is introduced in place of Ti^{4+} in $BaTiO_3$, electrical neutrality may be restored by

(1) adding additional oxygen ions,

(2) converting appropriate number of Ti^{4+} ions into Ti^{3+} ions, or

(3) creating cation vacancies.

Since oxygen ions are in close packed arrangement in perovskite lattice, introduction of more of the large anions is unlikely. The presence of Ti^{3+} with Ti^{4+} should lead to increased electrical conductivity. From the work of Sauer and Flaschen (105) and Saburi (103, 104) on semi-conducting barium titanate, it may be concluded that at low niobium concentrations ($<0.2\%$), Ti^{3+} ions are indeed formed and give rise to enhanced electrical conductivity. With niobium contents greater than 0.2 to 0.3%, the samples become as good insulators as barium titanate itself. At these compositions, the presence of Ti^{3+} ions may therefore be ruled out. Preliminary x-ray intensity studies are consistent with the notion that some of barium sites are vacant at these compositions (119). In this connection, it may be noted that in WO_3, which crystallizes with the perovskite structure, all the A ions are missing.

Non-stoichiometric compositions in the system $BaTiO_3$–$Ba_{0.5}NbO_3$ were first investigated by Smolenskii et al. (114) and later by Isupov (65) and by Subbarao and Shirane (119). Solid solutions are formed up to about 14% $Ba_{0.5}NbO_3$. The Curie temperature of $BaTiO_3$ decreases steeply with the addition of $Ba_{0.5}NbO_3$, reaching a value of -140°C at the solubility limit. Part of this decrease no doubt is due to the replacement of Ti^{4+} ions by ions of a different valency (Nb^{5+}). Perhaps differences in size and polarizability of Ti^{4+} and Nb^{5+} ions also have an influence. However, $Ba_{0.5}TaO_3$ was found to have an effect similar to that of $Ba_{0.5}NbO_3$ in these systems, though Nb^{5+} and Ta^{5+} lead to substantially different Curie temperatures (T_C), in other ferroelectric oxides ($PbNb_2O_6$, T_C 570°C; $PbTa_2O_6$, T_C 260°C; $KNbO_3$, T_C 430°C; $KTaO_3$, T_C -260°C). This suggests that the replacement of Ti^{4+} ions by pentavalent ions is not the predominant factor. It must therefore be concluded that cation vacancies have a significant influence on the Curie temperature of $BaTiO_3$. The transition temperatures of solid solutions based on $BaTiO_3$ are summarized in Fig. 15 to illustrate the influence of ions of different size, charge and polarizability (*15, 41, 62, 107*) and also the role of non-stoichiometry. Cation vacancies and replacement of Ba^{2+} and Ti^{4+} by two trivalent ions (e.g., $La^{3+}Al^{3+}$) (*64*) have the strongest effect on the Curie temperature of $BaTiO_3$.

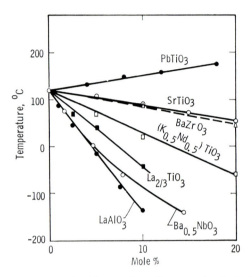

FIG. 15. Influence of ions with different size, charge, and polarizability and of non-stoichiometry on the ferroelectric Curie temperature of $BaTiO_3$.

The addition of $La_{2/3}TiO_3$ to $BaTiO_2$ leads to analogous results (*72, 115*) (Fig. 15). It is interesting to note that $La_{2/3}TiO_3$, which leads to fewer cation vacancies for the same amount of addition, is less severe than $Ba_{0.5}NbO_3$ in lowering the Curie temperature. If, however, a plot of the transition temperature versus the number of cation (A site) vacancies in these two systems is made, a straight line with a negative slope of about 50°C per 1% of cation vacancies is obtained.

B. Other Examples

Sodium niobate crystallizes with perovskite structure and is antiferroelectric in its pure form. In the non-stoichiometric systems $NaNbO_3$–

$Cd_{0.5}NbO_3$ and $NaNbO_3$–$Pb_{0.5}NbO_3$ (see Chapter 3, Section II,E,2,a), single phase perovskite-type solid solutions are formed up to 25% $Cd_{0.5}$-NbO_3 or 35% $Pb_{0.5}NbO_3$ (*34, 80, 83, 131*). Two Na^+ ions are believed to be replaced by one Cd^{2+} (or Pb^{2+}) ion and a cation vacancy. The phase transitions in the non-stoichiometric systems were studied. Defect solid solutions based on ferroelectric $PbTiO_3$ (*120*) and antiferroelectric $PbZrO_3$ (*79*) are also formed.

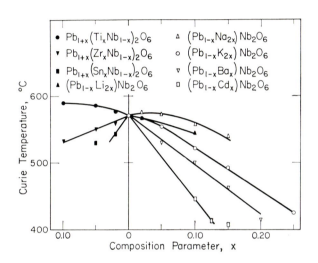

FIG. 16. Effect of substitutional ions and of guest ions in vacant metal sites on the ferroelectric Curie temperature of $PbNb_2O_6$ (*122*).

In Chapter 3, Section II,F, it has been demonstrated that ferroelectric $PbNb_2O_6$ (*39*) belongs to a class of non-stoichiometric materials with tetragonal tungsten-bronze type structure (*35, 87, 128*), possessing the general formula $A_{1+x}B_2O_6$ ($A_{\frac{1}{2}(1+x)}BO_3$) where A and B may be composed of one or more types of ions and x can vary over a limited range of positive and negative values. For positive values of x the ferroelectric phase is stabilized and the Curie temperature changes only slightly (Fig. 16). On the other hand, for negative values of x, i.e., increased number of A site vacancies, the Curie temperature decreases steeply (*118, 122*) (Fig. 17). Further, the non-stoichiometry induces an additional phase at some compositions (*121*). Other ferroelectric compositions related to this family are discussed by Goodman (*40*) and Fang and co-workers (*30*).

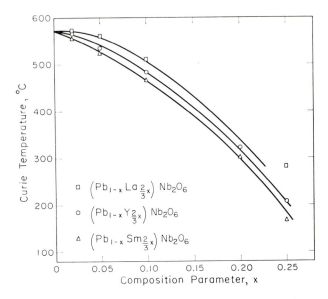

Fɪɢ. 17. Influence of metal site vacancies on the ferroelectric Curie temperature of
PbNb₂O₆ (*122*).

V. MAGNETIC PROPERTIES

A. Magnetic and Neutron Diffraction Studies on $Fe_{1-x}O$

The magnetic consequences of non-stoichiometry may be illustrated by
an examination of wüstite, $Fe_{1-x}O$. It has already been pointed out that
$Fe_{1-x}O$ crystallizes with rock-salt-type, *B1*, structure and has a filled anion
lattice and vacant metal sites. Electrical neutrality is preserved by promoting the appropriate number of Fe^{2+} ions into trivalent state. The
transport properties of wüstite were discussed in terms of this defect
structure.

Ferrous oxide becomes antiferromagnetic at 198°K by an ordering of
the magnetic moments associated with the iron atoms (*8*). Neutron diffraction studies have shown that the magnetic moments are arrayed in
ferromagnetic sheets parallel to the (111) planes; the moment directions are
perpendicular to the ferromagnetic sheets and point alternately up and
down in adjacent sheets (Fig. 18) (*98, 108, 109*). Associated with the
magnetic ordering, there is a slight elongation along the [111] direction
and the symmetry becomes rhombohedral. The x-ray study of Willis and
Rooksby (*138*) showed a decrease of rhombohedral deformation at 90°K
as the iron content decreases.

To examine the influence of non-stoichiometry (metal site vacancies and the presence of Fe^{3+} ions) on the magnetic exchange interactions, neutron diffraction studies were carried out by Roth (*100*) on wüstite specimens, quenched from 1000°C. These studies were made at room temperature (in the paramagnetic state) and at 90° and 4.2°K (in the antiferromagnetic state). Magnetic measurements were performed on the same specimens (*99*).

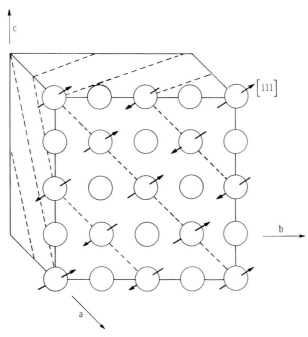

Fig. 18. Antiferromagnetic structure of stoichiometric FeO, with atomic spins directed along the [111] axis (*100*).

The correlation between the observed and calculated neutron intensities at room temperature is better for a model with a random distribution of an appropriate number of vacancies in metal sites than for stoichiometric FeO. However, the agreement was still not quite satisfactory. For example, the concentration of iron ions in the ferrous oxide determined by chemical analysis was about 20% greater than that estimated by the neutron diffraction analysis. To improve the agreement, Roth located the excess iron atoms in the tetrahedral interstices of the rock-salt structure on the basis of space group O_h^7–$Fd3m$. If the interstitial positions were occupied in a regular fashion, the space group $Fd3m$ requires Bragg reflections forbidden for the simple rock-salt structure. No such superstructure lines were observed in the x-ray or neutron diffraction patterns, but intense diffuse scattering was observed at angles where the superstructure lines were expected. This suggests that the major contribution to the diffuse scattering is the structural disorder created by the more or less random choice of different sets of tetrahedral sites available for occupancy by interstitial iron atoms.

The low temperature neutron diffraction patterns showed additional lines due to magnetic scattering (see Chapter I, Section VI,A). Within experimental error, the neutron scattering at 90° and 4.2°K is the same.

The structure of ferrous oxide is conveniently visualized as a framework of oxygen atoms in cubic close packing with cations occupying the interstices. In the non-stoichiometric compound, coulombic repulsion between cations in adjacent tetrahedral and octahedral sites are minimized if the defects coalesce such that an octahedral vacancy is shared by two interstitial cations. The coalescence of defects is a step toward the formation of magnetite, Fe_3O_4 (52). It is noteworthy that wüsite and magnetite have similar lattice parameters (8.54 Å for $Fe_{30}O_{32}$ and 8.39 Å for $Fe_{24}O_{32}$) (38) and atomic arrangements. A good epitaxial relationship also exists between these two compounds (89). These considerations, plus the fact that the neutron intensities indicate two vacancies per interstitial cation in $Fe_{1-x}O$, as in magnetite, suggest that the cation distribution in the vicinity of defects in wüstite represent magnetite-like clusters (Table IV). The distributions of iron atoms in the quenched wüstite specimens used for neutron experiments may be compared to those employed for high temperature diffusion studies (51), since the neutron specimens represent the frozen-in distribution of the high-temperature equilibrium. The existence of interstitial iron atoms in $Fe_{1-x}O$ is consistent with the cation diffusion data, because in the close-packed oxygen structure, the diffusion path from a filled to a vacant octahedral site is through a tetrahedral site.

The predominant magnetic interaction in FeO, as in MnO, NiO, and CoO, is due to the antiparallel super-exchange (1, 81) between moments on next-nearest neighbor cations connected by oxygen anions:

$$Fe^{2+}\text{—}O\text{—}Fe^{2+}\text{—}O\text{—}Fe^{2+}\text{—}O\text{—}Fe^{2+}$$
$$\uparrow \qquad \downarrow \qquad \uparrow \qquad \downarrow$$

The moment per iron atom should be somewhat greater than $4\mu_B$. The presence of Fe^{3+} ions in octahedral sites in $Fe_{1-x}O$ would cause a slight decrease in the average moment per octahedral site if antiparallel coupling between next-nearest-neighbors is retained. Alternatively, the double exchange (142) interaction of $Fe^{2+}\text{—}O\text{—}Fe^{3+}$ provides a mechanism for ferromagnetic coupling. The additional exchange of $Fe_{(tetra.)}\text{—}O\text{—}Fe_{(oct.)}$

type is also possible. These sites are not crystallographically equivalent and hence a negative interaction is expected regardless of valence state. By analogy to the ionic distribution in magnetite, there may be a slight preference of Fe^{3+} for tetrahedral interstices, and the antiferromagnetic octahedral-tetrahedral exchange will result in a net ferrimagnetic moment. However, neutron diffraction experiments revealed only antiferromagnetic coupling. Magnetic studies did not show appreciable ferromagnetic remanence. Consequently, the spin correlation in the defect appears to be antiferromagnetic or paramagnetic.

The average magnetic moment per octahedral site computed from neutron intensities is compared with calculated value in Table IV. The calculation is based on the assumption that the moment is proportional to the number of Fe—O—Fe bonds in superexchange contact. No account is taken of the orbital contribution to the spin moment.

The smaller magnetic moment observed experimentally suggests that approximately 20% of the octahedral sites are not contributing to the neutron scattering from the ordered structure. Further, they are not coupled to produce a ferromagnetic remanence. Thus, Roth concluded,

TABLE IV

CATION DEFECTS IN FERROUS OXIDE   (100)

		I	II
$Fe_{1-x}O$	$1-x$	0.945	0.926
Content of average unit cell	n_{oxygen}	32	32
	n_{cation}	30.2	29.6
	$n_{Fe^{3+}}$	3.5	4.7
Ratio of vacancies to interstitial cations		1.9	2.2
Fraction octahedral sites occupied		0.88	0.86
Next-nearest-neighbor shell	$n_{vacancies}$	0.71	0.83
	$n_{cations}$	5.29	5.17
	$n_{Fe—O—Fe\ bonds}$	4.66	4.46
	Per cent $_{Fe—O—Fe\ bonds}$	77.6	74.3
Average moment per octahedral site	calc.	$3.10\mu_B$	$2.98\mu_B$
	obs.	$2.96\mu_B$	$2.36\mu_B$

that there are in FeO small "paramagnetic islands" of approximately two interstitial cations plus six octahedral sites per unit cell.

The magnetic structure in a (11$\bar{1}$) plane of wüstite is described in Fig. 19 (*100*). Three defect regions are shown ranging from that about a single interstitial to a "magnetite-like" block derived from the coalescence of six interstitial cations. Formation of large clusters of cations and vacan-

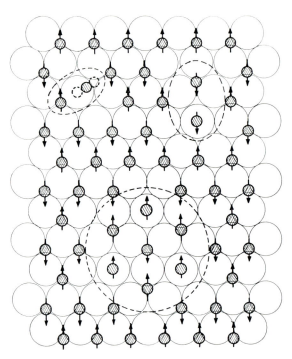

FIG. 19. Magnetic structure of defects in FeO. The projection on (11$\bar{1}$) of three clusters formed from 1, 2, and 6 interstitial cations is shown. The isolated interstitial occupies an intermediate position between tetrahedral interstices (*100*).

cies is favored because of the reduction of coulombic repulsion. The cations situated on octahedral and tetrahedral sites produce a ferrimagnetic moment in the vicinity of the defect due to super-exchange. The co-existence of ferromagnetic components in an antiferromagnetic matrix is consistent with a small ferromagnetic remanence observed at room temperature, which increases with decreasing temperature. In addition, an asymmetric hystersis loop was observed (*99*). These results have been explained as follows. The spin within the magnetite-like clusters are ferro-magnetically coupled, but at room temperature the applied magnetic field is able to orient the magnetization of only the larger clusters against the randomizing effects of thermal motion. As the temperature is lowered, increasingly smaller clusters can be oriented and the remanence increases. In similar fashion, the asymmetric hysteresis loop is the result of the unidirectional anisotropy developed when the antiferromagnetic and ferrimagnetic volumes are magnetically ordered by the applied field.

B. Mössbauer Study of $Fe_{1-x}O$

Wertheim (*136*) observed two Mössbauer absorption peaks in $Fe_{1-x}O$. Recently Shirane et al. (*106*) made a Mössbauer study of $Fe_{1-x}O$ and (Fe, Mg)O. They assigned the two peaks to Fe^{2+} and Fe^{3+}. These authors observed also a quadrupole splitting of Fe^{2+}, even though the over-all symmetry of the crystal is cubic (Fig. 20). This might mean that the symmetry of the crystal is not really cubic, although the distortion is too small to be detected by x-ray techniques. Or, more likely, the cation vacancies in $Fe_{1-x}O$ remove local cubic symmetry at Fe nuclei. It may be noted that in $Fe_{0.915}O$, 66% of the Fe ions have at least one vacancy somewhere among the twelve nearest neighboring metal positions, if the vacancies

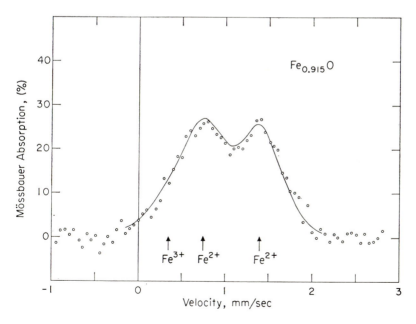

FIG. 20. Mössbauer absorption of $Fe_{0.915}O$ (*106*).

are distributed at random. Similar quadrupole splittings were observed in the system (Fe, Mg)O, where the over-all symmetry again is cubic.

C. Other Examples

Crystal structure determinations of $Fe_{1-x}S$ ($B8-C6$; cf. Chapter 3, Section III,A) revealed an ordering of vacancies (7, 46, 47, 71). The magnetic studies of FeS (47, 53, 71, 90, 91, 93) showed it to be antiferromagnetic when it is stoichiometric or nearly so. With about 10% of iron ions missing, the compound becomes ferrimagnetic. The iron deficiency is accompanied by the formation of some Fe^{3+} ions to maintain electrical neutrality, as in the case of $Fe_{1-x}O$. The ferrimagnetism has been interpreted in terms of the ordering of ferric and ferrous ions on alternate layers perpendicular to the c-axis of the hexagonal crystal (54, 86, 140).

The systems (La, Sr)CoO_3 (69) and (La, Ca)MnO_3 (48) also present interesting examples of the magnetic consequences of non-stoichiometry.

VI. CONCLUDING REMARKS

Rather detailed discussions of ionic and electrical conductivity, and ferroelectric and magnetic properties of non-stoichiometric compounds have been presented. Now a brief mention will be made of other properties.

Dielectric absorption studies on $Ba_x(Ti_{8-x}Mg_x)O_{16}$ (with $0.67 < x < 1.14$) showed a strong anisotropy between the c and a directions of the tetragonal crystal (25). The Ba ions are located in interstitial sites in the tunnels formed by a framework of (Ti, Mg)O_2 octahedron. The tunnels are along c and the absorption has been interpreted in terms of the movement of Ba ions to the adjacent vacant site in the tunnel (see Chapter 3, Section II,B,2). The dielectric relaxation behavior observed in barium zirconium metaniobate [(40) cf. also Chapter 3, Section II,F] appears similar to that in $Ba(Ti, Mg)_8O_{16}$. Inasmuch as the metaniobate has tetragonal tungsten bronze type structure with unfilled sites in the tunnels, similar phenomena may be operative.

It has been known that non-stoichiometry influences diffusion in inorganic compounds and therefore it may be expected that creep and other mechanical properties at elevated temperatures are affected by non-stoichiometry. However, no clear-cut evidence of the relation of variable composition and mechanical behavior of non-metallic materials is available at present.

The thermal properties, e.g., thermal conductivity, of alloy systems are known to be influenced by the formation of solid solutions and the presence of point defects (78). It is therefore reasonable to expect that thermal conductivity of non-stoichiometric systems is related to composition. No detailed studies of this type on inorganic compounds seem to be available.

ACKNOWLEDGMENT

The author is indebted to several members of these laboratories, particularly Drs. G. Shirane, R. R. Heikes, and P. H. Sutter, for helpful discussions.

REFERENCES

1. Anderson, P. W., *Phys. Rev.* **79**, 350 (1950).
2. Appel, J., and Kurnick, S. W., *J. Appl. Phys.* **32**, 2206 (1961).
3. Atoji, M., and Rundle, R. E., *J. Chem. Phys.* **32**, 627 (1960).
4. Baenziger, N. C., Eick, H. A., Schmidt, H. S., and Eyring, L., *J. Am. Chem. Soc.* **83**, 2219 (1961).
5. Baumback, H. H., and Wagner, C., *Z. physik. Chem. (Leipzig)* **B22**, 199 (1933); **B24**, 59 (1934).
6. Belyaev, I. N., Novosil'tsev, N. S., Fesenko, E. G., and Khodakov, A. L., *Doklady Akad. Nauk S.S.S.R.* **83**, 675 (1952).
7. Bertaut, F., *Acta Cryst.* **6**, 557 (1953).
8. Bizette, H., and Tsai, B., *Comp. rend, acad. sci.* **217**, 390 (1943).
9. Breckenridge, R. G., *in* "Imperfections in Nearly Perfect Crystals" (W. Schockley, J. H. Hollomon, R. J. Maurer, and F. Seitz, eds.), p. 219. Wiley, New York, 1952.
10. Brimm, E. O., Brantley, J. C., Lorenz, J. H., and Jellinek, M. H., *J. Am. Chem. Soc.* **73**, 5427 (1951).
11. Brindley, G. W., and Hoare, F. E., *Proc. Phys. Soc. (London)* **B49**, 619 (1937).
12. Brown, B. W., and Banks, E., *Phys. Rev.* **84**, 609 (1951).
13. Brown, B. W., and Banks, E., *J. Am. Chem. Soc.* **76**, 963 (1954).
14. Brown, F. H., Jr., and Duwez, P., *J. Am. Ceram. Soc.* **38**, 95 (1955).
15. Buhrer, C., *Tech. Rept. 160, Lab.* Insulation Research, Mass. Inst. Technol., Cambridge, March, 1961.
16. Carter, F. L., Miller, R. C., and Ryan, F. M., *J. Advanced Energy Conversion* **1**, 165 (1961).
17. Condit, R. H., *in* "Kinetics of High Temperature Processes" (W. D. Kingery, ed.), p. 97. Wiley, New York, 1959.
18. Conroy, L. E., and Sienko, M. J., *J. Am. Chem. Soc.* **74**, 3520 (1952).
19. Curtis, C. E., and Johnson, J. R., *J. Am. Ceram. Soc.* **40**, 63 (1957).
20. Darken, L. S., and Gurry, R. W., *J. Am. Chem. Soc.* **67**, 1398 (1945).
21. de Jong, W. F., *Z. Krist.* **81**, 314 (1932).
22. Dekker, A. J., "Solid State Physics," Chapter 7. Prentice Hall, Englewood Cliffs, New Jersey, 1957.
23. DeVries, R. C., *J. Am. Ceram. Soc.* **43**, 226 (1960).
24. Dietzel, A., and Tober, H., *Ber. deut. keram. Ges.* **30**, 47, 71 (1953).
25. Dryden, J. S., and Wadsley, A. D., *Trans. Faraday Soc.* **54**, 1574 (1958).
26. Duwez, P., Brown, F. H., Jr., and Odell, F., *J. Electrochem. Soc.* **98**, 356 (1951).
27. Duwez, P., Odell, F., and Brown, F. H., Jr., *J. Am. Ceram. Soc.* **35**, 107 (1952).

28. Ebert, F., and Cohn, E., *Z. anorg. u. allgem. Chem.* **213**, 321 (1933).
29. Ellerbeck, L. D., Shanks, H. R., Sidles, P. H., and Danielson, G. C., *J. Chem. Phys.* **35**, 298 (1961).
30. Fang, P. H., Roth, R. S., and Johnson, H., *J. Am. Ceram. Soc.* **43**, 169 (1960).
31. Foëx, M., *Comp. rend. acad. sci.* **220**, 359 (1945).
32. Forsbergh, P. W., Jr., *in* "Handbuch der Physik" (S. Flügge, ed.), Vol. XVII, p. 318. Springer, Berlin, 1956.
33. Foster, P. K., and Welch, A. J. E., *Trans. Faraday Soc.* **52**, 1626 (1956).
34. Francombe, M. H., and Lewis, B., *J. Electronics* **2**, 387 (1957).
35. Francombe, M. H., and Lewis, B., *Acta Cryst.* **11**, 696 (1958).
36. Gardner, W. R., and Danielson, G. C., *Phys. Rev.* **93**, 46 (1954).
37. Garner, W. E. (ed.) "Chemistry of the Solid State," p. 20. Academic Press, New York, 1955.
38. Goldschmidt, H. J., *J. Iron Steel Inst.* (*London*) **146**, 157 (1942).
39. Goodman, G., *J. Am. Ceram. Soc.* **36**, 368 (1953).
40. Goodman, G., *J. Am. Ceram. Soc.* **43**, 105 (1960).
41. Gränicher, H., and Jakits, O., *Nuovo cimento* [9] **11**, 480 (1954).
42. Gray, T. J., "The Defect Solid State," Chapter VII. Interscience, New York, 1957.
43. Greiner, J. D., Shanks, H. R., and Wallace, D. G. (Private Communication).
44. Hägg, G., *Z. physik. Chem.* (*Leipzig*) **B29**, 192 (1935); *Nature* **135**, 874 (1935).
45. Hägg, G., and Magnéli, A., *Revs. Pure and Appl. Chem.* (*Australia*) **4**, 235 (1954).
46. Hägg, G., and Sucksdorff, I., *Z. physik. Chem.* (*Leipzig*) **B22**, 444 (1933).
47. Haraldsen, H., *Z. anorg. u. allgem. Chem.* **231**, 78 (1937); **246**, 169, 195 (1941).
48. Harwood, M. G., *Proc. Phys. Soc.* (*London*) **B68**, 586 (1955).
49. Hauffe, K., "Oxydation von Metallen und Metallegierungen." Springer, Berlin, 1956.
50. Heikes, R. R., and Johnston, W. D., *J. Chem. Phys.* **26**, 582 (1957).
51. Himmel, L., Mehl, R. F., and Birchenall, C. E., *Trans. Am. Inst. Mining, Met. Petrol. Engrs.* **197**, 827 (1953).
52. Himmel, L., *in* "Kinetics of High Temperature Processes" (W. D. Kingery, ed.), p. 137. Wiley, New York, 1959.
53. Hirahara, E., and Murakami, M., *J. Phys. Chem. Solids* **7**, 281 (1959).
54. Hirone, T., and Tsuya, N., *Phys. Rev.* **83**, 1063 (1951).
55. Houston, M. D., *in* "Rare Earth Research" (W. Kleber, ed.), p. 255. Macmillan, New York, 1961.
56. Huibregtse, E. J., Barker, D. B., and Danielson, G. C., *Phys. Rev.* **84**, 142 (1951).
57. Hund, F., *Z. Elektrochem.* **55**, 363 (1951).
58. Hund, F., *Z. physik. Chem.* (*Leipzig*) **B199**, 142 (1952).
59. Hund, F., *Z. anorg. u. allgem. Chem.* **274**, 105 (1953).
60. Hund, F., and Mezger, R., *Z. physik. Chem.* (*Leipzig*) **B201**, 268 (1952).
61. Hund, F., and Dürrwächter, W., *Z. anorg. u. allgem. Chem.* **265**, 67 (1951).
62. Ikeda, T., *J. Phys. Soc. Japan* **14**, 1286 (1959).
63. Ingold, J. H., and DeVries, R. C., *Acta Met.* **6**, 736 (1958).

64. Ismailzade, I. G., *Izvest. Akad. Nauk S.S.S.R.* **22**, 1483 (1958).
65. Isupov, V. A., *Izvest. Akad. Nauk S.S.S.R.* **21**, 402 (1957).
66. Jette, E. R., and Foote, F., *J. Chem. Phys.* **1**, 29 (1933); *Trans. AIME* **105**, 276 (1933).
67. Johnson, J. R., and Curtis, C. E., *J. Am. Ceram. Soc.* **37**, 611 (1954).
68. Jones, W. H., Jr., Garbaty, E. A., and Barnes, R. G., *J. Chem. Phys.* **36**, 494 (1962).
69. Jonker, G. H., and van Santen, H. J., *Physica* **19**, 120 (1953).
70. Juretschke, H. J., *Phys. Rev.* **86**, 124 (1952).
71. Juza, R., and Biltz, W., *Z. anorg. u. allgem. Chem.* **205**, 273 (1932).
72. Kainz, J., *Ber. deut. keram. Ges.* **35**, 69 (1958).
73. Känzig, W., *Solid State Phys.* **4**, 1 (1957).
74. Keller, J. M., *J. Chem. Phys.* **33**, 232 (1960).
75. Kingery, W. D., Pappis, J., Doty, M. E., and Hill, D. C., *J. Am. Ceram. Soc.* **42**, 393 (1959).
76. Kittel, C., "Introduction to Solid State Physics," Chapter 8. Wiley, New York, 1956.
77. Kiukkola, K., and Wagner, C., *J. Electrochem. Soc.* **104**, 379 (1957).
78. Klemens, P. G., *Phys. Rev.* **119**, 507 (1960).
79. Krainik, N. N., *Zhur. Tekh. Fiz.* **28**, 525 (1958).
80. Krainik, N. N., *Izvest. Akad. Nauk S.S.S.R.* **22**, 1492 (1958).
81. Kramers, H., *Physica* **18**, 101, (1952).
82. Kupka, F., and Sienko, M. J., *J. Chem. Phys.* **18**, 1296 (1950).
83. Lewis, B., and White, E. A. D., *J. Electronics* **1**, 646 (1956); *Acta Cryst.* **8**, 849 (1955).
84. Lidiard, A. B., *Phys. Rev.* **94**, 29 (1954).
85. Lidiard, A. B., *in* "Handbuch der Physik" (S. Flügge, ed.), Vol. XX, p. 246. Springer, Berlin, 1957.
86. Lotgering, F. K., *Philips Research Repts.* **11**, 190 (1956).
87. Magnéli, A., *Arkiv Kemi* **1**, 213 (1949).
88. Martin, R. L., *Nature* **165**, 202 (1950).
89. Mehl, R. F., and McCandless, E. L., *Trans. Am. Inst. Mining Met. Petrol. Engrs.* **125**, 531 (1957).
90. Miyahara, S., *Proc. Phys. Math. Soc. Japan* **22**, 358, (1940).
91. Neél, L., *Revs. Modern. Phys.* **25**, 58 (1953).
92. Novosil'tsev, N. S., and Khodakov, A. L., *Doklady Akad. Nauk S.S.S.R.* **85**, 1263 (1952).
93. Pauthenet, R., *Compt. rend. acad. sci.* **234**, 2261 (1952).
94. Picon, M., Darange, L., Flahaut, J., and Guittard, M., *Bull. soc. chim. France* **2**, 221 (1960).
95. Rees, A. L. G., "Chemistry of the Defect Solid State," Chapter VI. Methuen, London, 1954.
96. Rosen, C., Post, B., and Banks, E., *Acta Cryst.* **9**, 477 (1956).
97. Roth, R. S., *J. Research Natl. Bur. Standards* **56**, 17 (1956).
98. Roth, W. L., *Phys. Rev.* **110**, 1333 (1958) ; **111**, 772 (1958).
99. Roth, W. L., *J. Appl. Phys.* **30**, 303S (1959).
100. Roth, W. L., *Acta Cryst.* **13**, 140 (1960).
101. Ruff, O., Ebert, F., and Stephan, E., *Z. anorg. u. allgem. Chem.* **180**, 215 (1929).

102. Ryan, F. M., Greenberg, I. N., Carter, F. L., and Miller, R. C., *J. Appl. Phys.* 33, 864 (1962).
103. Saburi, O., *J. Phys. Soc. Japan* 14, 1159 (1959).
104. Saburi, O., *J. Am. Ceram. Soc.* 44, 54 (1961).
105. Sauer, H. A., and Flaschen, S. S., *Proc. 7th Electronics Components Symposium, Washington, D. C., May, 1956* p. 41.
106. Shirane, G., Cox, D. E., and Ruby, S. L., *Phys. Rev.* 125, 1158 (1962).
107. Shirane, G., and Suzuki, K., *J. Phys. Soc. Japan* 6, 274 (1951).
108. Shull, C. G., Strauser, W. A., and Wollan, E. O., *Phys. Rev.* 83, 333 (1951).
109. Shull, C. G., Wollan, E. O., and Koehler, W. C., *Phys. Rev.* 84, 912 (1951).
110. Shusterius, C., and Padurow, N. N., *Ber. deut. keram. Ges.* 30, 235 (1953).
111. Sienko, M. J., *J. Am. Chem. Soc.* 81, 5556 (1959).
112. Slater, J. C., *Phys. Rev.* 78, 748 (1950).
113. Smith, J. F., and Danielson, G. C., *J. Chem. Phys.* 22, 266 (1954).
114. Smolenskii, G. A., Isupov, V. A., and Agranovskaya, A. I., *Doklady Akad. Nauk S.S.S.R.* 113, 1053 (1957).
115. Smolenskii, G. A., Isupov, V. A., and Agranovskaya, A. I., *Fiz. Tverd. Tela. Akad. Nauk S.S.S.R.* 1, 1573 (1959).
116. Straumanis, M. E., and Dravnieks, A., *J. Am. Chem. Soc.* 71, 683 (1949).
117. Stubbin, P. M., and Mellor, D. P., *J. Roy. Soc. New South Wales* 82, 225 (1948).
118. Subbarao, E. C., *J. Am. Ceram. Soc.* 42, 448 (1959).
119. Subbarao, E. C., and Shirane, G., *J. Am. Ceram. Soc.* 42, 279 (1959).
120. Subbarao, E. C., *J. Am. Ceram. Soc.* 43, 119 (1960).
121. Subbarao, E. C., *J. Am. Ceram. Soc.* 43, 439 (1960).
122. Subbarao, E. C., and Shirane, G., *J. Chem. Phys.* 32, 1846 (1960).
123. Tilk, W., and Klemm, W., *Z. anorg. u. allgem. Chem.* 240, 355 (1939).
124. Trombe, F., and Foëx, M., *Compt. rend. acad. sci.* 233, 254 (1951).
125. Trombe, F., and Foëx, M., *Compt. rend. acad. sci.* 236, 1783 (1953).
126. Vest, R. W., Griffel, M., and Smith, J. F., *J. Chem. Phys.* 28, 293 (1958).
127. Wachtman, J. B., Jr., Thesis, University of Maryland, College Park, Maryland, 1961.
128. Wadsley, A. D., *Revs. Pure and Appl. Chem. (Australia)* 5, 165 (1955).
129. Wagner, C., *Z. physik. Chem. (Leipzig)* B22, 181 (1933).
130. Wagner, C., and Koch, E., *Z. physik. Chem. (Leipzig)* B32, 439 (1936).
131. Wainer, E., and Wentworth, C., *J. Am. Ceram. Soc.* 35, 207 (1952).
132. Ward, R., *in* "Progress in Inorganic Chemistry" (F. A. Cotton, ed.), Vol. I, p. 465. Interscience, New York, 1959.
133. Weissbart, J., *J. Chem. Educ.* 38, 267 (1961).
134. Weissbart, J., and Ruka, R., *Rev. Sci. Instr.* 32, 593 (1961).
135. Weissbart, J., and Ruka, R., *Extended Abstr., Fuel Cell Symposium, Electrochem. Soc., Detroit, Michigan, October, 1961.*
136. Wertheim, G. W., *J. Appl. Phys.* 32, 110S (1961).
137. White, J., *Trans. Brit. Ceram. Soc.* 56, 553 (1957).
138. Willis, B. T. M., and Rooksby, H. P., *Acta Cryst.* 6, 827 (1953).
139. Wöhler, F., *Ann. Physik* [2] 2, 350 (1824).
140. Yosida, K., *Progr. Theor. Phys. (Kyoto)* 16, 356 (1956).
141. Zachariasen, W. H., *Acta Cryst.* 1, 265 (1948); 2, 57 (1949).
142. Zener, C., *Phys. Rev.* 82, 403 (1951).

CHAPTER 6

R. M. Barrer
Chemistry Department,
Imperial College of Science and Technology,
London, England

Inorganic Inclusion Complexes

I. Introduction... 310
II. Guest Molecules in Isolated Cavities......................... 313
    A. Gas and Liquid Hydrates............................... 313
    B. Felspathoids... 324
III. Guest Molecules in Parallel Channels: Cancrinites and Fibrous
    Clays.. 327
IV. Guest Molecules between Chains............................. 330
    A. Alkylammonium Polyphosphates......................... 330
    B. Mercuryamidosulfonates............................... 332
V. Guest Molecules between Layers............................. 333
    A. Layer Silicates...................................... 333
    B. Uranium Micas....................................... 343
    C. Trititanates.. 346
    D. Layer Lattice Cyanides............................... 351
    E. Inclusion Complexes of Basic Salts.................... 352
    F. Graphitic Oxide...................................... 352
    G. Graphite.. 354
VI. Some Additional Complexes................................ 363
VII. Zeolites with Intersecting Channel Networks................. 367
    A. General Aspects...................................... 367
    B. Structural Features.................................. 371
    C. Channel Systems and Cavity Dimensions................ 384
    D. Molecular Sieve Properties........................... 388
    E. Saturation Capacities of Some Porous Crystals......... 392
    F. Synthesis of Some Host Lattice Silicates............. 394
VIII. Inclusion Isotherms....................................... 399
    A. Isotherms Showing Discontinuities.................... 399
    B. Isotherms without Discontinuities.................... 402
    C. The Empty Host Lattices.............................. 411

IX. Thermochemistry... 412
    A. Hydrate Inclusion Complexes............................. 412
    B. Guest Molecules in Zeolites.............................. 415
X. Molecule Diffusion in Some Porous Crystals.................. 421
    A. Diffusion of Zeolitic Water.............................. 422
    B. Diffusion of Permanent and Rare Gases in Mordenite and Levynite... 425
    C. Diffusion in Chabazite and Linde Sieve 4A................ 427
XI. Conclusion.. 429
    References.. 430

I. INTRODUCTION

In this chapter an account will be given of structural and general aspects of inorganic inclusion complexes, and of equilibrium between the volatile constituents of the complexes and the host lattices which contain them. Equilibrium and thermochemical considerations will be restricted to several kinds of system which nevertheless point the direction of progress. Applications of some of these complexes in industry and the laboratory have been the subject of two recent reviews (27, 250) and will, for reasons of space, not be considered in this chapter.

Inclusion complexes can be classified according to the distribution of the guest molecules within the frameworks formed by the host species. Such a classification is given in Table I. Various inorganic or organic molecules may be enclosed in the structures of column 2, in the distribution patterns of column 1. In principle none of these complexes need be fully stoichiometric, and in practice some very large departures from stoichiometry arise because it is not necessary for guest molecules to occupy every available gap in the host structure before a stable complex is formed.

Repeating patterns in host crystals may be based upon chains, sheets, or polyhedra. A familiar and simple sheet pattern is that in graphite. Other layer structures have more complex sheets, for example, vermiculite or montmorillonite, which are discussed later. In three-dimensional networks any cavities may be polyhedral in character. There are only five polyhedra with which one may fill all space by stacking a given polyhedron with others of the same kind and in the same orientation—the cube, hexagonal prism, rhombic dodecahedron, elongated dodecahedron, and cubo-octahedron. These are Fedorov's space-filling polyhedra shown in Fig. 1 (288). Many combinations of different polyhedra can also fill all space. Andreini (7) listed the combinations of Archimedean solids and prisms which can pack without interstices. Archimedean and other polyhedra are illustrated stereographically by Wells (288), together with certain three-dimensional arrangements of polyhedra of interest in the study of clathrate phases

TABLE I

STRUCTURAL CLASSIFICATION OF SOME INCLUSION COMPLEXES

Arrangement of guest molecules	Examples of corresponding host lattices
1. Molecules in isolated cavities	Water in water clathrates Nosean-sodalite-ultramarine felspathoids Scapolites
2. Molecules in parallel channels	Cancrinites Fibrous clays (attapulgite and sepiolite)
3. Molecules between parallel chains	Quaternary alkylammonium polyphosphates Alkylammonium mercuryamidosulfonates
4. Molecules between layers	Montmorillonites Vermiculites Basic salts Mg-hexamethylenetetraminehexacyanoferric salts Nickel cyanide ammoniate MoS_2 and WS_2 n-Alkylammonium trititanate Graphite oxide Graphite
5. Molecules in channel networks	Zeolites

(e.g., dodecahedra and tetradecahedra; dodecahedra and hexadecahedra; cubo-octahedra). Other combinations include tetrahedra and octahedra (in 2:1 proportions); truncated cubes and octahedra (1:1); cubo-octahedra and octahedra (1:1). Figure 2 shows the appropriate stacking in the last two cases. One may likewise form combination stackings of tetrahedra and truncated tetrahedra; octagonal prisms and truncated cubo-octahedra; octagonal prisms and cubes; 3-prisms and 12-prisms; 3- and 6-prisms; and 3- and 4-prisms. More complex polyhedra and stackings of polyhedra are referred to later in connection with some zeolite structures.

The tetrahedron found in silicates, germanates, or phosphates comprises a group of four oxygen atoms in contact and centered on the tetrahedron apices, the small interstitial gap being occupied by P, Al, Si, B, Ge, or Ga. These tetrahedra may then be linked to form polyhedra. Thus a group of eight tetrahedra, linked by sharing appropriate apical oxygens, forms a cubic unit; a group of twelve tetrahedra can form a hexagonal prism; and one of twenty-four can give a cubo-octahedron. In each of these groupings an Al, Si, etc., is centered on each polyhedral apex, and an O atom is near

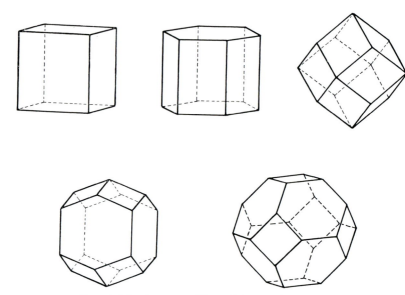

FIG. 1. The five space-filling solids of Fedorov (28).

but not necessarily on the mid-point of each edge. In a similar way one may visualize other polyhedra.

When the polyhedra are large (for example, the cubo-octahedron, dodeca-hedron, tetradecahedron, and other still larger polyhedral groupings) it proves possible to have quite large free volumes inside each polyhedron. These cavities may themselves be occupied by chemical species, con-

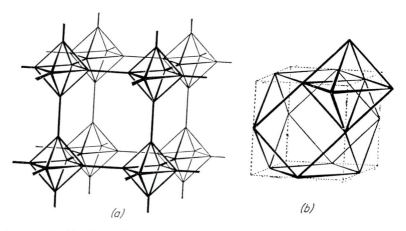

FIG. 2. Combinations of (a) truncated cubes and octahedra, and (b) cubo-octahedra and octahedra (288).

veniently referred to as guest molecules, while the stacked polyhedra form a host lattice. We shall see also that in structures involving the larger polyhedra (e.g., zeolites) there may be polygonal faces which are common to each of two polyhedra and which themselves have considerable free diameters. These faces then allow migration of guest molecules between polyhedra, so that three-dimensional channel networks result. In other structures the polygonal faces are all of too small a diameter for such diffusion, the guest molecules then being locked within the structure during its formation. In many structures the polyhedra show degrees of distortion from their ideally regular forms. This is true for instance of the dodecahedra in gas hydrates or of cubo-octahedra in sodalite-nosean minerals.

With these general geometrical considerations in mind one may now describe characteristic complexes selected from Table I.

II. GUEST MOLECULES IN ISOLATED CAVITIES

A. Gas and Liquid Hydrates

1. STRUCTURE

The first known *gas* hydrate was that of chlorine, which was considered to be a compound by Sir Humphrey Davy (*104*) in 1811. The number of species now known to take part, as guest molecules, in the formation of these hydrates is very large, but all such hydrates can be described in terms of two structures only. These structures were elucidated by Claussen (*92, 93*), Pauling and Marsh (*201*), and von Stackelberg and Müller (*185, 268, 269*). In each structure the pentagonal dodecahedron (Fig. 3b) is an essential unit. This polyhedron is here composed of twenty water molecules, each with an oxygen atom at one of the twenty apices and hydrogen bonded to four other oxygens, three in the given polyhedron and the remaining one belonging to another polyhedron. The hydrogen bonds are distributed nearly tetrahedrally about any oxygen, and the thirty edges of the dodecahedron are hydrogen bonds about 2.8 Å long. Because it has fivefold axial symmetry around the normal through the center of any face the dodecahedron cannot be close packed with itself only, to fill all space. Instead it is found to be stacked together with tetradecahedra, having twelve pentagonal and two hexagonal faces in Type I hydrate structures, and with hexadecahedra with twelve pentagonal and four hexagonal faces in Type II hydrates.

Isolated tetra- and hexadecahedra are shown in Figs. 3*a* and 3*c*, and the arrangement of polyhedra in the Type I clathrates in Fig. 4*a* and in the Type II clathrates in Fig. 4*b*. Each structure is cubic with cube edges of about 12 and 17.4 Å respectively. In the Type I hydrates, dodecahedra are centered at the eight corners and the center of the unit cell. Those at the corners of the cube are joined to adjacent corner dodecahedra by two

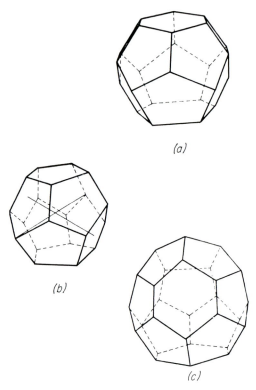

FIG. 3. The pentagonal dodecahedron (*b*), found in coordination with the 14-face (*a*) and the 16-face (*c*) polyhedra in gas hydrates of Types I and II respectively.

additional hydrogen bonds to form hexagonal rings of water molecules, belonging to tetradecahedra. The body-centered dodecahedron is attached to all the corner dodecahedra by single hydrogen bonds and also to two of the added *hexagon* water molecules. There are two dodecahedral and six tetradecahedral cavities in each unit cell containing forty-six water molecules. The volume of a dodecahedron is about 169 Å³ and of a tetradecahedron about 216 Å³. Twenty-four water molecules are required to form one tetradecahedron. If guest molecules, M, occupied every cavity the

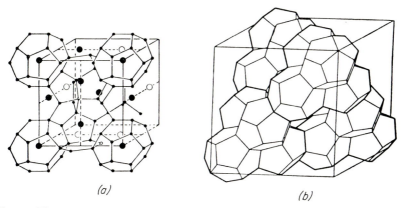

(a)   *(b)*

FIG. 4. The stacking of dodecahedra in hydrates of Type I (Fig. 4a) and of Type II (Fig. 4b) (22).

limiting composition would be $5\frac{3}{4}H_2O \cdot M$; if only the larger cavities were occupied this composition would be $7\frac{2}{3}H_2O \cdot M$. The stacking of these polyhedra is seen to be such that faces rather than edges or apices are shared between nearest neighbor polyhedra.

Type II hydrates may be constructed as follows (92). First, the dodecahedron is slightly deformed so that the angles around two opposite molecules are exactly tetrahedral. These two tetrahedral points are then superimposed on the positions of pairs of carbon atoms in a diamond lattice. This leads to a stacking of dodecahedra in which the cubic cell edge is that observed if the hydrogen bonds are of length ~ 2.8 Å, and in which hexadecahedral cavities are also formed, each hexadecahedron being enclosed by 28 water molecules and having a volume of 250 Å^3. There are then 136 water molecules per unit cell, each of which contains 16 dodecahedral and 8 hexadecahedral voids. When only these larger voids are occupied, the limiting composition for a guest molecule M is $17H_2O \cdot M$. It should be noted that Fig. 4b indicates in outline the arrangement of some dodecahedra only. The larger voids are not shown.

2. GENERAL CONSIDERATIONS

Hydrates of Types I and II are usually formed between water and species with which they show little compatibility, such as chloroform, methylene chloride, bromine, simple aliphatic hydrocarbons, or the heavier inert gases. There are, however, some species which are freely soluble in water and which form hydrates, such as acetone (274), ethylene oxide, and tetrahydrofuran (267). Hydrates do not form with species which are

TABLE II

Physicochemical Properties of Some Type I Hydrates (270)

Guest molecule M	Molecular volume of liquid M (cm³)	Dissociation pressure of hydrate at 0°C	Decomposition temperature at 1 atm (°C)	Exothermal heat of formation (kcals/mole of M, from liquid H₂O)	Lattice constant (Å)
N_2 (257)	—	160 atm	—	—	—
O_2 (257)	—	120	—	—	—
Ar	(29)	105	−42.8	—	—
CH_4	(39)	26	−29.0	14.5	—
Kr	(43)	14.5	−27.8	13.9	—
CO_2	(29)ᵃ	12.3	−24	14.4	12.04
N_2O	36	10.0	−19.3	14.7	12.03
C_2H_2	(42)	5.7	−15.4	15	—
C_2H_4	(49)	5.5	−13.4	15.2	—
C_2H_6	(55)	5.2	−15.8	15.0	—
CH_3F	—	2.1	—	—	—
PH_3	(46)	1.6	−6.4	—	—
Xe	(43)	1.5	−3.4	16.7	11.97
H_2S	(36)	731 mm	+0.35	—	12.00
AsH_3	(55)	613	+1.8	—	—

C_2H_5F	(60)	530	+3.7	—	—
H_2Se	38	346	+8.0	—	12.06
CH_3Cl	53	311	+7.5	18.1, 18.1 (81)	12.00
SO_2	44	297	+7.0	16.6	11.94
Cl_2	45	252	+9.6	16.0	12.03
CH_3SH	54	239	+10.0	16.6	12.12
CH_3Br	55	187	+11.1	19.5	12.09
Br_2	51	45	—	19.6, 20.83 (105)	12.01
CHF_3 (265)	—	—	—	—	12.05
CH_2CHF (265)	—	—	—	—	12.11
CH_3CHF_2 (265)	—	—	—	—	12.12
$CH_2=CH_2$ (267)	—	—	—	—	12.0

^{a} As solid CO_2.

capable of strong hydrogen bonding (halogen halides, ammonia, or organic acids) probably because specific interactions then perturb the *open ice* structure of the host lattice. There is also no evidence that soluble inorganic salts can be incorporated into the polyhedral cavities, although a number of different *open ice* hydrates can be formed with certain alkyl-ammonium, -sulfonium, or -phosphonium salts having rather bulky organic ions (e.g., (isoamyl)$_4$N$^+$)(*127, 157, 176*).

Whether the hydrate formed is of Type I or Type II depends on the dimensions of the guest molecules. Table II gives some examples of Type I hydrates, together with physicochemical information of interest. The unit cell dimensions can vary slightly according to the guest molecule and the equilibrium pressure. The relation between the unit cell size and that of the guest molecule is not clear, however. Some small guest molecules (e.g., CO_2, N_2O, H_2S) have unit cells as large or larger than those containing rather big guest molecules (Cl_2, Br_2, CH_3Cl, Xe). In part this may be due to the inability, for steric reasons, of large molecules to occupy the small dodecahedral cavities, so that the compositions are essentially poorer in the large molecule. Thus the composition of chlorine hydrate at 0°C has recently been given by Allen as 7.27 ± 0.17H$_2$O·Cl$_2$ (*2*). In this hydrate the smaller cavities may therefore be occupied only very incompletely. The bromine hydrate has been found to have a composition of 8.47 ± 0.05H$_2$O·Br$_2$ (*183*) which would indicate that not only the smaller cavities but also some of the larger are unoccupied by Br$_2$ molecules. On the other hand, small guest molecules can occupy both types of cavity. The evidence is that Cl$_2$ (molecular volume 44 cm^3) is about the smallest molecule which is yet big enough to be largely excluded from the dodecahedral voids, while C$_2$H$_5$F of molecular volume about 60 (Table II) is the biggest molecule which can be accepted by the tetradecahedral voids. The free* diameter of the two cavities in this open ice structure was estimated by Barrer and Stuart to be 5.2 and 5.9 Å for the smaller and larger voids respectively (*69*). Platteeuw and van der Waals (*205*) give 5.1 and 5.8 Å for these diameters. Molecules believed small enough to occupy both cavities include Ar, CH$_4$, C$_2$H$_2$, PH$_3$, H$_2$S, CO$_2$, N$_2$O, and H$_2$Se. On the other hand C$_2$H$_6$, C$_2$H$_4$, C$_2$H$_5$F, SO$_2$, CH$_3$Cl, CH$_3$Br, Cl$_2$, Br$_2$, CH$_3$SH, CHF$_3$, CH$_2$CHF, and CH$_3$CHF$_2$ should occupy only, or primarily, the larger cavities. It follows that the SO$_2$ or Br$_2$ hydrates, for example, if formed in the presence of small molecules such as argon or methane, might also occlude quantities of these gases during crystal growth. Blankenship (*81*) has reported the evolution of air enriched in oxygen from hydrates such as that of bromine.

---

* By *free* here and elsewhere is meant not occupied even by the peripheries of the molecules or atoms forming the host lattice.

When one has larger guest molecules than C_2H_5F the second *open ice* lattice is formed in which the free diameter of the hexadecahedral voids is about 6.9 Å and that of the dodecahedral voids is now about 4.8 Å (Type II hydrates). The bigger voids can accommodate quite large molecules, as the results in Table III indicate, but these molecules are much too large to occupy the smaller cavities and also are not very volatile. Accordingly, the hydrates of these molecules should approach the composition $17H_2O \cdot M$. For example, Barrer and Ruzicka (*67*) have made careful analyses of the chloroform hydrate, for which, in the vicinity of 0°C, the mean composition was found to be $17.9H_2O \cdot CHCl_3$.

The small unoccupied cavities are 16 in number per unit cell as compared with 8 which are occupied. If a Type II hydrate is formed in the presence of a small molecule (e.g., H_2S) one can readily obtain double hydrates approaching the composition $17H_2O \cdot M \cdot 2N$, where M denotes the large guest molecule and N the small one. A number of these are listed in Table IV, of which the most interesting feature is the relatively high decomposition temperature at 1 atm. Filling both types of void

TABLE III

PHYSICOCHEMICAL PROPERTIES OF SOME TYPE II HYDRATES (*270*)

Guest molecule M	Molecular volume of liquid M (cm³)	Dissociation pressure at 0°C (mm)	Exothermal heat of formation (kcals/mole of M from liquid H_2O)	Lattice constant (Å)
C_3H_8	(75)	760	—	—
$(CH_3)_2O$	—	—	—	17.44
$(CH_3)_3CH$	—	—	—	17.53
C_2H_5Cl	70	201	31.9	17.30
CH_2Cl_2	63	116	29, 32.4[a]	17.31
CH_3I	62	74	31.4, 30.1[a]	—
CH_3CHCl_2	84	(55)	—	—
$CHCl_3$	80	(50)	31, 30.6[a], 30.6[b]	17.30
$CBrClF_2$ (*136*)	—	139.2	32.57 ±0.07[a]	—

[a] Determined from vapor pressure data (*81*, *136*).
[b] Determined calorimetrically (*81*).

stabilizes the open ice lattice considerably. Stabilization is also possible when in place of H_2S we have Ar, O_2, N_2, H_2, CO_2, etc. as *help gases* [this term was used by von Stackelberg and Meinhold (*266*)]. The increase in decomposition temperature of hydrates of CCl_4, $CHCl_3$, and CH_2Cl_2 is shown in Fig. 5 as a function of the pressure of the help gases CO_2 or N_2 (*263*). An explanation of the role of help gases was first given by Barrer and Stuart (*69*) in terms of the statistical thermodynamic formulation of equilibria in clathrate phases, which will be outlined later. The less volatile the help gas the greater the fraction of the voids it will occupy, and the

TABLE IV

DOUBLE CLATHRATE PHASES OF WATER OF TYPE II (*270*)

Component N	Component M	Decomposition temperature (°C) at 1 atm	Lattice constant (Å)
H_2S	COS	~0	17.30
	C_3H_8	+8	17.40
	CH_3Br	—	17.31
	C_2H_5Cl	7.2	17.26
	$(CH_3)_2S$	14.	17.39
	C_2H_5Br	13.	17.26
	CH_2Cl_2	14.	17.28
	CH_3I	14.2	17.37
	CS_2	8	17.30
	$CHCl_3$	16.3	17.29
	$n\text{-}C_3H_7Br$	—	17.42
	CCl_4	17.3	17.46
	C_6H_6	3.5	17.48
	CH_2ClCH_2Cl	—	17.51
	CCl_3Br	11.3	17.57
	CCl_3NO_2	13.	17.60
H_2Se	C_2H_5Cl	10.	17.41
	$CHCl_3$	15.	17.45
	CCl_4	19.	17.60

TABLE V

DECOMPOSITION TEMPERATURES OF HYDRATES OF TYPE II AT 1 ATM PRESSURE (274)

Help gas	Guest molecule			
	CH₃COCH₃	CH₂Cl₂	CHCl₃	CCl₄
Ar	−8.0	−7.0	−4.8	−1.6
Kr	−5.0	+6.2	+9.0	+11.3
Xe	+3.0	+8.6	+10.9	+13.7

greater its stabilizing role. This is excellently illustrated by the data of Waller (274) in Table V. The stabilizing of several Type II hydrates at 1 atm pressure is much greater for the less volatile xenon than for the more volatile argon. Xenon occupies a greater proportion of voids than argon on account of this lower volatility.

The role of molecular size and shape of the included species in determining the type of clathrate phase, or whether such phases will form at all, is illustrated in Fig. 6a and b (270). It is apparent that the host lattices could show remarkable selectivity in encaging certain guest molecules but not others. Few attempts have so far been made to utilize this potentiality, despite one or two orienting experiments. Hammerschmidt (141) found the fractionation of natural gas shown in Table VI. All the com-

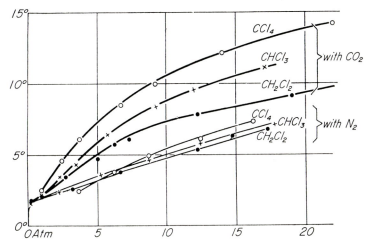

FIG. 5. The decomposition temperatures of some hydrates of chloromethanes under pressures of carbon dioxide and nitrogen (266).

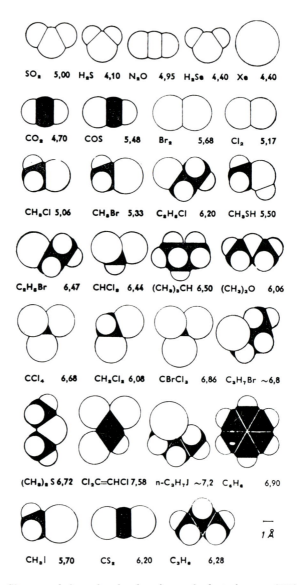

FIG. 6 (a). Shapes and sizes of molecules of some hydrate formers (270).

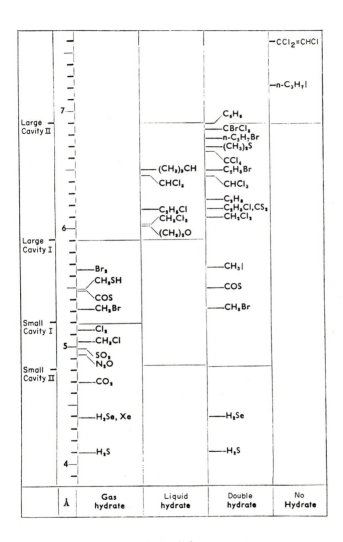

(b)

Fig. 6 (*b*). Comparison of molecular diameters of hydrate formers with the diameters of the cavities (*270*).

TABLE VI

FRACTIONATION BY CLATHRATION OF A NATURAL GAS

Component	Per cent in gas phase	Per cent in hydrate	Ratio
CH_4	82.5	56.95	0.7
C_2H_6	5.99	5.66	1.0
C_3H_8	3.26	24.97	8.0
Iso-C_4H_{10}	0.30	4.69	16.0
n-C_4H_{10}	0.49	0.83	1.7
C_5H_{12} etc.	0.07	0.00	0
CO_2	0.20	0.44	2.2
N_2	7.19	6.46	0.9

ponents are in competition for the available cavities, and it is clear that very high selectivities are shown for C_3H_8 and iso-C_4H_{10}. Pentanes are excluded. The smallest molecules (N_2, CO_2, CH_4, C_2H_6) have access to the dodecahedral cavities from which the more bulky C_3 and C_4 paraffins are excluded.

B. Felspathoids

The felspathoids include a number of complexes in which the guest molecules are salts. Two mineral families which occur naturally are the scapolites and the nosean-sodalite minerals. These all have three-dimensional aluminosilicate frameworks carrying a net negative charge. In interstices and cavities in the frameworks a sufficient number of cations are located to neutralize the negative charge, together with salt molecules. In order to have sufficient room for salt molecules the frameworks must be comparatively open in structure.

Scapolite compositions range between marialite, $3(NaAlSi_3O_8)NaCl$, and meionite, $3(CaAl_2Si_2O_8)Ca(SO_4, CO_3)$. Wernerite is a third variety intermediate in composition between the other two. The salts included in these phases are sodium and calcium chlorides, sulfates, and carbonates. The frameworks have the compositions of the corresponding felspars, albite and anorthite. The structure was suggested by Pauling (199) and confirmed in essentials by Schiebold and Seumel (233). A typical hexagonal unit cell has $a = 12.11$ and $c = 7.59_5$ Å. So far synthetic scapolites do not appear to have been prepared.

The nosean-sodalite felspathoids include the species sodalite, $6[NaAlSiO_4]2NaCl$; nosean, $6[NaAlSiO_4]Na_2SO_4$; ultramarine, $6[NaAlSiO_4]Na_2S_x$; helvite, $6[(Mn, Fe, Zn)BeSiO_4](Mn, Fe, Zn)S$; hauynite, $6[(Na, \frac{1}{2}Ca)AlSiO_4](Na_2, Ca)SO_4$; and lazurite, $6[(Na, \frac{1}{2}Ca)AlSiO_4](Na_2, Ca)(SO_4, S, 2Cl)$. In this series the Al:Si ratio is nearly constant at 1:1, except for helvite which does not contain Al. Synthetic species in the same family have also been prepared in which H_2O, NaOH, NaBr, and $NaNO_3$ replace those salts found in the natural species (75, 126). Na_2CO_3 and $CaCO_3$ may also be present in the naturally occurring minerals. The structures of all these phases are very similar. The unit cells are cubic, and the aluminosilicate framework is based on cubo-octahedral units (Fig. 1) stacked in 8-fold coordination to produce the structure formally represented in Fig. 7. Al or Si atoms are present at each apex and O atoms are centered near but not on the mid-points of each edge. The free diameter of each cubo-

Fig. 7. The stacking of cubo-octahedra in 8-fold coordination which is found in sodalites, noseans, and ultramarines. Al or Si atoms are centered at the corners and O atoms near but not on the mid-points of the edges (25).

octahedral unit is about 6.6 Å, so that there is room in these units for the salt molecules as well as the extra cations needed to neutralize the framework charge. Each cubo-octahedron has six 4-ring faces and eight 6-ring faces. (The term *4-ring* refers to a ring made from four linked (Al, Si)O_4 tetrahedra, and a *6-ring* to one made from six of these tetrahedra). The 6-rings have free diameters of 2.2–2.4 Å, which are sufficient to permit exchange of smaller cations but not normally of anions. An interesting demonstration of this property was provided by exposing a synthetic *basic* sodalite to the action of dry hydrochloric acid gas (*75*). The basic sodalite contained H_2O + NaOH in place of the usual NaCl. If the subscript *o* denotes outside and *i* inside the crystal, the observed reaction can be represented as:

$$OH_{(i)}^- + Na_{(i)}^+ + HCl_{(o)} \rightarrow NaCl_{(o)} + H_2O_{(i)}$$

The formation of crystalline sodium chloride outside the sodalite crystals was shown by x-ray powder photography. We thus have a demonstration of the ready intracrystalline migration of Na^+ ions while the Cl^- ions (diameter $\sim$3.62 Å) remain outside the crystal.

One of the most interesting members of the nosean-sodalite family is ultramarine, which was once imported as the semiprecious stone, lapis lazuli, prized for its vivid blue color. Like other nosean felspathoids, ultramarine undergoes ion exchange. A synthetic ultramarine exchanged its Na^+ ion for such ions as Li^+, K^+, Ag^+, Tl^+, Pb^{2+}, Zn^{2+}, and Cd^{2+} (*58, 156*), with modifications of color. For the Ag^+-exchanged compound the color was green or yellow, with Pb^{2+} ion it was brown. Li- or Tl-containing ultramarines were a still richer, darker shade of blue than the Na- or K-varieties. The color depends on the presence of unreduced sulfur, as indicated in the accompanying data (cf. *113*), which represent approximately the compositions of various preparations:

White	$6(NaAlSiO_4) \cdot 2Na_2S$
	$6(NaAlSiO_4) \cdot 3Na_2S$
	$6(NaAlSiO_4) \cdot 4Na_2S$
Green	$6(NaAlSiO_4) \cdot Na_2S, S$
	$6(NaAlSiO_4) \cdot 1.5(Na_2S, S)$
	$6(NaAlSiO_4) \cdot 2(Na_2S, S)$
Blue	$6(NaAlSiO_4) \cdot 2S$
	$6(NaAlSiO_4) \cdot 0.5(Na_2S), 2.5S$
	$6(NaAlSiO_4) \cdot Na_2S, 3S.$

In the above formulas, the aluminosilicate framework neutralized by interstitial ions is represented by $(NaAlSiO_4)$; the sulfur or sodium sulfides are also present interstitially as guest molecules. It is possible to reduce the sulfur or polysulfide in these ultramarines, for example by fusion with sodium formate or by heating with hydrogen at 400°C, giving a white or pale blue product. On the other hand when this material is heated in air, or even *in vacuo* at 200°C, the deep blue color is restored. Ultramarines have also been reported in which the sulfur is replaced by selenium and which are blood red, while tellurium ultramarines are yellow (*156*). A wide range and variety of colors is obtainable, together with innumerable degrees of tint and hue.

Synthetic ultramarines can be made pyrolytically, for example by heating kaolin to redness, in absence of air, admixed with sulfur, or sodium sulfate and carbonaceous reducing agents. The first product, a yellow-green mass, is heated in air and the color deepens to dark blue. Soluble sodium salts are then leached out to leave the pigment. Several variations of this process are available (*156*). The nosean-sodalite felspathoids (but not ultramarine) can also be prepared hydrothermally (e.g., *75*). In all these species the guest molecules must be regarded as stabilizing the relatively porous host lattices by filling the cavities, just as for the gas hydrates. Indeed this quite general phenomenon is amenable to thermodynamic treatment (*28*), and to experimental study (*34, 54*). It is a significant aspect of mineral chemistry.

Color associated with variable oxidation states such as those of sulfur in ultramarine is not uncommon. One may briefly refer, as an additional example, to the tungsten bronzes. Tungsten can exist in both W^V and W^{VI} valence states, and tungsten bronzes are intermediate between WO_3, which has a structure based on the combination of WO_6 octahedra of Fig. 2a, leaving the truncated cubic cavity shown there. If $NaWO_3$ could be formed, we would then have one Na^+ ion in each of these cavities, the substance being given the formula $Na^+[W^VO_3]^-$. The tungsten bronzes are obtained by heating Na_2WO_4, WO_3, and WO_2 *in vacuo*, or by reducing Na_2WO_4 by hydrogen or molten zinc. They may be represented by the formula Na_xWO_3 where $0 < x < 1$. They are good electrical conductors, have a metallic luster, and vary in color according to the value of x. Thus for x approaching unity this color is golden yellow; for $x \sim 0.6$ it is red, and for $x \sim 0.3$ violet. Phases with $x > 0.32$ are all cubic and of perovskite structure, with the Na^+ ions statistically distributed in the truncated cubic interstices. The formula may be more correctly written as $Na_x W_x^V W_{1-x}^{VI} O_3$ (e.g., *114*). A detailed discussion of these bronzes appears in Chapter 3.

III. GUEST MOLECULES IN PARALLEL CHANNELS: CANCRINITES AND FIBROUS CLAYS

The principal cancrinite phases occurring naturally are cancrinite $(6[(Na, \frac{1}{2}Ca)AlSiO_4], (Na_2, Ca)CO_3)$ and davynite $(6[(Na, \frac{1}{2}Ca)AlSiO_4]$

$(Na_2, Ca)(CO_3, SO_4, 2Cl))$. Other species which may be included are NaOH and H_2O, which are found in synthetic phases, termed *basic cancrinites* on account of their caustic soda content (75). The part of the formula in the square brackets represents the aluminosilicate framework together with the cations Na^+ or Ca^{2+} needed to neutralize the framework anionic charge. This framework has the same Al:Si ratio as that found in the nosean-sodalite minerals. The structure which was first suggested by

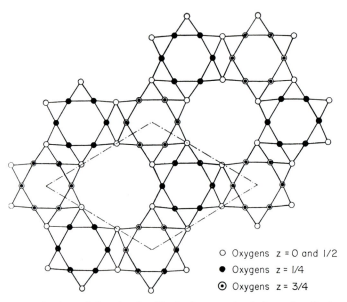

○ Oxygens z = 0 and 1/2
● Oxygens z = 1/4
◉ Oxygens z = 3/4

Fig. 8. A projection of the aluminosilicate framework of the unit cell of cancrinite normal to the c axis (188).

Pauling (199) and more fully developed by Nithollon (188) is however different. A projection of the hexagonal unit cell normal to the c axis is shown in Fig. 8. Very wide channels circumscribed by rings of twelve (Si, Al)O_4 tetrahedra, and also narrower channels circumscribed by rings of six tetrahedra run parallel to the c axis. Cations are present in both types of channel, and carbonate or other anions are in the wide tunnels which have free diameters of about 6 Å. The cancrinite framework can be constructed from a sequence of layers of linked 6-rings, every third layer being superposed upon the first. Sodalite on the other hand can be constructed from the same kind of layer, but with every fourth layer superposed on the first.

Two other species in which well-defined channels, containing water as guest molecules, run parallel to the c axis, are attapulgite (or palygorskite) and sepiolite (83, 85, 186). The cross sections of the unit cells normal to this axis are shown in Fig. 9. An idealized composition is $(Si_8O_{20})Mg_5$-$(OH)_2(OH_2)_4 \cdot 4H_2O$, the water being present as hydroxyl groups, bound water, and zeolitic water, the last named being the most readily displaced on heating. The channels in sepiolite have the same depth but about 50% greater width than those in attapulgite, but otherwise the structural arrangement of channels is similar. The tunnels do not appear to be of sufficient depth to allow ready replacement of water by other species, except

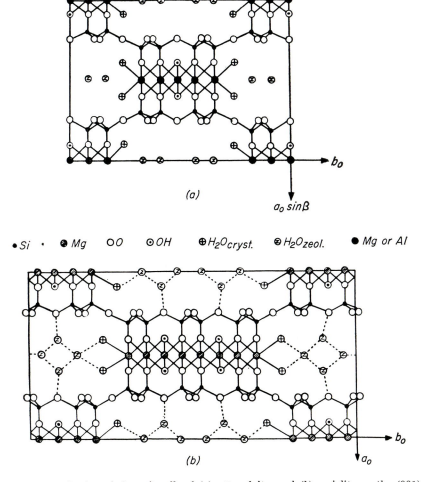

(a)

$a_0 \sin\beta$

$\bullet Si$ $\cdot$ $\bullet Mg$ OO $\odot OH$ $\oplus H_2O_{cryst.}$ $\otimes H_2O_{zeol.}$ $\bullet Mg\ or\ Al$

(b)

FIG. 9. Projection of the unit cells of (a) attapulgite, and (b) sepiolite on the (001) plane (85).

possibly by ammonia (50), although as sorbents both attapulgite and sepiolite have large effective areas and interesting selectivities.

IV. GUEST MOLECULES BETWEEN CHAINS

A. Alkylammonium Polyphosphates

An interesting series of complexes may be formed between organic liquids and certain n-alkylammonium polyphosphates (282, 283). Substituted ammonium polyphosphates may be made directly, if sometimes very slowly, by ion exchange from Kurrol's salt $(KPO_3)_n$, or Maddrell's salt $(NaPO_3)_n$, both of which are chain polyphosphates with Na^+ or K^+ ions between the chains. The chain arrangement in $(KPO_3)_n$ is indicated in Fig. 10, the chains being shown in the plane of the b and c axes. The respective repeat distances of about 4.6 and 14.1 Å for these directions tend to be preserved in the exchanged forms in which n-alkyl- and di-n-alkylammonium ions replace K^+ ions. The a dimension, however, expands in proportion to the length of the alkyl chains, and the increment per CH_2 group is such as to indicate a double layer of alkyl groups between each pair of polyphosphate layers. The chains are somewhat tilted. A second type of structure is found with alkyl-(α, ω)-diammonium ions, in which a

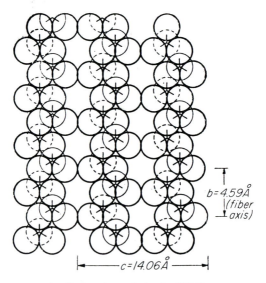

$b = 4.59 Å$
(fiber axis)

$c = 14.06 Å$

FIG. 10. Arrangement of polyphosphate chains in $(KPO_3)_n$. A wholly similar arrangement occurs in the mono-n-alkylammonium polyphosphates (282).

single layer of chains is interpolated between each pair of polyphosphate layers, the terminal —NH_3^+ groups being firmly attached to exchange sites on upper and lower sheets respectively.

The n-alkylammonium polyphosphates show limited swelling in long-

TABLE VII

Two-Dimensional Intracrystalline Swelling of Quaternary Alkylammonium Polyphosphates

Swelling condition	Chain distance $\perp^{1\mathrm{r}}$ to b axis (Å)	Repeat distance along b axis (Å)
(a) Trimethylcetylammonium polyphosphate		
Dried at 60°C and 0.1 atm	22.2	4.8_4
Under: water	27.7	—
ethanol	29.8	$5._0$ (diffuse)
nonanol-1	40.3	$4._6$ (diffuse)
decanol-1	42.5	$4._6$ (diffuse)
toluene	30.9	$5._0$ (diffuse)
xylene	31.4	$5._0$ (diffuse)
nitrobenzene	27.4	—
acetonitrile	32.6	$4._8$ (diffuse)
n-butyl ether	29.4	$4._6$ (diffuse)
butyl acetate	26.2	$4._8$ (diffuse)
diethyl ketone	30.0	$4._6$ (diffuse)
(b) Octadecylpyridinium polyphosphate		
Dried at 60°C and 0.1 atm	24.2	4.5_5
Under: water	28.2	4.5_3
ethanol	105 (?)	—
decanol-1	43.5	4.5_5
benzene	28.5	4.6 (diffuse)
toluene	33.9	4.6_0
nitrobenzene	26.0	4.5_8

chain alkanols, aldehydes, and fatty acids. If the penetrant is a n-alkanol, and if

$$R = \frac{\text{No. of C atoms in the interlayer alkylammonium ion}}{\text{No. of C atoms in the } n\text{-alkanol}}$$

then for $R > 1$, negligible increase in the spacing between the polyphosphate layers occurs. For $R = 1$, or a little less than one, however, the expansion, though not large, reaches its maximum value.

A tetragonal type of structure was also prepared by Weiss and Michel (282) from long-chain quaternary alkylammonium ions in which polyphosphate chains were separated from one another equally in both a and c directions, without alteration of the repeat distance of about 4.6 Å along the b axis. These structures freely imbibed a variety of organic species with the two-dimensional swelling recorded in Table VII. No equilibrium studies of these systems have been reported, but one might seek for a connection between cohesive energy density of the penetrant and the extent of swelling, as investigated by Barrer and Kelsey (46) for dimethyldioctadecylammonium bentonite.

B. Mercuryamidosulfonates

The monovalent metal salts of mercuryamidosulfonic acid $A^+[\text{Hg-NSO}_3]^-$, can exchange the metal ions for other cations in the same way as a zeolite (284). In particular, quaternary alkylammonium and alkylpyridinium ions may replace other metal ions quantitatively. These exchange forms readily undergo two-dimensional intracrystalline swelling in the presence of a variety of penetrants, in a similar manner to the corresponding polyphosphates (Table VIII). In this unusual inorganic crystalline polymer the anionic chains may be represented as (I).

(I)

From the table it is seen that the greatest swelling takes place in decane, a liquid of low cohesive energy density. There is also considerable uptake of toluene.

TABLE VIII

REPEAT DISTANCES (IN Å) BETWEEN CHAINS IN $(CH_3)_3\overset{+}{N}(n\text{-}C_{16}H_{33})[HgNSO_3]^-$ AND IN

$(CH_3)_2\overset{+}{N}(n\text{-}C_{18}H_{37})_2[HgNSO_3]^-$

Swelling condition	Trimethylcetyl-ammonium form	Dimethyldioctadecyl-ammonium form
20°C, dried at 0.1 atm	32.6	35.8
Under: water	42.2	36.9
toluene	46.7	38.2
butyl acetate	40.5	—
decane	55.4	50.4
nitrobenzene	40.3	—
acetonitrile	34.6	36.9
capronitrile	41.0	36.9
n-decanol	45.3	—
n-dodecanol	49.3	—

V. GUEST MOLECULES BETWEEN LAYERS

A. Layer Silicates

Many layer lattices possess the property of being able to expand in the presence of appropriate fluids, and of intercalating the molecules of these fluids. Perhaps the most numerous group is found among the silicates. Figure 11 (87) gives a cross section of a portion of two aluminosilicate layers in pyrophyllite. These layers appear, with various substitutions of Al for Si, Mg for Al, in a variety of natural layer minerals, such as micas, chlorites, vermiculites, and a number of clay minerals such as montmorillonite. Each layer is a threefold one, in which SiO_4^{4-} tetrahedra are linked with each other to form upper and lower layers consisting of sheets of six-rings (i.e., rings of six tetrahedra). These layers are also linked via Si—O—Al bonds to some of the oxygens surrounding aluminum in octahedral coordination in a central layer as shown in Fig. 12 (88). In pyrophyllite, the resultant triple layers carry no net charge. However, replacements of Si by Al in the tetrahedral or of Al by Mg, Fe^{II}, etc. in the octahedral layers result in varied anionic charges developing over the triple layers. In this case, additional cations such as K^+, Na^+, Ca^{2+}, Ba^{2+}, or Mg^{2+} are located between these layers, in numbers sufficient to produce a neutral structure. These ions may or may not be hydrated, and the charge density may vary greatly among the resultant species.

The capacity of liquids to swell such species depends on their ability to penetrate between the silicate layers. Water is one of the most penetrating fluids in this respect, but not all layer silicates swell in contact with this

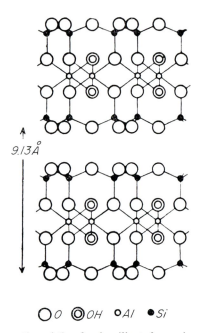

$\bigcirc O$ $\bigcirc OH$ $\circ Al$ $\bullet Si$

Fig. 11. A cross section of the aluminosilicate layers in pyrophyllite (88).

liquid. According to Weiss (276) the extent of swelling depends in the first instance upon the number of charges per unit area on the silicate layers in the manner indicated in Table IX. Water does not swell very highly charged layer silicates or the uncharged layer silicates. The most highly swollen structures are those with a small layer charge, and monovalent interlayer ions promote swelling more than divalent ions. Included in the table are three types of layer lattices which are not silicates, and which will be referred to later. These structures—uranium micas $(A^+(H_2O)_n\{UO_2XO_4\}^-$, where X is P, As, or V); the complex cyanides (e.g., $Mg[Mg((CH_2)_6N_4)_2Fe(CN)_6]_2 \cdot nH_2O)$; and graphitic acid $(C_7O_4H_2)$—fall reasonably into place with the silicates.

The swelling properties of the micaceous silicates are influenced by con-

$$5\overset{\circ}{A}$$

Fig. 12. The superposition of the tetrahedral siliceous layer on the octahedral layer in minerals of the mica, vermiculite, and montmorillonite groups. The thin lines represent the uppermost oxygens of the octahedral layer and the thick lines the outer sheet of tetrahedral oxygens. The unit cell is outlined in the center of the diagram (88).

centrations of dissolved electrolytes, the general effect being to reduce the extent of swelling. However, the results of Table X show that electrolytes have less effect when the original charge density of the silicate layers is high (as in batavite). A Donnan membrane equilibrium clearly influences this situation. In addition, specificity of swelling properties can sometimes be observed. Single crystals of Li-vermiculite show macroscopic swelling when immersed in water or lithium salt solutions (193, 272). The degree of swelling is related to the electrolyte concentration, but the swollen crystals collapse at once if the lithium salt solution is replaced by other solutions. Single vermiculite crystals containing interlayer butylammonium ions also swell macroscopically when placed in water or butylammonium chloride solutions (271). Interlayer spacings of about 500 Å arise with distilled water, and this spacing declines linearly with $C^{-1/2}$, where C is the concentration of aqueous butylammonium chloride in moles/liter. When C increases above 0.06 N, the spacing collapses abruptly from about 170 Å. Apart from these two particular ion-exchanged forms of vermiculite no other interlayer ions in this mineral are known to behave in this extreme

TABLE IX

DEPENDENCE OF INTRACRYSTALLINE SWELLING ON CHARGE DENSITY (276)

Layer lattice	Equivalent area per unit charge ($Å^2$)	Extent of swelling in $Å$ in distilled water when the interlayer ions are:	
		Na^+	Ca^{++}
(a) *Micaceous silicates*:			
Margarite (Insel, Elba)	12	0	0
Margarite (Pfitsch-Tal)	12	0	0
Muscovite (Norway)	24	1.9	2.8
Biotite (Monroe, New York)	24	1.9	2.8
Lepidolite	24	1.9	2.8
Zinnwaldite	24	1.9	2.8
Seladonite (Vesuvius)	27	2.4	2.8
Glauconite (New Jersey)	31	3.8	2.8
Dioctahedral illite (Sarospatak)	32	4.2	2.8
Trioctahedral illite (Kropfmuhl by Passau)	36	5.1	4.3
Vermiculite (S. Africa)	36	5.1	4.3
Vermiculite (Spanish Morocco)	36	5.0	4.2
Vermiculite (Kropfmuhl)	37	5.1	4.3
Batavite (Kropfmuhl)	36	5.1	4.3
Beidellite I (Unterrupsroth)	41	5.4	4.9
Saponite (Fichtelgebirge)	42	4.9	4.9
Nontronite (Untergriesbach)	46	∞	9.2
Beidellite (Unterrupsroth)	57	∞	9.2
Montmorillonite (Cyprus)	60	∞	9.2
Montmorillonite (Geisenheim)	75	∞	9.6
Hectorite (California)	100	∞	10.6
Pyrophyllite	∞	0	0
Talc	∞	0	0
(b) *Nonsilicates*:		Na^+	Mg^{2+}
Uranium mica	25	3.3	2.9
Hexacyano complexes of Fe^{III}, Co^{III}, Cr^{III}, Mn^{III}, and Rh^{III} with hexamethylene-tetramine and Mg^{II} or Ni^{II}	$\sim$25	3.6(?)	2.4
Graphitic acid	$\sim$70 to 150	∞	9 to 11

TABLE X

INFLUENCE OF ELECTROLYTE CONCENTRATION ON INTRACRYSTALLINE SWELLING
OF MICACEOUS SILICATES (276)

| | Interlayer distances in Å for: | | | | | |
| | montmorillonite; area per ion 73 Å² | | montmorillonite; area per ion 56 Å² | | batavite; area per ion 36 Å² | |
Concentration of aqueous electrolyte	LiCl aq	NaCl aq	LiCl aq	NaCl aq	LiCl aq	NaCl aq
~5 N	15.1	15.6	15.6	15.9	14.6	14.8
2 N	17.5	16.6	18.1	17.6	14.7	14.8
1 N	19.2	19.1	20.1	20.4	14.7	14.8
Distilled H₂O	∞	∞	∞	∞	14.7	14.9

fashion. Unlimited swelling also takes place, however, with water and the sodium forms of the clay minerals nontronite, beidellite, montmorillonite, and hectorite with equivalent areas per cation in the range 46–100 Å² (Table IX). Some basic phenomena have been considered in a more quantitative way [for example by Verwey and Overbeek (262) and by Norrish (193)]. Norrish found the same kind of linear dependence of swelling upon $C^{-1/2}$ for Na-montmorillonite in aqueous NaCl and Na₂SO₄ as did Walker (271) for butylammonium vermiculite in aqueous butylammonium chloride.

Intercalation in natural montmorillonites and some other clay minerals is observed for other polar molecules besides water, for example, ammonia, methanol, ethanol, pyridine, glycol, or glycerol. The intercalation isotherms are usually continuous, and demonstrate a hysteresis (Fig. 13) between sorption and desorption which is associated with the lattice expansion (51). In several instances one or more rather ill-defined steps can be observed, which correspond to particular stages in the sorption process.

By means of ion exchange (278) a great range of modified layer lattice silicates may be prepared, which are hydrophilic when simple inorganic ions replace the Na⁺ or Ca²⁺ ions of the species of Table IX, and which show modified powers of intercalation depending inter alia on the charge and size of the entering cations. When Na⁺ or Ca²⁺ are replaced by organic ions, the degree of hydrophilic or hydrophobic character can be modified, largely at will, according to the nature and amounts of the organic and inorganic constituents of the resultant crystals. This character then governs the types of neutral molecule which may subsequently be intercalated, and the extent of this sorption.

The rate of exchange of inorganic ions by organic ones varies greatly according to the size of the exchanging crystals, the temperature, the density of interlayer cations, and the character of the exchanging ions. Exchanges in clay minerals such as montmorillonite, hectorite, or beidellite occur

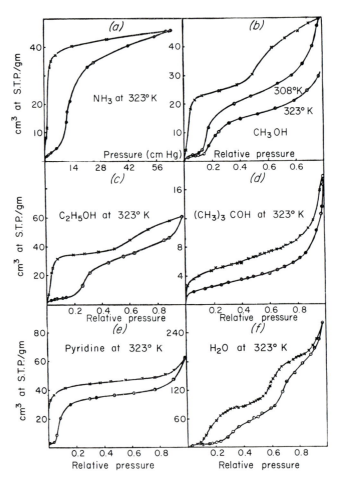

FIG. 13. Isotherms for polar sorbates on natural montmorillonite (Na-rich) at 308° and 323°K. KEY: ⊙, adsorption points; ✕, desorption points (*51*).

rapidly because here the crystals are small and the interlayer charge density is low. As we proceed to species such as the vermiculites of higher interlayer cation density (Table IX), the exchange rates are much reduced. The exchange proceeds from the edges of the crystallites inwards, with a relatively sharp boundary between the swollen crystal containing large interlayer organic ions and the parent crystal containing small inorganic interlamellar ions. In the case of micas, such as muscovite, with very high charge density between layers, the rate of exchange has become very slow indeed (277). Thus, after three months the exchange of K^+ ion by oleylammonium ion in muscovite was incomplete (281). Nevertheless the oleylammonium muscovite finally prepared was itself much expanded, and also imbibed a considerable range of neutral molecules with varied additional swelling of the mica (e.g., benzene, nitrobenzene, pyridine, n-primary amines, and alcohols). Tertiary and quaternary alkylammonium ions exchanged with muscovite much more slowly even than monoalkyl-ammonium ions.

By far the most extensive measurements have been made upon the swelling and other properties of organic derivatives of montmorillonoid clay minerals, which (Table IX) have considerably fewer interlamellar ions per unit area than have micas and vermiculites. The alkyl chains between the aluminosilicate sheets are usually at an angle to the planes of the sheets, with the polar end groups in contact with the oxygen atoms of the sheets. Franzen (128) determined the structure of a montmorillonite containing cetyltrimethylammonium ions and interlamellar cetyltrimethyl-ammonium bromide or chloride molecules in the ratio 1:1.4. The structure as found by one-dimensional Fourier synthesis is shown in Fig. 14. Although the figure shows all organic ions with Cl^- or Br^- as counter ions, in fact there are vacant positions for these anions according to the above composition. The halogen ions are distributed statistically among the available positions. Similar regular arrangements of alkyl chains are considered to occur in vermiculites and micas (276), although the angles of inclination may vary. When imbibition of small neutral molecules takes place among the chains there must be swelling of the lattice and presumably more or less disordering of the chains (46).

We may now consider briefly some more salient features associated with sorption of neutral molecules by these organic ion-exchanged layer silicates. If the organic ions introduced into montmorillonites are small and relatively globular [$CH_3NH_3^+$, $(CH_3)_2NH_2^+$, $(CH_3)_3NH^+$, $(CH_3)_4N^+$, and $(C_2H_5)_4N^+$] the silicate layers are separated by amounts depending on the dimensions of the ions, and are held in this position (cf. Table X). These layers may expand a little more but they cannot collapse on to one another. There is then some space between adjacent cations, and so an intracrystalline porosity develops which transforms the sorptive proper-ties of the clay mineral. It has now a substantial intracrystalline surface freely available to such species as inert gases, permanent gases, n-paraffins, and simple aromatic and cycloparaffins (52, 59). The repeat distances of these ion-exchanged montmorillonites are compared with those of some other species having the same kind of silicate layers in Table XI. The free

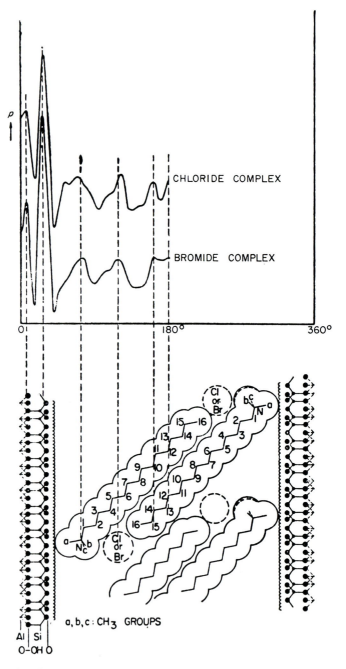

Fig. 14. One-dimensional Fourier syntheses of montmorillonite cetyltrimethylammonium bromide and chloride complexes (128).

TABLE XI

REPEAT DISTANCES OF SOME LAYER SILICATES

Mineral	Repeat distance, $d_{(001)}$ normal to silicate layers (Å)	Free distance between layers	Remark
Talc	9.2_6	0	No cations occur between lamellae
Pyrophyllite	9.1_3	0	
Muscovite	9.9_8	0.7–0.8	K^+ ions between layers
Paragonite			Na^+ ions between layers
Na-montmorillonite (60)	9.6	0.2	Outgassed
NH$_4$-montmorillonite (60)	Diffuse first order lines and irrational series of (001) reflections	—	Outgassed
Cs-montmorillonite (60)		—	Outgassed
CH$_3$NH$_3$-montmorillonite (59^a)	12.0	2.6	Outgassed
(CH$_3$)$_2$NH$_2$-montmorillonite (59^a)	12.2	2.8	Outgassed
(CH$_3$)$_3$NH-montmorillonite (59^a)	13.0	3.6	Outgassed
(CH$_3$)$_4$N-montmorillonite (52, 59^a)	13.5–13.6	4.1	Outgassed
(C$_2$H$_5$)$_4$N-montmorillonite (52, 59^a)	13.95	4.5_5	Outgassed

^{a} Slightly smaller values were recorded in some instances by Barrer and Kelsey (45). The spacing is influenced to a minor extent by sorbed water.

distances between the lamellae are of the order of molecular dimensions. When sorbate molecules penetrate between the sheets there is sometimes a slight additional expansion. Thus benzene expands the $d_{(001)}$ spacing of $N(CH_3)_4$-montmorillonite to 14.6 Å even at relative pressures as low as 0.06. This spacing in the $NH_3(CH_3)$-clay rises to 15 Å (56, 57). Benzene molecules are considered to be oriented nearly vertically or vertically, respectively, between the silicate layers, though keyed to some extent into the surface layers of oxygen atoms of Fig. 12, in conformity with the free distances of 5.2 and 5.6 Å between the layers.

TABLE XII

AMOUNTS SORBED BY SEVERAL ALKYLAMMONIUM CLAYS AT $P/P_0 = 0.2$, AS CM^3
AT S.T.P. PER GM OF CLAY (52, 59)

Sorbate	Temp. °K	Natural clay	$NH_3(CH_3)$- clay	$NH(CH_3)_3$- clay	$N(CH_3)_4$- clay	$N(C_2H_5)_4$- clay
O_2	90	7	50	44	52	29
N_2	90	6	47	42	45	18
Ar	90	—	44	41	—	14
CH_4	90	—	38	36	—	5
n-C_4H_{10}	273	—	17.8	13.2	—	—
Iso-C_4H_{10}	273	—	12	9.2	—	—
Benzene	323	1.7	—	—	27	8
Toluene	323	—	—	—	20	—
o-Xylene	323	—	—	—	14	—
m-Xylene	323	—	—	—	13.2	—
p-Xylene	323	—	—	—	15	—
Cyclohexane	323	—	—	—	12.5	—
Cyclopentane	323	—	—	—	14.5	—
n-Pentane	323	—	—	—	13.5	—
Isopentane	323	—	—	—	12.0	—
Neopentane	323	—	—	—	9.0	—
n-Heptane	323	—	—	—	10.5	—
Isooctane	323	—	—	—	7.5	—

The lateral free distances between the organic ions can play a dominant role in determining the entry of penetrants between the silicate layers (57). n-Perfluoroheptane cannot penetrate into either the methyl- or the tetramethylammonium clay, while isooctane and cyclohexane do so to a much smaller extent than n-heptane, n-hexane, or benzene. When considering this penetration it must always be remembered that some adsorption upon the external surfaces of the small clay crystallites can occur, and that when the relative pressures exceed 0.5 or 0.6 capillary condensation can begin. However, external surfaces normally prove small in comparison with those accessible between the silicate layers. Some amounts sorbed estimated as cm³ at S.T.P. per gm of alkylammonium clay at a relative pressure of 0.2 are given in Table XII, which shows the much increased sorption by the alkylammonium ion-exchanged clays as compared with that on the parent Na-clay. However, the amount of interlamellar space available in the $N(C_2H_5)_4$-clay is considerably smaller than, for example, that in the $N(CH_3)_4$-clay. The larger ion, which assumes a flattened configuration, fills more of this space than the smaller (52).

For long-chain alkylammonium ions the interlamellar space is filled by the alkyl radicals (cf. Fig. 14) and the sorptive properties of such sorbents change radically (46). Instead of isotherms which have the curvature of Types I or II in the B.E.T. classification (90) they now show that of isotherms of Type III, such as are observed when benzene is sorbed by rubber (e.g., 135). Instead of sorptions which take place from the liquids exothermally and with a decrease in entropy, this process now occurs with a very small heat and with an increase in entropy. Comparisons of isotherms and of differential heats and entropies of sorption for n-heptane, benzene, and isooctane in $N(CH_3)_4$-, $NH_3(CH_3)$-, and $N(CH_3)_2(C_{18}H_{37})_2$-montmorillonites are shown in Fig. 15. These changed characteristics are fully compatible with different mechanisms of sorption. Molecules are intercalated in the $N(CH_3)_4$- and $NH_3(CH_3)$-clays into pre-existing holes or interstices between the layers. They are intercalated into the $N(CH_3)_2(C_{18}H_{37})_2$-clay by mixing with the long alkyl chains, displacing and disordering them and swelling the clay in order to do so.

B. Uranium Micas

Weiss, Hartl, and Hofmann (279, 280) have shown that the compounds $H(H_2O)_4[UO_2PO_4]$ and $H(H_2O)_4[UO_2AsO_4]$, which have tetragonal unit cells with $a = 6.90 \pm 0.02$ Å, $c = 17.12 \pm 0.04$ Å and $a = 7.10 \pm 0.02$ Å, $c = 17.50 \pm 0.04$ Å, respectively, are readily prepared and can yield a variety of compounds of the uranium mica group. The latter can be repre-

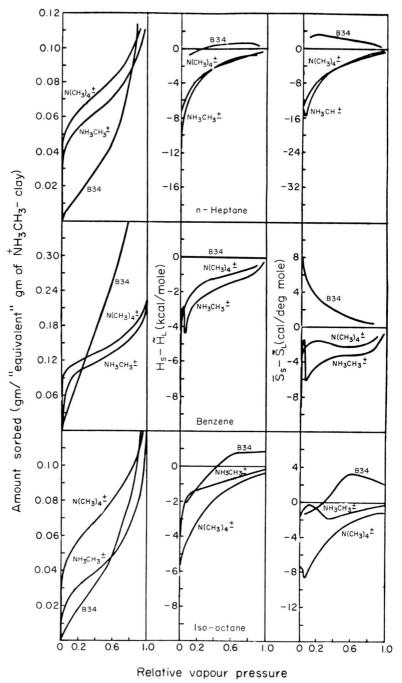

FIG. 15. Comparisons of adsorption isotherms, and of differential heats and entropies of adsorption of liquid hydrocarbons, for monomethyl-, tetramethyl-, and dimethyl-dioctadecylammonium (Bentone 34) montmorillonites (46).

344

sented by the general formula

$$(A^+, \tfrac{1}{2}A^{2+})xH_2O[UO_2XO_4]^-$$

where X may be P, As, or V, and A^+ or A^{2+} are cations such as Na^+, K^+, Ca^{2+}. The group of compounds is represented by such naturally occurring species as autunite, $Ca[UO_2PO_4]_2xH_2O$; torbernite, $Ca[UO_2PO_4]_2xH_2O$; zeunerite, $Cu[UO_2AsO_4]_2xH_2O$; trogerite, $UO_2[UO_2AsO_4]_2xH_2O$; or carnotite, $K[UO_2VO_4]$. In all these formulas the part enclosed in the square brackets gives the composition of the uranium mica layers, between which are located water molecules and exchangeable cations. From Table IX it is seen that the cation density between layers is almost the same as that between layers in micas such as muscovite, biotite, lepidolite, or zinnwaldite. The interlayer cations are exchangeable and may also be introduced by neutralizing the oxonium ion forms such as $H(H_2O)_4[UO_2PO_4]$. The inorganic cations may be exchanged inter alia by alkylammonium ions, which then appear to be oriented vertically or nearly vertically between the $[UO_2XO_4]$ layers. Direct synthesis of these alkylammonium uranium micas is also possible (*280*).

When the alkylammonium uranium micas were exposed to various liquids, these liquids were intercalated between the $[UO_2XO_4]$ layers. A number of the spacings are given in Table XIII for mono-*n*-alkylammonium uranylphosphates, taken from the more extensive data of Weiss et al. (*279*). The repeat distance of the layers of dried $NH_4[UO_2PO_4]$ is 6.3 Å. Then the observed layer repeat distance of the alkylammonium uranylphosphates dried at 65°C less this distance for the ammonium form (6.3 Å), is represented reasonably well (in Å) by

$$(n - 1)1.26 + 3.54$$

where n denotes the number of carbon atoms in the alkyl chain. When a neutral chain molecule is intercalated along with the alkylammonium ions the same formula still remains approximately valid where n now denotes the total number of carbon atoms in both chains. For example, the layer expansion distances for $(n\text{-}C_8H_{17})\overset{+}{N}H_3$ and for $(n\text{-}C_6H_{13})\overset{+}{N}H_3 + C_2H_5OH$ as the interlayer components are respectively 12.3 and 12.1 Å. In the latter system the formula gives correctly the swelling expected for both chains in the numerical ratio 1:1, one on top of the other, and each stretched normal to the plane of the $[UO_2PO_4]$ layers. A thermodynamic study of the intercalation of neutral guest molecules would however be of interest here, to indicate the signs and magnitudes of heats and entropies of intercalation of liquids, and so to give a better indication of the nature of the process of mixing of the long-chain ions and the neutral molecules. This approach

TABLE XIII

LAYER REPEAT DISTANCES IN Å FOR MONO-*n*-ALKYLAMMONIUM URANYLPHOSPHATES
(*279*)

Swelling condition	Ion-exchanged form				
	$C_4{}^a$	C_6	C_8	C_{12}	C_{18}
Dried at 65°C	14.2	16.6	18.6	23.5	28.0
Under: water	23.6	19.8	21.2	31.8	—
benzene	18.6	21.1	24.5	32.8	—
toluene	17.9	—	24.6	33.5	44.0
nitrobenzene	17.1	21.5	24.2	—	34.6
pyridine	16.0	21.0	—	30.0	—
acetonitrile	17.0	—	22.2	—	32.2
methyl ethyl ketone	—	22.9	24.0	—	31.0
n-butylamine	18.9	—	—	—	—
n-hexylamine	—	22.8	—	—	—
n-octylamine	—	—	29.8	—	—
ethanol	15.4	18.4	—	24.5	33.4
n-butanol	18.6	20.3	22.7	27.0	32.6
n-hexanol	—	22.6	24.8	29.4	35.6
n-heptanol	21.5	23.6	27.0	32.1	39.2
n-octanol	22.7	25.2	29.2	34.4	40.6
n-decanol	24.6	27.8	32.5	37.6	45.3

a C_n denotes $n\text{-}(C_nH_{2n+1})\overset{+}{N}H_3$ as the interlayer cation.

has, as previously noted, been helpful in the case of the alkylammonium montmorillonites.

C. Trititanates

Weiss and Weiss (*286*) reported some interesting intercalation phenomena associated with primary *n*-alkylammonium trititanates.* Andersson

---

* Although this work was considered by Weiss and Weiss to relate to the dititanate, $M_2Ti_2O_5$, Andersson and Wadsley reported that the diffraction spacings given by Weiss and Weiss are those of the trititanate.

and Wadsley (*6*) prepared $Na_2Ti_3O_7$ and determined its structure. The space group is $P2_{1/n}$ with unit cell dimensions $a = 8.571$, $b = 3.804$, $c = 9.135$, $\beta = 101°57'$. The structure consists of layers of TiO_6 octahedra. These layers are built of blocks of six TiO_6 octahedra sharing edges, three at one level, three at a distance $(b/2)$Å above. A cross section of the layers of linked octahedra is shown in Fig. 16; between these sheets the Na^+

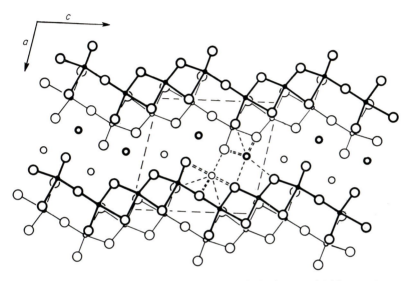

FIG. 16. Part of a projection in the ac plane of the layers of TiO_6, octahedra in $Na_2Ti_3O_8$. Bonds to oxygen (large circles) from titanium (smallest circles) are shown, the lighter circles representing atoms at the level $y = \frac{1}{4}$, the heavier at $y = \frac{3}{4}$. The bonds from interlayer sodium (medium circles) to oxygen are the dotted lines. The unit cell is also outlined (*6*).

ions are located as indicated. These ions can be replaced by primary *n*-alkylammonium ions very slowly as they are in muscovite or biotite micas, the titanate layers being preserved in the process. The complete exchange at 60°C required one or two months in crystals of 1–2 mm dimensions. The $d_{(001)}$ spacing rose from 3.8 Å for the Na-form to 18.0_3 Å for *n*-hexylammonium trititanate to 35.1_7 Å for the *n*-octadecylammonium trititanate. The alkylammonium trititanates then swelled additionally and reversibly in the presence of water, alcohols, ethers, aldehydes, ketones, esters, carboxylic acids, nitriles, nitro compounds, and hydrocarbons. When *n*-alcohols were intercalated the layer repeat distance increased linearly with the total number of carbon atoms in the alkylammonium ion and the *n*-alkanol. This behavior recalls that found in the uranium micas.

   It has been seen that *n*-alkylammonium forms of polyphosphates, layer lattice silicates, uranium micas, and trititanates can be prepared under appropriate conditions. Some comments on the alkylammonium layers may be relevant. Much information has been gained on the stereochemistry of long alkyl chains present as monolayer films on aqueous surfaces and on metals or glasses [e.g., Adam (1); Rideal (213)]. Lattice-like arrangements of steeply oriented chains are possible when the monolayers are formed of closely packed chains, the limiting area per chain under zero compression then being about 20.5 $Å^2$. On water surfaces the area per chain can be varied at will, by the Langmuir trough procedure. However, between lattice layers of inorganic compounds the area available per chain is equal to the area per exchange ion. These areas are given in Table IX. The greatest cation density found in the margarite micas corresponds to 12 $Å^2$, and if the interlayer ions could be exchanged the alkyl chains could not be arranged even as a vertically oriented monolayer, for which the area per chain is about 20 $Å^2$. Instead it would be possible to have a double layer with half the —NH_3^+ groups terminating on the upper and half on the lower silicate layers. In micas such as muscovite or biotite the area per exchangeable ion is 24 $Å^2$, and in the *uranium micas* it is 25 $Å^2$, so that oriented monolayers are just possible at full exchange. The *free* distance between the inorganic layers is often close to that given by $(n - 1)1.26 + 3.54$ Å, where n is the number of carbon atoms in the

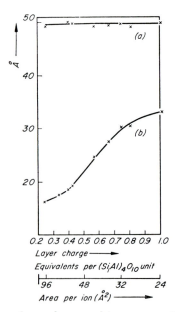

FIG. 17. Relation between layer charge and layer separation of mica-like minerals exchanged with stearylammonium ions, (a) under n-dodecyl alcohol, and (b) dried at 60° and 0.1 mm pressure (276).

TABLE XIV

CYANIDES AND RELATED COMPOUNDS WHICH FORM INCLUSION COMPLEXES

Compositions of host lattices	Limiting compositions of complexes	Typical guest molecules
$Ni(CN)_2 \cdot NH_3$	$Ni(CN)_2 NH_3 \cdot M$	M = benzene, pyridine, pyrrole, thiophene, furan, phenol, aniline; biphenyl, 4-NH_2-biphenyl, 4-OH-biphenyl ($\frac{1}{2}$M)
$ANi(CN)_4(NH_3)_2$ A = Cu^{II}, Cd^{II}, Zn^{II}	$ANi(CN)_4(NH_3)_2 \frac{3}{2}M$	M = benzene
$Mg[Mg((CH_2)_6N_4)_2 \cdot A^{III}(CN)_6]_2$ A = Fe^{III}, Co^{III}, Cr^{III}, Mn^{III}, and Rb^{III}	—	H_2O, acetone, aniline, ethylene, glycol, glycerine
A(4-methylpyridyl)$_4X_2$ A = Ni^{II}, Mn^{II}, Fe^{II}, Co^{II}, and Cu^{II}; X = CN^-, CNO^-, SCN^-, Cl^-, or $HCOO^-$	—	Benzene, toluene, ethylbenzene, o-, m-, and p-xylenes, o-, m-, and p-diethylbenzene, ethyltoluenes, cymenes, naphthalene, anthracene, 1-methylnaphthalene, biphenyl, dichlorobenzene, toluidines, nitrotoluenes, methylanisoles

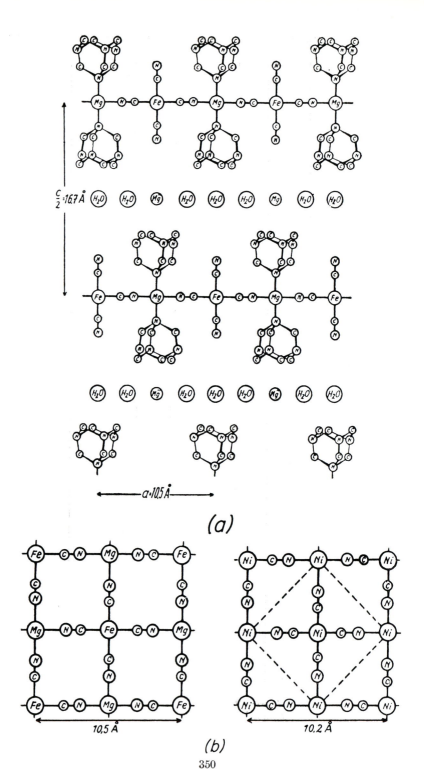

(a)

(b)

chain. This corresponds to a vertically oriented close packed monolayer of alkyl chains. When the area per cation increases still more [e.g., muscovite < glauconite < vermiculite < montmorillonite (Table IX)], the alkyl chains tilt more and more, net attraction between the two inorganic layers ensuring that the free space is reduced to a minimum. The variation of the repeat distance with the area per cation in micaceous silicates is shown in Fig. 17, curve *b* (*276*). The angle of tilt corresponding to the lowest repeat distance is only about 19° from the horizontal.

The angle of tilt can be increased for low interlayer charge densities by intercalation of chain molecules as well as the exchange ions. An example of this has been referred to in Fig. 14, in which cetyltrimethylammonium chloride or bromide molecules are included in montmorillonite alongside the cetyltrimethylammonium exchange ions. When *n*-dodecanol is intercalated into the stearylammonium layer silicates these all swell to the same repeat distance of a little less than 50 Å. This corresponds to a free distance between silicate layers equal to the combined length of dodecanol and stearylammonium when vertical and end to end (Fig. 17, curve *a*), although the detailed arrangement of chains does not follow from this observation alone. The organic layer is of constant thickness, independent of the area available to each stearylammonium ion. It is much richer in dodecanol at the left than at the right of curve *a*. When the intercalated molecules are small much disorder may be expected, since diverse arrangements of these molecules and of the long chain ions could, as required, fill all the interlayer space.

D. Layer Lattice Cyanides

Several different groups of cyanides and related compounds which form inclusion complexes are indicated in Table XIV. The structures of $Ni(CN)_2\cdot NH_3\cdot C_6H_6$ and of $Mg[Mg((CH_2)_6N_4)_2Fe(CN)_6]_2\cdot 24H_2O$ have been determined respectively by Powell and Rayner (*208, 209*) and by Weiss *et al.* (*287*). The cyanide layers of each type of compound are extremely similar in form and dimensions, as shown by Fig. 18*a* and *b*. A cross section through the layers of $Mg[Mg((CH_2)_6N_4)_2Fe(CN)_6]_2\cdot 24H_2O$ is shown in Fig. 18*a*. The interlayer Mg^{2+} ions are exchangeable for NH_4^+, Li^+, Co^{2+}, Ni^{2+} and Cu^{2+} ions, and the water molecules by other small polar molecules (Table XIV), with variations in the layer repeat distance.

In the complex $Ni(CN)_2NH_3\cdot C_6H_6$ the sheets of Fig. 18*b* have NH_3 groups projecting both above and below every Ni atom, and the sheets

---

Fig. 18. (*a*) Section through the *ac* plane of $Mg[Mg((CH_2)_6N_4)_2Fe(CN)_6]_2\cdot 24H_2O$. (*b*) Comparison of layers in $Mg[Mg((CH_2)_6N_4)_2Fe(CN)_6]_2\cdot 24H_2O$ and $Ni(CN)_2NH_3\cdot C_6H_6$ (*287*).

are stacked so that the projecting NH_3 groups in adjacent layers are above one another, forming the cages which trap the benzene molecular. Baur and Schwarzenbach (76) observed that some ammoniacal solutions of the double cyanides, $ANi(CN)_4$ of Table XIV also gave clathrate complexes with benzene. These may resemble the $Ni(CN)_2NH_3 \cdot C_6H_6$ complex, but with A and Ni atoms alternating in the layers portrayed in Fig. 18b.

The crystal structures of the $A(4\text{-methylpyridyl})_4X_2$ complexes have not yet been determined, but from the types of molecule intercalated (231) they may also be based upon a layered host lattice. These and similar Werner complexes are of considerable interest for selective inclusion of certain aromatic species (231) and for separations of nitro compounds (161).

E. Inclusion Complexes of Basic Salts

An extensive study has been made by Feitknecht and his collaborators of basic salts of divalent metals (e.g., 124). These are often layer compounds in which sulfate, chloride, or nitrate are intercalated between metal hydroxide layers. This work suggested that certain metal hydroxides, such as those of zinc and copper, should be able to intercalate flat organic molecules. The truth of the suggestion was demonstrated by forming layer structures such as zinc hydroxide nitrophenolates (118), zinc, cadmium, and copper hydroxide flavianates (122), inclusion complexes of Napthogelb S with Mg, Cu, Ni, Co, Mn, and Cd hydroxides (119, 120, 121), and a variety of similar structures (123). The layer repeat distance varied with the compositions, n, of the basic zinc flavianate, $Zn(OH)_2 \cdot nZnFla$ where Fla denotes the divalent ion (II).

$$\left[O_3S\text{———}\underset{NO_2}{\overset{O}{\text{naphthalene}}}\text{———}NO_2 \right]^{2-}$$

(II)

These spacings are summarized in Table XV, which also records them for a variety of other complexes. All these complexes are essentially ionic in character.

F. Graphitic Oxide

Graphitic oxide (graphitic acid) may be prepared by oxidation of graphite (239). The method is described also by de Boer and van Doorn (107) who gave the empirical composition $C_7O_4H_2$ to the compound. Despite

TABLE XV

LAYER REPEAT DISTANCES IN SOME Zn(OH)$_2$ COMPLEXES

Complex	Approximate composition[a] n in $Zn(OH)_2 \cdot nZnR^{II}$ (or R_2^I)	Layer distance in Å
Flavianate	0.065	14.2
	0.130	15.3
	0.254	16.2
	0.286	18.3
	0.316	19.5
	0.315	19.5
o-Nitrophenolate	—	~20
p-Nitrophenolate	—	14.9
Fully crystallized p-nitrophenolate	0.25	11.4
Fully crystallized picrate	0.20	18.2
Benzoate	—	19.4
Salicylate	—	16.5
Fully crystallized salicylate	—	12.8
Benzene sulfonate	—	15.8
Erioflavinate	—	20.6
Erioglaucinate	0.14$_7$	27
Swiss blue complex	—	27–28

[a] R^{II} and R^{I} denote the divalent or monovalent organic ions referred to in column 1.

considerable work, summarized for example by Croft (102) and by Ubbelohde and Lewis (254), the detailed structure of graphitic oxide is not fully understood. However, there is no doubt that the oxide has a layer lattice based on sheets of carbon atoms. These layers are not fully graphitic since the (10$\bar{1}$0) and (11$\bar{2}$0) lines indicate a C—C distance of 1.44 Å as compared with 1.41 Å in graphite. The projection on to a plane of a buckled aliphatic carbon hexagon network with the C—C distance equal to 1.53 Å would give a projected C—C distance of 1.45 Å in the plane of the network, so that the figure of 1.44 Å is compatible either with a partly aromatic or with a puckered aliphatic carbon sheet. Each sheet probably has attached OH groups, oxygen bridges, and keto groups. The interplanar spacing in the air-dried oxide is about 9 Å which falls to 6.3 Å when drying is effected by phosphoric oxide. The hydroxyl groups, still present even after drying over phosphoric oxide, can be esterified and also neutralized with caustic soda. Membranes of lamellar texture may be prepared from the oxide that are permeable to water, because of imbibition of this molecule, but not to nonpolar gases such as nitrogen. This allows measurement of partial pressures of water vapor in mixtures with permanent gases (91).

One of the most interesting properties of graphitic oxide is its power to absorb polar liquids. When water is imbibed, there is little swelling for the first 4.5% uptake of this sorbate, but for larger amounts of interlayer water the c spacing increases linearly with the amount imbibed, reaching values of about 120 Å for 50% by weight of water sorbed (108). Swelling may result even in sheet dispersion as giant two-dimensional molecules, just as for Na-montmorillonite. Aragon et al. (9) have compared the changes in interlayer spacings of graphitic oxide and of montmorillonite when n-amines, diamines, and alcohols are the penetrants. In both, for n-amines having from 4 to 16 carbon atoms in the chain, the spacing increased by ~2.6 Å per carbon atom. This increment is close to the projected length of two C—C single bonds, and could mean a double layer of vertical chains sandwiched between each pair of layers. On the other hand, the values of the interlayer spacings are insufficient for two such vertical and fully extended sheets of amine one on the other, and so it was suggested that the free ends may overlap to some extent or that the first two or three carbon atoms adjacent to the —NH₂ group may lie on the surfaces of the lamellae. The diamines give less regular curves of interlayer spacing against chain length. Also these spacings are smaller, and it would now seem that only a single sheet of diamine molecules is located between a pair of lamellae of the host lattice.

Considerable similarities thus exist between montmorillonite and graphite oxide. Some parallels also exist for their intercalation complexes with n-alcohols and glycols, but the results are in general less regular, with layer spacings usually smaller for n-alcohols than for n-amines. Both montmorillonite and graphite oxide give electron micrographs which demonstrate the filmy nature of the crystallites. These can sometimes be folded and wrinkled, being so thin as to be flexible.

G. Graphite

Intercalation complexes formed by graphite have been the subject of several recent reviews (102, 146, 217, 254). They are formed with alkali metals, with halogens and some oxyacids, and with a variety of halides such as $FeCl_3$ or $AlCl_3$ (Table XVI).

Fredenhagen and his co-workers first showed that graphite reacts strongly with vapor or liquid K, Rb, and Cs (129, 130), while Asher (10) prepared a sodium-graphite layer complex of considerably less stability. The lithium-graphite complex is the least stable, but this metal has been

TABLE XVI

GRAPHITE INCLUSION COMPLEXES

Substances included	Limiting compositions
Li, Na, K, Rb, and Cs	$C_{64}Na$ C_8K, $C_{16}K$, $C_{24}K$, $C_{36}K$, $C_{64}K$
Br_2, F_2; ICl, ICl_3	CF, C_4F, C_8Br
H_2SO_4, HNO_3, H_2SeO_4, $HClO_4$, HPO_3, $H_4P_2O_7$, H_3AsO_4, HF	$C_{24}^+ \cdot HSO_4^- \cdot 2H_2SO_4$ $C_{24}^+ HF_2^- \cdot 2H_2F_2$
CrO_2Cl_2, CrO_2F_2, UO_2Cl_2	—
Chlorides of: Fe^{III}, Cu^{II}, B^{III}, Al^{III}, Ga^{III}, In^{III}, Tl^{III}, Zr^{IV}, Hf^{IV}, Sb^V, Ta^V, Cr^{III}, Mo^{III}, W^{VI}, U^{IV}, Re^{IV}, Co^{III}, Ru^{III}, Rh^{III}, Pd^{IV}, Pt^{IV}, Y^{III}, Gd^{III}, Yb^{III}, Dy^{III}, Eu^{III}	$C_m^+[AlCl_4^- + nAlCl_3]$
Bromides of: Cu^{II}, Al^{III}	
Oxides CrO_3, Sb_2O_4, MoO_3	—
Sulfides Sb_2S_3, Tl_2S, CuS, FeS_2, Cr_2S_3, V_2S_3, WS_2, PbS (with disproportionation in some cases)	—

intercalated by special methods, such as allowing graphite to react with lithium dissolved in ammonia or methylamine (223). A number of limiting compositions of these and other graphite layer complexes are given in Table XVI. Certain of these compositions may be less exactly defined than is sometimes assumed. Thus Fig. 19 shows the isobar of the potassium-graphite system when the potassium is at 250°C (255). While steps appear corresponding approximately to C_8K and $C_{24}K$, the curve becomes more or less continuous for higher carbon:potassium ratios than 24:1.

1. COMPLEXES WIYH ALKALI METALS

At the composition C_8M (e.g., C_8K) each carbon layer is separated by a layer of potassium (Fig. 20). The metal atoms are located over the

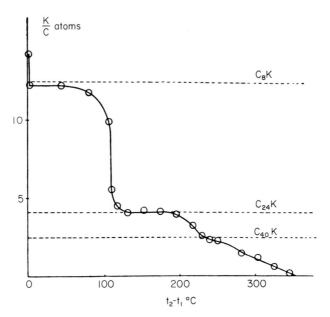

FIG. 19. Isobar of potassium graphite complex. Graphite at t_2°C. Potassium at $t_1 = 250$°C (*256*).

centers of alternate hexagons of carbon atoms, forming a triangular array. In complexes of composition $C_{16}M$ the alkali metal atoms are supposed to form the same triangular arrays located between every alternate pair of graphite layers. Thus, there is one layer of metal atoms to every two graphite layers. Similarly, the layer arrangement can be traced for other compositions $C_{24}M$ up to $C_{64}M$. In the latter case the metal atoms are intercalated to give one metal layer for every eight carbon layers. Whether the sequence of occupied and unoccupied layers is strictly a regular one in such a phase may be a subject for still further x-ray study. The intercalation of metal atoms (or of halogens, metal halides, or acids) expands the graphite layers, the interlayer distances being those given in Table XVII.

The alkali metals probably exist between the carbon layers as ions. Even if this is true, the expansions shown in column 3 of Table XVII are less than the cationic diameters. This illustrates a behavior found also for neutral molecules in layer silicates, where the expansion is always rather less than the van der Waals dimensions of the intercalated species (e.g., *45, 84, 138, 242*). Such behavior can in part be considered as due to keying of the molecules or ions into the six-membered rings of carbon atoms in the case of graphite, or oxygen atoms in layer silicates.

Graphitic carbon layers can act either as sources or as sinks of electrons. Thus, the formation of positive alkali metal ions between layers involves transfer of electrons to the conduction band of the graphitic layers, with a great increase in electrical conductivity. On the other hand when halogens (Br_2, Cl_2, or ICl) are intercalated, electrons are drawn from the filled π

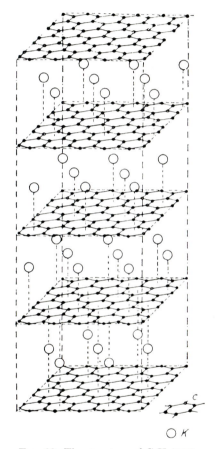

$\bigcirc$ K

Fig. 20. The structure of C_8K (256).

band by the halogens, leaving positive holes. Once more the conductivity is greatly increased. The specific resistance of C_8K in the direction of the a axis is between that of nickel and aluminum, and is many times less than this resistance for graphite. The resistance in the direction of the c axis is greater, but compared with graphite itself the decrease is even more spectacular (Fig. 42 in ref. 256).

It is of interest that other alkali metal inclusion complexes have been

TABLE XVII

INTERLAYER SPACINGS OF INTERCALATION COMPLEXES OF GRAPHITE

Approximate formula	Spacing in Å	Expansion in Å	Reference
C (graphite)	3.35	—	—
$C_{64}Na$	4.6	1.25	(10)
C_8K, $C_{24}K$, $C_{36}K$	5.4	2.05	(222)
C_8Rb, $C_{24}Rb$, $C_{36}Rb$	5.65	2.30	(222)
C_8Cs	5.94	2.69	(232)
$C_{12}M(NH_3)_2$	6.6	3.25	(223)
(M = Li, Na, K, Rb, or Cs)			
$C_{12}Li(CH_3NH_2)_2$	6.9	3.55	(223)
C_8Br, $C_{16}Br$	7.05	3.70	(216)
C_5ICl	7.24	3.89	(225)
$C_{24}{}^+HSO_4{}^-2H_2SO_4$	7.98	4.63	(215)
C_nFeCl_3	9.37–9.45	6.02–6.10	(221)
$C_m{}^+[GaCl_4{}^-+nGaCl_3]$	9.5	6.15	(219)
$C_m{}^+[AlCl_4{}^-+nAlCl_3]$	9.52	6.17	(227)

prepared from the layer lattice compounds MoS_2 and WS_2, complexes which are also thought to be partially ionic in character (224). These were made from the sulfides by interaction with the alkali metals dissolved in liquid ammonia, and were reported as having compositions:

$2MoS_2\ 1.0Cs$	$2WS_2\ 0.9Cs$
$2MoS_2\ 1.2K$	$2WS_2\ 1.0Rb$
$2MoS_2\ 1.6Na \cdot 0.4NH_3$	$2WS_2\ 0.9K$
$2MoS_2\ 2.2Li \cdot 1.2NH_3$	$2WS_2\ 1.2Na \cdot 0.2NH_3$
	$2WS_2\ 1.0Li \cdot 1.2NH_3$

The repeat distance normal to the layers increases after intercalation. Thus it is 12.35 Å in pure WS_2, and increases by 4.03, 4.84, and 5.53 Å when K, Rb, and Cs respectively are present between layers. It is interesting that the expansion is considerably higher than in the corresponding graphite complexes, and may thus correspond more nearly to the atomic than to the ionic dimensions of the alkali metals.

2. COMPLEXES WITH HALOGENS

As noted above, the bromine-graphite complex is a better electrical conductor than graphite, and it thus seems likely that it also has a partially salt-like character. The formula $C_n{}^+Br^-3Br_2$ may then be a better representation of its limiting composition than C_8Br. The expansion of 3.70 Å on intercalating bromine does not support this argument, being actually a little less than the van der Waals diameter of Br, and appreciably less than that of Br^- ion. However, keying of Br^- ion into hexagons of carbon, and some compression of the ion between graphitic layers may be important in determining the magnitude of the expansion. A number of measurements have been made of sorption isotherms of bromine by graphite and graphitic carbon (e.g., *152, 212*). These often show hysteresis between sorption and desorption cycles which persists to the lowest pressures, a behavior characteristic of lattice swelling and shrinking and found also with some of the layer lattice silicates. In addition some bromine is fixed irreversibly to the carbon, either at edges or at defect centers such as those of "hole" or "claw" type (*253*). Recent measurements by Hooley (*153, 154*) using ICl and Br_2 have demonstrated that the extent of sorption, as well as the isotherm contours and hysteresis, are strongly influenced by the crystallite size. The carbons examined were flake graphite, GI (1–2 mm), various graphites obtained from this by milling, and microcrystalline graphitic carbons with >200 Å crystals in 5000 Å blocks (Sterling MT), and with 80 Å crystals in 300 Å blocks (Spheron 6). Figure 21 shows the relations between amount sorbed, and temperature, pressure or relative pressure for the largest flakes and for Spheron 6 and Sterling MT. In view of this work it seems likely that the many reported variations in the compositions of bromine lamellar complexes with graphitic carbon are due to a combination of capillary condensation of bromine and its incomplete intercalation especially in microcrystalline carbons. The composition in the flake graphite does, however, approach C_8Br and is nearly independent of pressure and temperature over a range in both these variables.

Graphite also combines with fluorine to form a hydrophobic insulating solid of composition approaching $(CF)_n$ (*228*). The most probable structure is a series of puckered aliphatic planes of carbon flanked on either side by planes of fluorine atoms. Evidently this is a phase of different nature from the graphite complexes previously considered. However, some anomalies in x-ray reflection intensities remain which are not easy to reconcile with the "aliphatic" structure (*198*). Various intersheet distances of 8, 8.17,

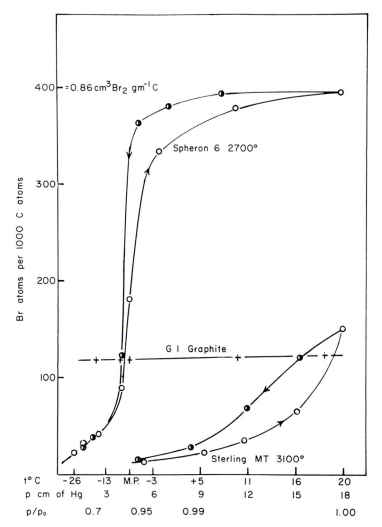

Fig. 21. Bromine uptake by Spheron 6 (sintered at 2700°C), graphite flakes, and Sterling MT carbon (154).

6.6, and 8.9 Å have been reported, distances which depend in part only upon the fluorine content (102). Compositions were reported as ranging from $CF_{0.676}$ to $CF_{0.998}$. Another insulating fluorine-graphite complex, first reported by Rüdorff and Rüdorff (220), has the composition C_4F. This phase, like CF, is nonreactive, but it is not considered to be 'aliphatic' in character because the intersheet distance is only 5.4 Å and the C—C distance in the layer planes is that of an aromatic compound, although this distance could still be a projected length of a C—C bond in a somewhat puckered carbon sheet. C_4F cannot be converted to CF by heating in the usual mixtures of hydrogen fluoride and fluorine (hydrogen fluoride normally catalyzes fluorine uptake). If it is slowly heated it loses fluorine progressively, but rapid heating causes deflagration with products such as CF_4 and C_2F_6 from both C_4F and CF.

The lamellar complexes of graphite can often be decomposed in a manner which leads to recovery of the guest component. However, a certain amount may be fixed within the graphite (e.g. *145*). The product is then referred to as a residue compound, an example being found in the bromine-graphite system. This residue compound is much more readily able to imbibe chlorine, aluminum chloride, or iodine than is the parent graphite (*145*, *158*). The chlorine-graphite residue compound has been shown to behave similarly in the subsequent imbibition of chlorine, and that of bisulfate-graphite in the uptake of bromine.

3. Complexes with Acids

The complexes formed, under oxidizing conditions, between graphite and oxyacids are partly ionic in character. Thus, when graphite is treated with strong sulfuric acid in the presence of a suitable oxidizing agent (nitric acid, chromium trioxide, potassium permanganate, ammonium persulfate, manganese dioxide, lead dioxide, arsenic pentoxide, iodic and periodic acids (*218*, *249*) it swells and intercalates HSO_4^- ions and H_2SO_4 molecules, forming a complex to which the limiting composition $C_{24}^+HSO_4^-$, $2H_2SO_4$ is attributed. This process is accompanied by the usual increase in electrical conductivity of the phase. The graphite-bifluoride complex is formed by anodic oxidation of graphite, or by oxidation with fluorine, in presence of anhydrous hydrogen fluoride. It has the limiting formula $C_{24}^+HF_2^-$, $2H_2F_2$. Like the bisulfate it can be reduced in stages to give lower levels of intercalation. The layer spacing of nearly 8 Å appears to be characteristic of a number of graphitic acid salts including bisulfate, bifluoride, and perchlorate. The acid salts can show interchange equilibria such as

$$\text{graphite phosphate} + H_2SO_4 \rightleftharpoons \text{graphite bisulfate} + H_3PO_4$$

this particular equilibrium lying well to the right. They react vigorously with water and caustic soda and readily with ethers, alcohols, glacial acetic acid, or esters. Reaction also occurs with dry benzene or toluene, but not with aliphatic hydrocarbons, carbon tetrachloride, chloroform, or carbon bisulfide.

4. "Molecular" Complexes

Perhaps the most numerous group of complexes formed by graphite is that in which halides, oxyhalides, oxides, and sulfides are intercalated (Table XVI). The guest molecules in some cases can be recovered unchanged, at least in part. The ferric chloride complex has been studied more fully than most of these phases.

This complex can have up to 56% of intercalated $FeCl_3$. In a product containing 55.5% of the chloride a recent x-ray study demonstrated the presence of about 17% of free graphite and 83% of the complex (97). As the amount of ferric chloride was diminished that of free graphite increased and the quantity of ferric chloride in the actual complex became less per layer. In the intercalation single layers of $FeCl_3$ lie between successive parallel planes of carbon atoms. At about 39% of ferric chloride the interlayer distance was 9.41 Å. The lateral positioning of layers relative to one another was essentially random, but there was some coordination between C and Cl atom positions, giving rise to some short-range order. The ferric chloride layers were about 92% filled in the system containing 55.5% $FeCl_3$. The ferric chloride – graphite complex has an enhanced electrical conductivity compared with that of graphite. The change in sign of the Hall coefficient indicates that there is transfer of electrons from the graphite layers to the ferric chloride. The phase richest in guest molecules has the blue iridescence which is typical of ionic graphite compounds.

The interaction of $AlCl_3$ and $GaCl_3$ is aided by the presence of an element such as chlorine (227). It seems likely that the halogen facilitates charge transfer and gives a proportion of intercalated anions like $AlCl_4^-$ yielding compositions such as $C_m^+[AlCl_4^- + nAlCl_3]$ (Table XVI). X-ray powder data for this system suggested three stages of intercalation as the temperature was increased progressively from 265° to 440°C. In the complex richest in $AlCl_3$ the deep blue product had a composition with $C:AlCl_3 = 9:1$. In the other stages these ratios were 18:1 and 36:1. Similar observations were made on the compositions of the $GaCl_3$-graphite complex (219).

Chromyl chloride vapor is intercalated by graphite provided a considerable threshold pressure of the volatile oxychloride is exceeded. The composition reached then approaches $C_{40} \cdot CrO_2Cl_2$ (155). From liquid CrO_2Cl the maximum composition has been reported as $C_{12} \cdot CrO_2Cl_2$ (225). The chromyl chloride intercalated, however, becomes slowly fixed in an irreversible manner, either by polymerization or by a reaction involving the lamellae. As a result, less and less chromyl chloride can be recovered by desorption the longer the time interval after the initial sorption (155).

When sulfides and oxides were intercalated there was a tendency for the intercalated metallic element to show a higher valence toward the sulfur or oxygen than in the parent oxide. The same blue iridescence appeared with most of the sulfides and with CrO_3 which was also observed with the chlorides (99).

The possibility of intercalation by the graphite-like compound, BN, was also investigated by Croft (100, 101). Positive results were reported for $SbCl_3$, $CuCl$, $FeCl_3$, and $AlCl_3$ although Rüdorff and Stumpp (226) did not observe any uptake, and also Hooley (155) found little evidence of intercalation of Br_2, ICl, or CrO_2Cl_2 by this substance. Boron nitride layers may be represented as (III).

(III)

The tendency to alternating polarity between N and B may mean a greater cohesion between successive lamellae, and so a lesser ability to intercalate than is shown by graphite. Nevertheless when boron nitride was heated with $FeCl_3$ at 400°C and with $AlCl_3$ at 250°C, 10.6% w/w of ferric chloride and 13.0% of aluminium chloride were occluded. Croft (101, 102) further commented upon the ability of other layer lattices to intercalate. Thus AlB_2 was reported as forming a sorption complex with ammonia, while chromic chloride incorporates up to 40% of $MoCl_5$. He considers this property should be general for layer lattices in the presence of appropriate guest molecules and under the right physical conditions. Reference has already been made to intercalation of alkali metals by WS_2 and MoS_2 (Section V,G,1). Hooley (153, 154, 155) studied the intercalation of Br_2, ICl, and CrO_2Cl_2 in MoS_2 and also observed formation of residue compounds between the halide or halogen and the molybdenum sulfide.

VI. SOME ADDITIONAL COMPLEXES

Before discussing zeolites as host crystals, a brief account may be given of some inclusion complexes largely of unknown structure. Several of these are Werner compounds. Kihara et al. (162) found that the complex

Fe^{III} salts derived from bis(salicylaldehydeethylenediimine) of the structure (IV)

(IV)

where X$^-$ denotes a monovalent anion, can yield various adducts. If X$^-$ was Cl$^-$, 1 mole of chloroform or bromoform, or 2 moles of pyridine were added. If X$^-$ was Br$^-$ the addition of a mole of bromoform was observed. When X$^-$ was $\frac{1}{2}$O^{2-}, 1.5 moles of chloroform could be incorporated. Some of these adducts proved to be very stable. Tsumaki et al. (252) observed that complexes were formed by certain metal phthalocyanines. Per mole of Mg-phthalocyanine the following additions occurred:

2H$_2$O	2CH$_3$OH
1.5 pyridine + 0.5H$_2$O	2C$_2$H$_5$OH
1.5 lutidine + 0.5H$_2$O	1CH$_3$COCH$_3$ + 1H$_2$O
2 quinoline	2C$_2$H$_5$SC$_2$H$_5$
1 aniline + 1H$_2$O	1 thiophene + 1H$_2$O
1 o-toluidine + 1H$_2$O	

The nature of the Mg-phthalocyanine molecule suggests that these complexes may be lamellar in character.

Other Werner complexes able to include water are magnesium platinocyanide, studied by Tammann (243), and hexamethylisocyanidoiron(II) chloride (206, 207). Hardt (142) reported that beryllium oxyacetate, Be$_4$O(O·COCH$_3$)$_6$, undergoes partial decomposition in absolute alcohol, giving a higher basic acetate. This, with undecomposed oxyacetate, forms a structure in which large amounts of ethanol are occluded. Osterlof (197) has suggested that acetylene, in the complexes 2CuCl·C$_2$H$_2$ and 3CuCl·C$_2$H$_2$ is located interstitially in a cuprous chloride host lattice. Weiss and Weiss (285) found that mercarbide can imbibe vapors of methanol and ammonia, and that water is sorbed zeolitically. McBain (175), following Katz (160), has listed a number of phases which appear able to contain a zeolitic guest molecule. It is evident that a wide variety of such complexes can exist.

As final examples we may consider alkali metal benzene sulfonates in which the metal ion is K^+, Rb^+, or Cs^+. These form a notable series of complexes (*42, 168, 169, 170*), a property which is not shared by the Li-, Na-, or NH_4-forms, nor by the alkali metal toluene sulfonates. Some of the sorption isotherms have contours recalling Langmuir's isotherm, but others show one or more steps. Typical examples are illustrated in Fig. 22 for water and several alcohols. Especially when stepwise sorption occurs, well-defined hysteresis loops may be found. In some cases these loops may be traversed reproducibly, for example, in the sorption of aromatic hydro-

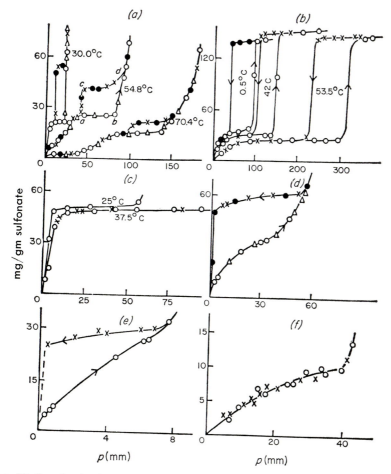

FIG. 22. Sorption isotherms in potassium benzene sulfonate: (*a*) water; (*b*) methanol; (*c*) ethanol; (*d*) isopropanol, all at 30.8°C; (*e*) *n*-butanol at 27°C; (*f*) *tert*-butanol at 25°C (*42*).

TABLE XVIII

Limiting Compositions of Some Complexes of Potassium Benzene Sulfonate (42)

Guest molecule	Moles of guest per mole of host	Temp. (°C)
Ethylene	0.22	−22.9
Propane	0.009	13
Cyclopentane	0.10	9.2
	0.08	25
Water (in lower hydrate)	0.27	30
	0.25	54.8
	0.17	70.4
Benzene	0.16	31.4
	0.14	54.8
	0.11	71.0
Toluene	0.11	31.6
	0.09	54.7
	0.05	70.7
o-Xylene	0.09	30.5
	0.07	54.8
	0.04	70.7
Naphthalene	0.050	54.8
	0.046	71.2
Water (in higher hydrate)	0.58	30.0
	0.42	54.8
	0.23	70.4
Methanol	0.96	30.5
	0.98	42.5
	0.95	53.5
Ethanol	0.23	25.0
	0.22	37.5
Iso-propanol	0.20	30.8
n-Butanol	0.08	27.0
tert-Butanol	0.03	25.0
Ethylamine	0.18	50.0
Thiophene	0.25	30.0
	0.25	54.6
p-Dioxane	0.28	30.0
	0.27	73.4

carbons. Occasionally, as for dioxane, successively determined loops changed in position and shape before finally settling down to become reproducible. Steps appear to be associated with intracrystalline rearrangements of the host lattice, and the x-ray evidence suggests that there may be several kinds of structure. Apparent limiting compositions are given for various included species in Table XVIII, most of which do not approach simple stoichiometric proportions, and decrease with increasing temperature. Among species of the same kind (e.g. aromatic hydrocarbons) the limiting amounts included decrease with increasing molecular size.

VII. ZEOLITES WITH INTERSECTING CHANNEL NETWORKS

A. General Aspects

The zeolites form a large and important group of crystals in which varied systems of intersecting channel networks traverse porous crystal frameworks. As a result they can often form complexes with a great variety of molecules, inorganic or organic, as well as with various salts. Because of their differing pore and channel geometries they are finding a range of applications as selective and molecular sieve sorbents and also have promise as selective ion exchangers (4, 24). All naturally occurring zeolites are aluminosilicates in which the exchangeable cations are predominantly Na, K, Ca, and Ba. The oxide formula is $(A_2^I, A^{II})O \cdot Al_2O_3 \cdot nSiO_2 \cdot mH_2O$ where, in any one zeolite, both n and m can normally vary. Synthetic crystalline zeolites conform to the same generic formula but the ions A^I may now be Li, Na, K, Rb, Cs, Tl, or NH_4 while A^{II} may be Ca, Sr, or Ba (23). Additional synthetic analogues have been prepared in which Ga replaces Al and Ge replaces Si (32, 137) and also in which A^I is replaced by such alkylammonium ions as $NH_3(CH_3)^+$, $NH_2(CH_3)_2^+$, $NH(CH_3)_3^+$, and $N(CH_3)_4^+$ (40). The variability of n in the oxide formulas arises from isomorphous replacements of the type

$$NaAl \rightleftharpoons Si; \quad CaAl \rightleftharpoons NaSi$$

Both kinds of isomorphous replacement may modify the molecular sieve character and so the power to form complexes, as considered later.

Table XIX lists a number of naturally occurring zeolites. The classification given in column 1 is based in part upon that of Dana (103), and in part upon more recent x-ray studies, but is neither exact nor complete. In the oxide formulas of column 2 the alumina:silica ratios must not be regarded as fixed, these ratios often being variable over a wide range, as

TABLE XIX

Some Naturally Occurring Zeolites

Zeolite	Typical oxide formula	Crystal chemical nature	Approx. intracrystalline volume for H_2O (cm^3/cm^3 of zeolite)
Mordenite group			
Mordenite	$(Ca, K_2, Na_2)O \cdot Al_2O_3 \cdot 10SiO_2 \cdot 6.7H_2O$	1[a]	0.29
Ptilolite	$(Ca, K_2, Na_2)O \cdot Al_2O_3 \cdot 10SiO_2 \cdot 4H_2O$	1	0.22
Dachiardite	$(Na_2, K_2, Ca)O \cdot Al_2O_3 \cdot 9SiO_2 \cdot 7H_2O$	1	0.31
Heulandite group			
Heulandite	$CaO \cdot Al_2O_3 \cdot 6SiO_2 \cdot 5H_2O$	2[b]	0.33
Clinoptilolite	$(Ca, Na_2, K_2)O \cdot Al_2O_3 \cdot 10SiO_2 \cdot 8H_2O$	2	0.34
Stilbite	$(Na_2, Ca)O \cdot Al_2O_3 \cdot 6SiO_2 \cdot 6H_2O$	2	0.37
Brewsterite	$(Sr, Ca, Ba)O \cdot Al_2O_3 \cdot 6SiO_2 \cdot 5H_2O$	—	0.33
Epistilbite	$CaO \cdot Al_2O_3 \cdot 6SiO_2 \cdot 5H_2O$	—	0.33
Ferrierite	$(Na_2, Mg)O \cdot Al_2O_3 \cdot 10SiO_2 \cdot 6H_2O$	—	0.27
Phillipsite group			
Phillipsite	$(K_2, Ca)O \cdot Al_2O_3 \cdot 4SiO_2 \cdot 4.5H_2O$	1	0.36
Harmotome	$(K_2, Ba)O \cdot Al_2O_3 \cdot 5SiO_2 \cdot 5H_2O$	1	0.34
Wellsite	$(Ca, Ba, Na_2, K_2)O \cdot Al_2O_3 \cdot 4SiO_2 \cdot 3.5H_2O$	1	0.36
Garronite	$(Ca, Na_2O) \cdot Al_2O_3 \cdot 3.3SiO_2 \cdot 4.5H_2O$[c]	1	0.41
Laumontite	$CaO \cdot Al_2O_3 \cdot 4SiO_2 \cdot 4H_2O$	—	0.35
Gismondite	$CaO \cdot Al_2O_3 \cdot 2SiO_2 \cdot 4H_2O$	—	0.49
Chabazite group			
Chabazite	$(Ca, Na_2)O \cdot Al_2O_3 \cdot 4SiO_2 \cdot 6H_2O$	1	0.46
Gmelinite	$(Na_2, Ca)O \cdot Al_2O_3 \cdot 4SiO_2 \cdot 6H_2O$	1	0.45
Levynite	$CaO \cdot Al_2O_3 \cdot 3SiO_2 \cdot 5H_2O$	1	0.39
Erionite	$(Ca, Mg, Na_2, K_2)O \cdot Al_2O_3 \cdot 6SiO_2 \cdot 6H_2O$	1	0.36
Natrolite group			
Natrolite[e]	$Na_2O \cdot Al_2O_3 \cdot 3SiO_2 \cdot 2H_2O$	3[d]	0.21
Scolecite	$CaO \cdot Al_2O_3 \cdot 3SiO_2 \cdot 3H_2O$	3	0.29
Mesolite	Between natrolite and scolecite	3	0.21–0.29
Edingtonite	$BaO \cdot Al_2O_3 \cdot 3SiO_2 \cdot 3H_2O$	3	0.30
Thomsonite	$(Na_2, Ca)O \cdot Al_2O_3 \cdot 2SiO_2 \cdot 3H_2O$	3	0.33
Gonnardite	$(Ca, Na_2)O \cdot Al_2O_3 \cdot 3SiO_2 \cdot 3.5H_2O$	3	0.31

TABLE XIX—*Continued*

Zeolite	Typical oxide formula	Crystal chemical nature	Approx. intracrystalline volume for H_2O (cm³/cm³ of zeolite)
Analcite group			
Analcite	$Na_2O \cdot Al_2O_3 \cdot 4SiO_2 \cdot 2H_2O$	1	0.176
Wairakite	$CaO \cdot Al_2O_3 \cdot 4SiO_2 \cdot 2H_2O$	1	0.176
Faujasite group			
Faujasite	$(Na_2, Ca)O \cdot Al_2O_3 \cdot 5SiO_2 \cdot 9H_2O$	1	0.54
Other species			
Paulingite	$(Na_2, K_2, Ca, Ba)O \cdot Al_2O_3 \cdot 8SiO_2 \cdot 12H_2O$ (approx.)	—	∼0.47
Ashcroftine	$(Na_2, K_2, Ca, Mg, Mn)O \cdot Al_2O_3 \cdot 2.5SiO_2 \cdot 4H_2O$	—	0.48
Yugawaralite	$CaO \cdot Al_2O_3 \cdot 5.7SiO_2 \cdot 4H_2O$	—	0.28

[a] 1 denotes a three-dimensional framework with bonding strengths comparable in three dimensions.

[b] 2 frameworks with a lamellar tendency.

[c] Dr. G. Walker, private communication.

[d] 3 frameworks with a fibrous tendency.

[e] There appears to be no significant difference between natrolite and laubanite.

noted above. All the zeolites are three-dimensional aluminosilicate networks, but appreciable differences can arise in the density of network bonds in different directions, so that laminar or near-fibrous character can appear. This is the basis of the crystal chemical classification of column 3. In the three-dimensional network structures bonding is comparably strong in all three dimensions. If network bonding is strong in two but less strong in the third dimension, platy zeolites appear; while if the bonding is strong in one dimension and less strong in the remaining two, the fibrous zeolites are obtained. In column 4 the volumes of zeolitic water displaced by heat and evacuation from the structures are given, expressed as cm³ of liquid water per cm³ of zeolite. This is taken as a measure of the intracrystalline free volume of the porous zeolite structures towards water, and often for many other guest molecules. It is seen that about 50% of a faujasite crystal may in this sense be represented as pore volume and something approaching this value for chabazite, gmelinite, and gismondite.

The crystal densities used to compute these free volumes are average values taken from Dana (*103*) and high accuracy cannot always be claimed. Also the co-volume per water molecule may vary within the crystals. Thus Barrer and Bratt (*34*) plotted the gm of water per Avogadro number of unit cells against the total volume occupied by cations per unit cell for a number of ion-exchanged chabazites and near-faujasites respectively. They then found for a given zeolite that its alkali metal forms gave a different

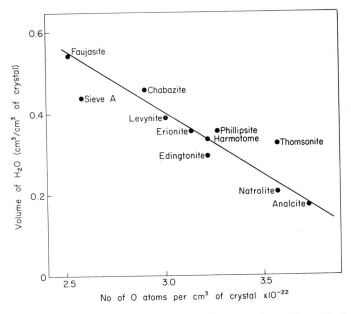

Fig. 23. Correlation of the density of framework oxygens in zeolites with the intracrystalline free volume.

curve from the alkaline earth metal forms, and these latter in turn gave a different curve from Ni-, Co-, and Cu-forms. The extrapolation of each of these curves to zero volume of occupying cations then demonstrated the different molar volume for the zeolitic water when associated with the three types of cation. These differences do not arise from alterations of the unit cell dimensions, with exchanges of cations, since such alterations are quite small (*39, 68, 86*). However, despite variations in the co-volumes of the zeolitic water molecule the figures in the last column of Table XIX form a reasonable comparison of free volumes within the crystals.

It is also possible to correlate the intracrystalline free volumes with the number of framework oxygen atoms per cm³ of crystal lattice, knowing the unit cell volumes and contents, as shown in Fig. 23 for a number of zeolites. Oxygen atoms are always the most numerous and are usually the largest atomic units in the structure. Al^{3+} and Si^{4+} are always buried in tetrahedra of oxygens in contact, so that only the intracrystalline Na, K, Ca, Si, or Ba ions are in competition with water for the free volume. Although, because of their differing sizes and numbers, the cations occupy varying fractions of the free volumes, these fractions are not large enough to obscure the correlation of Fig. 23. One or two zeolites do not show this correlation, for example, ashcroftine. However, only one analysis of this zeolite exists.

B. Structural Features

Structures have been proposed for the aluminosilicate frameworks of a number of zeolites, including analcite (*245, 246*); natrolite, scolecite, thomsonite, and edingtonite (*178, 247, 248*); chabazite, gmelinite, levynite, and erionite (*47, 109, 238*); phillipsite and harmotome (*37, 229*); mordenite (*179*); dachiardite (*180*); and faujasite (*79, 89*). To these zeolites we may add the purely synthetic material, Linde Sieve A (*55, 89, 210*). No detailed account of this work will be given, but essential features of a number of structures are described. Interesting zeolites so far studied as molecular sieves include faujasite (and synthetic near-faujasites such as Linde Sieves X and Y); Linde Sieve A; chabazite, gmelinite, levynite, and erionite; and mordenite, ptilolite, and dachiardite. The diversity of molecular sieve behavior has been added to by preparation of synthetic variants of the natural species, having novel compositions and properties, as described later.

Table XX summarizes the unit cell dimensions of a number of zeolites, the subdivisions being essentially structural, except that paulingite, ashcroftine, bikitaite, and yugawaralite are four not necessarily related and so far unclassified species.

The basic structural unit in zeolites is the tetrahedron $SiO_4{}^{4-}$ or $AlO_4{}^{5-}$. These units are linked according to certain rules. Thus a given tetrahedron shares one of its four apical oxygen atoms with each of four others, but does not share edges or faces. There is good evidence that an AlO_4 tetrahedron links in this way only with SiO_4 tetrahedra, never with other AlO_4 tetrahedra (*174*). No true zeolite is known in which there are unshared apical oxygen atoms, so that the resulting network is negatively charged only because of isomorphous replacements of Si^{IV} by Al^{III}. Network charge is then neutralized by an electrochemical equivalent of interstitial, mobile, exchangeable cations. As consequences, the ratio base:Al_2O_3 is 1:1 and $(Al + Si):O = 1:2$. Since the anionic frameworks are very open, and

TABLE XX

Unit Cells of Some Naturally Occurring Zeolites

Zeolite	Cell type	Dimensions (Å)			Angle
		a	b	c	
Mordenite[a] (143, 179, 275)	Orthorhombic	7.52 ⎱ 7.54 ⎰ 7.50	18.13 ⎱ 18.16 ⎰ 18.25	20.49 ⎱ 20.45 ⎰ 20.35	
Dachiardite (82)	Monoclinic	18.31	7.52	10.23	107°49'
Epistilbite (241)	Monoclinic (χ-orthorhombic)	14.8 (8.92)[b]	17.73 (17.73)	10.21 (10.21)	90°35' (124°20')
Heulandite (261)	Monoclinic (χ-orthorhombic)	7.45 (7.45)[b]	17.80 (17.80)	15.85 (17.35)	91°24' (113°56')
Clinoptilolite (241)	Monoclinic (χ-orthorhombic)	7.46 (17.11)[b]	17.84 (17.84)	15.88 (7.46)	91°26' (116°20')
Ferrierite (237)	Orthorhombic	19.12 ± 0.06	14.14 ± 0.03	7.48 ± 0.02	
Stilbite (241)	Monoclinic (χ-orthorhombic)	13.63 (13.63)[b]	18.17 (18.17)	17.62 (11.31)	92°00' (129°10')
Brewsterite (241)	Monoclinic (χ-orthorhombic)	6.77	17.41	7.66	93°04'
Phillipsite (290)	Monoclinic[c]	9.80	14.10	8.66	55°10'
Harmotome (235)	Monoclinic[c]	10.00	14.25	8.62	54°20'
Garronite (87, 273)	Tetragonal	10.01	10.01	9.8₇	
Gismondite (125)	Monoclinic (χ-orthorhombic) (Orthorhombic)	10.02 ± 0.02 (13.71)[b]	10.62 ± 0.02 (14.33)	9.84 ± 0.02 (10.62)	92°25' ± 15'
Laumontite (94)	Monoclinic	14.90 ± 0.05	13.17 ± 0.02	7.55 ± 0.05	111.5 ± 0.5°
Leonhardite (94)	Monoclinic	14.75 ± 0.03	13.10 ± 0.02	7.55 ± 0.01	112.0 ± 0.2°

Mineral	Crystal system	a	b	c	angle
Chabazite (109, 195, 196)	Hexagonal (Rhombohedral)	$13.7_4, 13.7_8$ $(9.40)^b$	—	$14.8_3, 15.0_6$	$(94°18')$
Gmelinite (196)	Hexagonal (Rhombohedral)	$13.7_2, 13.7_6$ $(10.75)^b$	—	$10.0_2, 10.0_6$	$(76°25')$
Levynite (196)	Hexagonal	13.3_2	—	22.5_1	
Erionite (238)	Hexagonal	13.2_6	—	15.1_2	
Natrolite[d] (178)	Orthorhombic	18.30 ± 0.01	18.63 ± 0.01	6.60 ± 0.01	
Mesolite (149)	Orthorhombic	18.44 ± 0.04	56.7 ± 0.01	6.54 ± 0.02	
Scolecite (248)	Orthorhombic	18.3	18.6	6.6	
Edingtonite (247)	Orthorhombic (x-tetragonal)	9.6	9.7	6.5	
Thomsonite (248)	Tetragonal	13.1	13.1	6.6	
Gonnardite (147)	Tetragonal	$13.3_5 \pm 0.05$	$13.3_5 \pm 0.05$	$6.6_5 \pm 0.05$	
Analcite (245)	Cubic	13.68 ± 0.04	—	—	
Wairakite (95)	Tetragonal	13.69	13.69	13.56	
Faujasite (79, 80)	Cubic	$24.65, 24.60$			
Paulingite (159)	Cubic	35.10 ± 0.02			
Ashcroftine (148)	Tetragonal	34.04	34.04	17.49	
Bikitaite (8)	Monoclinic	8.611	4.960	7.610	$114°26' \pm 5'$
Yugawaralite (230)	Monoclinic	13.26	13.65	9.73	$68°28'$

[a] There appears to be no significant distinction between mordenite and arduinite as far as unit cells are concerned.

[b] Figures in brackets refer to an alternate choice of unit cell.

[c] B-face-centered orthorhombic unit cells are also possible (37) for these two minerals, which are for phillipsite, $a = 9.84$, $b = 13.85$, $c = 14.3$ Å, and for harmotome, $a = 9.78$, $b = 14.00$, and $c = 14.23$ Å.

[d] There appears to be no real distinction between natrolite and laubanite (240).

filled with water molecules, sometimes these molecules may in part be replaced by additional base, as is the case with the *basic* cancrinites and sodalites of Barrer and White (*75*). However, here the additional base is, like the water molecules, a guest species within the host lattice, not essential for its stability. Sometimes also hydrolysis may cause part of the exchangeable cation to be replaced by an electrochemical equivalent of H_3O^+ ion.

Even where aluminosilicate frameworks have been determined it has often proved less easy to locate either cations or water molecules. Positions for ions and molecules have been suggested for some less porous frameworks, such as those of analcite (*245*) and natrolite (*178*). Some but not all of the cation positions have also been indicated for Ca-chabazite (*236*), and Linde Sieves A and X (*89*). In considering cation positions one must recall that cation densities in a given framework vary with Al:Si ratios, which can often change over a considerable range. Thus, chabazite-like phases have been prepared or exist naturally in which the ratio Al_2O_3: $SiO_2 = 1:2.3$ to about $1:6$ (*31*). Similarly, the amount of water varies continuously with pressure, temperature, and zeolite composition. This almost certainly means some disorder in the distribution of ions and water molecules, especially since both species are in any case rather mobile within the aluminosilicate frameworks. It is, in the most porous zeolites, a reasonable working hypothesis to regard the cations and water molecules as approximating a dense fluid within the pores of the giant aluminosilicate anions. Also, the cations are not necessarily similarly located in the water-free and water-containing states of the zeolite.

Although the ultimate structural unit in the aluminosilicates is a tetrahedron, SiO_4^{4-} or AlO_4^{5-}, the complex frameworks with which one is concerned in the zeolites are sometimes more clearly visualized in terms of polyhedra, constructed from groups of tetrahedra. The polyhedra are then linked in various relatively simple coordinations yielding the relevant frameworks. These secondary, polyhedral, structural units are conveniently represented with an aluminum or silicon centered at each apex and with oxygens centered near, but not usually on, the mid-point of each edge. Thus, a suitable cluster of eight tetrahedra forms a cubic unit, and one of twelve tetrahedra a hexagonal prism (see Fig. 1). Both these units have only a small internal volume, which in the hexagonal prism is accessible through either of two six-ring windows of free diameters 2.2–2.4 Å. Ions such as Ca^{2+}, Sr^{2+}, or Na^+ could then enter the prism through these openings.

The cubic unit appears to be a component of some phases belonging to the harmotome-phillipsite zeolites (*37*). This group includes the species of

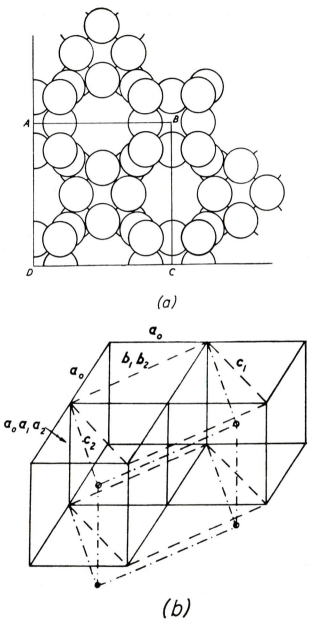

(a)

(b)

FIG. 24. (a) A portion of the oxygen framework of a synthetic zeolite, Na–P1, of the harmotome-phillipsite group. (b) Relation between cubic, orthorhombic, and monoclinic unit cells based on the structure of Na–P1. Cubic cell, a_0; orthorhombic cell, $a_1b_1c_1$; monoclinic cell, $a_2b_2c_2$; mid-points of cubic cells, $\odot$ (37).

Table XIX and also the three closely related synthetic zeolites having the unit cells (*32*):

Na-P1 Cubic	$a = 10.01$ Å
Na-P2 Tetragonal	$a = 10.01$ Å, $c = 9.8$ Å
Na-P3 Orthorhombic	$a = 14.1, b = 14.0, c = 9.8$ Å

The cubic phase Na-P1 can be derived from a simple fully symmetrical arrangement of the cubic units of eight (Si, Al)O$_4$ tetrahedra. Starting from one such unit at the center of the unit cell, each corner is linked by one Si—O—(Si, Al) bond to the corner one of eight other identical units centered on the corners of the unit cell. A portion of the oxygen atom framework of Na-P1 is then shown in plan in Fig. 24*a*. A system of channels, circumscribed by nonplanar eight-rings, intersects in three dimensions mutually at right angles, there being one channel per 100 Å^2 of surface. Cations and water molecules are located in the channels. Orthorhombic or monoclinic cells can be chosen which are related to the cubic cell as shown in Fig. 24*b*. The monoclinic cell of Na-P1 for example is then

$$a = 10.01, \qquad b = 14.15, \qquad c = 8.67 \text{Å}, \qquad \beta = 55°44'.$$

It is very nearly the same as the unit cells given for harmotome and phillipsite in Table XX. However, a recent study (*229*) suggests that harmotome is based upon a different arrangement of 4- and 8-rings from that in Fig. 24*a*, leading to the same monoclinic unit cell dimensions, but having similarities with the structures of sanidine and paracelsian. It remains to be seen which of the two structural patterns is followed by phillipsite and garronite.*

The hexagonal prism as a secondary unit of structure is found in the related species chabazite, gmelinite, levynite, and erionite, the unit cells of which are given in Table XX (*47, 109, 238*). The anionic frameworks of chabazite and gmelinite can be represented as sequences of layers of hexagonal prisms, firmly bonded to one another in such a way as to produce rigid frameworks containing substantial cavities communicating with one another by way of eight-ring apertures. The layer sequence is 123123 . . . in chabazite and 121212 . . . in gmelinite. The large cavities are then as shown in Fig. 25*a* and *b*, in which can also be seen the arrange-

---

* *Added in proof* : Phillipsite has recently been shown to have a framework closely related to that of harmotome [Steinfink, H., *Acta. Cryst.* **15**, 644 (1962)]. There are moreover seventeen simplest ways of cross-linking the kind of silicate chain found in these structures, which include Na-P1. Thus other zeolites of this family are possible, one of which appears to be gismondite [Smith, J. V., and Rinaldi, F., *Mineral. Mag.* **258**, 202 (1962)].

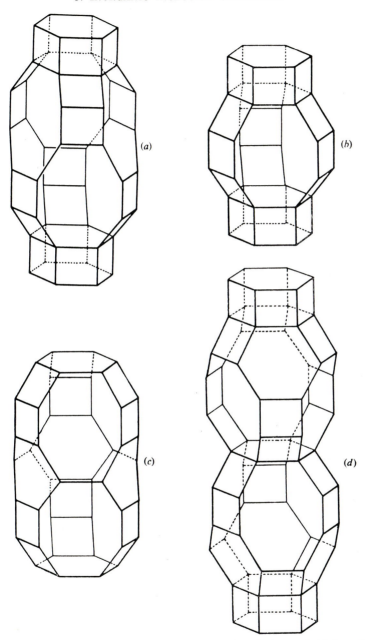

FIG. 25. Cavities in (a) chabazite, (b) gmelinite, (c) erionite, and (d) levynite. In (d) two superposed cavities are shown. Aluminum and silicon atoms are centered on each corner; oxygen atoms near but not on the mid-points of edges. All diagrams are to the same scale (47).

ment of eight-ring openings leading from one cavity to others. In erionite and levynite layers of hexagonal prisms and hexagonal rings alternate, the layer sequences being 12341234 . . . and 123456123456 . . . in erionite and levynite respectively. Cavities thereby formed in these two zeolites are shown in Figs. 25c and d. The apertures leading between cavities are again eight-rings, the stereochemistry of which is shown, along with that for the eight-rings of other zeolites, in Fig. 26. These openings play an important part in determining the molecular sieve properties. Their free

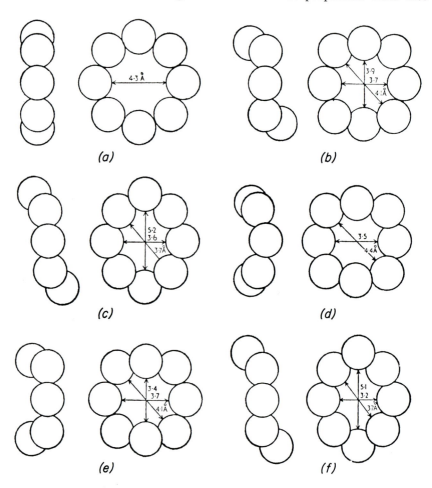

FIG. 26. The stereochemistry and free dimensions of 8-membered rings in (a) Linde Sieve A, (b) chabazite, (c) erionite, (d) *cubic harmotome* (Na–P1), (e) gmelinite, and (f) levynite (47).

diameters vary within limits from structure to structure and according to the direction of measurement. The maximum free dimensions range from 5.2 to 4.1 Å, but may be modified somewhat when water is expelled from the zeolites by heat and evacuation.

Another more complex polyhedral unit is the cubo-octahedron (Fig. 1) formed in silicate structures from 24(Si, Al)O$_4$ tetrahedra. As previously noted this polyhedron has a considerable free volume, and a sphere of ∼6.6 Å diameter can be inscribed within it. The cubo-octahedron in 8-fold

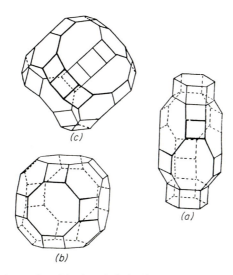

FIG. 27. The contours of cavities in (a) chabazite, (b) Linde Sieve A, and (c) faujasite or Linde Sieves X and Y. Representation is as indicated for Fig. 25, with the chabazite cavity to permit comparison with Fig. 25 (72).

coordination gives the sodalite-nosean structure of Fig. 7. It can also be present in 4- or 6-fold coordination to give the Linde Sieve X or faujasite structure and the Linde Sieve A structure respectively. The arrangement in 6-fold coordination involves six cubic units as 'bonds' linking pairs of cubo-octahedra (see Fig. 5 in reference 25). The resultant structure encloses a third very large cavity outlined in Fig. 27b (73). The chabazite cavity is shown on the same scale enabling comparison of the cages in Fig. 27 to be made with those of the chabazite group in Fig. 25. The openings leading to and from the cavities of Sieve A are the eight-rings of Fig. 26a of ∼4.3 Å free diameter.

When the cubo-octahedra are linked in 4-coordination, four hexagonal prism units serve as bonds linking four of the eight six-ring faces of pairs of cubo-octahedra (see Fig. 6 in reference 25). This is the faujasite structure in which cubo-octahedra are arranged just as are the carbon atoms in diamond. The configuration of the polyhedra encloses the very large cavities shown in Fig. 27c, to which entry of guest molecules is effected through the very wide twelve-ring windows seen in the diagram. These large cavities are themselves in tetrahedral coordination with one another.

Not all zeolites are as simply represented in terms of stacked polyhedra as those so far discussed. Thus the zeolites of the natrolite group are based upon clusters of five $(Al, Si)O_4$ tetrahedra, linked in chains in the manner shown in Fig. 28a (178). In all the natrolite zeolites these chains occur, running parallel to the c axis but crosslinked differently with one another (248). All the crosslinks are single Si—O—(Si, Al) bonds, so that the density of bonds in the direction of the c axis is greater than that of the crosslinks. This property accounts for the fibrous tendency of zeolites of the natrolite group, while some flexibility of the framework is possible by rotation around the single bonds. In Fig. 28b an end-on view of the chains in natrolite shows their arrangement relative to each other and indicates also the positions of Na^+ ions and water molecules. Dehydration and cation exchange have until recently been considered to occur along these channels parallel with the c axis. However, Meier (178) pointed out that their free width of 2.08 Å is less than that of other channels normal to the c axis, for which the free width is 2.6 Å. In the related structures of thomsonite or edingtonite it is also the case that the widest channels are normal to the c axis.

The arrangement of Al and Si atoms in natrolite is apparently a fully ordered one. If this is always true it implies that no variation in the Al:Si ratio can occur. Conversely in those zeolites such as chabazite, where substantial variations in Al:Si ratios are recorded, there must be considerable randomness in the distribution of Al and Si among sites. Al and Si alternate quite regularly in their positions in Linde Sieve A specimens in which Al:Si = 1:1. Recently, however, preparations of this type of structure have been made in which there is good reason to suppose that the Al:Si ratios are considerably less than 1:1 (i.e. siliceous forms of the structure) (40). Here some randomness of Al and Si atom distributions on the regular sites is to be expected. Finally, one may note that the repeat distance of 6.5–6.6 Å along the c axis is characteristic of the clusters of five tetrahedra of Fig. 28a (cf. Table XX).

So far, all the zeolite structures considered have even numbered rings of

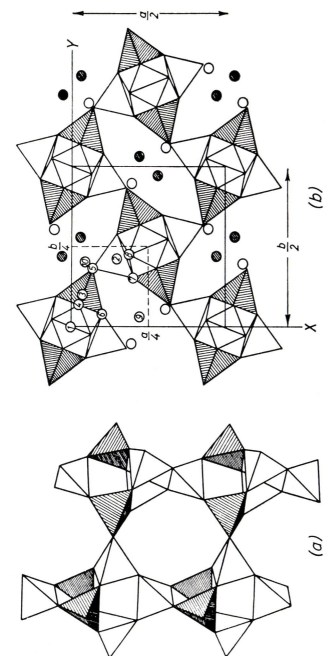

FIG. 28. (a) The chains in natrolite. The lower SiO_4 tetrahedra are linked to the upper AlO tetrahedra (shaded) of neighboring chains. (b) (001) projection of natrolite structure. Repeat distances are $a/2$ and $b/2$ in this projection. The notation used for atoms of the asymmetric unit is: (1) Si_I; (2) Si_{II}; (3) Al; (4) O_I; (5) O_{II}; (6) O_{III}; (7) O_{IV}; (8) O_V; (9) Na; (10) H_2O (178).

tetrahedra (Al, Si)O_4 in the frameworks, the main rings being as summarized in the accompanying tabulation:

Faujasite	4-, 6-, and 12-rings
Linde Sieve A	4-, 6-, and 8-rings
Chabazite	4-, 6-, and 8-rings
Gmelinite	4-, 6-, 8-, and 12-rings
Erionite	4-, 6-, and 8-rings
Levynite	4-, 6-, and 8-rings
Harmotome and phillipsite	4- and 8-rings
Natrolite group	4- and 8-rings

In the non-zeolitic minerals, scapolite and petalite, and in keatite, however, 5-rings may be identified, and there are also some zeolites where 5-rings occur. Mordenite and ptilolite come into this category (*179*), as also do heulandite (*261*) and probably other zeolites of this group (Table XIX). In mordenite, for example, 4-, 5-, 6-, 8-, and 12-rings occur, and the stability of the mineral has been tentatively attributed to the predominance of 5- and 6-rings in the lattice (*179*). Stability may also arise from the low Al:Si ratio and hence the low content of exchangeable cations. Stability to

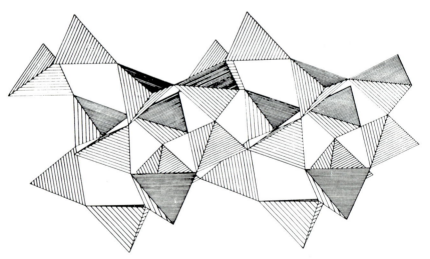

Fig. 29. A portion of the characteristic chain of tetrahedra found in the structures of mordenite and of dachiardite (*179*).

heating in the outgassed, water-free state must further be distinguished from stability in presence of potentially reactive substances such as water or weathering solutions.

The aluminosilicate network in mordenite can be referred to chains of the type shown in Fig. 29, in which the 5-membered rings can be identified. These chains are so linked with one another as to give very wide channels parallel to the fiber axis [001], which have free diameters of 6.6 Å. These channels are interconnected by passages parallel to [010] having a minimum free diameter of 2.8 Å. The full diameter of 6.6 Å does not accord with the molecular sieve behavior as found by Barrer (15, 19), but Meier (179) has shown how stacking faults can reduce the free diameter to about 4 Å. Mordenite could then have a system of channels parallel to the b axis at least 2.8 Å in diameter and another (in presence of stacking faults) with occasional restrictions of 4 Å. This could probably accord with the observed molecular sieve behavior. The structure obtained by Meier also accounts for the fibrous nature and perfect prismatic cleavage of mordenite, since the bond densities per 100 Å² for different cleavage planes are

$$2.60 \text{ for } [100]$$

$$2.58 \text{ for } [010]$$

$$4.30 \text{ for } [001]$$

Known tectosilicates with 5-rings all show one axial length of about 7.5 Å. Since epistilbite, brewsterite, ferrierite, and dachiardite all show this spacing (Table XX) structures based on 5-rings may be anticipated for them also. A structure for dachiardite, based upon a union of the mordenite chains of Fig. 31 different from that in mordenite itself, has indeed been found (180).

Although not of importance as a molecular sieve, analcite was one of the first zeolites for which a structure was obtained (245). The framework is relatively stable. In it occur 4-, 6-, and distorted 8-rings. The cubic unit cell (Table XX) contains $16(NaAlSi_2O_6 \cdot H_2O)$, the sixteen Na^+ ions being distributed statistically over the 24-fold positions $(0, \frac{1}{4}, \frac{1}{8})$. Analcite, with wairakite, is the least hydrated of all zeolites. It is a member of a considerable family of synthetic mineral-type compounds, some of which are felspathoids rather than zeolites (23). Some members are anhydrous, as is the case when the framework charge is neutralized by the larger cations K^+, Tl^+, Rb^+, or Cs^+. The mobility of the cations decreases rapidly as their diameter increases (63).

C. Channel Systems and Cavity Dimensions

1. ANALCITE

The channels in zeolites and felspathoids form well-defined space patterns which assist in understanding diffusion in, and molecular sieve behavior of, the crystals. The channels in analcite lie along the trigonal axes and do not intersect directly. They connect with one another through distorted 8-ring apertures, the spatial distribution being shown in Fig. 30a. The channels are so narrow that only small polar molecules (H_2O, NH_3) and some cations can diffuse within them.

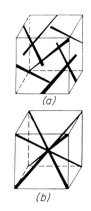

(a)

(b)

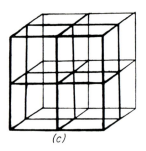

(c)

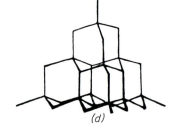

(d)

FIG. 30. The patterns made by the interconnected or intersecting channels in (a) analcite, (b) sodalites, noseans, and ultramarines, (c) Linde Sieve A, and (d) faujasite and Linde Sieves X and Y (25).

2. STRUCTURES CONTAINING THE CUBO-OCTAHEDRAL UNIT

The channel pattern in the nosean-sodalite felspathoids is shown in Fig. 30b. Channels can be regarded as diverging from the center of each unit cell through the eight corners, the crossing points being repeated at every cell center and corner. A very simple three-dimensional network of channels is thus formed, the molecular sieve behavior of which is determined by the free diameters of 6-rings, which form the narrowest openings at ~7.7 Å intervals along each channel. The free diameters of 2.2–2.4 Å allow the diffusion only of ions of radii up to that of K^+ ion (58) or, in basic sodalite, of small molecules such as water.

The channel pattern in Linde Sieve A is shown in Fig. 30c. The channels intersect in three dimensions at right angles, emerging from the six 8-ring faces of the large cavity of Fig. 27b. These 8-rings lie at the middle of, and in the planes of, the six faces of the unit cell, and so occur at intervals of 12.3 Å along each channel. As the free diameters of the 8-rings are ~4.3 Å, molecules of substantial cross-sectional diameter are freely occluded (e.g., n-paraffins). The cavities are large enough to inscribe within them spheres of about 11.4 Å diameter. In addition, cations, or possibly water, could pass through any of the eight 6-ring windows in each cavity, so having access to each cubo-octahedral unit. However, as far as the molecular sieve behavior is concerned these smaller units are relatively unimportant.

In faujasite or Linde Sieve X or Y the channels are distributed in space exactly as are the bonds in diamond (Fig. 30d). In length each "bond" represents the center-to-center distance of two adjacent large cavities, is ~12.4 Å long and is bisected by a 12-ring window of 8–9 Å free diameter. These apertures are wide enough to allow diffusion of some very big molecules, while in each cavity a sphere of about 12–13 Å diameter could be inscribed. If one projects on to the (011) plane, the Si + Al atom positions of the smaller cubo-octahedral cages centered on this plane the projected cross section of a channel can be obtained as shown in Fig. 31, the longest free path being about 20 Å.

3. STRUCTURES CONTAINING HEXAGONAL PRISM UNITS (CHABAZITE GROUP)

The elongated cavities in chabazite (Fig. 25a) are not wholly symmetrical, but have major and minor free dimensions of ~11 and ~6.6 Å respectively. Six channels lead from each cavity through the 8-ring windows of Fig. 25a into each of six other cavities, producing an intersecting three-dimensional channel pattern well able to permit diffusion of molecules up

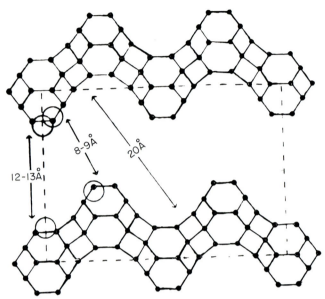

FIG. 31. (011) projection of (Al + Si) atoms of cubo-octahedral cages in faujasite centered on this plane. Some important free distances are indicated which illustrate the openness of the framework of faujasite (25).

to and including n-paraffins, as an almost but not wholly isotropic diffusion medium (47).

In gmelinite (109) very wide channels circumscribed by 12-rings of free diameters ~6.4 Å run parallel to the c axis. There is also an intersecting channel system in planes normal to the c axis. This system has the hexagonal symmetry shown in Fig. 32a. Eight-rings open from the wide channels (outlined by the dotted lines only), into the cavities of Fig. 25b (represented by full and dotted lines in Fig. 32a) which have free dimensions of ~7.8 Å normal to the c direction and ~6.5 Å in this direction. As Fig. 25b shows, in any one plane three 8-ring windows open from every cavity into one of three wide channels, and conversely from each wide channel into three cavities. In an ideal gmelinite the wide channels should allow very rapid diffusion of molecules in the c direction. However, occasional stacking faults will always interfere with diffusion down parallel nonintersecting systems of channels. In gmelinite occasional sequences of the hexagonal prism layers as in chabazite (123123), rather than the 1212 sequence of gmelinite, would effectively interrupt the wide channels. The molecular sieve behavior would then be governed by the two-dimensional networks of Fig. 32a, which are repeated at ~5 Å intervals along the c direction, each third network being superposable upon the first. The 8-ring windows controlling diffusion in these networks have maximum and

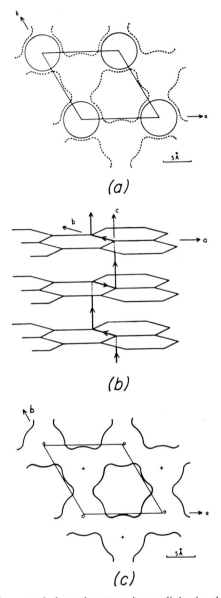

(a)

(b)

(c)

FIG. 32. (a) The hexagonal channel pattern in gmelinite in planes normal to the c direction. Dashed lines give maximum free dimensions of channels and cavities, and full lines give the minimum free diameter of the channels running in the c direction. (b) The arrangement of diffusion paths in erionite, illustrating how molecules may move both along the c direction and normal to it. (c) The hexagonal channel pattern in levynite, normal to the c direction. ○ denotes a cavity center in a reference plane, and + a cavity center above this plane. Thus the channel network is puckered. The free dimensions are given by the line contour (47).

minimum dimensions of 4.1 and 3.4 Å, leading one to expect as observed
(15) that only slow diffusion of n-paraffins could occur in such a crystal.

In erionite columns of elongated cavities of free length ~15.1 Å and free
diameter ~6.3 Å (Fig. 25c) lie along the c direction of the hexagonal unit
cell, one on top of another. As with chabazite, there is a slight waist in
the cavities and the 6.3 Å represents the free diameter of this waist. Six
8-ring windows lead from each long cavity into one of six other such
cavities, producing, in planes spaced at 7.5 Å along the c direction, the
intersecting networks of channels shown in Fig. 32b. Molecules may pass
from one such plane to another by moving up the elongated cavities as
indicated in Fig. 32b, so that a three-dimensional if anisotropic channel
network is formed, the narrowest apertures in which are the 8-ring windows
having in the hydrated crystals maximum and minimum free dimensions
of 5.2 and 3.6 Å respectively (Fig. 26c).

As a final example we may consider levynite in which the spheroidal
cavities of Fig. 25d have a free diameter near 7.8 Å. Each cavity is connected by a shared 8-ring having major and minor axes of ~5.1 and 3.2
Å (Fig. 26f) with each of three like cavities so as to form the channel
pattern shown in Fig. 32c. This system is in the form of a puckered hexagonal network in a plane normal to the c direction, the planes recurring at
intervals of 7.5 Å. There is no diffusion path allowing molecules to move
from one network into the ones above or below, except through 6-rings of
free diameter ~2.7 Å.

The channel systems described are in general compatible with the
molecular sieve properties of the crystals outlined below and with their
behavior as diffusion media, although in both functions exchangeable
cations may play an important moderating role (see next section).

D. Molecular Sieve Properties

Considerable progress has been made in evaluating the molecular sieve
properties of zeolites (e.g. *16, 20, 27, 33, 86, 177, 250*). The free dimensions
of the apertures in the channel systems described in the previous section
can be usefully compared with critical van der Waals dimensions of typical
molecules.

The critical dimension which determines the ability of a molecule to
pass through an aperture is, for a spherical molecule such as argon, its
diameter. This must not be significantly greater than the smallest free
dimension of the apertures. At the same time molecules of argon are not
hard spheres, nor are the oxygen atoms comprising the 8-ring openings in
Linde Sieve A, chabazite, gmelinite, levynite, or erionite. Also, these rings
are not themselves entirely rigid. It is thus usual to find that a molecule
will pass through a ring having a rather smaller minimum free dimension

than the critical dimension of the molecule. As the overlap in dimensions increases the energy barrier which must be surmounted increases rapidly. The relation between energy barriers and critical dimensions has been studied for mordenites (19), and calculations made for passage of typical molecules through 6-rings (163) (see Section X). In the accompanying tabulation we merely note the following correlation for argon which has a critical dimension of 3.8_3 Å.

Zeolite	Minimum dimension of 8-ring	Rate of occlusion of Ar at $-183°C$ in outgassed zeolite
Linde Sieve 5A	4.3	Very rapid
Ca-rich chabazite	3.7	Very rapid
Erionite (synthetic)	3.6	Rapid
Gmelinite	3.4	Less rapid
Levynite	3.2	Slow

At the same time the cation distribution is also important. Thus, Linde Sieve 4A sorbs argon at a negligible rate at $-185°C$, and Na-chabazite is also a much more sluggish sorbent than Ca-chabazite. Small changes may also occur in the aperture dimensions during outgassing. Despite such complications a correlation exists in the above examples, with an overlap which in levynite may approach $(3.8_3–3.2) \sim 0.6$ Å.

The critical dimensions of some spherical or very symmetrical molecules, using van der Waals radii given by Pauling (200) are (in Å):

He	2.0	Kr	3.9_4	CF_4	$5.3_3(5.4_4)$	CI_4	$8.2_2(8.5_0)$
Ne	3.2_0	Xe	4.3_7	CCl_4	$6.8_8(7.1_2)$	$C(CH_3)_4$	$6.8_8(7.0_8)$
Ar	3.8_3	CH_4	$4.0(4.5_8)^*$ 4.4_4	CBr_4	$7.4_6(7.7_2)$	SF_6	$6.0_6(6.0_6)$

For molecules such as CF_4, CCl_4, the critical dimension in the nonrotating state will tend to be the diameter of the circle circumscribing the triangular base of the molecule. If the molecules are freely rotating then the critical dimension will be the diameter of the circumscribing sphere. These latter dimensions are given in parentheses.

---

* The van der Waals diameter of CH_4 could be taken, after Pauling, as 4.0 Å when the molecule is regarded as spherical and structureless. If, however, it is regarded as tetrahedral the somewhat larger dimension of 4.4_4 Å is obtained.

For diatomic or diradical molecules the critical molecular dimension will usually approximate to the diameter of the largest circle required to circumscribe the molecule normal to its length. These diameters are illustrated below, and also the molecular length is given in parentheses:

$$H_2 \quad 2.4(3.1_4) \qquad C_2H_6 \quad 4.4_4(4.6_0)$$

$$O_2 \quad 2.8(3.9_0) \qquad C_2F_6 \quad 5.3_3(5.1_1)$$

$$N_2 \quad 3.0(4.0_8) \qquad C_2Cl_6 \quad 6.8_8(6.2_3)$$

In the case of n-paraffin molecules the critical dimension is again the diameter of the largest circle needed to circumscribe the molecule in a plane normal to its length. This dimension of about 4.9 Å is the same for all n-paraffins in a stretched-out configuration. Normal to the plane of the zigzag of the chains the thickness of the CH_2 group can be taken as the Pauling value of ~ 4.0 Å. n-Paraffins pass slowly into Ca-chabazite (44), for which the maximum and minimum free dimensions of the 8-ring windows are 4.1 and 3.7 Å respectively (Fig. 26b), and more rapidly into Linde Sieve 5A which has ~ 4.3 Å as diameter of the symmetrical circular 8-ring apertures (Fig. 26a).

When a substituent group is attached to a secondary carbon atom along a n-paraffin chain it is once more the diameter of the largest circle needed to circumscribe the molecule in a plane normal to the chain length which constitutes the critical dimension for passage through a circular aperture. If the aperture is elliptical a second critical dimension may be the thickness of the chain normal to the plane of the zigzag (~ 4 Å) or the thickness of the substituent group in the same direction, whichever is the greater. With disc-shaped molecules the diameter of the circle circumscribing the disc is the important dimension, with the thickness of the disc as a subsidiary one if the apertures are elliptical. If the penetrants are unsymmetrical molecules such as $CHFCl_2$ or CHF_2Cl, the diameter of the smallest circumscribing circle is a critical dimension (35). With still more complex molecules other critical dimensions are possible.

In Table XXI (27) is given a classification into five main groups of some rigid framework molecular sieves, together with examples of the guest molecules which each category of sieve can accommodate once the intracrystalline water has been removed by heat and evacuation. There are opportunities for further subdivision within the major groups of molecular sieve crystals. For example, Linde Sieve 5A and Ca-chabazite are both placed as Type 3 sieves. However, one may distinguish between these two zeolites on the basis of their capacity to differentiate between *Freons*. Thus, CHF_3 and CHF_2Cl are occluded by both zeolites, but CF_3Cl and CF_2Cl_2 are sorbed only by Sieve 5A.

TABLE XXI

CLASSIFICATION OF SOME MOLECULAR SIEVES

Molecular size increasing ⟶

He, Ne, Ar, CO, H_2, O_2, N_2, NH_3, H_2O	C_3H_8	CF_4	SF_6	$(CH_3)_3N$	C_6H_6	Naphthalene	1,3,5-triethyl benzene	$(n\text{-}C_4F_9)_3N$
Size limit for Ca- and Ba-mordenites and levynite about here (≈3.8 Å)	$n\text{-}C_4H_{10}$	C_2F_6	Iso-C_4H_{10}	$(C_2H_5)_2N$	$C_6H_5CH_3$	Quinoline	1, 2, 3, 4, 5, 6, 7, 8, 13, 14, 15, 16-decahydrochrysene	
Kr, Xe	$n\text{-}C_7H_{16}$	CF_2Cl_2	Iso-C_5H_{12}	$C(CH_3)_4$	$C_6H_4(CH_3)_2$	6-decyl-1,2,3,4-tetrahydronaphthalene		
CH_4	$n\text{-}C_{14}H_{30}$	CF_3Cl	etc.	$C(CH_3)_3Cl$	Cyclohexane	2-butyl-1-hexylindane		
C_2H_6	etc.	$CHFCl_2$	$CHCl_3$	$C(CH_3)_3Br$	Methylcyclohexane	$C_6F_{11}CF_3$		
CH_3OH	C_2H_5Cl		$CHBr_3$	$C(CH_3)_3OH$	Thiophene			
CH_3CN	C_2H_5Br		CHI_3	CCl_4	Furan			
CH_3NH_2	C_2H_5OH		$(CH_3)_2CHOH$	CBr_4	Pyridine			
CH_3CN	$C_2H_5NH_2$		$(CH_3)_2CHCl$	$C_2F_2Cl_4$	Dioxane			
CH_2Br	CH_2Cl_2		$n\text{-}C_3F_8$		$B_{10}H_{14}$			
CO_2	CH_2Br_2		$n\text{-}C_4F_{10}$					
C_2H_2	CHF_2Cl		$n\text{-}C_7F_{16}$					
CS_2	CHF_3		B_5H_9					
Size limit for Na-mordenite and Linde Sieve 4A about here (≈4.0 Å)	$(CH_3)_2NH$							
	CH_3I							
	B_2H_6							
	Size limit for Ca-rich chabazite, Linde Sieve 5A, synthetic Ba-zeolite, and gmelinite about here (≈4.9 Å)					Size limit for Linde Sieve 10X about here	Size limit for Linde Sieve 13X about here (≈10 Å)	

Type 5

Type 4

Type 3

Type 2

Type 1

391

E. Saturation Capacities of Some Porous Crystals

The numbers of guest molecules which saturate the large cavities in porous zeolite crystals of several of the kinds discussed are illustrated in Table XXII. As the molecular volumes of the guest molecules increase the numbers accommodated decrease. These numbers are however not integral, since molecules may be shared between two cages, if they happen to be located in the windows uniting the cages. Also, the numbers decrease as temperature rises, and are thus only approximate, the co-volume per molecule being temperature-dependent. The numbers of small molecules per large cavity are considerable, and it is quite appropriate to regard them as present in clusters. These clusters, especially for the more open lattices, are not isolated from one another, and the guest molecules may probably be regarded as an intracrystalline fluid in so open a structure as that of faujasite. However, even in less open structures such as chabazite, which can accommodate only two iodine molecules per cage (Table XXII), these molecules can touch other iodine molecules through the 8-ring windows, and the average coordination number of iodine in chabazite, faujasite, and Linde Sieve 5A lattices saturated by this guest molecule is in all three cases about four with respect to other iodines (73).

We may suppose that the zeolite crystals are first saturated with a given guest species such as nitrogen, and that all the occluded molecules are then used to form a saturated monolayer on a plane surface. The area of this surface can then be compared with the surfaces of typical known sorbents (e.g. charcoals, silica gels, activated alumina, porous glass). The results of such a comparison are contained in Table XXIII. It includes the alkylammonium bentonites among porous crystals. Sepiolite and attapulgite, which are not capable of intracrystalline sorption of nitrogen, nevertheless are sorbents of very considerable external surface areas. The table shows that porous crystalline aluminosilicates can have equivalent monolayer capacities fully comparable with those of typical commercial adsorbents.

We may also compare the intracrystalline free volumes of zeolites as given in Table XIX with these volumes for several other types of host lattice. We then find (25):

β-hydroquinone-SO$_2$ clathrate	$\sim$0.09 cm^3/cm^3
β-hydroquinone-Ar clathrate	$\sim$0.05 cm^3/cm^3
Urea-n-paraffin adducts	$\sim$0.37 cm^3/cm^3
Thiourea-hydrocarbon adducts	$\sim$0.41 cm^3/cm^3
Type I water clathrates	$\sim$0.46 cm^3/cm^3
Type II water clathrates	$\sim$0.46 cm^3/cm^3

TABLE XXII

SATURATION OF CAVITIES BY GUEST MOLECULES (*25, 35, 38, 65, 71, 72, 86*)

Crystal	Largest cavities	Guest molecules per cavity
Basic sodalite	14-hedra (8 × 6-rings 6 × 4-rings)	$\sim(4H_2O + 0.5NaOH)$
Chabazite	20-hedra (6 × 8-rings 2 × 6-rings 12 × 4-rings)	$12-14H_2O$ $\sim7.7NH_3$ $\sim6\ Ar,N_2,O_2$ $\sim4.9CH_3NH_2$ $\sim4.3CH_3Cl$ $\sim3.1CH_2Cl_2$ $\sim2.0I_2$
Linde Sieve A	26-hedra (6 × 8-rings 8 × 6-rings 12 × 4-rings)	$\sim29H_2O\ (25 + 4)^a$ $19-20NH_3$ $14-16\ Ar,N_2,O_2$ $\sim15H_2S$ $\sim12CH_3OH$ $\sim10SO_2$ $\sim9CO_2$ $\sim5.5I_2$ $\sim5.4\ n\text{-}C_3H_7OH$ $\sim4\ n\text{-}C_4H_{10}$
Faujasite	26-hedra (4 × 12-rings 4 × 6-rings 18 × 4-rings)	$\sim32H_2O\ (28 + 4)^a$ $17-19\ Ar,N_2,O_2$ $\sim7.5I_2$ $\sim7.8CF_4$ $\sim6.5SF_6$ $\sim5.8C_2F_6$ ~5.6 cyclopentane ~5.4 benzene ~4.6 toluene $\sim4.5\ n\text{-}C_5H_{12}$ ~4.1 cyclohexane ~4.1 perfluorocyclobutene $\sim4.1\ C_2F_4Cl_2$ $\sim3.5\ n\text{-}C_7H_{16}$ $\sim3.4\ C_3F_8$ $\sim2.9\ n\text{-}C_4F_{10}$ $\sim2.8\ \text{iso-}C_8H_{18}$ ~2.3 perfluoro-Me-cyclohexane ~2.1 perfluoro-diMe-cyclohexane

a The division of water molecules in this way would represent 4 as full occupation of the smaller cubo-octahedral cages with water, as for basic sodalite. This may not always happen, since sometimes there is $NaAlO_2$ in these cages, at least for Linde Sieve A (*54*).

TABLE XXIII

SURFACE AREAS OF SOME ACTIVE SORBENTS AND EQUIVALENT AREAS OF SOME
POROUS CRYSTALS (25)

Porous crystal	Monolayer equivalent N₂ area (m²/gm)	Active sorbent	N₂ area (m²/gm)
Linde Sieve 13X	1030	*Carbolac* carbon	1060
Linde Sieve 10X	1030	*Carbolac* carbon compressed	890
Linde Sieve 4A	∼800	to porosity 0.53	
Linde Sieve 5A	750–800	Carbon wear dust	770
Ca-chabazite	750	Silica gel	610
Mordenite	440	Silica gel	580
CH₃NH₃-bentonite	160(135)ᵃ	Activated alumina	230–380
(CH₃)₂NH₂-bentonite	150(110)ᵃ	Sepiolite	310(max)
(CH₃)₃NH-bentonite	130(95)ᵃ	Attapulgite	260(max)
(CH₃)₄N-bentonite	140(110)ᵃ	*Vycor* porous glass	140

ᵃ Figures in parentheses give estimated interlamellar areas only. The figures not in parentheses include the contribution due to external areas of the small clay crystallites.

The 'porosity' of the host lattices in the last four systems compares with that of the more highly hydrated among zeolites. In these cases, however, the hypothetical empty host lattices cannot be obtained. Only for the rather less porous β-hydroquinone has this proved possible. In some other organic host lattices, such as those formed by the cyclodextrins (98), or by tri-*o*-thymotide (171) (see Chapter 7), the cavities are permanent features of the structures (12), just as for the zeolites.

F. Synthesis of Some Host Lattice Silicates

In this section a brief account of the synthesis of host lattice silicates is given. For details the original references may be consulted. No comment is made upon the preparation of other host lattices such as graphite oxide, alkylammonium polyphosphates, or the Werner complexes for which again the original references are available.

Zeolite synthesis is achieved by the hydrothermal method, in which aluminosilicate magmas, powders, and gels, containing appropriate amounts of alkali, are heated with water in sealed vessels. Without over-much elaboration stainless steel autoclaves can be used for this purpose up to 400 atm or more, and at temperatures rising to 450°C. However, the more elevated the temperature the less highly hydrated tend to be the species formed, and the most important ranges for zeolite synthesis may be the lowest at which crystallization can be made to take place. Frame-work structures tend to crystallize from highly alkaline media, and since also high alkalinity promotes ready crystal growth by increasing the solubility of the solid oxides and gels in the aqueous phase, framework zeolites can be made even at 100°C or below. Under such mild conditions sealed autoclaves may be dispensed with, and crystallizations carried out on a water bath. Somewhat above 100°C, stout sealed glass tubes may be used as reaction vessels, or reaction may be carried out in pressure vessels, the reaction mixtures being contained in sealed jars with water also out-side the jars as a pressure equalizer. To obtain ready crystallizations the gels need to be as reactive as possible, and may conveniently be prepared from stabilized silica sols, and freshly prepared aluminum hydroxide, with additions of alkali often in excess of the amount required for stoichiometric reaction. Because of its metastability with respect to the crystallizing species the reactive gel tends to yield a shower of small crystallites, after which the mother liquor is depleted of essential feed material and the re-action ceases. The crystals as prepared are of a size convenient for many purposes, whether the zeolites are required as sorbents or ion exchangers. For large scale uses the crystals may require to be pelleted with smaller amounts of admixed clay as a bond.

A full account of the hydrothermal method and its results will not be given. Among other syntheses using this method that of zeolites has been systematically examined in the author's and in other laboratories for a considerable period. There have been studies of hydrothermal reactions going back over many years, in which reports of zeolite syntheses have appeared (5, 23, 86, 181, 211). Currently there is much interest in the hydrothermal procedure owing to its versatility, and to the geological and mineralogical as well as the chemical significance of many of the re-sults obtained (96, 112). It bids fair to be an important method of growing crystals of considerable dimensions as well as for the production of crystal-line powders (289). Although details are often as yet unpublished, the Linde Co. reported the formation of a number of zeolites related to natural species (86) such as mordenite, chabazite, erionite, faujasite, and gis-mondite, as well as some which do not appear to occur naturally, and of which the most important is Linde Sieve A. An interesting feature of hydrothermal synthesis arises in possibilities of forming crystals related to naturally occurring species but modified in various ways, for example

TABLE XXIV

SYNTHESES OF ZEOLITES AND RELATED STRUCTURES

Zeolite and group	Syntheses	Reference
Mordenite group	Na-mordenite	17, 75
	Ca-mordenite	41
	Sr-mordenite	53
	Ca-epistilbite	41
Harmotome-phillipsite group	Ca-, Sr-, and Ba-harmotomes	41, 53
	(Na, K)-phillipsite	32
	K-phillipsite	30
	(K, Na)-harmotome	32
	(Ca, N)-P1 (cubic)ᵃ	40
	Na-P1 (cubic)	
	Na-P2 (tetragonal, near garronite)	32, 37
	Na-P3 (orthorhombic)	
	NH₄-harmotome	40
	N-harmotomeᵃ	40
	Na-aluminogermanate analogue of harmotome	32
Chabazite group	(K, Na)-chabazite	32
	Sr-chabazite	53
	K-chabazite-like phases	30
	(Ca, N)-gmeliniteᵃ	40
	Na-gmelinite	32
	Sr-gmelinite	53
Natrolite group	Ca-thomsonite	41
	Na-gallosilicate analogue of thomsonite	32
	Na-gallogermanate analogue of thomsonite	
Analcite group	Na-form (cubic)	75
	Ca-form (cubic)	41
	Ca-form (tetragonal)	
	Sr-form	53
	NH₄-form	40
	K-form (cubic)	30
	K-form (tetragonal; leucite)	
	Rb-forms (two tetragonal species)	49
	Cs-form (cubic; pollucite)	
	(Na, K)-forms	32
	Tl-form	244

TABLE XXIV—*Continued*

Zeolite and group	Syntheses	Reference
Faujasite (Linde Sieve X)	Na-form Na-aluminogermanate analogue Na-gallogermanate analogue	*32*
	N(CH$_3$)$_4$-form (silica-rich)	*40*
Linde Sieve A	Na-form Na-aluminogermanate analogue Na-gallogermanate analogue	*32*
	N(CH$_3$)$_4$-form (silica-rich)	*40*
Zeolites with no natural counterpart, or unidentified	Li-zeolite, Li$_2$O·Al$_2$O$_3$·2SiO$_2$·4H$_2$O Li-zeolite, Li$_2$O·Al$_2$O$_3$·2SiO$_2$·5H$_2$O	*74*
	K-zeolite, K$_2$O·Al$_2$O$_3$·2SiO$_2$·3H$_2$O	*80*
	Rb-zeolite, Rb$_2$O·Al$_2$O$_3$·2SiO$_2$·H$_2$O	*49*
	Ba-zeolite, probably BaO·Al$_2$O$_3$·4SiO$_2$·nH$_2$O	*18*

[a] The symbol N means containing a nitrogenous cation which may be any ion between NH$_4^+$ and N(CH$_3$)$_4^+$.

in the cation present, in the alumina:silica ratios and hence in the number of cations present. Thus Linde Sieve X is close to the natural zeolite faujasite, but differs in certain respects from it. These modifications may confer useful variations in molecular sieve or catalytic properties upon the zeolite. The feasibility of such changes was well demonstrated in a series of chabazite-like phases, in which the power to sorb gases like oxygen was reduced progressively as the phases became more aluminous, while the capacity to sorb water remained largely unaltered. This behavior is shown in Fig. 33 for Ca and Na ion-exchanged forms of the series (*31*). One may

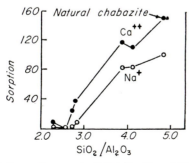

FIG. 33. Influence of the replacements ($\frac{1}{2}$Ca)Al$\rightleftharpoons$Si and NaAl$\rightleftharpoons$Si on the sorption of oxygen at $-183°$C and 20 cm Hg pressure. Sorption is in cm^3 at S.T.P. in the amount of chabazite containing the same number of unit cells as 1 gm of the Na-form (*31*).

synthesize the same kind of zeolite directly, but with a diversity of cations in it, as shown in Table XXIV, which summarizes some formations of zeolites and related structures carried out in the author's laboratory and for nearly all of which preparative details have been published. Changing the cations without altering the alumina:silica ratio of the zeolite may also have dramatic effects upon the molecular sieve behavior, as was first demonstrated with Na-, Ca-, and Ba-mordenite (*19*). Linde Sieves 4A and 5A, and 10X and 13X, respectively, differ only in the cation present, but their molecular sieve functions are significantly altered.

Among the zeolites of Table XXIV are a number of examples of species of cationic compositions differing from those which occur naturally [inter alia NH_4-, Rb-, and Tl-'analcites,' NH_4-, and alkylammonium-'harmotomes,' $N(CH_3)_4$-'faujasites' and analogues of Linde Sieve A]. There are also structures closely related to naturally occurring species, but of differing symmetries. This is the case with the phases Na-P1, Na-P2 and Na-P3 belonging to the harmotome-phillipsite group of zeolites. Finally, there are zeolites which do not appear to have any natural counterparts. For further details of the crystallization fields and conditions of synthesis the original papers may be consulted. No further account of these and of syntheses by other workers can be given here.

Under less alkaline conditions the hydrothermal method leads readily to minerals of the clay group, some of which are, as we have seen, able to intercalate many kinds of guest molecule. Typical syntheses are given below:

> Kaolinite (e.g. *117, 139, 189, 190, 191, 192, 194, 234, 258*)
> Dickite (*117, 258*)
> Beidellite (*117, 166, 258*)
> Sericite (*189, 190, 191, 192*)
> Nontronite (*117*)
> Saponite (*166*)
> Montmorillonite (*40, 189, 190, 191, 192, 214, 258*).

The syntheses of montmorillonoids by Barrer and Denny (*40*) were carried out in the presence of excess of base in the form of methylammonium hydroxides. In this respect the syntheses differed from all the others. The products were montmorillonoids with interlamellar $N(CH_3)_4^+$, $N(CH_3)_3H^+$, $N(CH_3)_2H_2^+$, and $N(CH_3)H_3^+$ ions replacing the usual interlamellar Na^+ and Ca^{2+} ions.

Felspathoids can be made both by hydrothermal and by pyrolytic methods. Ultramarine is made only by the pyrolytic method (cf. *113*) since under hydrothermal conditions the included polysulfide hydrolyzes and decomposes. Sodalites and noseans with included NaCl, or Na_2SO_4, can be prepared pyrolytically (*182*), or they can be made hydrothermally, after adding excess of NaCl or Na_2SO_4 to the alkaline magma. Modifications of these species are also readily made from such magmas without adding salts. In these circumstances one may prepare basic sodalite-nosean species, and basic cancrinites in which included salts are replaced by NaOH + H_2O (*75*). These materials then possess the properties of zeolites more than those of felspathoids.

VIII. INCLUSION ISOTHERMS

In this section a short account will be given of equilibrium between guest molecules in the vapor phase and in the inclusion complex. Isotherms are of several general forms, the complexes being in all cases non-stoichiometric (*22*). These are:

(*a*) continuous curves such as are found when gases or vapors are included in various zeolites; hydrocarbons are sorbed by tetramethylammonium montmorillonites; and ammonia, ethylamine, or ethanol by potassium benzene sulfonate. The isotherm contours qualitatively resemble Langmuir's isotherm, as indicated by the family of isotherms for CF_4 in a near-faujasite shown in Fig. 34;

(*b*) isotherms showing continuous sections with one more or less well-defined step. Examples are benzene and naphthalene in potassium benzene sulfonate (Fig. 35*a*); ammonia, methanol, or ethanol in montmorillonite (Fig. 13); or hydrogen in some transition metals below a critical temperature;

(*c*) isotherms showing two steps alternating with continuous sections, such as have been found with water in potassium benzene sulfonate (Fig. 22), or, more clearly, in Na-rich montmorillonite (Fig. 13).

A. Isotherms Showing Discontinuities

Isotherms with steps also show hysteresis between sorption and desorption branches. The steps are often associated with pronounced lattice alterations, equivalent to the nucleation of a new phase richer in guest molecules on or in a matrix of the old. Similarly, at the step on the desorption branch, the phase poor in guest molecules is nucleated on or in that rich in the guest species. The intimate contact of phases involves in each case two extra free energy contributions due to strain and to surface tension at the interfaces between nuclei and parent matrix. These free energy contributions, being positive, delay the appearance of stable nuclei

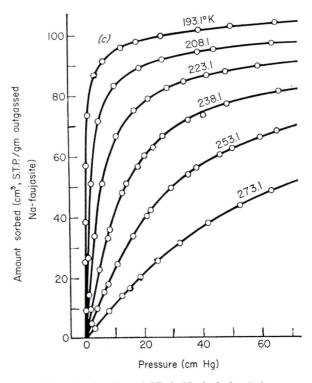

FIG. 34. Sorption of CF₄ in Na-faujasite (65).

of the new phase both on sorption and desorption branches of the isotherm, and so result in hysteresis. Such hysteresis loops can be reproducible, or may be dependent upon the number of sorption-desorption cycles to which the system has been submitted. Individual loops are not rectangular because germ nuclei of differing shapes may form, which may also appear in different locations on what are often finely divided parent crystals. Thus a distribution of strain and surface tension terms may arise for different germ nuclei, so that spontaneously growing nuclei develop from these germ nuclei over a range of pressures, often yielding rather sloping and ill-defined steps in the isotherms. Under conditions where nucleation is involved the kinetics of formation of the complexes are sometimes "autocatalytic" in character (42).

It is sometimes found that, in these isotherms showing discontinuities, limiting compositions of the complex can vary rather strongly with temperature but not with pressure (excluding capillary condensation as the relative pressure nears unity). Examples are seen in the sorption of naphthalene (Fig. 35a) and other aromatic hydrocarbons by potassium

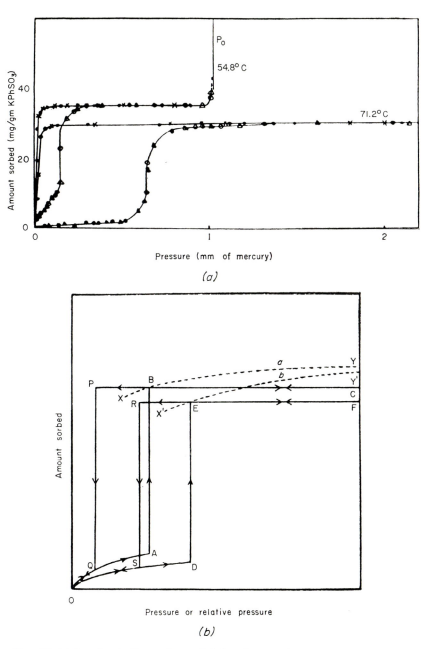

FIG. 35. (a) Sorption isotherms for naphthalene in potassium benzene sulfonate. KEY: ⊙, first sorption; ●, first desorption; △, second sorption; ×, second desorption. (b) Expected course of isotherms for formation of clathrate inclusion complex at temperatures T_1 and T_2 (full lines), compared with true equilibrium (dotted lines) (21).

benzene sulfonate (see also Table XVIII). An explanation which may be general in such circumstances is as follows (21).

In Fig. 35b, XY, $X'Y'$ represent the only parts of the true inclusion isotherms of the naphthalene-rich phase which at temperatures T_1 and T_2 ($T_1 < T_2$) are theoretically realizable without instability of the host lattice. If outgassed potassium benzene sulfonate is bathed in naphthalene vapor the complex cannot form until the pressure at T_1 exceeds the value corresponding to the point X. Even here, however, it will not normally form owing to the difficulty of nucleating the naphthalene-rich phase on or in the matrix of parent crystals. For similar reasons the ideally vertical section AB in Fig. 35b is often replaced by a sloping line because, as already noted, nuclei may form at differing pressures according to their shape and location. The isotherm path initially followed is OA corresponding to a little physical sorption of naphthalene on the external surfaces of the crystals of benzene sulfonate. At A the naphthalene-rich phase of composition corresponding to point B is formed. B is a true isotherm point and reaction is now terminated because the guest molecules are so encaged that no more naphthalene can enter or leave the host lattice without decomposition of the clathrate structure. Thus, the phase once formed remains of fixed composition even though the naphthalene vapor pressure is increased substantially corresponding to the isotherm section BC. On lowering the pressure the complex persists to the metastable point P, again owing to difficulties in nucleating crystals of the naphthalene-free benzene sulfonate. At point P nucleation occurs and the path PQO is followed. Thus, at T_1, $OABC$ is the isotherm path with rising pressure and $CBPQO$ as pressure is decreased.

Similarly at temperature T_2 the isotherms are $ODEF$ for rising and $FERSO$ for falling vapor pressure of naphthalene. Thus PBC and REF represent two non-stoichiometric phases metastable except at B and E, respectively, and having compositions independent of pressure (within the existence limits), but for normal isotherms XY, $X'Y'$, sensitive to temperature.

B. Isotherms without Discontinuities

Isotherms without discontinuities are normally reversible on sorption and desorption cycles, and are obtained when the host lattice remains stable in presence or absence of guest molecules. In this field, sorption of gases and vapors by zeolites has been the most extensively investigated. The guest molecules now have ready access to the intracrystalline cavities by reversible diffusion processes.

Even when access is impossible once the complex has been formed, and when the empty host lattice cannot exist, parts of continuous isotherms may still be realized. For example, and in effect by forming the β-hydroquinone-argon clathrate phase at a series of different fixed argon pressures, Platteeuw (204) succeeded in obtaining the isotherm over the existence range of the complex. The experiment further demonstrated the validity of Langmuir's isotherm for this particular clathrate solid solution.

Three physical situations can so far be recognized in inclusion complexes. In the first, each cavity is to be regarded as a fixed site in Langmuir's sense (Type I and Type II hydrates, or β-hydroquinone clathrates). In the second, multiple occupancy of cavities is possible, and sites and cavities in the Langmuir sense cannot be identified with one another. Guest molecules in any one cavity can be in physical contact with other guest molecules, and the cluster in a given cavity may make contact with clusters in other cavities to produce a continuous intracrystalline fluid (guest molecule-porous zeolite complexes). In both these situations the host lattice is relatively inert, and the thermal entropy of inclusion is negative. In the third situation, the heat of inclusion of *liquid* guest molecules is very small, and the entropy of inclusion of the liquid is positive (dimethyldioctadecylammonium montmorillonite-hydrocarbon complexes). We may consider the three physical situations briefly in order.

1. COMPLEXES WHERE EACH CAVITY IS AN INCLUSION SITE

From the thermodynamic and statistical thermodynamic viewpoint it does not matter whether sorption sites are located only on the surface of a solid or are distributed throughout its volume. The latter is the case in inclusion complexes. In β-hydroquinone the cavities are small enough to be able to contain only one guest molecule at a time, and there is only one kind of cavity. The next simplest systems are found in the gas hydrates, where we have already seen that two kinds of cavity are found, each large enough to contain only one guest molecule. However, the cavities are sufficiently different in size for situations to arise (in the Type II structures) in which only the larger kind of cavity is big enough to contain certain guest molecules (e.g., $CHCl_3$), and the position reduces again to that in β-hydroquinone (see Chapter 7, Section IV). Systems in which cavity and Langmuir sites are to be identified are the easiest to treat on a theoretical basis, and considerable success has been achieved in the description and understanding of the behavior of the corresponding clathrate structures as solid solutions (69, 205, 259). The fundamental equations for these solutions are, for a single guest molecule in a host lattice containing two kinds of cavity:

$$K_1 = \frac{\theta_1}{P(1 - \theta_1)}$$

(1)

$$K_2 = \frac{\theta_2}{P(1 - \theta_2)}$$

and

$$\Delta\mu = \frac{n}{(n + 1)m} \ln (1 - \theta_1) + \frac{1}{(n + 1)m} \ln (1 - \theta_2)$$

(2)

where the subscripts $_1$ and $_2$ refer to cavities of the two kinds, of which fractions θ_1 and θ_2 are occupied at the pressure P. $\Delta\mu$ is the difference in chemical potential of the lattice-forming units of the host lattice when the cavities are partly filled and empty respectively. n is the ratio of the numbers of cavities of the two kinds, and m is the ratio of the total number of lattice units to the total number of available cavities. K_1 and K_2 are the Langmuir equilibrium constants for the two kinds of cavities. These equilibrium constants are in turn given by:

$$K_1 = \frac{1}{kT} \frac{h^3}{(2\pi mkT)^{3/2}} \frac{Z_1(T)}{Z_A(T)} \exp (\epsilon_1/kT)$$

(3)

$$K_2 = \frac{1}{kT} \frac{h^3}{(2\pi mkT)^{3/2}} \frac{Z_2(T)}{Z_A(T)} \exp (\epsilon_2/kT)$$

where m is the mass of the guest molecule, h is Planck's constant, and k is Boltzmann's constant. ϵ_1 and ϵ_2 are respectively the least energies needed to remove a guest molecule from a cavity of kinds 1 and 2 to the gas phase. $Z_1(T)$ and $Z_2(T)$ are the partition functions of the included guest molecules in the two kinds of cavity, including their motions relative to the walls of the cavities, and $Z_A(T)$ is the partition function, excluding that for translations, of the gaseous guest molecule.

Using the cell theory of liquids (151, 172), which was presented in Chapter 2, Section III, for the evaluation of the ratio of partition functions, van der Waals and Platteeuw (205) and Barrer and Stuart (69) were able to achieve success in calculating the experimental equilibrium constants and other properties for simple gases in gas hydrates. Van der

TABLE XXV

DISSOCIATION PRESSURES, CALCULATED AND OBSERVED, FOR SOME TYPE I HYDRATES AT 0°C (205)

Guest molecule	θ_1	θ_2	Dissociation pressure (atm)	
			Obs.	Calc.
Ar	0.83	0.84	95.5	95.5
Kr	0.83	0.83	14.5	15.4
Xe	0.81	0.84	1.15	1.0
CH_4	0.82	0.84	26.	19.
CF_4	0.28	0.89	~1.	1.6
C_2H_6	0.84	0.83	5.2	1.1
C_2H_4	0.52	0.88	5.44	0.5
O_2	0.82	0.84	120.	63.
N_2	0.81	0.85	160.	90.

Waals and Platteeuw allowed themselves one adjustable parameter; Barrer and Stuart made an absolute calculation for Ar, Kr, and Xe, using only known physical constants for these gases and for water. Table XXV then gives some observed and calculated dissociation pressures at 0°C of some Type I gas hydrates, together with estimated values of θ_1 and θ_2 for the smaller and larger cavities respectively (260). The adjustable parameter was determined by making calculation and experiment agree for the argon hydrate, and was then available for the other systems. The treatment is adequate for symmetrical molecules, but is less appropriate for diatomic or diradical molecules. These molecules, it would appear, suffer hindrances to rotation which cannot be treated in terms of the cell theory of liquids.

2. COMPLEXES WHERE EACH CAVITY PROVIDES A NUMBER OF SORPTION SITES

In Table XXII are given for various guest molecules and for several porous crystals the number of guest molecules required to fill a single cavity. These numbers can be rather large. They are not integers because, as noted previously, a guest molecule can be shared between two cavities. Also the co-volumes of the guest molecules tend to increase with temperature, the coefficients of thermal expansion being in fact not very different from those of the corresponding bulk liquids (38, 65, 71). This behavior supports the idea that in such open structures as faujasite, chabazite, or Linde Sieve A the isotherm behavior might be described in terms of an equation of state. Barrer and Rees (62) successfully used an equation of state found valid for bulk fluids up to their critical densities (150) to reproduce sorption isotherms of nitrogen and argon up to $\theta \sim 0.3$ in several ion-exchanged faujasites. After the equation of state for the intracrystalline fluids was modified to allow for the smaller thermal entropy of the partially encaged guest molecules, and for the smaller molecule-molecule coordination numbers due to the restricted space available for molecule clusters, the experimental isotherms were rather well reproduced, as shown in Fig. 36.

Other treatments, assuming the simpler equations of state of Volmer or of van der Waals, lead respectively to the isotherms

$$K = \frac{\theta}{P(1 - \theta)} \exp \frac{\theta}{(1 - \theta)} \tag{4}$$

and

$$K = \frac{\theta}{P(1 - \theta)} \exp \left(\frac{\theta}{1 - \theta} - \alpha\theta \right) \tag{5}$$

where α is a coefficient depending upon temperature and upon the constants a and b of van der Waals' equation. The constant K is again defined by Eq. (3), and the ratio $Z_1(T)/Z_A(T)$ can be evaluated after appropriate assumptions about the degrees of freedom of the guest molecules (131). Both these equations have received attention, notably by Kington and his co-workers (132, 134), and it has been found that Eq. (4) represents the isotherms of argon and oxygen in chabazite at liquid oxygen temperatures. However, the equation proved valid over a range of values in θ far beyond any for which so simple an equation of state as that of Volmer could reasonably be expected to apply. Thus its validity should probably be regarded as accidental. This is especially so because the curves of differential heat, $\overline{\Delta H}$, against amount sorbed show that this heat is a function of θ (cf. Fig. 37), whereas Eq. (4) is derived assuming that the gas is occluded in a uniform field of potential.

The third approach to the behavior of intracrystalline fluids in zeolites is based upon the model for localized sorption, without interaction and

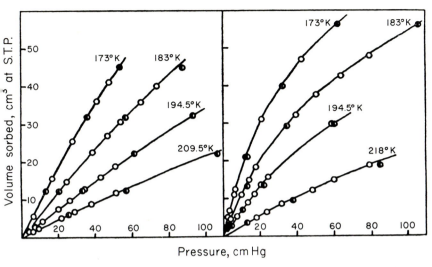

FIG. 36. (*a*) Observed isotherms and isotherms calculated using an equation of state in the crystal for argon in (*a*) Na-faujasite, and (*b*) Ba-faujasite. KEY: ●, point from which argon-argon coordination number was obtained; ◐, calculated isotherm points; ○, observed isotherm points (*62*).

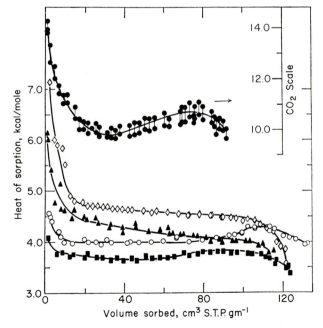

FIG. 37. Differential heats of sorption in natural chabazite. KEY: ■, argon; ○, oxygen; ▲, nitrogen; ◇, carbon monoxide; ●, carbon dioxide (*164*).

with interaction, leading respectively to the isotherms of Langmuir [Eq.
(1)] and of Lacher (167) as given in Eq. (6):

$$K = \frac{\theta}{P(1 - \theta)} \left\{ \frac{2 - 2\theta}{\beta - 1 - 2\theta} \right\}^z \tag{6}$$

In this equation z denotes the coordination number of a site and

$$\beta = \left\{ 1 - 4\theta(1 - \theta) \left[1 - \exp\left(- \frac{2\omega}{zkT} \right) \right] \right\}^{\frac{1}{2}}.$$

Here $2\omega/z$ is the interaction energy between a pair of guest molecules.
Both Eqs. (1) and (6) are derived assuming that the interaction between
guest and host lattice does not vary with θ, and so must usually be idealiza-
tions. In the actual case of a number of guest molecules occluded by
chabazite the variations of $\overline{\Delta H}$ with θ are shown in Fig. 37 (164).

Nevertheless it is of interest that Langmuir's isotherm is sometimes
valid over a wide range in the values of θ, as shown in Table XXVI for
the ethane-faujasite system (38). The table shows the inadequacy of
Volmer's isotherm for this particular system. The differential heat of
inclusion of the ethane does not in this system vary greatly over the

TABLE XXVI

SORPTION OF ETHANE AT 297.9°K IN A NEAR-FAUJASITE (SIEVE 13X)ᵃ

Equilibrium pressure (cm Hg)	θ	$\frac{P(1 - \theta)}{\theta}$	$\frac{P(1 - \theta)}{\theta} \exp - \frac{\theta}{(1 - \theta)}$	$-\Delta H$ (kcal/mole)
4.8	0.187	23	19	6.2
6.6	0.250	19	14	6.4
8.4	0.312	18	12	6.5
10.7	0.375	18	9.8	6.4
13.2	0.438	17	7.8	6.5
16.5	0.500	17	6.1	6.8
20.9	0.562	16	4.5	7.2
28.0	0.625	17	3.2	7.1
38.8	0.688	18	2.0	7.1

ᵃ $\theta = 1$ corresponds to the sorption of 80 cm³ at S.T.P. per gm.

range in θ studied, a factor which may contribute to the success of the ideal localized model.

Sometimes, however, Langmuir's isotherm provides a good description of the inclusion isotherm even when $\overline{\Delta H}$ is changing with θ. An example is found in the iodine-zeolite systems studied by Barrer and Wasilewski (73). Values of the Langmuir quotients are summarized for I_2-Sieve 5A in

TABLE XXVII

LANGMUIR QUOTIENTS FOR THE I_2-SIEVE 5A COMPLEX

θ	120°	155°	195°	230°	265°	300°C
				$K = \dfrac{\theta}{P(1-\theta)}$		
	$\times 1$	$\times 10$	$\times 10$	$\times 10^2$	$\times 10^3$	$\times 10^3$
0.1	—	—	1.69	5.91	2.70	9.83
0.2	—	6.69	1.41	4.98	2.10	8.87
0.3	—	5.92	1.37	5.16	1.98	8.77
0.4	—	6.47	1.50	5.33	1.96	8.95
0.5	—	6.94	1.60	5.26	1.93	9.09
0.6	—	7.01	1.57	5.05	1.92	8.98
0.7	3.89	6.85	1.50	4.91	1.82	8.73
0.8	3.47	5.86	1.23	4.47	1.72	—
0.9	2.29	3.63	0.89	4.06	—	—

Table XXVII. Here the validity of Langmuir's isotherm is due not to the constancy of $\overline{\Delta H}$, but to the almost complete compensation between the variation of $\overline{\Delta H}$ and of $T\overline{\Delta S}_{th}$ with θ. Here $\overline{\Delta S}_{th}$ denotes the thermal entropy change associated with inclusion. Since $(\overline{\Delta H} - T\overline{\Delta S}_{th})$ is constant over the relevant ranges of θ, the chance of occupation of any site remains independent of θ and Langmuir's isotherm is recovered, written in the form:

$$P = \frac{\theta}{(1-\theta)} \exp\left[-\left(\frac{\overline{\Delta H} - T\overline{\Delta S}_{th}}{RT}\right)\right] \tag{7}$$

where the equilibrium constant of Eq. (3) is now given by

$$- \ln K = \frac{\overline{\Delta H} - T\overline{\Delta S}_{\text{th}}}{RT} \tag{8}$$

It was further pointed out that these systems differ from the physical picture in the original statistical thermodynamic derivation of Langmuir' isotherm in that the number of sites available changes according to the size of the guest molecule and according to the variation of the co-volume of the guest with temperature. It was suggested that the site model in the derivation of Langmuir's isotherm may have about the same status as the lattice cells in the lattice theory of polymer-penetrant mixtures. That is, the site is here a rather artificial device which enables the correct configurational entropy to be estimated.

The localized sorption model is likely to be at its worst for smaller values of θ where in the case of energetically heterogeneous systems $\overline{\Delta H}$ changes most rapidly with θ. Also, as θ tends towards unity no localized isotherm equation remains indefinitely valid, the direction of the trend always corresponding to a greater escaping tendency of the guest molecules from the complex than is predicted. This effect is to be traced to the caging action of the guest molecules upon one another. The loss of thermal entropy associated with this stage becomes important and the affinity of guest molecules for the zeolite falls.

3. COMPLEXES IN WHICH THE ENTROPY OF INCLUSION OF LIQUID GUEST IS POSITIVE

The first examples of inclusion complexes in which the entropy of inclusion of liquid guest species is positive have only recently been observed (46). Positive entropies were found when hydrocarbons were imbibed by dimethyldioctadecylammonium montmorillonite (Fig. 15); the physical interpretation is given in Section V, A. There is now no free space between the aluminosilicate lamellae of the clay derivative, so that the guest molecules are imbibed by a process of mixing of the sorbed molecules with the long alkyl chains of the alkylammonium ions. The process takes place with appropriate swelling of the clay. The system thus resembles rubber-benzene mixtures more than superficially, and by a modification of the lattice theory of polymer-penetrant mixtures it was possible to calculate approximately the curve of the entropy of mixing versus amount of guest species imbibed. It would be expected that positive entropies of imbibition of liquids would be found with other systems in which all the interlamellar space is occupied by long-chain cations, such as the alkylammonium forms of uranium micas or vermiculites. However, experimental evidence on this point is as yet not available.

C. The Empty Host Lattices

From Eq. (2) we may evaluate differences in chemical potential of the partly filled and the empty host lattices in clathrate phases such as gas hydrates, at the temperature at which the clathrate phase has formed. At this temperature, however, the chemical potential of water in the hydrate equals that of water in the aqueous phase from which the hydrate forms if equilibrium conditions are obtained. Thus, one may evaluate differences in chemical potential between liquid water, or ice, and the hypothetical empty host lattice. Van der Waals and Platteeuw (260) evaluated for Type I hydrates the quantity

$$\Delta\mu = \mu_{H_2O}^{ice} - \mu_{H_2O}^{o} \tag{9}$$

where $\mu_{H_2O}^{ice}$ and $\mu_{H_2O}^{o}$ are the chemical potentials of water in ice and empty host lattice respectively. They used the composition $Br_2 \cdot 8.47H_2O$ obtained for the bromine hydrate, for which only the larger cavities are occupied. Also for the Type II SF_6-hydrate, the vapor pressure in equilibrium with ice at $-3°C$ was determined as 0.85 atm, and the equilibrium value of θ_1 as given by Eq. (1) was then in effect calculated from the theory, and $\Delta\mu$ estimated. The results obtained are summarized in Table XXVIII, together with $\Delta\mu$ for α-hydroquinone and the metastable empty β-hydroquinone host lattice in which argon or krypton were the actual guest molecules. The differences $\Delta\mu$ are very small, although sufficient in the case of the hydrates to ensure that the *open ice* host lattices have never been prepared in absence of guest molecules to stabilize them. The values of $\Delta\mu$ for these empty clathrate structures and the stable phase will vary to some extent according to the guest molecules present, since the host lattice is not

TABLE XXVIII

$\Delta\mu$ for the Stable Phase and the Empty Host Lattice

Host lattice	Stable phase	Temperature (°C)	$-\Delta\mu$ (cal/mole)
Type I hydrate	Ice	0	167
Type II hydrate	Ice	0	$\sim$190
β-Hydroquinone	α-Hydroquinone	25	82

entirely inert, as shown by small changes in unit cell dimensions of the unit cells with the guest molecule included (Tables II, III, and IV).

IX. THERMOCHEMISTRY

The thermochemical considerations of this section will be confined to some aspects of hydrate and of zeolite inclusion complexes.

A. Hydrate Inclusion Complexes

Heats of reaction which are important in the theory of clathrate phases of water relate to the processes:

(a)   ice → empty host lattice   (ΔH_1)

(b)   ice (or liquid H_2O) + hydrate former → hydrate   (ΔH_2)

(c)   hydrate former → hydrate former included   (ΔH_3)
               (gas or liquid)   in the host lattice

These three heats are not independent: if ΔH_1 and ΔH_2 were available for ice, ΔH_3 would follow. Thus when reaction (b) refers to one mole of hydrate former, n molecules of water then actually participate in reaction (b), and the relationship between the three heats is

$$n\Delta H_1 + \Delta H_3 = \Delta H_2 \qquad (10)$$

However, ΔH_1 is not known. In the analogous case in which α-hydroquonine → empty β-hydroquinone host lattice, ΔH_1 has been estimated as 160 cal/mole at 25°C (116). This heat would also be expected to be small for the formation of empty host lattice from ice. Eucken (115) made the assumption that ΔH_1 is zero, so that then

$$\Delta H_3 \simeq \Delta H_2 \qquad (11)$$

The weakness of this argument is that even if ΔH_1 is very small, n may be considerable and so $n\Delta H_1$ may not be negligible compared with ΔH_3. Nevertheless it provides one with a means of estimating heats of intercalation ΔH_3, since heats of formation, ΔH_2, may be determined either calorimetrically, or by application of the Clapeyron-Clausius equation to the variation of total pressure, P, with temperature, T, along the equilibrium P–T line:

$$\frac{dP}{dT} = \frac{\Delta H_2}{T\Delta V} \qquad (12)$$

Here ΔV is the volume change when hydrate formation occurs. In order to determine ΔH_2 accurately per mole of guest species, analytical data must be available. Also, since the clathrate phase is non-stoichiometric its composition may change along the P–T line. Lack of accurate information of an analytical character is one of the main sources of error in estimates of ΔH_2. Fortunately, θ approaches 1 for many of the clathrate phases studied. Heats of formation and other thermodynamic quantities have been determined for the Type II hydrate of CBrClF$_2$, and may be quoted as typical (Table XXIX). Since $\theta \rightarrow 1$, its composition approaches CBrClF$_2 \cdot$17H$_2$O very nearly. The heat of 8254 $\pm$ 29 cal/mole can be regarded on the basis of Eucken's assumption ($\Delta H_1 = 0$) as an approximation to the heat of intercalation of CBrClF$_2$ in the water host lattice.

TABLE XXIX

THERMODYNAMIC FUNCTIONS FOR CBrClF$_2 \cdot$17H$_2$O AT 0°C (136)

	CBrClF$_2 \cdot$17H$_2$O(s) $\rightarrow$ CBrClF$_2$(g) + 17H$_2$O(l)	CBrClF$_2 \cdot$17H$_2$O(s) $\rightarrow$ CBrClF$_2$(g) + 17H$_2$O(s)
ΔG (cal/mole)	923.3 $\pm$ 0.5	923.3 $\pm$ 0.5
ΔH (cal/mole)	32,567 $\pm$ 70	8254 $\pm$ 29
ΔS (cal/deg mole)	115.8 $\pm$ 0.3	26.8 $\pm$ 0.1
ΔC_p (cal/deg mole)	138.6 $\pm$ 10.8	$-1.2 \pm$ 5.9

A second estimate of the heat of intercalation can be made for some guest species by measuring heats of formation of single and double hydrates, such as CHCl$_3 \cdot$17H$_2$O and CHCl$_3 \cdot$2H$_2$S$\cdot$17H$_2$O. By subtraction of one heat from the other, the heat of intercalation of hydrogen sulfide may be estimated. However, neither hydrate is strictly stoichiometric, so that this method also lacks rigor. In a third method heats of intercalation, ΔH_3, are estimated from the empirical combining rule

$$\Delta H_3 = \sqrt{\Delta H_h \Delta H_{ice}} \qquad (13)$$

where ΔH_h is the heat of condensation of hydrate former to its liquid, and ΔH_{ice} is this heat for water vapor condensing to ice. Some estimates of ΔH_3 by this last method for Type I hydrates are given in Table XXX, taking ΔH_{ice} as 8000 cal/mole, together with heats evaluated from the heats of formation using Eq. (11). Agreement is rather satisfactory.

TABLE XXX

HEATS OF INTERCALATION FROM EQ. (13) (*264*)

Heat (kcal/mole)	Hydrate former									
	Kr	Xe	CH_4	C_2H_6	N_2O	CO_2	SO_2	Cl_2	Br_2	CH_3I
$-\Delta H_h$	~3.3	~3.7	2.2	~5.8	6.	6.3	8.5	7.3	11.	8.
$-\Delta H_3 = \sqrt{\Delta H_h \cdot \Delta H_{ice}}$	5.0	5.5	4.2	6.8	6.9	7.1	8.2	7.6	9.4	8.
$-\Delta H_3$ from heat of reaction	5.3	8.0	4.4	6.3	6.2	6.0	7.9	7.3	8.3	7.3

Heats of intercalation may also be calculated from the dispersion + repulsion energy of an interacting guest molecule and water molecule. Barrer and Stuart (69) used the Lennard-Jones and Devonshire (172) potential, in conjunction with the Kirkwood-Müller (165, 184) approximation for the dispersion energy constant to evaluate this energy. They integrated throughout the volume of the crystals outside the cavities to obtain the total energy, using the average water molecule density. Barrer and Ruzicka (67) used London's (173) approximation with the more rigorous method of summation over all pairs contributing appreciably to the interaction energy. Neglecting any temperature coefficient of the energy due to heat capacity changes on inclusion, the heats of inclusion

TABLE XXXI

Calculated Heats of Intercalation in Small Cavities of Type II Hydrates (kcal/mole)

Guest molecule	Barrer and Stuart (69)	Barrer and Ruzicka (67)
Ar	−3.6	−3.6
Kr	−5.5	−4.7
Xe	−7.8	−5.8
CH$_4$	—	−4.6

may be evaluated. One may illustrate the results obtained by reference to the calculated heats of intercalation in the small cavities of Type II hydrates for Ar, Kr, Xe, and CH$_4$ (Table XXXI). These values may be compared with those of Table XXX, again showing reasonable correspondence. Heats of intercalation vary somewhat according to the sizes of the several cavities, as shown by Barrer and Stuart, but not sufficiently to affect reasonable agreement.

B. Guest Molecules in Zeolites

Differential heats of inclusion, $\overline{\Delta H_3}$, of gases or vapors in zeolites have been determined directly, or by application of the relationship

$$\left(\frac{\partial \ln P}{\partial T}\right)_a = \frac{\overline{\Delta H_3}}{RT^2} \tag{14}$$

where P is the equilibrium pressure for a constant amount sorbed, a. In the gas hydrates, although differential heats of inclusion as a function of the quantity of guest species included have not so far been determined, there seems every likelihood that $\overline{\Delta H}_3$ would not vary appreciably with amount included for any one kind of cavity, since the cavity can contain one molecule only, and its environment relative to the host lattice is always the same. Thus, for any one type of cavity, integral and differential heats would be nearly equal. In Type I clathrate phases of water in which the two kinds of cavity are simultaneously occupied by one guest species, $\overline{\Delta H}_3$ might vary with amount of guest, because in one type of cavity θ might approach unity more rapidly than in the other.

In zeolite crystals where, as we have seen, clusters of guest molecules may be present, possibilities for variations of $\overline{\Delta H}_3$ with amount included are more diverse. In the first place, the environment is more strongly polar, so that polarization energies, and interactions of electrostatic fields and field gradients with permanent electric moments in guest molecules may contribute to $\overline{\Delta H}_3$. Since fields and field gradients may not be uniform throughout a large cavity, such contributions could vary with θ. Even the dispersion and repulsion energies may vary substantially according to the positions of the guest molecules in the cavities, and hence according to θ, as demonstrated for iodine in the large cavities in faujasite by Barrer and Wasilewski (73). Also, as θ increases, guest molecules make increasing numbers of contacts with each other, and so give a self-potential contribution to $\overline{\Delta H}_3$. As a consequence of these considerations one expects that $\overline{\Delta H}_3$ may become dependent upon θ for zeolite sorbents. Figure 37 shows that this is very definitely the case for a number of gases sorbed by chabazite (164).

The initial heterogeneity observed in these systems is of particular interest, since of the series of guest molecules H_2, O_2, N_2, CO, and CO_2 only CO has a dipole moment which is very small, while N_2, CO, and CO_2 have considerable quadrupole moments increasing in the order given, and H_2 and O_2 have only very small quadrupole moments. If one neglects the field-dipole contribution from CO, and assumes the dispersion + repulsion energy to be independent of θ, at least for smaller values of θ, then the observed energetic heterogeneity is to be attributed to variations in electrostatic interactions. The relevant interactions of this kind are polarization and quadrupole-field gradient energy. Thus with dispersion and repulsion energy independent of θ we may write:

$$\overline{\Delta H}_3{}^{(2)} - \overline{\Delta H}_3{}^{(1)} = \frac{\alpha}{2}(E_1{}^2 - E_2{}^2) + \frac{Q}{4}\left(\frac{\partial E_{t_2}}{\partial t} - \frac{\partial E_{t_1}}{\partial t}\right) \qquad (15)$$

where $\overline{\Delta H}_3{}^{(2)}$ and $\overline{\Delta H}_3{}^{(1)}$ are differential heats of inclusion when the values of θ are θ_2 and θ_1 respectively ($\theta_2 > \theta_1$), E_1 and E_2 are the appropriate electrostatic fields, and $\partial E_{t_2}/\partial t$ and $\partial E_{t_1}/\partial t$ are the corresponding gradients of these fields along the quadrupole axes of the guest molecules; α and Q denote respectively polarizability and quadrupole moment of the guest molecules. Equation (15) can now be rewritten as

$$(\Delta H_3^{(2)} - \Delta H_3^{(1)}) - a\alpha = cQ \qquad (16)$$

where a and c are taken as constants for the series of guest molecules. Since argon has no quadrupole moment, the value of a was determined for $\theta_1 = 0.01$ and $\theta_2 = 0.30$, and the left hand side of Eq. (16) was then plotted against the quadrupole moment for the other guest species, H_2, O_2, N_2, CO, and CO_2. The result, shown in Fig. 38, is a linear plot as required by Eq. (16) and supports the view that energetic heterogeneity in chabazite is largely of electrostatic origin. It also gives support to a tacit assumption underlying Eq. (16). Thus for the equation to be valid, all guest molecules, at least up to $\theta = 0.3$, must perferentially be entering the same elements of the interstitial volume and in the same order. Kington and Macleod further considered the heterogeneity as arising only from

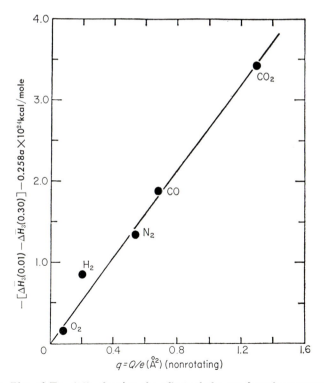

FIG. 38. Plot of Eq. (16), showing the effect of the quadrupole moment upon the energetic heterogeneity of chabazite (164).

variations of dispersion and repulsion energy (the converse of the above situation). On this basis, however, no treatment could be reconciled with the measured heterogeneities shown in Fig. 37, further supporting the view that this heterogeneity is of electrostatic origin.

Energetic heterogeneity is not always apparent, and is a specific property of both the host lattice and the guest molecule. Properties of guest molecules which favor increased energetic heterogeneity are high polarizability and high permanent electric moments. Properties of host lattices which favor such heterogeneity include small size and high valency of the intracrystalline cations (70). Even in a system where there is considerable heterogeneity among the sorption sites, however, when the sorption follows Henry's law (amount sorbed proportional to pressure) the differential heat of inclusion, $\overline{\Delta H_3}$, remains independent of the amount of the guest species (64). The heterogeneity can now manifest itself in a considerable temperature coefficient in $\overline{\Delta H_3}$ because, although Henry's law remains valid for each group of sites (and hence for the total sorption), there is a redistribution of populations of guest species among site groups as the temperature is changed, and each group binds guest species with a different energy.

Energetic heterogeneity disappears almost completely, even for sorptions well outside Henry's law, when large fluorocarbon molecules are included by sodium near-faujasite (66), as shown in Fig. 39. The fluorocarbons have

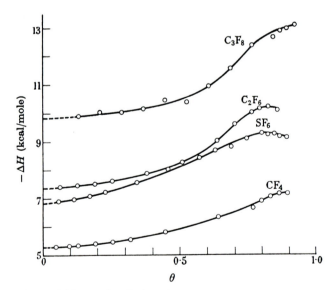

FIG. 39. Differential heats of occlusion of some perfluoro compounds in Na-faujasite, as functions of the fraction of saturation, θ (66).

rather low polarizabilities for their size, and if only limited parts of these bulky molecules can be inserted into regions of high field, the polarization energies should be small. On the other hand, the fluorocarbons interact with one another giving a considerable self-potential contribution to $\overline{\Delta H_3}$ for larger values of θ. This contribution has its origin in dispersion forces, and has been shown to have the magnitude to be expected from the properties of liquid fluorocarbons. The ultimate fall in $-\overline{\Delta H_3}$ as θ approaches 1 is ascribed to the sorption of fluorocarbon molecules upon external surfaces of the crystals, which at this stage begins to become important.

Heats of inclusion can become very large, for example reaching values of over 20 kcal/mole for inclusion of n-hexane, n-heptane or isooctane in Na-near-faujasite. Ratios of some heats of inclusion (for larger values of θ except in the case of methane) to heats of liquefaction are illustrated in the accompanying tabulation (71).

Hydrocarbon	CH_4	C_2H_6	C_3H_8	n-C_4H_{10}	Iso-C_4H_{10}	
$\dfrac{\overline{\Delta H_3} \text{ (sorption)}}{\Delta H \text{ (liquefaction)}}$	2.2	1.94	2.48	2.66	2.84	
Hydrocarbon	n-C_5H_{12}	Iso-C_5H_{12}	Neo-C_5H_{12}	n-C_6H_{14}	n-C_7H_{16}	Iso-C_8H_{18}
$\dfrac{\overline{\Delta H_3} \text{ (sorption)}}{\Delta H \text{ (liquefaction)}}$	2.78	2.90	2.41	2.96	2.69	2.84

These high ratios might be taken to indicate that heats are greatly enhanced by the intracrystalline environment. However, the mechanism of desorption from a zeolite also has an important bearing. When, from a saturated zeolite, all the guest molecules are removed, the host lattice does not collapse into the cavities. On the other hand, if an equal number of clusters of the same size were removed endothermally from the interior of a liquid, the liquid would collapse exothermally into the cavities formed, thus reducing the over-all heat of vaporization as compared with the integral heat of desorption from the zeolite (48). The maximum ratio to be expected from this cause alone however is 2, and if sizable clusters were being removed, as is the case in the Na-faujasite, the ratio would be reduced below 2. Thus, there must remain a considerable effect due to the actual environment of the guest species.

Another interesting comparison may be made between heats of intercalation on the one hand and heats of adsorption on the other. De Boer and Custers (106) showed that, if the dispersion energy for an adsorbed molecule on a plane surface containing N atoms of substrate per cm^3 is E_1, and if this energy is E_2, E_3, and E_4 when the sorbed molecule is re-

TABLE XXXII

Some Differential Heats of Intercalation and Adsorption (kcal/mole)

Sorbent or host lattice	N (atoms of sorbent or host lattice per cm³ $\times 10^{-22}$)	Sorbate or guest molecule	Exothermal heat values	
			as $\theta \to 0$	as $\theta \to 0.5$ (or for amount sorbed in cm³ at S.T.P./gm given by figures in parentheses)
β-Hydroquinone (259)	2.27(C) 0.76(O) 2.27(H)	Ar[a]	4.8	4.8
Clathrate structure of water (69)	2.66(H_2O)	Ar[a] Kr[a] Xe[a]	~3.0 ~5.3 ~8.0	~3.0 ~5.3 ~8.0
Chabazite (outgassed at 480°C) (14)	3.0(O)	Ar H_2	~6.0 ~3.8	3.0 (50) 2.0 (40)
Chabazite (outgassed at 300°C) (133) Faujasite (13, 70)	2.47(O)	Ar Ar O_2	4.6 2.70 2.80	3.6 2.70 (25) 2.80 (25)
Rutile (110)	10.6(O)	Ar O_2	3.50 4.00	2.50 2.80
Carbons: Spheron heated to 2700°C (3, 11, 78)	11.5(C as graphite)	Kr Ar Ne	3.97 2.70 0.87	4.55 2.80 0.88
Graphon (77) Saran S84 (78) Saran S600H (78)		Ar Ar Ar	2.60 3.50 3.90	2.75 2.63 3.63

[a] Heats for intercalation in β-hydroquinone and in gas hydrates are independent of θ.

spectively in a hemispherical pocket, at the end of a long tube with hemispherical end, and in a completely closed cavity, each having a free diameter, d, equal to that of the sorbed molecule, then $E_2 = 4E_1$, $E_3 = 6.36E_1$, and $E_4 = 8E_1$. For two plane parallel surfaces distant d apart, $E_5 = 2E_1$. Thus in slit-shaped cavities, such as arise with methylammonium montmorillonites, or in zeolite channels, or in the cavities of the clathrate phases of water, large enhancements of the heats of intercalation as compared with corresponding heats of adsorption are possible. In fact, however, comparisons of heats of adsorption and of intercalation as shown in Table XXXII do not reveal these enhancements (26). There are two reasons for this. Firstly, the cavities or channels in which the guest molecules are intercalated do not have free diameters exactly equal to the molecular diameters of the guest species. Secondly, the values of N vary greatly as between porous crystals and massive sorbents. Among carbon-rich sorbents, β-hydroquinone may be compared with the various carbons in the table, and it is then seen that N (carbon + oxygen) for β-hydroquinone is to N for nonporous carbons as about 1:4. Therefore the maximum enhancement in the heat for β-hydroquinone as compared with that for the carbons would be about 2, assuming the most ideal size of cavity in β-hydroquinone. In fact for argon in this host lattice and on nonporous *Spheron* the ratio is about 1.7. The *Saran* carbons of Table XXXII are microporous, and here there is at least initially a considerable enhancement of the heat of sorption of argon as compared with the heat on the nonporous *Spheron* or *Graphon* carbons. The *Saran* carbons are in fact initially tending to behave more nearly like β-hydroquinone.

Among the oxygen-rich sorbents, N in rutile is about four times its value in faujasite. Also the cavities in faujasite are very large, and so heats of intercalation for larger amounts sorbed (outside the region of energetic heterogeneity on rutile) prove nearly equal to heats of adsorption.

X. MOLECULE DIFFUSION IN SOME POROUS CRYSTALS

In terms of Fick's law, diffusion in a two-component solution of guest species A in host lattice B can be considered using five diffusion coefficients, D_A, D_B, D_A^*, D_B^* and D_{AB} (144). D_A and D_B are the intrinsic diffusion coefficients of A and B, D_A^* and D_B^* are the corresponding self-diffusion coefficients, and D_{AB} is the mutual diffusion coefficient, describing interdiffusion of A and B. The surface of the crystal represents a section such that the mass of host lattice B is fixed on each side. Then D_{AB} relative to this section is (144):

$$D_{AB} = V_B C_B{}^v (V_B{}^0 C_B{}^v)^2 \left[D_A + D_B \frac{(C_A{}^v V_A + C_A{}^v d V_A/dC_A{}^v)}{(C_B{}^v V_B + C_B{}^v d V_B/dC_B{}^v)} \right] \quad (17)$$

where V_A and V_B are the constant volumes of the unit amounts used to define A and B. $V_B{}^0$ is the specific volume of pure host lattice, B, and $C_B{}^v$, $C_A{}^v$ are the concentrations of B and A in unit volume of the mixture. When certain zeolites are the host lattices two special properties apply. Firstly, $D_B = D_B{}^* = 0$; and secondly, the host lattices accept the guest molecules with negligible swelling or shrinking, and so V_B is independent of $C_A{}^v$. Then $V_B{}^0 = V_B$ and $C_B{}^v V_B = 1$, and so Eq. (17) reduces to

$$D_{AB} = D_A \quad (18)$$

Also, if gradients in chemical potential are the driving forces, the relation between D_A and $D_A{}^*$ is

$$D_A = D_A{}^* \frac{d \ln a_A}{d \ln C_A{}^v} \quad (19)$$

where a_A is the activity of the guest molecules. Thus, the diffusion processes for a single guest species in isotropic nonswelling lattices can be fully described in terms of two diffusion coefficients only.

A. Diffusion of Zeolitic Water

In many host lattices, such as zeolites, an important naturally occurring guest molecule is water. Water has been the subject of several investigations both of self-diffusion and of intrinsic diffusion. One of the earliest of these was concerned with intrinsic diffusion in heulandite (251); a later study (202) examined self-diffusion; and still more recently both self- and intrinsic diffusion coefficients were measured in each of three zeolites (43).

Tiselius used an optical method for following the progress of diffusion. Parallel to the (010) cleavage planes of heulandite diffusion was $> 10^5$ times as rapid at room temperatures as normal to it. Moreover D_A was not the same in all directions in this plane, the diffusion coefficients at 20°C in Tiselius' sample normal to (001), (201), and (20$\bar{1}$) planes being in the ratio 1:11.6:11.6. The self-diffusion coefficients of Pemsler in heulandite and other zeolites were measured using heavy water and an infrared method for its analysis. However, the results were interpreted as though the heulandite crystals were isotropic and so must give less accurate values of $D_A{}^*$. Barrer and Fender measured the self- and intrinsic diffusion coefficients in heulandite, chabazite, and gmelinite by a gravimetric method, and allowed for the effective lack of diffusion in heulandite normal to (010) in interpreting the data.

The concentration dependence of D_A normal to the (201) plane and in the (010) plane of heulandite is shown in Table XXXIII. The value of D_A increases strongly with increasing water content, but approaches a nearly constant value as the water content nears the saturation value. The absolute values of D_A in section (b) of Table XXXIII are rather different in the heulandite sample studied by Tiselius (columns 2 and 3) and in the sample of Barrer and Fender (column 5), but such variability in different zeolite specimens is fully possible. The energy barrier for the mean D_A (8.4 kcal/mole) lies between those for diffusion normal to (201) and (001) planes (5.4 and 9.14 kcal/mole) as might be expected.

The diffusion coefficients can be represented very satisfactorily in terms of the Arrhenius equation, $D_A = D_0 \exp [-E/RT]$. The constants D_0 and E are then compared in the accompanying tabulation for chabazite, gmelinite, and heulandite (43):

	$10^6 \times D_A$ (cm^2 sec^{-1} at 45°C)	D_0 (cm^2 sec^{-1})	E (kcal/mole)
Chabazite	4.8	1.2×10^{-3}	6.7 ± 0.3
Gmelinite	1.5	5.6×10^{-2}	8.5 ± 2.0
Heulandite	1.6	4.9×10^{-2}	8.4 ± 0.4

Since essential features of the structures of these crystals are known, the results could in principle be related to the dimensions and character of the channel systems (Section VII,C). Not enough information is yet available, however, about the positioning of the cations for such considerations.

The relation between self- and intrinsic diffusion coefficients given in Eq. (19) was examined by Barrer and Fender. The activity correction

$$d \ln a_A/d \ln C_A = d \ln P/d \ln C_A$$

was obtained from the equilibrium isotherms. Its values were large, in the range 23–37, and the products $D_A^*(d \ln a_A/d \ln C_A)$ correspond closely with the experimental values of D_A. The self-diffusion study by Pemsler covered a number of zeolites, but the results show considerable scatter. Some values of D_A^* and of the Arrhenius energies are summarized in Table XXXIV, together with the similar results of Barrer and Fender. All Pemsler's self-diffusion data were interpreted as though the crystals

TABLE XXXIII

(a) Concentration Dependence of D_A in Heulandite [Normal to (201)]. $T = 20°C$, Saturation is 19.67% by Weight of Water (251)

Concentration % by wt. of water	$D_A \times 10^7$ (cm^2 sec^{-1}) with H$_2$O content initially $C_0 = 8.3\%$	$D_A \times 10^7$ (cm^2 sec^{-1}) $C_0 = 13.20\%$	$D_A \times 10^7$ (cm^2 sec^{-1}) $C_0 = 16.20\%$
10	0.04	—	—
11	0.2	—	—
12	0.7	—	—
13	1.3	—	—
14	2.0	2.1	—
15	2.7	2.6	—
16	3.0	3.5	—
17	4.0	4.2	4.0
18	4.0	4.1	4.2
19	3.3	3.5	4.1

(b) Temperature Dependence of D_A in Heulandite (43, 251)

Temp. (°C)	$D_A \times 10^7$ (cm^2 sec^{-1}) normal to (201)[a]	$D_A \times 10^7$ (cm^2 sec^{-1}) normal to (001)[b]	Temp. (°C)	$D_A \times 10^6$ (cm^2 sec^{-1}) mean value in cleavage planes[c]
20.0	2.7	0.23	35.0	1.05
33.8	4.1	0.45	45.0	1.6
46.1	4.8	0.66	55.0	2.4
60.0	7.6	1.45	65.0	3.5
75.0	11.1	2.8	75.0	4.9

[a] $E = 5.4$ kcal/mole.
[b] $E = 9.14$ kcal/mole.
[c] $E = 8.4 \pm 0.4$ kcal/mole.

were isotropic. This accounts in part for the low value of $D_A{}^*$ for heulandite; indeed only chabazite among the zeolites studied approximates to an isotropic medium. The values of D_0 obtained by Barrer and Fender are close to those for diffusion in liquid water, suggesting that the entropy of activation may be similar in the zeolites and in liquid water. The energy barriers involved in migration within the zeolites are, however, usually considerably higher than in liquid water. This must in part be ascribed to the restriction of the intracrystalline fluid by the zeolite frameworks, so that this fluid is essentially more viscous than bulk water. The self-diffusion coefficients of Barrer and Fender extrapolated to $-2°C$ are, however, somewhat higher than is $D_A{}^*$ for ice at $-2°C$. These experiments thus shed considerable light upon the physical character of zeolitic water. It is of interest that energy barriers for self-diffusion of monovalent cations in chabazite are only a little less than those for self-diffusion of water (29), but these barriers for Ca^{2+} and Sr^{2+} are about twice their values for the monovalent ions. Some correlation between such rate processes is possible because water molecules and cations jostle one another in the same channels, and cooperative movements involving small groups of water molecules plus cation may be concerned in successful unit diffusion processes of either water or ion. Ducros (111) using a nuclear magnetic resonance method, observed a relaxation process for water in chabazite which obeyed the Arrhenius equation

$$\tau = 5 \times 10^{-11} \exp\left(-5800/RT\right) \text{ sec,}$$

τ being the relaxation time. This process has a rather smaller activation energy than self-diffusion, and probably involves rotation of water molecules.

B. Diffusion of Permanent and Rare Gases in Mordenite and Levynite

From studies of the sorption kinetics of gases in mordenite and levynite (19, 36) values of D_A were obtained for relatively small amounts sorbed. Diffusion coefficients were obtained in Ca-, K-, Ba-, Na-, and Li-forms of mordenite, as well as in Ca-rich natural levynite. The results in Table XXXV may be regarded as typical. They show that the diffusion coefficients increase rapidly as the critical dimensions of the diffusing molecules decrease, while the energy barriers decrease. For electrically neutral molecules these barriers are the result of periodic variations in polarization, dispersion and repulsion energies as the guest molecules move through successive constrictions within the aluminosilicate framework. Even for ions, when they diffuse in the still less open structure of analcite, a direct connec-

TABLE XXXIV

SELF-DIFFUSION OF WATER IN SOME ZEOLITES

Author	Zeolite	D_A* (cm² sec⁻¹)	Temp. (°C)	D_0 (cm² sec⁻¹)	E (kcal/mole)	
Pemsler (202)	Chabazite	1×10^{-7}	30	—	(9.2, 12.6, 8.8, 10.2)	mean 10.2
	Heulandite	2.5×10^{-10}	30	—	(10.5, 9.9)	mean 10.2
	Stilbite	0.8×10^{-7}	30	—	(6.9, 3.6, 6.0)	mean 5.5
	Natrolite	1×10^{-9}	30	—	(9.0, 3.0)	mean 6.0
	Scolecite	10×10^{-8}	30	—	(6.7, 7.3)	mean 7.0
	Mesolite	5×10^{-7}	30	—	(4.3)	mean 4.3
Barrer and Fender (43)	Chabazite	1.26×10^{-7}	45	1.2×10^{-1}	8.7	
	Gmelinite	5.4×10^{-8}	45	2.0×10^{-2}	8.1	
	Heulandite	2.07×10^{-8}	45	7.6×10^{-1}	11.0	
	Liquid water	3.87×10^{-5}	45	5.6×10^{-2}	4.6	
	Ice	1.0×10^{-10}	-2	—	—	

TABLE XXXV

MOLECULAR DIFFUSION IN K-MORDENITE

Molecule	Critical dimension (Å)	D_A (cm² sec⁻¹) at −78°C	Energy of activation (cal/mole)
Kr	3.9₄	1.8×10^{-18}	10,000
Ar	3.8₃	2.4×10^{-16}	8,400
N₂	3.0	9.2×10^{-16}	4,800
O₂	2.8	2.0×10^{-15}	4,400
H₂	2.4	2.7×10^{-13}	2,500

tion has been observed between cation radii and energy barriers, again indicating that dispersion and repulsion energies associated with very narrow apertures are an important factor (63). On the other hand, in very open structures such as that of chabazite the energy barriers for self-diffusion of the monovalent ions Na⁺, K⁺, Rb⁺, and Cs⁺ are almost independent of the ionic radius, and so seem to be governed primarily by periodic variations in electrostatic potential. Further evidence of this is found in the energy barriers for Na⁺ and Ca²⁺ ions which are twice as large for the divalent cation as for the monovalent ion, in both chabazite (29) and in Linde Sieve A (203).

C. Diffusion in Chabazite and Linde Sieve 4A

Larger molecules of CH_2Cl_2, $(CH_3)_2NH$, and $n\text{-}C_4H_{10}$ diffuse in the more open structure of chabazite at rates which are comparable with those at which argon or krypton diffuse in the ion-exchanged mordenites or in levynite only when the temperatures are considerably higher. Diffusion coefficients for several concentrations of sorbate and temperatures are recorded in Table XXXVI (36). The diffusion coefficients for n-butane tend to decrease as the intracrystalline concentration increases, although the change is not large. It is not clear how general this result is; a decrease was established also for CH_2Cl_2 in chabazite, but it has previously been noted that D_A for water increases with concentration in heulandite (Table XXXIII).

Habgood (140) determined integral values of the diffusion coefficient for nitrogen and methane in Linde Sieve 4A. These integral values over a

TABLE XXXVI

MOLECULAR DIFFUSION IN CHABAZITE

Molecule	Temp. (°C)	Concentration of guest (cm³ at S.T.P./gm)	D_A at this concentration (cm² sec⁻¹)
CH_2Cl_2	0	70.0	2.17×10^{-16}
	50	47.0	4.92×10^{-15}
$(CH_3)_2NH$	0	87.0	1.90×10^{-19}
	50	78.5	1.35×10^{-17}
	100	70.0	2.51×10^{-15}
$n\text{-}C_4H_{10}$	200	13.5	2.10×10^{-13}
	200	17.1	1.85×10^{-13}
	200	19.1	1.70×10^{-13}

concentration range $(C_1 - C_2)$ are defined as

$$\bar{D}_A = \frac{1}{C_1 - C_2} \int_{C_2}^{C_1} D_A dC$$

The concentration dependence of these diffusion coefficients is not clear, since both an increase and a decrease were observed for nitrogen at 0° and −79.4°C, respectively, and increases for methane at each of these temperatures. At zero concentration the diffusion coefficients in the zeolite powder outgassed at 350°C could be represented by

$$D_{N_2} = 2.3 \times 10^{-9} \exp\left(-\frac{4070}{RT}\right) \text{ cm}^2 \text{ sec}^{-1}$$

$$D_{CH_4} = 5.8 \times 10^{-8} \exp\left(-\frac{7420}{RT}\right) \text{ cm}^2 \text{ sec}^{-1}$$

The concentration dependence may inter alia be modified by the completeness of water removal in the initial outgassing, and hence the physical state of the molecular sieve crystals (e.g., powder or pellets). The great changes in the diffusion coefficient which can be effected by leaving controlled amounts of strongly sorbed guest molecules in the crystals have been demonstrated by Barrer and Rees (61). These modifiers (e.g., water, ammonia, and methylamine) were immobile at the temperatures at which the diffusion of additional guest molecules was then studied. The modifier may change the diffusion coefficient of the guest molecules by many decades, the modifying action being different for guest species of different dimensions.

The cations within a given structural framework can have an influence on diffusion rates and energy barriers as important as that of the modifier molecules. This has been shown quantitatively in the diffusion of gases in ion-exchanged mordenites (19), and in Linde Sieves 3A, 4A, and 5A which are respectively the K^+-, Na^+-, and Ca^{2+}-ion-exchanged forms of the A zeolite (187). Some energy barriers for this latter zeolite are given in the accompanying tabulation.

Propane in Sieve 5A	$E = 0.54$ kcal/mole
Propane in Sieve 4A	$E = 8.7$ kcal/mole
Ethane in Sieve 4A	$E = 3.0$ kcal/mole
Argon in Sieve 3A	$E = 14.0$ kcal/mole
Nitrogen in Sieve 3A	$E = 16.2$ kcal/mole

It is interesting that in Sieve 3A the cation is so located that the *length* of the nitrogen molecule (4.08 Å) rather than its cross-sectional diameter (3.0 Å) may govern the barrier height opposing diffusion, since this barrier for nitrogen exceeds that for argon for which the diameter is 3.83 Å.

XI. CONCLUSION

The account given in the foregoing pages has indicated progress being made in certain directions in the study of non-stoichiometric complexes involving inorganic compounds. The number of substances able to act as host lattices is large, and the range of their applications seems likely to grow rapidly. One may consider that if suitable penetrants could be found, most crystals would be able to imbibe them, the imbibition being preliminary to solution in some instances, but in others being halted at a certain stage, due either to the crosslinked network character of the crystalline host or to other physicochemical factors. In an account such as this it is impossible to review many valuable contributions for it has been necessary to be selective in the topics chosen for discussion and comment. The author is conscious of these omissions, and hopes it may be possible sometime to remedy them by a fuller account. In the meantime it is confidently expected that the subject of inclusion complexes will develop in interest and importance.

REFERENCES

1. Adam, N. K., *in* "The Physics and Chemistry of Surfaces," Chapter II. Oxford Univ. Press, London and New York, 1941.
2. Allen, K. W., *J. Chem. Soc.*, p. 4131 (1959).
3. Amberg, C. H., Spencer, W. B., and Beebe, R. A., *Can. J. Chem.* **33**, 305 (1955).
4. Ames, L. L., Jr., *Am. Mineralogist* **45**, 689 (1960).
5. Ames, L. L., Jr., and Sand, L. B., *Am. Mineralogist* **43**, 476 (1958).
6. Andersson, S., and Wadsley, A. D., *Acta Cryst.* **14**, 1245 (1961).
7. Andreini, A., *Mem. mat. fis. soc. ital. sci. (Rome)*, *Ser. 3* **14**, 75 (1907).
8. Appleman, D. E., *Acta Cryst.* **13**, 1002 (1960).
9. Aragon, F., Ruiz, J. C., and MacEwan, D. M. C., *Nature* **183**, 740 (1959).
10. Asher, R. C., *J. Inorg. & Nuclear Chem.* **10**, 238 (1959).
11. Aston, J. G., and Greyson, J., *Proc. 2nd Intern. Congr. Surface Activity, London, 1957* p. 39 (1958).
12. Baron, M., *in* "Physical Methods in Chemical Analysis" (W. G. Berl, ed.), Vol. 4, Chapter 6. Academic Press, New York, 1961.
13. Barrer, R. M., unpublished result.
14. Barrer, R. M., *Proc. Roy. Soc.* **A167**, 392 (1938).
15. Barrer, R. M., *Trans. Faraday Soc.* **40**, 555 (1944).
16. Barrer, R. M., *J. Soc. Chem. Ind. (London)* **64**, 130, 133 (1945).
17. Barrer, R. M., *J. Chem. Soc.*, p. 2158 (1948).
18. Barrer, R. M., *J. Chem. Soc.* p. 127 (1948).
19. Barrer, R. M., *Trans. Faraday Soc.* **45**, 358 (1949).
20. Barrer, R. M., *Quart. Revs. (London)* **3**, 293 (1949).
21. Barrer, R. M., *Nature* **176**, 745 (1955).
22. Barrer, R. M., *Inst. intern. chim. Solvay, 10th Conseil, Brussels, 1956* p. 1.
23. Barrer, R. M., *Trans. Brit. Ceram. Soc.* **56**, 155 (1957).
24. Barrer, R. M., *Proc. Chem. Soc.* p. 99 (1958).
25. Barrer, R. M., *in* "The Structure and Properties of Porous Materials," Proc. 10th Symposium Colston Research Soc. (D. H. Everett and F. S. Stone, eds.), p. 8. Butterworths, London, 1958.
26. Barrer, R. M., *Nature* **181**, 176 (1958).
27. Barrer, R. M., *Brit. Chem. Eng.*, **4**, 267 (1959).
28. Barrer, R. M., *Phys. and Chem. Solids* **16**, 84 (1960).
29. Barrer, R. M., Bartholomew, R. F., and Rees, L. V. C., in preparation.
30. Barrer, R. M., Baynham, J. W., *J. Chem. Soc.* p. 2882 (1956).
31. Barrer, R. M., and Baynham, J. W., *J. Chem. Soc.* p. 2892 (1956).
32. Barrer, R. M., Baynham, J. W., Bultitude, F. W., and Meier, W. M., *J. Chem. Soc.* p. 195 (1959).
33. Barrer, R. M., and Belchetz, L., *J. Soc. Chem. Ind. (London)* **64**, 131 (1945).
34. Barrer, R. M., and Bratt, G. C., *Phys. and Chem. Solids* **12**, 130 (1959).
35. Barrer, R. M., and Brook, D. W., *Trans. Faraday Soc.* **49**, 940 (1953).
36. Barrer, R. M., and Brook, D. W., *Trans. Faraday Soc.* **49**, 1049 (1953).
37. Barrer, R. M., Bultitude, F. W., and Kerr, I. S., *J. Chem. Soc.* p. 1521 (1959).

38. Barrer, R. M., Bultitude, F. W., and Sutherland, J. W., *Trans. Faraday Soc.* 53, 1111 (1957).
39. Barrer, R. M., Buser, W., and Grütter, W. F., *Helv. Chim. Acta* 39, 518 (1956).
40. Barrer, R. M., and Denny, P. J., *J. Chem. Soc.* p. 971 (1961).
41. Barrer, R. M., and Denny, P. J., *J. Chem. Soc.* p. 983 (1961).
42. Barrer, R. M., Drake, J., and Whittam, T. V., *Proc. Roy. Soc.* A219, 32 (1953).
43. Barrer, R. M., and Fender, B. E. F., *Phys. and Chem. Solids* 21, 12 (1961).
44. Barrer, R. M., and Ibbitson, D. A., *Trans. Faraday Soc.* 40, 206 (1944).
45. Barrer, R. M., and Kelsey, K., *Trans. Faraday Soc.* 57, 452 (1961).
46. Barrer, R. M., and Kelsey, K., *Trans. Faraday Soc.* 57, 625 (1961).
47. Barrer, R. M., and Kerr, I. S., *Trans. Faraday Soc.* 55, 1915 (1959).
48. Barrer, R. M., and Langley, D. A., *J. Chem. Soc.* p. 3817 (1958).
49. Barrer, R. M., and McCallum, N., *J. Chem. Soc.* p. 4029 (1953).
50. Barrer, R. M., and MacKenzie, N., *J. Phys. Chem.* 58, 568 (1954).
51. Barrer, R. M., and MacLeod, D. M., *Trans. Faraday Soc.* 50, 980 (1954).
52. Barrer, R. M., and MacLeod, D. M., *Trans. Faraday Soc.* 51, 1290 (1955).
53. Barrer, R. M., and Marshall, D. J., in preparation.
54. Barrer, R. M., and Meier, W. M., *J. Chem. Soc.* p. 299 (1958).
55. Barrer, R. M., and Meier, W. M., *Trans. Faraday Soc.* 54, 1074 (1958).
56. Barrer, R. M., and Perry, G. S., *J. Chem. Soc.* p. 842 (1961).
57. Barrer, R. M., and Perry, G. S., *J. Chem. Soc.* p. 850 (1961).
58. Barrer, R. M., and Raitt, J. S., *J. Chem. Soc.* p. 4641 (1954).
59. Barrer, R. M., and Reay, J. S. S., *Trans. Faraday Soc.* 53, 1253 (1957).
60. Barrer, R. M., and Reay, J. S. S., *J. Chem. Soc.* p. 3824 (1958).
61. Barrer, R. M., and Rees, L. V. C., *Trans. Faraday Soc.* 50, 989 (1954).
62. Barrer, R. M., and Rees, L. V. C., *Trans. Faraday Soc.* 55, 992 (1959).
63. Barrer, R. M., and Rees, L. V. C., *Trans. Faraday Soc.* 56, 709 (1960).
64. Barrer, R. M., and Rees, L. V. C., *Trans. Faraday Soc.* 57, 999 (1961).
65. Barrer, R. M., and Reucroft, P. J., *Proc. Roy. Soc.* A258, 431 (1960).
66. Barrer, R. M., and Reucroft, P. J., *Proc. Roy. Soc.* A258, 449 (1960).
67. Barrer, R. M., and Ruzicka, D. J., *Trans. Faraday Soc.* 58, 2239 (1962); Ruzicka, D. J., Ph.D. thesis, University of London, 1961.
68. Barrer, R. M., and Sammon, D. C., *J. Chem. Soc.* p. 2838 (1955).
69. Barrer, R. M., and Stuart, W. I., *Proc. Roy. Soc.* A242, 172 (1957).
70. Barrer, R. M., and Stuart, W. I., *Proc. Roy. Soc.* A249, 464 (1959).
71. Barrer, R. M., and Sutherland, J. W., *Proc. Roy. Soc.* A237, 439 (1956).
72. Barrer, R. M., and Wasilewski, S., *Trans. Faraday Soc.* 57, 1140 (1961).
73. Barrer, R. M., and Wasilewski, S., *Trans. Faraday Soc.* 57, 1153 (1961).
74. Barrer, R. M., and White, E. A., *J. Chem. Soc.* p. 1267 (1951).
75. Barrer, R. M., and White, E. A., *J. Chem. Soc.* p. 1561 (1952).
76. Baur, R., and Schwarzenbach, G., *Helv. Chim. Acta* 43, 842 (1960).
77. Beebe, R. A., Millard, B., and Cynarski, J., *J. Am. Chem. Soc.* 75, 839 (1953).
78. Beebe, R. A., and Young, D. M., *J. Phys. Chem.* 58, 93 (1954).
79. Bergerhoff, G., Baur, W. H., and Nowacki, W., *Neues Jahrb. Mineral. Monatsh.* 9, 193 (1958).

80. Bergerhoff, G., Koyama, H., and Nowacki, W., *Experientia* 12, 418 (1956).
81. Blankenship, F. F., Final O. N. R. Rept. on "Hydrates of Hydrocarbons and Hydrocarbon Derivatives" (1951).
82. Bonatti, S., *Atti soc. toscana sci. nat. pisa* 50, 14 (1942).
83. Bradley, W. F., *Am. Mineralogist* 25, 405 (1940).
84. Bradley, W. F., *J. Am. Chem. Soc.* 67, 975 (1945).
85. Brauner, K., and Preisinger, A., *Tschermak's mineral. u. petrog. Mitt.* 6, 120 (1956).
86. Breck, D. W., Eversole, W. G., Milton, R. M., Reed, T. B., and Thomas, T. L., *J. Am. Chem. Soc.* 78, 5963 (1956).
87. Brindley, G. W., "X-ray Identification and Crystal Structures of Clay Minerals," p. 89, Fig. IV. 2. Mineralogical Society, London, 1951.
88. Brindley, G. W., "X-ray Identification and Crystal Structures of Clay Minerals," p. 141, Fig. V. 3. Mineralogical Society, London, 1951.
89. Broussard, L., and Shoemaker, D. P., *J. Am. Chem. Soc.* 82, 1041 (1960).
90. Brunauer, S., "Physical Adsorption of Gases and Vapours," Chapter VI. Oxford Univ. Press, London and New York, 1945.
91. Clauss, A., and Hofmann, U., *Angew. Chem.* 68, 522 (1956).
92. Claussen, W. F., *J. Chem. Phys.* 19, 259 (1951).
93. Claussen, W. F., *J. Chem. Phys.* 19, 1425 (1951).
94. Coombs, D. S., *Am. Mineralogist* 37, 812 (1952).
95. Coombs, D. S., *Mineral. Mag.* 30, 699 (1955).
96. Coombs, D. S., Ellis, A. J., Fyfe, W. S., and Taylor, A. M., *Geochim. et Cosmochim. Acta* 17, 53 (1959).
97. Cowley, J. M., and Ibers, J. A., *Acta Cryst.* 9, 421 (1956).
98. Cramer, F., and Henglein, F. M., *Angew. Chem.* 68, 649 (1956).
99. Croft, R. C., *Australian J. Chem.* 9, 184, 194 (1956).
100. Croft, R. C., *Australian J. Chem.* 9, 201 (1956).
101. Croft, R. C., *Proc. 3rd Carbon Conf., Buffalo, New York* p. 315 (1959).
102. Croft, R. C., *Quart. Revs. (London)* 14, 1 (1960).
103. Dana, J. D., "A System of Mineralogy," 6th Ed., 1892.
104. Davy, Sir H., *Phil. Trans. Roy. Soc. London* 101, 1 (1811).
105. Deaton, W. M., and Frost, E. M., "Gas Hydrates and their Relation to the Operation of Natural-Gas Pipe Lines," Monograph 8, U.S. Bur. Mines, 1946.
106. de Boer, J. H., and Custers, J. F. H., *Z. Physik. Chem. (Leipzig)* B25, 225 (1934).
107. de Boer, J. H., and van Doorn, A. B. C., *Koninkl. Ned. Akad. Wetenschap.* B57, 181 (1954).
108. de Boer, J. H., and van Doorn, A. B. C., *Koninkl. Ned. Akad. Wetenschap.* B61, 242 (1958).
109. Dent. L. S., and Smith, J. V., *Nature* 181, 1794 (1958).
110. Drain, L. E., and Morrison, J. A., *Trans. Faraday Soc.* 48, 840 (1952).
111. Ducros, P., *Bull. soc. franç. minéral. et crist.* 83, 85 (1960).
112. Ellis, A. J., and Fyfe, W. S., *Revs. Pure and Appl. Chem. (Australia)* 7, 261 (1957).
113. Eméleus, H. J., and Anderson, J. S., "Modern Aspects of Inorganic Chemistry," p. 213. Van Nostrand, Princeton, New Jersey, 1938.

114. Emeléus, H. J., and Anderson, J. S., "Modern Aspects of Inorganic Chemistry," p. 462. Van Nostrand, Princeton, New Jersey, 1938.
115. Eucken, A., cited by von Stackelberg, M., in *Naturwissenschaften* **36**, 359 (1949).
116. Evans, D. F., and Richards, R. E., *Proc. Roy. Soc.* **A223**, 238 (1954).
117. Ewell, R. H., and Insley, H., *J. Research Natl. Bur. Standards* **15**, 173 (1935).
118. Feitknecht, W., and Blatter, F., *Chimia (Switz.)* **8**, 261 (1954).
119. Feitknecht, W., and Burki, H., *Experientia* **5**, 154 (1949).
120. Feitknecht, W., and Burki, H., *Chimia (Switz.)* **3**, 146 (1949).
121. Feitknecht, W., and Burki, H., *Helv. Chim. Acta* **39**, 564 (1956).
122. Feitknecht, W., and Burki, H., *Helv. Chim. Acta* **39**, 576, 584 (1956).
123. Feitknecht, W., and Burki, H., *Helv. Chim. Acta* **39**, 589 (1956).
124. Feitknecht, W., and Weidmann, H., *Helv. Chim. Acta* **26**, 1560, 1564, 1911 (1943).
125. Fischer, K., and Kuzel, H., *Naturwissenschaften* **45**, 488 (1958).
126. Flint, E., Clarke, W., Newman, E. S., Shartsis, L., Bishop, D., and Wells, L. S., *J. Research Natl. Bur. Standards* **36**, 63 (1946).
127. Fowler, D. L., Loebenstein, W. V., Pall, D. B., and Kruas, C. A., *J. Am. Chem. Soc.* **62**, 1140 (1940).
128. Franzen, P., *Clay Minerals Bull.* **2**, 223 (1954).
129. Fredenhagen, K., and Cadenbach, G., *Z. anorg. u. allgem. Chem.* **158**, 249 (1926).
130. Fredenhagen, K., and Suck, M., *Z. anorg. u. allgem. Chem.* **178**, 353 (1929).
131. Garden, L., and Kington, G. L., *Proc. Roy. Soc.* **A234**, 24 (1956).
132. Garden, L., and Kington, G. L., *Trans. Faraday Soc.* **52**, 1397 (1956).
133. Garden, L., Kington G. L., and Laing, W., *Trans. Faraday Soc.* **51**, 1558 (1955).
134. Garden, L., Kington, G. L., and Laing, W., *Proc. Roy. Soc.* **A234**, 35 (1956).
135. Gee, G., *Trans. Faraday Soc.* **38**, 418 (1942).
136. Glew, D. N., *Can. J. Chem.* **38**, 208 (1960).
137. Goldsmith, J. R., *Mineral. Mag.* **29**, 952 (1952).
138. Greene-Kelly, R., *Trans. Faraday Soc.* **51**, 412 (1955).
139. Gruner, J. W., *Econ. Geol.* **39**, 578 (1944).
140. Habgood, H. W., *Can. J. Chem.* **36**, 1384 (1958).
141. Hammerschmidt, E. G., *Am. Gas Assoc. Monthly* **18**, 273 (1936).
142. Hardt, H. D., *Z. anorg. u. allgem. Chem.* **286**, 254 (1956).
143. Harris, P. G., and Brindley, G. W., *Am. Mineralogist* **39**, 819 (1954).
144. Hartley, G. S., and Crank, J., *Trans. Faraday Soc.* **45**, 801 (1949).
145. Hennig, G. R., *J. Chem. Phys.* **20**, 1438, 1443 (1952).
146. Hennig, G. R., *in* "Progress in Inorganic Chemistry" (F. A. Cotton, ed.), Vol. 1, pp. 127-205. Wiley (Interscience), New York, 1959.
147. Hey, M. H., and Bannister, F. A., *Mineral. Mag.* **23**, 51 (1932).
148. Hey, M. H., and Bannister, F. A., *Mineral. Mag.* **23**, 305 (1933).
149. Hey, M. H., and Bannister, F. A., *Mineral. Mag.* **23**, 421 (1933).
150. Hirschfelder, J. O., Buehler, R. J., McGee, H. A., Jr., and Sutton, J. R., *Ind. Eng. Chem.* **50**, 375 (1958).

151. Hirschfelder, J. O., Curtiss, C. F., and Bird, R. B., "Molecular Theory of Gases and Liquids," p. 293. Wiley, New York, 1954.
152. Hooley, J. G., *Can. J. Chem.* 37, 899 (1959).
153. Hooley, J. G., private communication.
154. Hooley, J. G., *Can. J. Chem.* 40, 745 (1962).
155. Hooley, J. G., private communication. (See also reference 154.)
156. Jaeger, F. M., *Trans. Faraday Soc.* 25, 320 (1929).
157. Jeffrey, G. A., Feil, D., McMullan, R., paper presented at *Symposium of Div. of Physical Chem., Am. Chem. Soc., Seattle, Washington, June, 1960.*
158. Juza, R., and Schmeckenberger, A., *Z. anorg. u. allgem. Chem.* 292, 46 (1957).
159. Kamb, W. B., and Oke, W. C., *Am. Mineralogist* 45, 79 (1960).
160. Katz, J. R., *Ergeb. exakt. Naturw.* 3, 323, 324, 333, 378, 393 (1924).
161. Kemula, W., and Sybilska, D., *Nature* 185, 237 (1960).
162. Kihara, Y., Ohta, H., and Tsumaki, T., *Mem. Fac. Sci. Kyushu Univ.* C3, 137 (1960).
163. Kington, G. L., and Laing, W., *Trans. Faraday Soc.* 51, 287 (1955).
164. Kington, G. L., and McLeod, A. C., *Trans. Faraday Soc.* 55, 1799 (1959).
165. Kirkwood, J. G., *Physik. Z.* 33, 57 (1932).
166. Koizumi, M., and Roy, R., *Am. Mineralogist* 44, 788 (1959).
167. Lacher, J. R., *Proc. Cambridge Phil. Soc.* 33, 518 (1937).
168. Lange, W., *Z. anorg. u. allgem. Chem.* 219, 305 (1934).
169. Lange, W., and Lewin, G., *Chem. Ber.* B63, 2156 (1930).
170. Lange, W., and von Krueger, G., *Z. anorg. u. allgem. Chem.* 216, 49 (1933).
171. Lawton, D., and Powell, H. M., *J. Chem. Soc.* p. 2339 (1958).
172. Lennard-Jones, J. E., and Devonshire, A. F., *Proc. Roy. Soc.* A163, 53 (1937); A165, 1 (1938).
173. London, F., *Z. physik Chem. (Leipzig)* B11, 222 (1930).
174. Loewenstein, W., *Am. Mineralogist* 39, 92 (1954).
175. McBain, J. W., "The Sorption of Gases and Vapours by Solids," p. 168. Routledge, London, 1932.
176. McMullan, R., and Jeffrey, G. A., *J. Chem. Phys.* 31, 1231 (1959).
177. Mair, B. J., and Shamaiengar, M., *Anal. Chem.* 30, 276 (1958).
178. Meier, W. M., *Z. Krist.* 113, 430 (1960).
179. Meier, W. M., *Z. Krist.* 115, 439 (1961).
180. Meier, W. M., private communication.
181. Morey, G. W., and Ingerson, E., *Econ. Geol.* 32, 607 (1937).
182. Morowicz, J., *Tschermak's mineral. u. petrog. Mitt.* 18, 20 (1899).
183. Mulders, E. M. J., Ph.D. thesis, University of Delft, Netherlands, 1937.
184. Müller, A., *Proc. Roy. Soc.* A154, 624 (1936).
185. Müller, H. R., and von Stackelberg, M., *Naturwissenschaften* 39, 20 (1952).
186. Nagy, B., and Bradley, W. F., *Am. Mineralogist* 40, 885 (1955).
187. Nelson, E. T., and Walker, P. L., Jr., *J. Appl. Chem. (London)* 11, 358 (1961).
188. Nithollon, P., *Publs. sci. et tech. ministère l'air,* No. N.T. 53 (1955).
189. Noll, W., *Centr. Mineral. Geol.* p. 80 (1934).
190. Noll, W., *Mineral. u. petrog. Mitt.* 45, 175 (1934); 48, 210 (1936).
191. Noll, W., *Neues Jahrb. Mineral. Geol. Beilage Bd.* A70, 65 (1935).

192. Noll, W., *Chem. Erde* 10, 129 (1936).
193. Norrish, K., *Discussions Faraday Soc. No.* 18, 120 (1954).
194. Norton, F. H., *Am. Mineralogist* 22, 1 (1937) ; 24, 1 (1939); 26, 1 (1941).
195. Nowacki, W., Aellen, M., and Koyama, H., *Schweiz. mineral. petrog. Mitt.* 38, 53 (1958).
196. Nowacki, W., Koyuma, H., and Mladeck, M. H., *Experientia* 14, 396 (1958).
197. Osterlof, J., *Acta Chem. Scand.* 4, 374 (1950).
198. Palin, D. E., and Wadsworth, K. D., *Nature* 162, 925 (1948).
199. Pauling, L., *Proc. Nat. Acad. Sci. U. S.* 16, 453 (1930).
200. Pauling, L., "The Nature of the Chemical Bond," p. 257. Cornell Univ. Press, Ithaca, New York, 1960.
201. Pauling, L., and Marsh, R. E., *Proc. Natl. Acad. Sci. U. S.* 38, 112 (1952).
202. Pemsler, P., Ph.D. thesis, University of New York, 1954; *Dissertation Abstr.* 18, 2005 (1958).
203. Peria, W. T., *Bull. Am. Phys. Soc.* 3, 230 (1958).
204. Platteeuw, J. C., *Rec. trav. chim.* 77, 403 (1958).
205. Platteeuw, J. C., and van der Waals, J. H., *Mol. Phys.* 1, 91 (1958).
206. Powell, H. M., *J. Chem. Soc.* p. 61 (1948).
207. Powell, H. M., and Bartindale, G W. R., *J. Chem. Soc.* p. 799 (1945).
208. Powell, H. M., and Rayner, J. H., *Nature* 163, 566 (1949).
209. Rayner, J. H., and Powell, H. M., *J. Chem. Soc.* p. 3412 (1958).
210. Reed, T. B., and Breck, D. W., *J. Am. Chem. Soc.* 78, 5972 (1956).
211. Regis, A. J., Sand, L. B., Calmon, C., and Gilwood, M. E., *J. Phys. Chem.* 64, 1567 (1960).
212. Reyerson, L. H., Wertz, J. E., Weltner, W., and Whitehurst, H., *J. Phys. Chem.* 61, 1334 (1957).
213. Rideal, Sir Eric K., "Surface Chemistry," Chapter III. Cambridge Univ. Press, London and New York, 1930.
214. Roy, R., and Sand, L. B., *Am. Mineralogist* 41, 505 (1956).
215. Rüdorff, W., *Z. physik. Chem. (Leipzig)* B45, 42, 174 (1939).
216. Rüdorff, W., *Z. anorg. u. allgem. Chem.* 245, 383 (1941).
217. Rüdorff, W., *Advances in Inorg. Chem. and Radiochem.* 1, 223 (1959).
218. Rüdorff, W., and Hofmann, U., *Z. anorg. u. allgem. Chem.* 238, 1 (1938).
219. Rüdorff, W., and Landel, A., *Z. anorg. u. allgem. Chem.* 293, 327 (1958).
220. Rüdorff, W., and Rüdorff, G., *Chem. Ber.* 80, 417 (1947).
221. Rüdorff, W., and Schulz, H., *Z. anorg. u. allgem. Chem.* 245, 121 (1940).
222. Rüdorff, W., and Schulze, E., *Z. anorg. u. allgem. Chem.* 277, 156 (1954).
223. Rüdorff, W., Schulze, E., and Rubisch, O., *Z. anorg. u. allgem. Chem.* 282, 232 (1955).
224. Rüdorff, W., and Sick, H. H., *Angew. Chem.* 71, 127 (1959).
225. Rüdorff, W., Sils, V., and Zeller, R., *Z. anorg. u. allgem. Chem.* 283, 299 (1956).
226. Rüdorff, W., and Stumpp, E., *Z. Naturforsch.* 13b, 459 (1958).
227. Rüdorff, W., and Zeller, R., *Z. anorg. u. allgem. Chem.* 279, 182 (1955).
228. Ruff, O., and Bretschneider, O., *Z. anorg. u. allgem. Chem.* 217, 1 (1934).
229. Sadanaga, R., Marumo, F., and Takeuchi, Y., *Acta Cryst.* 13, 1003 (1960); 14, 1153 (1961).

230. Sakurai, K., and Hayashi, A., *Sci. Repts. Yokohama Natl. Univ. Sect. II* **1**, 69 (1952).

231. Schaeffer, W. D., Dorsey, W. S., Skinner, D. A., and Christian, C. G., *J. Am. Chem. Soc.* **79**, 5870 (1957).

232. Schleede, A., and Wellmann, M., *Z. physik. Chem. (Leipzig)* **B18**, 1 (1932).

233. Schiebold, E., and Seumel, G., *Z. Krist.* **81**, 110 (1932).

234. Schwarz, Robert, and Trageser, G., *Naturwissenschaften* **23**, 512 (1935).

235. Sekanina, J., and Wyart, J., *Bull. soc. franç. minéral.* **60**, 139 (1937).

236. Smith, J. V., *Conf. on Zeolites, Penn. State Univ.* 1959.

237. Staples, L. W., *Am. Mineralogist* **40**, 1095 (1955).

238. Staples, L. W., and Gard, J. A., *Mineral. Mag.* **32**, 261 (1959).

239. Staudenmaier, L., *Chem. Ber.* **31**, 1481 (1898).

240. Strunz, H., *Neues Jahrb. Mineral. Monatsch.* **5**, 116 (1957).

241. Strunz, H., and Tennyson, C., *Neues Jahrb. Mineral. Monatsh.* **1**, 1 (1956).

242. Talibudeen, O., *Trans. Faraday Soc.* **51**, 582 (1955).

243. Tammann, G., *Ann. Physik.* [3] **63**, 16 (1897).

244. Taylor, H. F. W., *J. Chem. Soc.* p. 1253 (1949).

245. Taylor, W. H., *Z. Krist.* **74**, 1 (1930).

246. Taylor, W. H., *Proc. Roy. Soc.* **A145**, 80 (1934).

247. Taylor, W. H., and Jackson, R., *Z. Krist.* **86**, 53 (1933).

248. Taylor, W. H., Meek, C. A., and Jackson, W. W., *Z. Krist.* **84**, 373 (1933).

249. Thiele, H., *Z. anorg. u. allgem. Chem.* **206**, 407 (1932).

250. Thomas, T. L., and Mays, R. L., in "Physical Methods in Chemical Analysis," (W. G. Berl, ed.), Vol. 4, Chapter 2. Academic Press, New York, 1961.

251. Tiselius, A., *Z. physik. Chem. (Leipzig)* **A169**, 425 (1934).

252. Tsumaki, T., Yoshiura, H., and Fukada, N., *Memo. Fac. Sci. Kyushu Univ.* **C3**, 143 (1960).

253. Ubbelohde, A. R., *Nature* **180**, 380 (1957).

254. Ubbelohde, A. R., and Lewis, F. A., "Graphite and its Crystal Compounds," Chapter 8. Oxford Univ. Press, London and New York, 1960.

255. Ubbelohde, A. R., and Lewis, F. A., "Graphite and its Crystal Compounds," Fig. 35. Oxford Univ. Press, London and New York, 1960; after Herold, A., *Bull. soc. chim. France* 999 (1955).

256. Ubbelohde, A. R., and Lewis, F. A., "Graphite and its Crystal Compounds," Fig. 39 and Fig. 42. Oxford Univ. Press, London and New York, 1960.

257. van Cleeff, A., and Diepen, G. A. M., *Rec. trav. chim.* **79**, 582 (1960).

258. van Nieuwenberg, C. J., and Pieters, H. A. J., *Rec. trav. chim.* **48**, 27 (1929).

259. van der Waals, J. H., *Trans. Faraday Soc.* **52**, 184 (1956).

260. van der Waals, J. H., and Platteeuw, J. C., *Advances in Chem. Phys.* **2**, 1 (1959).

261. Ventriglia, U., *Periodico mineral. (Rome)* **24**, 49 (1955).

262. Verwey, E. J., and Overbeek, J. T., "Theory of Stability of Lyophobic Colloids." Elsevier, Amsterdam, 1948.

263. Villard, M. P., *Ann. chim. et phys.* **11**, 289 (1897).

264. von Stackelberg, M., *Naturwissenschaften* **36**, 327, 359 (1949).

265. von Stackelberg, M., and Jahns, W., *Z. Elektrochem.* **58**, 162 (1954).

266. von Stackelberg, M., and Meinhold, W., *Z. Elektrochem.* **58**, 40 (1954).
267. von Stackelberg, M., and Meuthen, B., *Z. Elektrochem.* **62**, 130 (1958).
268. von Stackelberg, M., and Müller, H. R., *Naturwiss.* **38**, 456 (1951).
269. von Stackelberg, M., and Müller, H. R., *J. Chem. Phys.* **19**, 1319 (1951).
270. von Stackelberg, M., and Müller, H. R., *Z. Elektrochem.* **58**, 25 (1954).
271. Walker, G. F., *Nature* **187**, 312 (1960).
272. Walker, G. F., and Milne, A., *Trans. 4th Intern. Congr. Soil Sci., Amsterdam, 1950* Vol. 2, p. 62 (1950).
273. Walker, G. P. L., *Mineral. Mag.* **33**, 173 (1962).
274. Waller, J. G., *Nature* **186**, 429 (1960).
275. Waymouth, C., Thornley, P. C., and Taylor, W. H., *Mineral. Mag.* **25**, 212 (1938).
276. Weiss, A., *Chem. Ber.* **91**, 487 (1958).
277. Weiss, A., *Z. anorg. u. allgem. Chem.* **297**, 17 (1958).
278. Weiss, A., *Z. anorg. u. allgem. Chem.* **297**, 232 (1958).
279. Weiss, A., Hartl, K., and Hofmann, U., *Z. Naturforsch.* **12b**, 351 (1957).
280. Weiss, A., Hartl, K., and Hofmann, U., *Z. Naturforsch.* **12b**, 669 (1957).
281. Weiss, A., Mehler, A., and Hofmann, U., *Z. Naturforsch.* **11b**, 431 (1956).
282. Weiss, A., and Michel, E., *Z. anorg. u. allgem. Chem.* **296**, 313 (1958).
283. Weiss, A., and Michel, E., *Z. anorg. u. allgem. Chem.* **306**, 277 (1960).
284. Weiss, A., and Michel, E., *Z. Naturforsch.* **15b**, 679 (1960).
285. Weiss, A., and Weiss, A., *Z. anorg. u. allgem. Chem.* **282**, 324 (1955).
286. Weiss, A., and Weiss, A., *Angew. Chem.* **72**, 413 (1960).
287. Weiss, A., Weiss, A., and Hofmann, U., *Z. anorg. u. allgem. Chem.* **273**, 129 (1953).
288. Wells, A. F., "The Third Dimension in Chemistry," Chapter 3. Oxford Univ. Press, London and New York, 1956.
289. White, E. A. D., *Quart. Revs. (London)* **15**, 1 (1961).
290. Wyart, J., and Chatelain, P., *Bull. soc. franç. minéral.* **61**, 121 (1938).

CHAPTER 7

H. M. Powell
Chemical Crystallography Laboratory,
Oxford University, England

Clathrates

I. Molecular Imprisonment.................................... 438
II. Early Observations on Clathrates........................... 439
III. Crystal Structures of Clathrates........................... 450
   A. Bonds of One Type Only................................ 450
   B. Bonds of Two Kinds: Covalent and Other Bonds............ 454
   C. Bonding of Three Kinds—Covalent Bonds and Hydrogen Bonds
      Combined with van der Waals Bonds.................... 480
   D. Bonds of Four Kinds—van der Waals Bonds Combined with
      Ionic, Covalent, and Hydrogen Bonds.................... 482
IV. Equilibrium Relationships and Non-Stoichiometry in Clathrates... 484
   References... 489

I. MOLECULAR IMPRISONMENT

The term *clathrate compound* was introduced to describe (*24*) a particular form of molecular compound in which one component formed a cage structure imprisoning the other. In 1947 the crystal structure of the molecular compound (*20*) formed by hydroquinone and sulfur dioxide became known. It was found that molecules of hydroquinone (I) are joined

$$HO—\langle\bigcirc\rangle—OH$$

(I)

to each other by hydrogen bonds, two acting through each oxygen atom, in such a way as to form two indefinitely extended three-dimensional networks which interpenetrate and make multiple enclosures of each other.

438

This double network of hydroquinone molecules (Fig. 3) acts as a series of cages, each of which is able to contain a sulfur dioxide molecule. At normal temperature the sulfur dioxide is retained in a manner that, previous to the elucidation of the structure, seemed surprising in view of its volatility. The particular structure of a double network is not essential to or characteristic of clathrates in general, but retention of very volatile components in this way is a sign of some form of imprisoning action and hence is a guide to the discovery of clathrates.

II. EARLY OBSERVATIONS ON CLATHRATES

1. HYDROQUINONE CLATHRATES

The sulfur dioxide compound itself was discovered nearly a century earlier (6) as a result of experiments on the preparation of hydroquinone by reduction of an aqueous solution of benzoquinone with sulfur dioxide. The composition was given as $3C_6H_4(OH)_2 \cdot SO_2$ and perhaps the first contribution to an understanding of its nature is to be found in the report that a detectable smell of sulfur dioxide resulted when the crystals were ground in a mortar. The quantity of gas that might be liberated from the opening of cages by mere subdivision during the grinding process may be estimated, and seems to be enough for the very sensitive smell test; but it is hardly possible to eliminate ordinary inclusions or decomposition by local heating as alternative sources. Even earlier, in 1849, Wöhler (35) had prepared the clathrate compound of hydroquinone with hydrogen sulfide. He reported two compounds: $4C_6H_4(OH)_2 \cdot H_2S$, and $3C_6H_4(OH)_2 \cdot H_2S$. At the time chemical theory naturally led an investigator to express the composition by the ratio of hydroquinone molecules to a single gas molecule. There was nothing to suggest that the hydroquinone content ought to be shown as fixed at three molecules, even if this resulted in a fractional number of the other molecule. This inclination to make an integer of the smallest subscript number in a chemical formula may have played a part in misdirecting thought and perhaps in discouraging further attention to these compounds which looked the more strange for every success in the unravelling of other chemical structures. Although these substances were not ordinary mixtures, and had some properties, e.g. crystalline form, different from those of the components, they could not be formulated in a chemically acceptable way. Clearly they did not obey some of the rules as then understood. Later observations confirmed this. Several other crystalline compounds of hydroquinone with normally gaseous or volatile substances were discovered but analysis did not reveal a constant molecular ratio of hydroquinone to the second component. The substances that combined in this way with hydroquinone seemed chemically unlikely to do so, or, if they did by some conceivable reaction, would have given products of different compositions and different properties. They include HCN, HCO₂H, HCl, and HBr. The compound with methanol was prepared and examined several times and even survived an early x-ray diffraction study without the presence of a component other than hydroquinone being suspected. It was described as β-hydroquinone. Had its methanol been detected and estimated the ratio 3:1 of molecules would have been found.

The history of this series of compounds shows that accurate analysis might have led to understanding as complete as would be possible without direct means of crystal structure determination. Some experiments of Mylius (17) are of special interest in this respect. He was attempting to prepare formyl derivatives of hydroquinone by heating formic acid and hydroquinone together in a sealed tube but obtained instead a crystalline product of remarkable properties. On solution in cold water or other solvent it liberated carbon monoxide, and hydroquinone could be recovered from the solution. It melted at 170°, also with liberation of carbon monoxide. However this is not simply a compound of hydroquinone and carbon monoxide since it contains some formic acid. Formic acid itself gives a clathrate compound with hydroquinone, and carbon monoxide is produced by decomposition of formic acid in the conditions used, but, perversely as it seemed, the compound could not be obtained when the mixture of formic acid and hydroquinone was heated in the same way but in an apparatus provided with an attachment to absorb the water resulting from decomposition of the formic acid. Mylius prepared and analyzed several samples. He found a variable carbon content, but hydrogen did not vary in a systematic way with the carbon percentage. His estimates of carbon monoxide and formic acid content can be understood if the hydroquinone clathrates are recognized as crystals which are nonstoichiometric because some of the sites for the volatile component may be vacant. In 1886 Mylius came near to an explanation when he supposed that somehow hydroquinone could retain carbon monoxide without combining with it. His analytical figure can all be explained now that it is known that hydroquinone traps the other molecules, each in a separate cage, and that the regularity of the crystal structure results in one cage for every three hydroquinone molecules. Table I, which includes later results, shows compositions of hydroquinone clathrates. The molecular ratio M/3Q, Q = hydroquinone, may approach the "ideal" value 1.0, corresponding to every available cage being occupied; it never exceeds this value and sometimes is much lower. When the clathrate is formed

TABLE I

OBSERVED COMPOSITIONS OF SOME β-HYDROQUINONE CLATHRATES OF IDEAL
MOLECULAR RATIO M/3Q (Q = HYDROQUINONE)[a]

M	Molecular ratio M/3Q
HCl	0.85
HBr	0.36
H_2S	0.64
CH_3OH	0.97
HCO_2H	0.82
SO_2	0.88
CO_2	0.74
CH_3CN	0.99
Ar	0.3–0.85
Kr	0.74
Xe	0.84

[a] Those ratios not close to 1.0 are in general variable according to conditions of preparation.

by simple recrystallization of hydroquinone from the second component used as a solvent, e.g. when the second component is methanol or methyl cyanide, there is a high concentration of solvent molecules available for enclosure. In these conditions nearly all the cavities become occupied. Most of the other substances listed are prepared from a solvent which dissolves both components and is itself not enclosed in the hydroquinone structure. In these conditions an enclosable molecule is evidently not always available at the instant when the cage is closed.

2. POSSIBLE RECOGNITION OF OTHER CLATHRATES

Before the structural characterization of the β-hydroquinone clathrates observations had been made on a large number of molecular compounds, some of which are of the clathrate type; it was not a simple matter to distinguish them and, in fact, they were not recognized. Although they are all potentially non-stoichiometric, many preserve a simple ratio of component molecules. The molecular ratio, if fixed, may have a value, such as the 3:1 of the hydroquinone compounds, that is determined basically by geometry. This might distinguish clathrates from some other molecular compounds in which a specific interaction of the molecules favors a simple ratio more closely related to the simple ratios that result when new chemical bonds are formed. The interactions between molecules of aromatic polynitro compounds and other aromatic systems result in formation of a large number of crystalline molecular compounds of 1:1 formula. In these the two different molecules are roughly of the same size. If several molecules are required to form one clathrate cage the molecular ratio will be higher. Even an enclosing component (*host*) which has the larger molecule is likely to be present in a ratio greater than 1. The smaller the enclosing molecules the greater the number required to enclose a given volume of space for the second component (*guest*). Study of compositions, expecially when a series of related compounds is available, may therefore provide evidence of clathrate formation, but although clathrates may be suspected they cannot, however, be distinguished from all other types of molecular compounds by any simple test based only on composition, whether stoichiometric or not. The retention of a volatile component, in the absence of some form of chemical bonding, is good supporting evidence, but the second component need not, in every case, be volatile. The following sections deal with early observations on some of the substances which are now known or suspected to form either clathrates or related molecular compounds.

3. Dianin's Compound, 4-*p*-Hydroxyphenyl-2,2,4-Trimethyl-chroman

In 1914 Dianin (*9*) prepared a substance later shown to have the struc-

(II)

ture shown (II). When attempts were made to crystallize it the product usually contained solvent. Analyses were given for adducts with diethyl ether (8:1), ethyl alcohol (4:1), acetone (4:1), acetic acid (4:1), and chloroform (4:1). All these compounds were stated by Dianin to crystallize as very stable crystals, which he supposed to be isomorphous. He commented on their great "durability" and noticed that they decompose only in the neighborhood of the fairly high melting point. The melting point of the ether compound was given as 171—172°C. This behavior suggests clathrate formation. The chroman appears to combine with other substances simply by crystallization from them as solvents. There is no chemical reason to expect such combination and the combining ratios of the two molecular components are not related to any likely reactions that might occur between them. Both the chroman and the solvents can be recovered from the "compounds," but direct removal of the solvent, e.g. by heating, is more difficult than would be expected from a simple agglomerate in the crystal of the chroman and the molecule of the more volatile solvent, without an imprisoning action.

4. Nickel Cyanide Ammine, $Ni(CN)_2 \cdot NH_3$

Solutions containing ammonia and the ions that could combine to form nickel(II) cyanide, slowly deposit powdery material of composition $Ni(CN)_2 \cdot NH_3 \cdot xH_2O$. Various values have been reported for x between 4.0 and 0.25. Hofmann and Küsper (14) showed in 1897 that such a solution when shaken with benzene quickly deposits a solid of composition $Ni(CN)_2 \cdot NH_3 \cdot C_6H_6$. Similar compounds were formed by some other aromatic substances such as pyrrole, furan, thiophene, pyridine, phenol, and aniline. The comparatively small molecular volumes of these aromatic substances were noticed a few years later by Hofmann and Arnoldi (13) who stated that fluorobenzene and other aromatic compounds of molecular volumes above a certain value do not give similar compounds. The benzene was very firmly retained, there being no detectable pressure at room temperature. Some of it could be removed by repeated washing with ether and it was evolved when the compound was heated to 120°.

This compound is of sufficiently constant and stoichiometric composition to have been used for the quantitative estimation of benzene. Attempts were made to devise chemical formulas based on the introduction of benzene into the coordination sphere of the nickel atom. However, the early recognition of molecular volume rather than aromatic character as the controlling factor strongly suggested clathrate formation to later workers and led directly to a structural examination.

5. Gas Hydrates

Many gases and easily volatile liquids are known to form solid hydrates. Most of these have become known since about 1890. They were at one time thought to have the formula $6H_2O \cdot M$ but there were difficulties of analysis due to the ready decomposition of these substances and this constancy of composition was never firmly established or left unquestioned. However, whether of this fixed molecular ratio or not, they showed a constant characteristic, that of crystallization in cubic forms easily recognized by their optical isotropy. Substances forming hydrates of this kind are of diverse chemical character. They may be described generally as hydrophobic, not liable to strong interaction with water, e.g. by hydrogen bonding. They include saturated and unsaturated hydrocarbons, chlorine, carbon tetrafluoride, halogen substituted derivatives of methane and ethane, and the inert gases argon, krypton, and xenon. Size and shape of molecule rather than chemical character determines whether a given substance forms a gas hydrate. Methane, ethane, propane, and isopropane form hydrates but higher homologues do not. 1,2-Dichloroethane which has an extended form does not give a hydrate although its more compact isomer 1,1-dichloroethane does so. The upper limit of size compatible with hydrate formation is represented by a molecular volume of about 85 cm³ in the liquid state. That molecular shape is important is shown by the failure of n-butane, in contrast to isobutane, to form a simple hydrate. These influences and the compositions all suggest that there is a structure of the clathrate type in which the hydrated molecule must be of suitable size to occupy some sort of cavity formed by water molecules. This is confirmed by the rough measure of stability provided by dissociation pressures. The xenon, krypton, and argon hydrates have at 0° respective pressures of 1.15, 14.5, and 105 atm (see Chapter 6, Section VIII, B, 1). These pressures increase markedly as the atomic diameter of the inert gas decreases, and some substances, such as hydrogen, of very small molecular dimensions do not give hydrates. The inference is, that, as with the hydroquinone clathrates, very small dimensions are unfavorable since an imprisoning action depends on a sufficient size of imprisoned molecule in relation to possible escape holes in the surrounding cage structure.

A further significant characteristic is the formation of hydrates which contain inert molecules of two different kinds. It is related to another factor. The gas hydrates are cubic crystals, and their water molecules must therefore be arranged in a way different from that of ordinary hexagonal ice. They must provide cavities for the hydrate formers and it might be supposed that the hydrate *ice* with empty cavities would be less dense and less stable than normal ice. There is in practice a close similarity to the behavior of hydroquinone. Normally the loose *ice* structure does not form in the absence of hydrate formers, just as normally the β-hydroquinone imprisoning lattice, although capable of independent existence, does not form in the absence of molecules suitable for clathrate formation. Instead the denser α-hydroquinone is formed. It is not the invariable rule (see under Dianin's chroman Section II, 3), but sometimes an imprisoning structure forms only when there are molecules to be imprisoned. Although the degree of attachment of an inert occupant to the cage former appears greater than is attributable to any attractive interaction, some interaction of this kind is necessary for the stable existence of the imprisoning structure. In some of the gas hydrates this factor requires the presence of two different kinds of included molecule. Not only can two different molecules be enclosed but the two kinds are essential for formation of a hydrate in which all components play a characteristic part. Examples are $17H_2O \cdot CHF_2CH_2 \cdot 2H_2S$ and $17H_2O \cdot CHCl_3 \cdot 2Xe$. Chloroform itself gives a hydrate $17H_2O \cdot CHCl_3$, but with water alone 1,1-difluorethane forms a 12:1 hydrate. A relevant observation is that the decomposition temperature of the chloroform hydrate is increased by the presence of the xenon. It was noticed also almost as soon as hydrates of this type were known that their stability was increased by a high pressure of the surrounding air. The effect seems to have been misunderstood at the time. It has more recently been noticed that, when suitably prepared in presence of air, many hydrates of liquids, e.g. bromine or chloroform, contain large quantities of air which is liberated when they decompose. These third component molecules of the structure are smaller than the hydrating chloroform or other molecules and from this it may be supposed that the hydrate structure contains cavities of two kinds, one set for the smaller and the other for the larger included molecules. Further, this structure can sometimes exist without the small molecules, but for some molecules, such as the difluorethane described, is only stabilized when the small molecules are also present.

6. COMPOUNDS OF PHENOL WITH VOLATILE SUBSTANCES

Terres and Volmer (32) established from the phase diagram that phenol and hydrogen sulfide form a compound. Later Nikitin and others (19) established more firmly that the composition is $3C_6H_5OH \cdot H_2S$. He also showed that (18) similar compounds are formed by a series of gases including HCl, HBr, CO_2, CH_3Br, CH_2Cl_2, and the inert gases argon and xenon. This behavior strongly suggests the formation of some kind of inclusion compound in which phenol molecules form the cage. The molecular ratio 3:1, or thereabouts, has no apparent explanation on the basis of electronic rearrangements such as lead to ordinary chemical combination. The molecules that associate with phenol are all rather small and some of them are chemically very inert. It has also been reported that when the included molecule is CS_2 there may be simultaneous inclusion of air, a phenomenon that recalls the behavior of the liquid hydrates (Section II, 5).

7. TRI-o-THYMOTIDE

The substance of composition $C_{33}H_{36}O_6$ and structure (III) was pre-

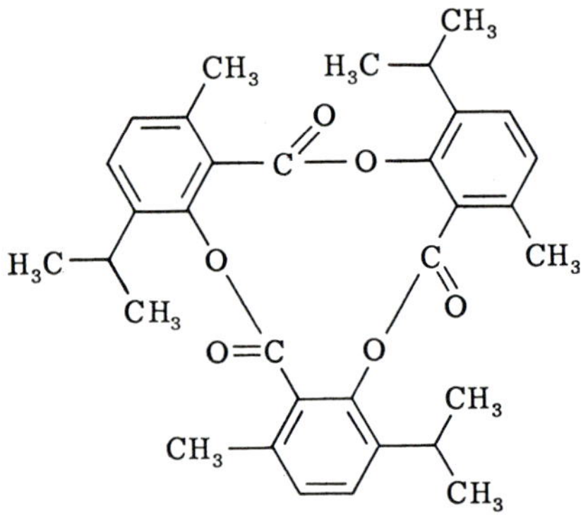

(III)

pared in 1909 by dehydration of thymotic acid (30). Its calculated molecular weight is 528.6. Di-o-thymotide (IV) obtained by the same procedure is indistinguishable from it by ordinary quantitative analysis but has a

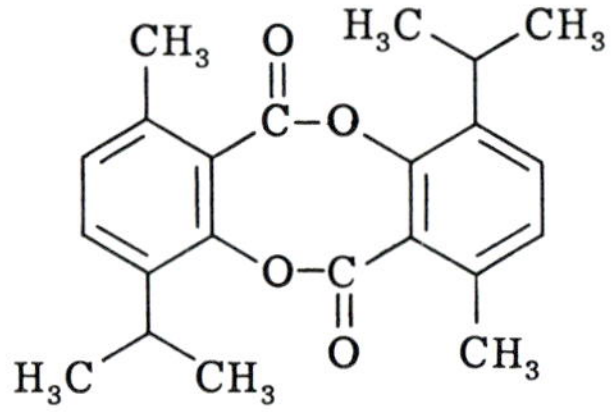

(IV)

molecular weight of 352.4. The original discoverers crystallized tri-o-thymotide from benzene. They obtained, unknown to themselves, crystals of a clathrate of composition $2C_{33}H_{36}O_6 \cdot C_6H_6$. As measured by its effect on the freezing point of a solvent other than benzene this crystalline substance will have an apparent molecular weight of 345.1 equal to one third of the formula weight. There is an accidental closeness to the molecular weight of di-o-thymotide and thus the formation of tri-o-thymotide was not recognized until many years later when Baker and co-workers (2) reinvestigated these substances.

The original failure to recognize a molecular compound (clathrates were not known as such at the time) is instructive. Addition of C_6H_6 to $2C_{33}$-$H_{36}O_6$ changes the weight ratio of carbon to hydrogen only from 10.9 to 10.98. The percentage weight of carbon changes only from 75.0 to 76.1. In view of the misleading molecular weight results it is therefore not surprising that the mistake was made. How such an error might now be easily avoided is considered because non-stoichiometric clathrates provide some difficult problems of the same kind. It is in the nature of clathrates that the enclosed molecule can be varied within limits which relate to dimensions rather than to weights. Any cage which forms around one kind of molecule will about as readily form around other available molecules of suitable dimensions. The solvent used for recrystallization is always present in high concentration and the solubility is itself evidence of interaction that must favor enclosure. It may happen therefore that a substance is obtained from a variety of common solvents in the form of solvent-enclosing clathrates, and that solvent-free material is obtainable only when specially selected solvents or conditions are used. Many organic solvents, e.g. alcohols of low molecular weight, might be substituted for benzene in the tri-o-thymotide cage without great apparent change in properties of the crystalline substance. Any of these might equally have passed for di-o-thymotide as a result of element analysis and molecular weight determination by freezing point depression. They all will have no appreciable vapor pressure at room temperature and no other readily noticed signs of the solvent. The error is avoidable by a more certain determination of molecular weight. If the material to be examined is recrystallized from the solvent used in the molecular weight measurement, formation of a solvent clathrate will affect the result only to the extent that the weight of solute used is in error by the weight of unsuspected solvent enclosed. This has the effect of raising the apparent molecular weight to equal the formula weight calculated on the basis of a single molecule of the enclosing substance. In the case of the benzene tri-o-thymotide clathrate $C_{33}H_{36}O_6 \cdot \frac{1}{2}C_6H_6$ the apparent molecular weight would then be about 7% high. If a series of solvents is used in this way, the molecular weight should always appear high and will tend to be higher the higher the molecular weight of the solvent itself. The exact behavior will depend on whether the compounds are stoichiometric and all of the same molecular ratio. Also the molecular weight determined in a different solvent will usually appear to be very much less than its true value. If the weight of enclosed material—usually a few per cent only—is, as a first approximation, neglected, the apparent molecular weight in a clathrate of composition C_nS, C = cage-forming molecule, S = solvent, will appear to be about $n/(n + 1)$ of the true molecular weight of C.

Determination of the density of the crystal and its unit cell dimensions gives a reliable value for the weight of the unit cell contents. Normally this may be directly related to the weight of a single molecule of the substance that has been crystallized, and any surplus weight due to the presence of enclosed solvent molecules is both revealed and determined quantitatively.

8. CHOLEIC ACIDS

Deoxycholic acid (V) has been known for some time to combine with

(V)

fatty acids, hydrocarbons, and a variety of other substances to form the choleic acids which have some resemblance to clathrates. In 1927, when *coordination number* was under discussion in relation to the developing electronic theory of valency (*28*), these compounds were distinguished by so-called coordination numbers, giving the number of deoxycholic acid molecules *coordinated* to each fatty acid. The values 1, 3, 4, 6, or 8, increasing with increasing chain length of fatty acid, show that the amount of material combined with deoxycholic acid is determined by its volume. If the formulas are rewritten for constant amount of deoxycholic acid the number of combined fatty acid molecules diminishes with increasing chain length of the fatty acid. This may be interpreted as a volume effect, the space available for the supposedly enclosed fatty acid being constant. However, there does not appear to be an upper limit of size and therefore this space is not in the form of closed cavities as in clathrates. (See also Chapter 8, Section II.)

9. COMPOUNDS CONTAINING COMMON SOLVENTS OF CRYSTALLIZATION

Many substances are obtained in the ordinary course of chemical synthesis in the form of solvates. This might be said of some clathrates, but the occurrence of the two components in one crystalline product is not sufficient evidence of clathrate formation. Some of these solvates resemble clathrates and it will sometimes be difficult to distinguish enclosure from other forms of association. The following examples illustrate some known types.

a. *Molecular Compounds of Triphenylmethane.* Triphenylmethane crystallizes normally in the orthorhombic system from mesitylene, o-, m, and p-xylene, toluene, benzyl alcohol, bromobenzene, acetone, chloroform, ethyl alcohol, ether, and various other solvents. From benzene, thiophene, pyrrole, and aniline it forms a different type of crystal (rhombohedral) containing solvent in the molecular ratio of 1:1. The four compounds are isomorphous (12). Crystals of the benzene compound lose the solvent readily on standing in the atmosphere. The selectivity of triphenylmethane for solvents is very similar to that of the nickel cyanide ammine (Section II, 4), which combines with the same four substances and there is little doubt that the behavior is controlled by size and shape factors. The ready loss of solvent, however, shows that there is not complete enclosure.

b. *α-Tetramethyl Ferrocyanide.* Two isomers of tetramethyl ferrocyanide are known. Of these the α-form has the (*cis*) structure shown (VI). This

$$\begin{array}{c}
CNCH_3 \\
| \quad CNCH_3 \\
| \; / \\
NC \text{———} Fe \text{———} CNCH_3 \\
/ \; | \\
NC \quad | \\
CNCH_3
\end{array}$$

(VI)

substance, like a number of others, normally forms crystalline solvates when attempts are made at recrystallization. It forms 1:1 compounds with acetonitrile, CH_3CN, and with methanol, CH_3OH. They do not seem to be clathrates since they lose solvent when exposed to the atmosphere. Their mode of decomposition, however, is instructive. The orthorhombic crystals which they form have roughly the shape of a hexagonal prism. When allowed to stand in the atmosphere they lose solvent and the decomposition is shown by the appearance of powdery unsolvated material on the surface of the crystal. The decomposition has a special directional nature, the sides of the hexagonal prism becoming opaque while the top and base faces remain for some time quite clear. There is however a steady change in the birefringence of the crystals as observed through these clear faces. It seems that solvent is restricted in that it may escape from the structure sideways but not in the direction of the pseudo-hexagonal axis. This is a direct demonstration of the reality of the imprisoning action which, when it acts for all directions, is the basis of clathrate formation.

III. CRYSTAL STRUCTURES OF CLATHRATES

Crystal structures of all clathrates must be alike in that they have enclosed spaces, occupied or not, for the trapped molecules, but there is evidently no other common structural characteristic of the enclosing part. The enclosed molecule has some interaction with its cage but cannot be very firmly trapped in a cage which is not itself firmly constructed. This implies that the component parts of this cage should be strongly bound together. Possible forms of binding between the component atoms of a cage structure may be conveniently, if roughly, classified as covalent bonds, ionic bonds, metallic bonds, hydrogen bonds, or van der Waals bonds. In any encaging structure more than one of these types may be involved. Various possible forms and combinations will be considered.

A. Bonds of One Type Only

1. COVALENT BONDS

A set of atoms might be linked entirely by covalent bonds to form the cage. If such a structure were made around an enclosed molecule, and the energy barrier to escape through the supposedly small spaces between atoms forming the walls of the cage were sufficiently high, it would be necessary to break bonds in order to release a trapped molecule. Such clathrates if they formed would therefore be difficult to decompose, but there may be a corresponding difficulty in their preparation.

Covalent bonds reach outwards from an atom in directions inclined to each other at angles which are restricted, if not completely constant, for a given atom in given conditions of valency and coordination. They might be bonds to atoms of the same kind. Among the nonmetallic elements which crystallize in structures satisfying the rule of $(8-N)$ close neighbors, where N is the number of the group in the periodic table, those in groups IV and V might form cage structures since any atom could link to three, or four, neighbors. Three is a sufficient number for the construction of a three-dimensional network, or of a finite closed cage. However the covalent distances between one atom and its neighbors are necessarily less than the van der Waals diameter of an atom such as argon, and it does not seem very probable that any such element will form a structure open enough to enclose other atoms. In diamond the tetrahedral direction of the bonds enforces a comparatively open structure but the cavities are small.

Cage-like structures formed by bonding of atoms all of the same kind are known. Silicon achieves such a structure in the neptunium compound $NpSi_2$ and related compounds. A three-dimensional network is formed by linkage of silicon atoms to three neighbors in a planar arrangement. Different sets of such atoms lie in different planes with one common atom to link them so that the three-dimensional network results. There is a geometrical resemblance to a clathrate, but the compound could be described as such only if there were no interaction, involving valency electrons, between the silicon atom and the metal atoms.

Boron, which, in its special position in the periodic table, forms electron deficient compounds with more bonds than electron pairs, gives some cage structures. In certain of these, twelve atoms grouped at the corners of an icosahedron each have five neighbors in the group which itself looks like a cage, but has little free space inside. These icosahedra may link further by a bond directed outwards from each boron atom. The resulting boron complex may be cage-like as in the hexagonal structure of carbon boride C_3B_{12}. This has a set of linked icosahedra forming a cage structure in which linear C_3 groups are located. There is formal geometrical similarity to a clathrate cage but there are bonds between carbon and boron. In some borides MB_6 (e.g. M = Ca, La, or Th) octahedral B_6 groups are linked to each other by bonds directed outwards from the octahedron through each boron atom. This results in a set of cavities that may be imagined at the centers of cubes which have the B_6 octahedra at each corner. The metal atoms are located in these cavities. There is a resemblance to the gas and liquid hydrate structures, and a large number, 24, of boron atoms surrounds each metal atom. Generally, in clathrates, many atoms are needed to form the walls of a single enclosing cage.

These structures show that cages may result from bonding of identical atoms when sufficient bonds can form in suitable directions. There are as yet no clathrates with gas atoms or molecules completely trapped in such cages. Partial trapping by layer structures is known, however, in the compounds of graphite (Chapter 6, Section V, G). In graphite, multiple bonding of carbon atoms to three neighbors, each of which has a similar linking restricted to the same plane, gives the sheet structure characteristic of this form of carbon. Hetero atoms or carbon atoms with a different valency function might in some conditions join portions of graphite sheets to form more complete enclosures.

Cages linked by covalent bonds alone are perhaps more likely to occur when atoms of different kinds are linked. It is possible to have a structural component larger and more like a cage bar or wall than the pair of linked identical atoms. A promising component is the M—CN—M' linear arrangement in which M and M' are different or identical metal atoms. The distance M—M' is in the region of 5.5 Å and bonds formed by the metal atoms will be at fixed angles to each other. If, for example, M and M' both formed six octahedral bonds the result would be a three-dimensional network resembling the framework of a large building constructed with girders. A framework of this kind exists in Prussian blue and perhaps in related compounds. Variations could be made by choice of metals with different covalent radii and different valency angles, and alternatives to the —CN— bridge could be devised. No definite series of clathrates based entirely on this kind of framework has been fully investigated structurally.

2. Ionic Bonds

Cages held by ionic bonds alone would be comparable in strength with those based on covalent bonds. Interionic forces, however, do not directly impose bond angle restrictions and it seems unlikely that they could compel a very open structure in a compound consisting of simple ions. They tend instead to result in rather closely packed structures determined by lattice energy. A rough rule is that an ion will have as many neighbors of opposite charge as is compatible with the chemical formula and the radius ratio of the ions, although there are many exceptions to the radius ratio rule among the simplest ionic compounds such as the alkali halides. But, even in closest packed structures there are vacant spaces between the spherical ions. Figure 1 shows a possible arrangement of anions in a cubic structure. If cations are put at the body centers of the small cubes marked 1–4 the structure is geometrically of the ZnS (blende) type in which each atom or ion has four neighbors placed tetrahedrally around

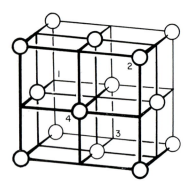

Fig. 1. Face-centered cubic lattice.

it. Clearly there are spaces unoccupied at the centers of the unnumbered cubes which might alternatively have been shown as containing cations. If both sets of spaces were occupied the formula and the structure would be similar to that of CaF_2. The tetrahedral spaces in the AX structure are thus seen to be the consequence of the 1:1 ratio of anions to cations combined with a coordination number of 4. In an ionic compound this low coordination number will be obtained only when the ratio of the smaller to the greater ionic radius is less than 0.41 and this means necessarily that the tetrahedral vacant space is small. The largest simple ions have radii not more than 2.5 Å and the corresponding oppositely charged ion in a tetrahedral hole will not have a radius greater than 0.41 × 2.5 or approximately 1 Å. This is less than the van der Waals radius of hydrogen (1.2 Å) and it is therefore unlikely that the tetrahedral spaces of the same capacity will act as clathrate cages. There are, however, other vacant spaces such as that shown at the body-center of the large cube in Fig. 1. This is also the center of an octahedron formed by the six ions at the centers of the cube faces. It is larger than the tetrahedral space and with suitable radii of the ions might have room for a sphere of about 1.6 Å radius, which could be increased if some distortion of the structure were possible. Although no clathrates of this kind are known it is possible that some may eventually be prepared.

A great deal of helium is trapped in cleveite and other uranium minerals but the nature of the traps is uncertain since considerable disturbance of the crystal structure takes place as a result of the radioactive disintegrations which produce the helium. Retention of the gas for prolonged periods suggests that atoms which are sufficiently small might be enclosed in some ionic structures.

3. Hydrogen Bonds

As a means of cage construction hydrogen bonding alone seems strictly to be possible only if there is a truly symmetrical bond with the hydrogen at the midpoint between the two atoms which it links. Such bonds, if they exist, are to be found in complex groups such as the diacetate ion which automatically brings in covalent bonds. Simple atoms, such as oxygen in water, have the hydrogen unsymmetrically placed so that it must be described as covalently linked to one neighboring oxygen. In a sense, however, all the bonds linking water to its neighbors, in ice or the gas hydrate structures, may be said to be equivalent since the hydrogen atom can occupy either of the two possible positions. Such structures will, however, be considered under the heading of covalent bonds combined with hydrogen bonding.

4. METALLIC BONDS

The structures of most metals are close packed or nearly so. They have tetrahedral and octahedral interatomic spaces similar in the geometrical sense to those discussed under ionic bonding (Section III, A, 2). The largest metal atom radii are less than 2 Å so that no other atom of radius greater than about 0.8 Å for an octahedral hole or 0.4 Å for the tetrahedral hole could fit into the undistorted structure. This excludes almost any atom if, as in a clathrate, it requires space corresponding to its van der Waals radius. There exists, however, a series of so-called interstitial compounds in which the small atoms—hydrogen, boron, carbon, nitrogen—fit into the interstices between metal atoms which in many instances have the same arrangement as in the pure metal. Although these structures retain some of the character of metals, e.g. metallic conductivity, they are often very hard and high melting to a degree that suggests interaction other than simple enclosure between metal and nonmetal (see Chapter 4). Although they may not be clathrates they have a further similarity in that they are stable when some of the available cavities are unoccupied.

5. VAN DER WAALS BONDS

The inert gas elements give crystal structures that contain empty space between the atoms, but are unlikely to enclose any material in these spaces. Argon has a cubic close packed structure and the cavities are small in relation to the size of the argon atoms themselves. Apart from the difficulty of finding any suitably sized enclosable atom, there is the certainty that these crystals are very weakly bound. They are mentioned, however, because van der Waals forces between *molecules* of sufficient complexity are known to provide the strength for stable clathrate formation.

B. Bonds of Two Kinds: Covalent and Other Bonds

There are two main advantages in combining bonds of different kinds. The first is that, by use of covalent bonds, atomic groups of varied dimensions and shapes may be used as components of enclosing cages. The second, and perhaps the more important, is that these rather rigidly bound components may be obtained in solution or otherwise as stable entities that may then be caused to join through some other form of bonding in conditions where the material to be enclosed is also present. There is a difference in quality and function between the covalent linkages and the others. The covalent bonding of a molecule or complex ion may, for this purpose, be regarded as permanent but any other form of bonding between such a group and any other components of a cage structure is more readily broken. Thus two ions may separate in solution, hydrogen bonded molecules or ions may similarly break loose from each other, and the van der Waals attachments of a set of molecules may be dissolved without change in the essential chemical character of the system.

1. COVALENT BONDS COMBINED WITH HYDROGEN BONDS

The combination of hydrogen bonds with covalent bonds is especially favorable to the construction of enclosing cages because the hydrogen bonds have something of the directional nature of covalencies. The hydrogen bond between the oxygen atom in a COH group and a suitable neighboring atom is found to point in a direction related to the carbon-oxygen covalent link in much the same way as two covalent links of an oxygen atom would be inclined at a definite angle. The angle is rather more variable over a range which includes 90° and the regular tetrahedral angle $109\frac{1}{2}°$. This directional restriction acts in the way that has been illustrated for purely covalent compounds (Section III, A, 1) and may lead to clathrate cage structures.

Figure 2 shows one of the simplest and most firmly established structures based on this combination of hydrogen bonding and covalent bonds. Hydroquinone, $C_6H_4(OH)_2$, would be expected to form hydrogen bonds through each of its two OH groups to the oxygen atoms of neighboring molecules. Each of these neighboring oxygen atoms will in turn be linked to some other oxygen atom and it thus appears that there will be a basic pattern of the form shown (VII)—where the broken lines represent hydro-

(VII)

gen bonds—controlling the association of hydroquinone molecules. The benzene ring, with its two links in the *para* positions completely fixes the positions of the two oxygen atoms which are about 5.5 Å apart, and the directions of the hydrogen bonds to two neighboring molecules are re-

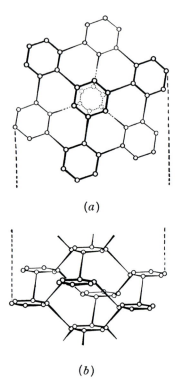

(a)

(b)

Fig. 2. Manner of hydrogen bonding of hydroquinone molecules. (a) In plan. Each regular hexagon denotes six hydrogen bonds between oxygen atoms. Hexagons at different levels are represented by different line thickness. The tapered lines, representing the O—O axis of a hydroquinone molecule, show the method of linking to form an infinite three-dimensional cagework. Each taper points downward from the observer. (b) Perspective drawing corresponding to the above. The hexagons denote the hydrogen bonds; the longer lines connecting different hexagons denote the O—O axis of the hydroquinone molecule. The complete structure as found in the molecular compounds consists of the cagework shown, together with a second identical interpenetrating cagework, which is displaced vertically half-way between the top and bottom hexagons.

stricted relative to each other and to the line joining the oxygen atom to the benzene ring. The same kind of restriction applies to the directions of the lines which must join the neighboring oxygen atoms to their own benzene rings. One structure which satisfies these directional and dimensional requirements is shown in Fig. 2. Every hydrogen atom of the OH groups forms one hydrogen bond, and the hydrogen bonds are all inclined at about the tetrahedral angle to the oxygen-carbon covalent bond. The hydrogen bonds are grouped into regular hexagons so that they are at 120° to each other.

This structure may be understood by a simplification. Each hexagon of six OH groups may be imagined as a single center of the whole structure. From it there radiate six lines joining it to six neighboring hexagons, which are at fixed distances determined by the dimensions of the hydroquinone molecule between its oxygen centers. Essentially this structure is the same as that of Prussian blue referred to in Section III, A, 1, the hexagons replacing the metal (Fe) atoms and the hydroquinone molecules bridging between hexagons as the CN groups bridge between iron atoms. It is the rigidity of the bridging groups, and the more or less fixed directions in which they must form, that in each case produce a three-dimensional cage-like structure.

This hydroquinone structure, which seems to be a natural requirement, is not in fact obtained when the material is recrystallized at ordinary temperatures, and so far it has not been obtained in any conditions. It is evident from the diameter of the cage, about 11.5 Å from the top to the bottom hexagons of Fig. 2, that there must be a lot of empty space in it. If it existed this form of hydroquinone would have a density of not much more than 0.6 gm/cm³. It is so open in structure that it is possible to construct a second identical extended three-dimensional network which interpenetrates the first. Each entangles and imprisons the other as though two steel girder frameworks had been built independently with the junctions of one set located at the centers of the rooms in the other.

It is evident that the single open hydroquinone structure has ample space to include other material but that it would not form an effective cage. If the channels that stretch throughout it are continuous enough to contain the second identical structure, any included single molecules that might alternatively fill them, would be expected to migrate readily through these channels and be easily removed at the surfaces. Possibly the single structure might be stabilized by trapped molecules of suitable shape, but since it must always form in the presence of other hydroquinone molecules, which fit into it so easily, there will always be the difficulty of keeping them out.

The double framework of two interpenetrating three-dimensional networks can be understood from Fig. 3, which also illustrates the manner in which the two networks jointly form cages in which small molecules may be trapped. These schematic figures in which, for clarity, single lines are used to represent the underlying pattern of linkage between the cage-forming components give a false impression in that the structure appears too open in character. The single lines, which give the impression of cage bars should be replaced by broad space-occupying components which block the apparently empty spaces through which the enclosed molecule is shown. If a model is constructed with all the atoms of the hydroquinone

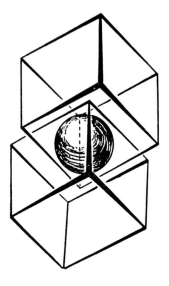

FIG. 3. Schematic representation of enclosure. The enclosed molecule is represented by a sphere imprisoned by two interpenetrating cage structures. Each edge of the cage may be looked upon as containing one hydroquinone molecule, and the real structure consists not of the limited cagework shown, but of the indefinitely extended pattern obtained by the prolongation of the edges to form an array of similar cages.

molecules represented to scale in their correct positions and with opaque part-spheres to denote the radii for contacts with unlinked atoms, the immediate group of molecules on any side of an enclosure completely obscures a sphere representing an enclosed molecule. The effect can be seen in Fig. 4 where in (b) most of the surrounding atoms have been omitted in order that a central enclosed atom should not be obscured. There are no holes through which an enclosed atom could escape from its cage without approaching atoms of the confining walls much closer than the normal van der Waals equilibrium distances.

Characteristics of clathrates illustrated by the hydroquinone compounds are: (a) that the limiting composition, corresponding to occupancy of every cage, is determined by geometrical rather than chemical factors; (b) that a large number of atoms is required to form the walls of a cage big enough to contain a single atom or small molecule which is at van der Waals distance from its surroundings; (c) that sometimes the clathrate structure is not that normally given by the cage former when it crystallizes alone.

The ratio of cavities to hydroquinone molecules is 1:3. This may be seen from Fig. 3 where the enclosed atom is surrounded by six bars, three from each framework. Each of the six serves as a bar of another cage on its opposite side and hence the ratio of bars to cages is 3:1.

The center of a cavity, when the occupying atom is small, is surrounded by 12 oxygen atoms at 3.9 Å, 6 carbon atoms at 3.8 Å, and 6 carbon atoms at 4.2 Å. This makes a total of 24 atoms not counting the hydrogen atoms, 18 in all, attached to some of them, or other carbon atoms which are not much further removed. The 24 close oxygen and carbon atoms lie fairly

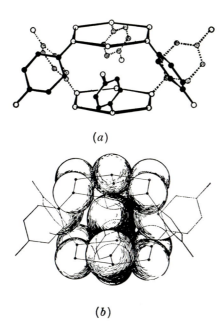

(a)

(b)

Fig. 4. (a) The positions of the six hydroquinone molecules that form the immediate surroundings of an argon atom are shown in a perspective drawing. This is deceptive because the centers of the atoms are shown, and the space occupied by the atoms cannot be shown at the same time. (b) The spaces occupied by the atoms are indicated in a drawing on the same scale as that above. A few only of the atoms surrounding the central argon atom are shown. They are distinguished from those which have been omitted by small circles drawn around their centers. Broken lines are used to indicate that a part of the structure so represented lies behind some portion drawn with full lines.

evenly distributed nearly on the surface of a sphere of radius 3.95 Å. If it is assumed that the effective space requirement of each such atom, including any attached hydrogen, is equivalent to a sphere of radius about 1.7 Å (half the effective thickness of an aromatic molecule in a crystal structure) the possible space left in the center for any enclosed molecule is roughly a sphere of radius about 2.25 Å.

These hydroquinone compounds have been described as β-hydroquinone clathrates because the enclosing structure illustrated does not readily form in the absence of enclosable material. Hydroquinone crystallized in normal conditions from solvents that cannot be enclosed in the β-hydroquinone cavities has a different structure known as α-hydroquinone. It has a slightly higher density than β-hydroquinone.

The gas and liquid hydrates show considerable similarity to β-hydroquinone clathrates. They do not have the complication of two interpenetrating systems of hydrogen bonded giant molecules, but are more complex in some other ways. As is well known ordinary ice is a hydrogen bonded structure, each water molecule being joined to four oxygen neighbors through its own or other hydrogen atoms. The hydrogen atoms are unsymmetrically placed, being closer to one oxygen of the linked pair than to the other, but the hydrogen atoms can switch to some extent between the two possible positions. The links from oxygen to oxygen are arranged tetrahedrally and effectively all the links are equivalent so that the resulting hexagonal structure is rather open in the same way as the tetrahedral 4-coordinated structure of ZnS (hexagonal, wurtzite). The empty spaces, which are revealed in the low density of ice, are not, however, very large. They are surrounded by 12 water molecules, a number insufficient to form a space large enough to enclose another atom or molecule.

Gas hydrates occur in two forms, Type I and Type II (5, 21, 31). These and their physical properties are described in Chapter 6 Sections II, A, VIII, B and C, and IX, A. Type I has a unit cube of side 12 Å, contains 46 water molecules and 2 small and 6 larger cavities. In Type II the unit cube cell is of 17 Å side, 136 water molecules, and 16 small and 8 larger cavities. Limiting compositions for each group of similar cavities may be accordingly set on the basis of every cavity being occupied by one molecule. The pentagonal dodecahedra which circumscribe the smaller cavities in both types are bound by 20 water molecules, and the tetradecahedra in Type I and the hexadecahedra in Type II are bound by 24 and 28 water molecules respectively. These high numbers contrast with the 12-molecule surroundings of the smaller empty spaces in ordinary ice and are similar to the large number of cavity forming atoms in hydroquinone clathrates and in some borides (Section III, A, 1). The diameters of the free space in these cavities, which are roughly spherical, are 5.1 and 5.8 Å in Type I and 5.0 and 6.6 Å in Type II. These are obtained from the O-to-O distances in the polyhedra and 1.4 Å is allowed for the space occupied by the water molecules themselves.

Among the inert gas clathrates reported are (34) a number of the double hydrate type (cf. Chapter 6, Table V) with unit cube dimension about 17.5 Å, Type II, in which argon, krypton, or xenon is combined with acetone, methylene dichloride, chloroform, or carbon tetrachloride. Some other small organic molecules such as dimethylamine and ethylamine appear also to be capable of giving double hydrates. This is of interest in view of the behavior of tetraalkylammonium salts, which form clathrate hydrates (Section III, D).

Gas hydrates show in a striking way how the dimensions of the caged molecules control the formation of clathrates. This is clearly apparent from Tables II, III, IV, and V in Chapter 6. Small molecules form Type I, larger ones form Type II, and Type II double hydrates contain small and large molecules. The larger molecules in the latter are enclosed in the 8 larger cavities and, generally, whether or not there is a third component there are 17 water molecules to each large enclosed molecule, i.e., Type II. In a few cases the single hydrates of the large molecules are Type I. The structural pattern adopted by the water molecules is thus determined by what else is present when the hydrate is formed.

Gas hydrates have for a long time been difficult to analyze accurately. They decompose readily and may lose some of the volatile component. Earlier results were affected by inclusions of mother liquor. It was natural perhaps that some regularity of composition should be expected, and that attempts should be made to discover some general formulas.

Chlorine hydrate first prepared by Davy (8) in 1811 was analyzed by Faraday (10) and, in 1823, represented as $10H_2O \cdot Cl_2$. Roozeboom (29) in 1884 gave $8H_2O \cdot Cl_2$ and later workers $6H_2O \cdot Cl_2$.

Although it is now known that the hydrate has the Type I structure with unit cube $a = 11.88$ Å, this does not settle the question even of what might be the ideal formula. There are 46 water molecules per unit cell with 2 smaller and 6 larger cavities. Possible molecular ratios of water: chlorine appear therefore to be 46:6 (or $7\frac{2}{3}:1$) if only the six larger cavities are occupied by chlorine, or 46:8 ($5\frac{3}{4}:1$) if all cavities are so occupied. These alternatives are fairly near to the simpler 8:1 or 6:1 which, previous to the crystal structure work, might have seemed chemically more desirable. Von Stackelberg assumed the composition to be $6H_2O \cdot Cl_2$, and explained this as due to a 96% filling of all the holes since $5\frac{3}{4} \times (100/96)$ is very close to 6.0. The assumption is evidently incorrect but is useful in showing that a simple ratio 6:1 may sometimes be good evidence of non-stoichiometry. From x-ray work Pauling and Marsh (22) concluded that the six larger cavities are occupied by chlorine, but a further complication is the suggestion that the smaller cavities may be occupied not by chlorine but by water. This would make $48H_2O$ per unit cell and give the composition $8H_2O \cdot Cl_2$, the whole number 8, so satisfying to the stoichiometric chemist, being in reality not the simple ratio he expects but the sum of two ratios 46/6 and 2/6.

Occupation of the smaller cavities by H_2O seems a reasonable possibility. There is certainly room in the cavity, and there is some ground for supposing that transient structures of the kind may exist in liquid water. However, the most recent purely chemical analysis of chlorine hydrate does not support the suggestion. By an application of Schreinmaker's wet residue method of analysis the composition was estimated as $(7.27 \pm 0.17)H_2O \cdot Cl_2$ (1), and 7.27 must be regarded as non-stoichiometric since it is *not* $7\frac{2}{3} = 46/6$. These apparently conflicting results are recorded to illustrate both how confusion may arise even in simple systems, and how it may be avoided. Determination of the absolute weight of the contents of one unit cell in a crystal structure is of great value. Unit cell dimensions can be measured, if necessary, to a high accuracy of one part in many thousands. Densities are sometimes more difficult to measure but an overall accuracy of 1 part in 1000 for the unit cell weight can be achieved without too great experimental elaboration. Apart from this knowledge of the absolute weight of the cell, crystal structures provide information of the *possible* cell contents in other ways. The space group symmetry, the nature and multiplicity of equivalent point positions that it permits, and the ultimate requirement that the intensities of the observed x-ray reflections must agree, within acceptable limits, with those calculated for any crystal structure that is postulated, provide definite information that must be reconciled with any suggested chemical formula. Thus, whatever else may be present, the 46 water molecules per unit of the cage structure in Type I hydrates must be included in any formula. The unit cell dimensions of chlorine hydrate being known, the density may be calculated for various supposed structures, with the following results: $46H_2O \cdot 6Cl_2$, 1.26; $46H_2O \cdot 8Cl_2$, 1.40; $6H_2O \cdot Cl_2$, 1.38; $7.27H_2O \cdot Cl_2$, 1.29. The reported experimental value for the density is 1.29 $\pm$ 0.02 gm/cm³, so that the last composition seems to be correct. It is identical with that found by the most recent analysis. According to this formula there is more chlorine present than required for filling of all the large cavities ($7\frac{2}{3}H_2O$ needed) and this additional chlorine can be explained if 20% of the small cavities are also occupied by chlorine molecules.

2. COVALENT BONDS COMBINED WITH IONIC BONDS

In complex ions, whether they are finite or polymeric, the covalent bonds linking their constituent atoms have, within narrow limits, lengths and angles to each other characteristic of the atoms and the bonds. This means that, as constituents of crystal structures, they, like molecules, have shapes to which other constituents must be adapted. These shapes may themselves be variable when groups are free to adopt various positions through rotation about bonds. The rotations are restricted, however, sometimes severely so, as in the case of double bonds. In triple bond systems such as —C≡C— or —C≡N the whole system is linear, or nearly so, and rotation about the triple bond has no effect on the positions of the two atoms immediately attached by the single bonds. Inflexibility of this kind does not necessarily lead to cage structures but, as in some of the other structures discussed above, it can be a favorable factor. Parts of a complex ion are restricted to definite relative positions, and it may be impossible to bring together a set of these ions and their oppositely charged partners, without leaving cavities, which may be large enough to contain other molecules. The bonding between ions will be strong and in the case when the cavities contain other molecules which are effectively barred from escape by the surroundings there is clathrate formation. Many structures of this kind may be expected because there is the same favorable factor as in the compounds of Section III, B, 1 above, that the cage components and the cage occupants can be assembled together in a solution from which the whole structure forms on crystallization. Dissolution of crystalline ionic compounds, whether the ions are single or polymerized, is often readily brought about by solvents of high dielectric constant. In the case under discussion this in effect weakens and destroys the cage but preserves its component parts. The oppositely charged ions necessary to form a cage which proves to be very insoluble could be brought separately into solution by use of two more soluble substances that each contain one of them.

Finite complex ions are responsible for a clathrate effect in hexamethylisocyanidoiron(II) chloride trihydrate, $[Fe(CNCH_3)_6]Cl_2 \cdot 3H_2O$. The cation is octahedral of geometrical form fixed by the Fe—CN—CH$_3$ sequence (25). In it Fe—CN—C atoms form a nearly straight group with a slight bend of the methyl carbon away from the line. The cation may be imagined as an octahedron stood on a triangular face and then pressed down slightly so that the C—CH$_3$ bonds both above and below the central iron atom are splayed out a few degrees. The trigonal symmetry is preserved, and top and bottom faces of the octahedron are each formed by a triangle of methyl groups. When these ions are packed as closely as possible in hexagonal array the methyl groups of one octahedron are in contact with those of its neighbors in a plane and with the methyl groups of the ions in similar planes immediately above and below. The methyl groups above and below fit as tightly as possible in between the arms of the complex ions. This closest possible packing of the cations occupies a space equal to that of the whole unit cell and consequently the two chloride ions and three water molecules which make up the complete formula are accommodated in spaces between the cations. These spaces arise in an obvious way. The six effectively linear and rigid arms of the octahedral complex have a length about 4.5 Å between iron and terminal carbon atom centers and there is a distance of about 3.8 Å between the carbon atom of one methyl group and that of one of its neighbors. Two octahedral ions can be fitted one on top of the other, with the projection arms of the upper one occupying the spaces between the arms of the lower, so that there is very little free space between them. Though the projecting arms of these ions fit in a simple way with their neighbors to the sides they inevitably leave large free spaces. These arise in a geometrical way which is similar to that applicable to the nickel cyanide ammine complex as discussed above and in Section III, B, 3. The straight $FeCNCH_3$ arms, analogous to the projecting NH_3 groups which place a limit on the approach of the layers, make it impossible for the iron atoms at the centers of the complex ions to approach closer than their observed separations. They hold the complex ions so far apart in certain directions that large spaces are left. To every unit cell there are five such spaces which fall, according to space group symmetry, into two sets. One of these sets, consisting of three equivalent positions seems suitable for the three water molecules and the other, consisting of two equivalent positions, seems suitable for the two chloride ions. The structure found is, however disordered. The threefold positions are occupied by two chloride ions and one water molecule per unit cell distributed statistically over these formally equivalent positions and the twofold positions are all occupied by water molecules. The chloride ions enter the threefold positions preferentially because they are closer to the positive charges than they would be in the twofold positions. The water molecules in either the twofold or threefold positions are firmly enclosed by the surrounding ions which form a strong cage. It is found that the water, which is not otherwise attached to the structure can be removed only to a small extent. Prolonged heating at a temperature just below 100°C—higher temperatures are impracticable owing to decomposition of the complex ion—causes very little loss of water. The water thus enclosed in the crystals is, in the first place, derived from the relatively small amount present in the ordinary laboratory methanol from which it is crystallized.

A three-dimensional extended complex based on the six octahedral iron bonds of ferrocyanide type group appears to be present in Prussian blue and related compounds. If a simple cubic network is imagined with iron atoms at each intersection and a CN group along each cube edge the resulting structure is a three-dimensional analogue of the planar $Ni(CN)_2$ part of the structure described in Sections II, 4 and III, B, 3. The composition may be represented $FeFe(CN)_6$, all the atoms being in the ferric state. This is ferric ferricyanide (Berlin green). If all iron atoms were ferrous, then, were the whole structure a single structural entity, it would be an anion such that a single unipositive cation, required for electrical neutrality, must be added to each of the cubic cages. The composition of such a structure might be represented as $K_2FeFe(CN)_6$ for potassium ferrous ferrocyanide. If half the atoms are ferrous and the other half ferric only half as many potassium ions are required for electrical neutrality. The composition becomes that of Prussian blue, $KFeFe(CN)_6$, and half the cube cages have no potassium ion. Soluble Prussian blue has enough water to provide one molecule for each of the cages and this must be regarded as trapped. The water molecule is not very different in size from the potassium ions that are known to be accommodated in the cages. As may be seen from Fig. 5, illustrating the general structure of the analogous $Ni(CN)_2$ sheet structure, the possible escape hole at the center of a square face of the cage is not large. It can be shown to be about 1.5 Å across, whereas a water molecule sometimes acts as roughly a sphere of diameter 2.8 Å. In any case every hole available for a water molecule in the Prussian blue structure is blocked by a potassium ion occupying the adjacent cube. For the present discussion it is not of great importance what is the precise chemical nature of the Prussian blue and

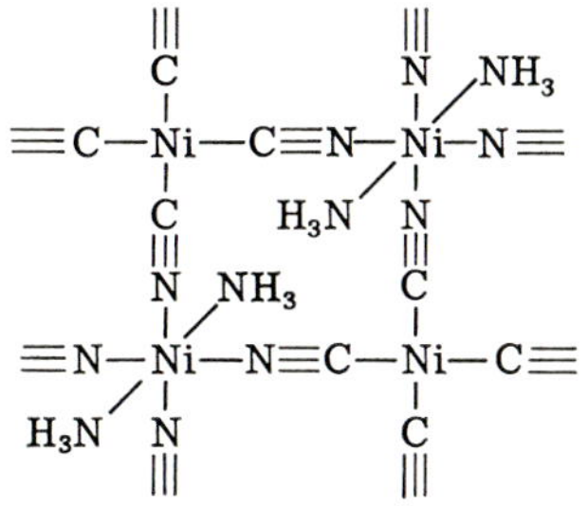

$$
\begin{array}{c}
\text{structure diagram} \\
\equiv C-Ni-C\equiv N-Ni-N\equiv \\
\equiv N-Ni-N\equiv C-Ni-C\equiv
\end{array}
$$

FIG. 5. Portion of sheet structure of composition $Ni(CN)_2 \cdot NH_3$.

similar structures. The argument concerning the availability of space, in a cage of sufficient strength to imprison, will hold whether or not individual atoms can be distinguished as ferric or ferrous. The $Fe(CN)_3$ structure may be regarded as a single complex anion or as a mixture of metal ions and octahedral complexes, without effect on the conclusion.

Space available for water molecules is produced in the crystal structure of the compound $KCu_2(CN)_3 \cdot H_2O$ by the same structural component, the —metal—CN—metal— bridge. This is a more complicated structure but the essential component is a polymer sheet of composition $[Cu_2(CN)_3]^-$. The sheet is formed by spiral chains of composition $(CuCN)_2$ and zigzag $(CuCN)$ chains (7). The copper atoms in these two chains are linked by CN groups of a third kind. The resulting sheet structure has rings of six sides each formed by a

$$
Cu—CN—Cu
$$

group of atoms. These hexagons are puckered and all the edges are shared so that, in projection, the whole sheet resembles a graphite layer, the carbon atoms being replaced by copper atoms which each link along CN sides of the hexagons to three other copper atoms. An approximate idea of the structure is obtained if the Cu atoms are pictured as having three

links arranged pyramidally. Two of the angles between the three bonds
of each copper atom are not far from the tetrahedral value and the third
is about 20° greater. The CuCN and CuNC sequences are nearly all close
to linear. The whole structure is similar to that which may be obtained
by joining up a set of tetrahedra, as in diamond or wurtzite, with the
limitation that only three of the tetrahedral bonds are to be used. Similar
sheets occur in the structure of arsenic.

The $[Cu_2(CN)_3]$ sheets are stacked parallel to form the main structure.
Potassium ions hold the negatively charged sheets together. In the sheet
each hexagon side is of length about 5 Å and this is also the approximate
distance from any copper atom to the center of the hexagon. The distances from C and N, along the sides, to the center of the hexagons will
be not much less. The part of this distance taken up by atoms of the
hexagonal network will not be greater than a layer 2 Å thick and there
is therefore a considerable empty space, of radius about 3 Å, which cannot
be filled by a potassium ion of effective radius about 1.3 Å. The water
molecules present in the structure lie within the hexagons and help to
fill up this space. Whether the trapping is as complete as in a clathrate
has not been determined but there is a close structural resemblance to
clathrates.

3. Covalent Bonds Combined with van der Waals Bonds

A combination of covalent and van der Waals bonds occurs when an
atom is enclosed between molecules of definite size or between macromole-
cules. Some molecules of these kinds have holes of molecular size through
the middle but most of them are close patterns of atoms that act as barriers to molecular movement. In compounds of graphite, carbon sheets
are interleaved with other material such as oxygen, HSO_4^- ions, water,
bromine, or alkali metal atoms (see Chapter 6, Section V, G). There is
relatively weak bonding between the layers and the perpendicular distance between them is variable according to the molecular dimensions of
the interlayer material. In some instances the swelling is reversible. The
imprisoning effect here is complete in one direction only, perpendicular
to the layers. It is possible to state a distinction between this kind of
interlayer enclosure and clathrates. In clathrates the cage is considered
to be enclosed completely and cannot vary much in form although minor
adaptations to the shape and size of the enclosable molecules are found.

In such structures the space available for an enclosed molecule is fixed
within narrow limits, and this in turn strictly limits the possible occupants
and the composition. There are, however, structures in which layers imprison other molecules in a way that amounts to clathrate formation. The

macromolecular layers must, like finite-sized molecules, be free to undergo displacements restricted by no more than their van der Waals interaction; however, in the molecular compounds that form, these displacements are small and there are additional structural factors which make the imprisonment more effective than that given by the flat graphite sheets.

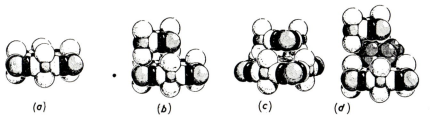

(a)   (b)   (c)   (d)

FIG. 6. (a) Approximate perspective drawing of part of the nickel cyanide ammine complex layer. Nitrogen atoms white; carbon, black; nickel, dotted. (b) and (c) Two different possible methods of interleaving the layers. (d) Superposition of layers as in (a), showing the included benzene molecules of the $Ni(CN)_2 \cdot NH_3 \cdot C_6H_6$ structure. Note the greater interlayer spacing than with (c).

One such series of compounds is that of nickel cyanide ammine with a number of molecules all about the size and shape of benzene (27). The structure is shown in Fig. 6(d). The basis of the layer structure is the square planar arrangement of bonds for a 4-coordinated nickel(II) atom. This nickel atom is the center of a $Ni(CN)_4$ group and each nitrogen atom coordinates to a nickel atom by a bond which is colinear with the NiCN arrangement. This produces a two-dimensional tetragonal layer that may be represented by the formula shown (VIII)

$$\left\{ \begin{array}{c} | \quad\quad | \\ -Ni-CN-Ni- \\ | \quad\quad\quad | \\ C \quad\quad\quad N \\ | \quad\quad\quad | \\ N \quad\quad\quad C \\ | \quad\quad\quad | \\ -Ni-NC-Ni- \\ | \quad\quad\quad | \end{array} \right\}_n$$

(VIII)

The nickel atoms in the layer are of two kinds, those attached to carbon atoms and those attached to four nitrogen atoms of the CN groups. The latter have two NH_3 groups in addition so that there is an octahedral arrangement of six bonds around them. The resulting structure is a flat extended sheet which has NH_3 groups projecting above and below at regular intervals. This is represented in Fig. 6(a). The distance between adjacent ammonia groups projecting on the same side of the sheet is that of the diagonal of the Ni—CN—Ni square $5.1\sqrt{2} = 7.2$ Å.

Any structure consisting of layers of this complex only must be an open one owing to the manner in which the projecting ammonia groups hold the layers apart in certain places and thus provide unoccupied spaces in others. Left to themselves such layers would be expected to adapt the projections of one as closely as possible to the hollows of its neighbors. Two ways of fitting one on top of another are shown in Figs. 6(b) and 6(c). Both fill space rather inefficiently as may be seen from the unoccupied regions. No structure composed simply of these layers appears to be formed from solutions that contain ammonia and the constituent ions of nickel cyanide. In the presence of benzene, or a few compounds having similar shaped molecules, the structure shown in Fig. 6(d) is produced. In this, the layers fit one above the other with the NH_3 groups projecting from one layer directly above or below similar NH_3 groups in neighboring layers. The spacing between the layers is much greater than that in Figs. 6(b) and 6(c), but with the inclusion of the benzene molecules the space-filling is very efficient, there being almost no visible free space. Even the small depressions in the centers of the squares bounded by Ni—CN—Ni sides are in part filled by the top and bottom CH groups of the benzene molecules. The other four CH groups in the benzene ring are in close contact with similar groups of other enclosed benzene molecules. In this structure the benzene molecules are clearly caged above and below by the nickel cyanide layers and to the sides by the ammonia groups. Benzene is not easily removed from the compound, a temperature of 120°, well above the boiling point of the liquid, being necessary for a ready decomposition.

Benzene may be replaced by pyrrole, thiophene, furan, or pyridine. This series of compounds has the characteristics of clathrates that the enclosure is firm, that there is selection according to molecular shape and size since larger homologues of these compounds do not form compounds, and that the cage need not form in the absence of enclosable molecules. There is no room for substituents on the four carbon atoms of the benzene molecule furthest removed from the layers [Fig. 6(d)] since the corresponding benzene CH groups are already as close as they can be to others of their own kind. Any substituted benzene would have to have the substituent attached by a bond pointing perpendicular to the layers, and the layers would have to be further apart to make room for the added group or atom. It has been found that aniline $C_6H_5NH_2$ gives a compound of similar structure but with the interlayer spacing increased by about 1 Å.

In the hydrate $Ni(CN)_2 \cdot NH_3 \cdot \frac{1}{4}H_2O$ a modified form of the structure occurs, the layers being slightly puckered and staggered so that the proecting ammonia groups of one point towards the holes in the square network of its neighbors. The staggering is as in Fig. 6(c) which, however, does not show puckering of the layers.

Cage structures may be formed by finite molecules which interact with each other through van der Waals forces. Molecular compounds of tri-o-thymotide of general formula $2C_{33}H_{36}O_6 \cdot M$ are known where M is a molecule which satisfies certain requirements concerning maximum dimensions (2). Among the substances represented by M are volatile liquids, such as benzene or chloroform, and some, such as CH_3Br, which are gaseous at room temperature. In addition to the size condition, the compounds have properties of clathrates in that the volatile constituent is firmly retained at temperatures far above its normal boiling point, many of the included molecules are chemically inert, and there is a common crystal structure for the series.

The tri-o-thymotide molecule (for formula, see Section II, 7) is itself fairly inert chemically and there is no possibility of hydrogen or other bonding between two or more such molecules. The van der Waals bonding between these molecules must therefore be strong enough to hold a firm cage around the enclosed components. As in other clathrates van der Waals interaction between cage and imprisoned molecule must contribute to stability and, as in some other cases, the tri-o-thymotide clathrate cage structure does not form in the absence of enclosable molecules. Tri-o-thymotide, when obtained pure, forms orthorhombic crystals entirely different from the trigonal crystals of the clathrates.

Since van der Waals bonding is the only form here available for maintaining a three-dimension cage action, there will be no necessary constancy of any structural dimension such as the spacings within a graphite or other sheet. All dimensions of a unit cell should be about equally variable. A greater adaptability to the shape of enclosed molecule is to be expected. The van der Waals equilibrium distances between neighboring atoms vary more than the lengths of stronger bonds. Also van der Waals attraction is not restricted to particular atoms which have definite positions in the molecule or to special directions in space relative to the rest of the molecule. The interaction between enclosed and enclosing molecule is, in this type of clathrate, qualitatively similar to that between any two molecules of the enclosing structure. The arrangement of cage-forming molecules may therefore be considerably influenced by their interaction with the enclosed component.

A structure analysis detailed enough to give atomic positions has not been carried out for these compounds but unit cell dimensions have been measured (15) accurately in order that the effects of varying the caged molecule may be seen. Table II gives unit cell dimensions and composi-

TABLE II

Tri-o-thymotide Clathrates

Included molecule	l^a	Unit cell dimensions, Å (probable errors in units of 0.001 Å)		Density (20°) (gm/cm³)	No. of included molecules per unit cell
		a	c		
CH_3OH^b	4.6	13.460 ± 1	30.223 ± 5	—	—
C_2H_5OH	5.6	13.453 ± 2	30.155 ± 1	1.1627 ± 0.0005	3.03 ± 0.05
CH_3Br	5.9	13.467 ± 3	30.119 ± 5	—	—
CH_3I	6.3	13.5	30.2	1.2597 ± 0.0006	(3)
C_2H_5Br	6.8	13.540 ± 2	30.140 ± 2	1.2125 ± 0.0006	3.05 ± 0.02
$n\text{-}C_3H_7OH$	6.9	13.515 ± 3	30.288 ± 4	1.1606 ± 0.0005	2.98 ± 0.06
CH_2Br_2	7.0	13.533 ± 1	30.174 ± 4	1.285 ± 0.004	3.07 ± 0.07
C_2H_5I	7.1	13.564 ± 5	30.28 ± 10	1.250 ± 0.002	2.96
CH_2I_2	7.7	13.655 ± 5	30.33 ± 10	1.347 ± 0.001	2.99 ± 0.03
$n\text{-}C_4H_9OH$	8.1	13.617 ± 4	30.603 ± 4	1.456 ± 0.0005	2.98 ± 0.05
$C_2H_5OC_2H_5$	8.9	13.623 ± 2	30.715 ± 10	1.408 ± 0.001	3.03 ± 0.04
$n\text{-}C_5H_{11}OH$	9.4	13.695 ± 6	30.742 ± 5	1.138 ± 0.002	2.9 ± 0.1

^{a} l = maximum length of included molecule, Å.

^{b} It is apparently impossible to obtain the methanol compound from pure solvent. The specimen used probably contained some acetone. This explains why the cell dimensions are slightly greater instead of slightly less than those of the ethanol compound.

tions. The second column gives the calculated maximum lengths required for packing each molecule into a space in the crystal. The molecule is assumed to have the normal form of an aliphatic chain. Each carbon-carbon bond of length 1.54 Å is projected on a line passing through alternate carbon atoms and the projected length 1.256 Å is taken as the contribution to the total distance between the centers of the terminal atoms. Distances C—Cl = 1.76, C—Br = 1.91, C—I = 2.10, C—O = 1.43 and O—H = 0.96 Å are projected similarly; the C—O—C angle in ether is taken as the tetrahedral. In this way a projected length between terminal atom centers is derived. Normally hydrogen atoms are ignored but in the case of n-alcohols the projection of the O—H distance is included. To find the maximum packing length, allowance is made for end groups. For alkanes and halogen derivatives the van der Waals radii Cl = 1.80, Br = 1.95, I = 2.15, or CH_3 = 2.0 Å, are added to the projected lengths between terminal atom centers. For the alcohols, a van der Waals radius of 1.2 Å is used for the hydroxyl-hydrogen atoms. The substances listed all give clathrates of similar structures which are here referred to a hexagonal unit cell containing six molecules of tri-o-thymotide. For a composition $2C_{33}H_{35}O_6 \cdot M$ the number of molecules included per unit cell, as given in the last column, should be 3. For some of these compounds the carbon and hydrogen percentages are of little value in fixing the ratio of tri-o-thymotide to the other component; they are more sensitive mainly when they are not necessary, i.e. when there is a large proportion of halogen. The OH hydrogen, which may be determined, is a very small proportion, but like halogen gives a direct measure of the amount of caged material. However, such direct chemical analyses will be erroneous if there is occluded solvent or moisture in the specimen. There is no certainty that the crystalline compound has been properly separated from its mother liquor; washing is of doubtful value since it may decompose the compound or add a new one. Drying of the analytical sample has a danger of decomposition to one side and the possibility of incompleteness on the other. Also tri-o-thymotide forms many different types of addition compound besides those already described and with some solvents it forms more than one solvate (e.g., with n-butyl iodide and n-pentanol). Consequently the sample analyzed may be a mixture. A sufficiently elaborate analytical process, including if necessary a wet residue method, might overcome the difficulties but direct determination of the unit cell weight seems easier and more certain. Conclusions concerning the stoichiometry of molecular compounds in general should not be made from chemical analyses carried out in ways that may be accurate and appropriate for other kinds of chemical investigation but which have not been undertaken with these special difficulties in view.

The accuracy required in the unit cell weight method can be seen from Table II and is illustrated further in Table III which gives the corresponding results for a set of tri-*o*-thymotide inclusion compounds containing chain type molecules ranging in length from 9.4 Å to considerably more. These are channel type enclosures in which the amount of tri-*o*-thymotide required to form the length of channel appropriate for a single enclosed molecule is proportional to the length of that molecule. Hence, as the table shows, the molecular ratio is not necessarily simple and is not constant for the series. Unit cell dimensions can be measured easily to the accuracy shown. They must be corrected if not measured at the same temperature as the densities which for this purpose are best found by flotation of the powdered material in a liquid column of determinable density gradient. This method is applicable to small quantities of material. It has the advantage of showing by the sharpness of the layer whether the material is of uniform composition. Two different crystalline substances present in the sample will separate into different layers and the individual densities may be determined. An accuracy usually better than 1:1000, as shown in Tables II and III, is sufficient to establish molecular ratios with the precision needed. The basis of the method and the precautions in its application are illustrated for the *n*-propanol clathrate. The weight of the unit cell is calculated from its dimensions and density. This is converted into atomic weight units on the scale O = 16.000. The unit cell dimensions being in Ångstrom units and the atomic weights being taken on the chemical scale, the conversion is made by using an adjusted value for Avogadro's number. The cell weight in grams multiplied by this number 0.60236×10^{24} gives 3350.8 as the total weight of the cell in atomic weight units. There are six molecules of tri-*o*-thymotide in the cell which thus contains, in addition to oxygen, 198 carbon and 216 hydrogen atoms. It is necessary therefore to use C = 12.01 and H = 1.008 to find the weight of these molecules which amounts to 3171.7. The difference, $3350.8 - 3171.7 = 179.1$, is the weight of caged molecules. Use of approximate atomic weights 12 and 1 would introduce an error of nearly 4 units. An error of one part in a thousand in the total cell weight causes an error of about 3 units in the estimated weight of caged material. This is approximately the error of the determinations recorded in the tables. To find the number of caged molecules per cell the extra weight is divided by the molecular weight of an included molecule, in this case $179.1/60.1 = 2.98$ with an estimated probable error ± 0.06. Non-stoichiometric ratios, as in Table III, can be established if the included weight is known to an accuracy of about 3 units of weight. For the compound with $C_7H_{15}OH$ (molecular weight 116.2) the included weight is about 310, and gives the number of molecules per unit cell as 2.67. When compounds are "analyzed"

TABLE III

TRI-o-THYMOTIDE CHANNEL TYPE COMPOUNDS

Included molecule	l^a	Unit cell dimensions, Å (probable errors in units of 0.001 Å)		Density (20°) (gm/cm³)	No. of included molecules per unit cell
		a	c		
$C_5H_{11}OH$	9.4	14.310 ± 1	28.987 ± 2	—	—
C_4H_9I	9.6	14.252 ± 3	29.030 ± 5	1.207 ± 0.001	2.95 ± 0.03
$CH_3OC_4H_9$	10.1	14.232 ± 2	29.153 ± 2	1.117 ± 0.001	3.05 ± 0.05
$C_5H_{11}Br$	10.5	14.255 ± 1	29.137 ± 4	1.1747 ± 0.001	3.02 ± 0.03
$C_6H_{13}OH$	10.7	14.268 ± 1	29.159 ± 3	1.1238 ± 0.0005	3.02 ± 0.03
$C_5H_{11}I$	10.9	14.288 ± 3	29.127 ± 6	1.2155 ± 0.0005	3.03 ± 0.02
$C_2H_5OC_4H_9$	11.4	14.252 ± 2	29.268 ± 2	1.1216 ± 0.0007	3.00 ± 0.03
$C_7H_{15}OH$	11.9	14.31 ± 10	29.055 ± 6	1.1217 ± 0.0005	2.67 ± 0.06
$C_7H_{15}Br$	13.0	14.323 ± 8	29.033 ± 3	1.1586 ± 0.0006	2.40 ± 0.04
$C_8H_{17}OH$	13.2	14.307 ± 2	29.033 ± 2	1.1184 ± 0.0005	2.28 ± 0.02
$C_7H_{15}I$	13.4	14.321 ± 3	29.030 ± 5	1.1972 ± 0.0003	2.42 ± 0.02
$C_8H_{17}I$	14.7	14.278 ± 3	29.024 ± 6	1.1791 ± 0.001	1.95 ± 0.02
$C_{10}H_{21}OH$	15.7	14.2825 ± 0.5	29.192 ± 2	1.1251 ± 0.0005	2.00 ± 0.01
$C_{12}H_{25}OH$	18.2	14.314 ± 1	29.012 ± 6	1.1231 ± 0.0005	1.68 ± 0.02
$C_{16}H_{33}OH$	23.2	14.302 ± 1	29.050 ± 2	1.1263 ± 0.0005	1.32 ± 0.01
$C_{16}H_{33}Br$	24.4	14.311 ± 3	29.039 ± 2	1.1555 ± 0.001	1.36 ± 0.02
$C_{16}H_{33}I$	24.7	14.306 ± 3	29.056 ± 9	1.1298 ± 0.001	0.95 ± 0.04
$C_{18}H_{37}OH$	25.7	14.304 ± 1	29.060 ± 5	1.1263 ± 0.0005	1.19 ± 0.01
$C_{18}H_{37}Br$	26.9	14.322 ± 1	29.078 ± 2	1.1540 ± 0.001	1.26 ± 0.01
$C_{18}H_{37}I$	27.2	14.320 ± 2	29.044 ± 8	1.1664 ± 0.001	1.19 ± 0.01

^{a} l = maximum length of included molecule, Å.

in this way the nearest possible integral number of molecules per unit cell is known—in this case 3. If the analysis is purely chemical it is not possible to determine what is the nearest integer. An accurate analysis corresponding to 2.67 included molecules per unit cell of 6 tri-o-thymotide molecules might be represented by a formula giving a molecular ratio 2.25:1. The nearest ratio of small whole numbers might be 2:1, the same as that given by the assumption that 2.67 is an approximation for 3, or it might be 5:2 (2.5:1). If larger numbers, such as are found among molecular compounds, are permitted 2.67 could be simply the ratio 8:3. The possible integral values being, however, known from the structure investigation, the significance of any observed integral or nonintegral value can be assessed. Three molecules of $C_7H_{15}OH$ per unit cell would require an included weight of 348.6 instead of 310, i.e. the ratio could be 2:1 if the error in estimated weight were 38.6 units, or 11% of the included weight. This amounts to about 1% of the total cell weight. It is about ten times the probable error and this shows that both the whole numbers of Table II and the nonintegral values of Table III are real.

Definite conclusions on the stoichiometry of these compounds can thus be reached without a determination of detailed crystal structure, and indeed the atomic positions in these very complex structures are not known. The compositions given in Tables II and III rest firmly on physical measurements, and would stand if no structural interpretation were given. They have, however, a logical pattern which illustrates some of the stoichiometric relationships found in clathrates and other structures. This can be shown by comparison of the two series—one clathrate, the other not.

The β-hydroquinone clathrates, it was concluded, can be non-stoichiometric because they are clathrates. It will be seen further, that some of them not only can, but must, be non-stoichiometric. It might appear from consideration of only the tri-o-thymotide compounds listed, that those of Table II are stoichiometric because they are clathrates and those of Table III are non-stoichiometric because they are not clathrates. The former have the composition $2C_{33}H_{36}O_6 \cdot M$ and the caged molecule M must not exceed 9.4 Å in greatest length. They all have similar structures that may be assigned to the space group $P3_121$ (or its enantiomorph $P3_221$). All the unit cell dimensions for one of these crystals are greater than the corresponding dimensions of the similar crystal that contains a lower homologue. This is illustrated by the clathrates of n-alcohols where a increases from about 13.45 (methanol) to 13.7 Å (n-pentanol) with intermediate values for the homologues between them. The c spacing increases similarly from about 30.2 to 30.74 Å. No general sequence is found for all the cell dimensions if they are compared simply with the maximum length of the included molecule. Although therefore the different homologous series cannot be combined to give an exact sequence of cell dimensions related only to the maximum length of included molecule there is, for all the substances listed in Table II, the general trend that the larger the included molecule the larger the cell dimensions. The total increase in the n-alcohol series is about 0.5 Å for the c (30 Å) spacing and about half that amount for a which itself is a little less than $\frac{1}{2}c$. This must be due to increased distances between the tri-o-thymotide molecules consequent on the substitution of a larger included molecule, but the increase is in no way comparable with the increase in maximum molecular length which is from 4.6 in methanol to 9.4 Å in n-pentanol. In contrast, the cell dimensions of Table III vary less than 0.1 Å for a and only in one case by more than 0.2 Å for c, a and c being of magnitudes comparable with the a and c of the clathrate series. Also the variations, unlike those of the clathrate series show no *trend* that may be related to length of the included molecule. They appear at first sight erratic but have been shown to be in part periodic in relation to the increasing maximum molecular length. The steady increase in the clathrate series is therefore an adaptation of the cage size to increasing size of its imprisoned molecule. The limit of its extension is clearly reached at 9.4 Å length of included molecule and has been confirmed by observations on many compounds not included in these tables. It may be supposed that molecules of this size, or perhaps rather less, fairly well fill the cages. At this stage addition of a further CH_2 group would need a considerable increase, more than 1 Å, in the length of the cavity, and this might involve the creation of empty spaces in other parts of the structure where they are not required. This would lead to instability. When the size of included molecule is decreased by removal of CH_2 groups the cage structure cannot, however, decrease by comparable amounts. Clearly some of the space in the cages is not filled but, from the compositions, it appears that every cavity is occupied. All the compounds are prepared by crystallizing tri-o-thymotide from a solvent which becomes caged. The conditions are comparable with those of the preparation of β-hydroquinone clathrates from solvent, rather than from a dissolved gas, and the high concentration of enclosable molecules leads to fairly complete occupation of the cages. Except perhaps in the case of methanol, which appears reluctant in any case to form the clathrate, the inclusion of one molecule in the cage must, from the calculated molecular dimensions, take up more than half the free space. This ensures that no second molecule may enter and the unavoidable empty space may be an additional indirect influence which makes it difficult for a molecule, once trapped, to be removed so as to leave a vacant cage.

The channel type structures can be seen to be such from general considerations. The cell dimensions vary little, the primary effect being that the channels which run along the c direction undergo minor variations with the length of the included molecule. If its length is rationally related to the periodicities of the trithymotide structure that surrounds it, a molecule and its fellows in close sequence can be fitted into a more ordered and therefore slightly more compact array. The width of the channel is slightly less when its indentations can fit rhythmically with the protuberances of its inclusions (Fig. 7). This indirectly produces a corresponding slight *increase* in the periodic length of the channel but the over-all effect is a slight contraction of unit cell volume. X-ray diffraction effects from included molecules labelled with heavy scattering atoms such as halogens, directly show the channel array of these molecules and give independent determinations of the periodicity of the included material which need not be simply related to that of the tri-*o*-thymotide structure. These effects include continuous streaks parallel to the layer lines, on single crystal oscillation photographs, which determine the c dimension. They may lie in intermediate nonrational positions. These streaks, which are observed also when the crystal is not oscillated, may be regarded as the diffraction

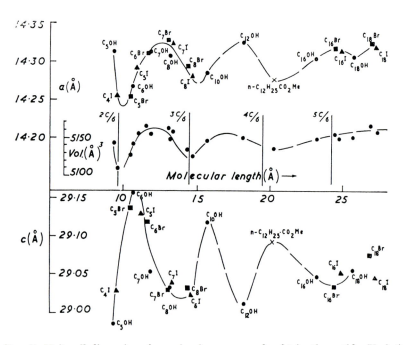

Fig. 7. Unit cell dimensions for molecular compounds of tri-*o*-thymotide. Variation of cell dimensions and volume with length of included molecule in channel. In the plots of a and c, alcohols shown by circles, bromides as squares, and iodides as triangles.

produced by the one-dimensional grating which the molecules in one channel constitute. When the spacing of this grating is divided into the corresponding value of the c dimension derived from the sharp diffraction spots produced by the thymotide structure, it should give the maximum number of molecules that can fit into a single channel of the unit cell containing six molecules of tri-o-thymotide. The result is an independent determination of an "ideal" composition. This is compared with the compositions found as described from unit cell weights. Figures are given in Table IV. A value from the cell weight less than the "ideal" could be explained by unoccupied spaces in the channels. The "ideal" value should not be lower than the other by an amount exceeding possible errors of measurement which are mainly in the "ideal" values derived from diffuse streaks. This error may be a few per cent and the requirement is seen to be satisfied by the results given in Table IV. The general agreement between the two sets of figures shows that in most cases the channels are completely filled. The inclusion in the channels of a molecule of the formula

$$CH_3 \cdot [CH_2]_7 \cdot CO \cdot CH_2 \cdot CO \cdot [CH_2]_7 \cdot CO \cdot CH_2 \cdot CO \cdot [CH_2]_7 \cdot CH_3$$

of maximum extended length 49.2 Å shows that the channels are continuous. It is the complete filling of continuous channels that requires the compounds to appear non-stoichiometric unless there is an accidental relationship between the length of included molecule and the c dimension. When such a relationship results in a simple ratio two possible general forms of structure could result. If there is a regular ordered structure with each included molecule related to its surroundings in the same way as every other, the unit cell may be a multiple of the original and there will be no streaks or similar anomalous x-ray diffraction. Such a compound would, in isolation, be regarded as stoichiometric. If, however, the material in the channels, though occupying space that leads to the simple ratio, is disordered in relation to its surroundings, e.g. by variable displacement in the direction of the channel length, the structure appears to be the same in nature as that of the non-stoichiometric members of Table III. In isolation such a compound would be described as stoichiometric as a result of chemical analysis. Structurally, if it were not known as one of a series, it might be regarded as stoichiometric but disordered. When it is known as one of a series it is perhaps best described as rational rather than stoichiometric. The ordered form (there are examples where one included substances gives both ordered and disordered forms) may be fairly described as stoichiometric but the difference between the two has become difficult to detect. One characteristic of simple compounds is that they have some range of existence with constant composition in

TABLE IV

Some Diffraction Effects Due to Molecules Included in the Tri-o-thymotide Channel Structure

Included molecule	Approx. length calc. for molecule in extended form (Å)	Spacing calc. from one-dimensional layer streaks (Å)	Assumed orders of observed streaks (c-axis oscillation)	No. of included molecules per unit cell	
				Ideal, calc. from spacing of third column	Calc. from unit cell weight
n-Butyl iodide	9.6	—	None observed	—	—
n-Pentyl bromide (A)[a]	10.5	8.8	1, 2	3.3	—
n-Pentyl bromide (B)[a]	10.5	9.6	1, 2[c]	3.0	3.02 ± 0.03
n-Pentyl iodide	10.9	—	None observed	—	—
n-Hexyl bromide	11.7	11	2	2.6	2.74 ± 0.12
n-Heptyl bromide	13.1	12	3	2.4	2.40 ± 0.04
n-Heptyl iodide	13.4	12.5	2, 3	2.3	2.40 ± 0.02
n-Octyl bromide	14.3	13.5	2, 3	2.1	2.14 ± 0.04
n-Octyl iodide (A)[a]	14.7	14.5	2, 4[b]	2.0	1.95 ± 0.02
n-Octyl iodide (B)[a]	14.7	—	None observed[e]	—	—
n-Hexadecyl bromide	24.4	24	3, 4, 5, 6, 7	1.2	1.36 ± 0.02

n-Hexadecyl iodide	24.7	24	4, 6, 7	1.2	0.95 ± 0.04
n-Octadecyl bromide	26.9	26	1, 2, 3, 4, 5	1.1	1.26 ± 0.01
n-Octadecyl iodide (A)[a]	27.2	27	2, 3, 4, 5, 6, 7, 8	1.1	1.19 ± 0.01
n-Octadecyl iodide (B)[a]	27.2	—	None observed	—	—
2-Bromooctane	13.1	12 × 2	1, 2, 3, 4, 6[f]	2.4	2.49 ± 0.02
Hexamethylene iodide	14.0	12.5	1, 2, 3[d]	2.3	—
Diethyl mercury	9.8	9.7	1, 3[c]	3.0	—
Methoxybutane	10.1	9.7	1[e]	3.0	3.03 ± 0.05
Ethoxybutane	11.4	9.7	1[e]	3.0	3.03 ± 0.04

[a] (A) (B) indicate that two crystalline forms are found.
[b] Coincident with 4th and 8th sharp layers.
[c] Coincident with 3rd, 3rd and 6th, or 3rd and 9th sharp layers.
[d] Also streaks corresponding to 3.5 Å.
[e] Additional sharp spots on 4th and 8th layers.
[f] Molecules presumed paired, head-to-head.

varying physical conditions. This applies, for example, to simple substances such as methane or sodium chloride. It might be possible to distinguish some of these more doubtful compounds by the application of
a test of this kind. A rational compound, whether ordered or not, might
have a very limited range of constancy. It is unlikely that the *coefficients
of thermal expansion* of the tri-*o*-thymotide channels and their molecular
contents will be the same. If the two parts of the structure could expand,
to some extent independently, a compound which was rational at one
temperature would not be so at another. It would then be regarded as
non-stoichiometric. There is a contrast here with clathrates for in this
case the cage controls the expansion. Small changes of temperature over
suitable ranges cannot alter the composition, whether stoichiometric or
not, unless there is decomposition through opening of the cages. In closed
cages there may be free space if the occupying molecule is too small, but
provided it is not large enough for another molecule, this space cannot
be occupied. Hence the fact of clathrate formation seems in this case to
favor a simple molecular ratio.

C. Bonding of Three Kinds—Covalent Bonds and Hydrogen Bonds Combined with van der Waals Bonds

When molecules are linked by hydrogen bonds some larger structural
component is formed. It may be a limited cluster of a definite number
of molecules or a polymer-like extended complex. This larger structure
can itself be treated as a molecule that may, with others, form the enclosing part of a clathrate. It could be argued that this applies to the two

TABLE V

RATIOS OF NUMBER OF CHROMAN MOLECULES $C_{18}H_{20}O_2$ TO ONE INCLUDED MOLECULE

2:1	6:1
Methanol	Bromobenzene
	1,3-Dibromopropane
3:1	*m*-Dichlorobenzene
Acetic acid	*o*-Dichlorobenzene
Carbon tetrachloride	Ethylene dibromide
Methyl iodide	Iodobenzene
Nitromethane	Tetrachlorethylene
Sulfur dioxide	Argon
4:1	7:1
Carbon disulfide	*p*-Bromanisole
Chloroform	2-Bromopyridine
Iodine	

TABLE VI

SUBSTANCES REPORTED TO FORM INCLUSION COMPOUNDS WITH THE CHROMAN

Acetone	Diethyl ether	Piperidine
Acetylacetone	Diisobutylene	Propionic acid
Benzene	Ethanol	Toluene
Benzylamine	Ethyl acetate	Triethylamine
Caproic acid	Formic acid	o-Xylene
Decalin	Isopropanol	m-Xylene
β,β-Dichlorodiethyl ether	Morpholine	p-Xylene
Diethylamine		

interpenetrating giant molecules of the β-hydroquinone clathrates. They are however more firmly linked than they would be by van der Waals forces alone. The hydrogen bonds and covalent bonds within each giant molecule are also the means of a binding, topological and not direct or chemical, between the two giant molecules. To this extent the strength of the cages depends on the strength of the hydrogen bonds and covalent bonds. The case has therefore been considered under bonds of two kinds.

All three types of bonding are involved in the cages formed by Dianin's compound (9). This compound forms crystalline inclusion complexes with a great variety of substances (see Tables V and VI). All the inclusion compounds examined are crystallographically similar (26). Referred to hexagonal axes they have a unit cell of $a = 27.0$ Å and $c = 11.1$ Å, the same as that of the chroman obtained without included material. A general interpretation of the crystal structure is shown in Fig. 8. The cluster

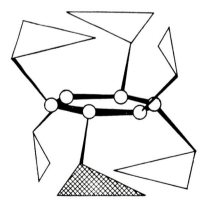

FIG. 8. Schematically the symmetrical relationship of six molecules of Dianin's chroman. Circles are OH groups. The lines pointing up or down from the hexagon of H-bonded OH groups are the links from OH to the rest of a molecule which is denoted by a triangle. Shaded triangle is nearest to observer from whom lines taper.

of six molecules forms a shape resembling a two-ended egg cup. This form is determined by the directions of the O—C links that slope outwards from the OH hexagon. These six bonds have a formal resemblance to the Fe—C octahedral bonds in $[Fe(CNCH_3)_6]^{2+}$ and basically the free space in the two instances is caused in the same way. Radiating arms make contacts with similar groups in neighboring clusters, thus fixing the total space between the center of the clusters. The projections of one group are prevented by these contacts from penetrating into the indentations of another group. The whole structure consists of these two-ended egg cups piled one on top of the other and it results in one cavity to every six molecules of the chroman. The distance in the c direction between equivalent hexagons of H-bonded OH groups is just over 11 Å so that the cavity is about twice as long in this direction as that in β-hydroquinone. Its other dimensions also must be correspondingly large. To include the molecules listed in the tables the cavities must be large, but evidence that they are nevertheless closed is provided by the formation of an argon clathrate which retains the gas firmly at room temperature. The molecular compositions may be represented as $6C_{18}H_{20}O_2 \cdot xM$ there being x molecules of M per cavity. Since from the observed cell dimensions the cavity is limited and very nearly the same in all compounds, the space required by a single molecule M fixes a maximum for x. All molecules listed in these tables are of a size that could be included. Some of the larger have $x = 1$ (ratio 6:1) but many smaller molecules give higher values for x, e.g. the ratio 3:1. When there is a sufficiently small molecule such as CH_3OH a ratio 2:1 is possible because three molecules may fit in a single cavity. For larger molecules a 3:1 ratio is possible if the included molecule is not more than half as long as the cavity, which then may contain two molecules.

For larger molecules up to a limiting size there can be only one molecule per cavity. The ideal compositions are therefore 2:1, 3:1, 6:1. If some available space is not occupied an included molecule may appear under a higher ratio than the ideal corresponding to its size. It never appears under a lower ratio.

D. Bonds of Four Kinds—van der Waals Bonds Combined with Ionic, Covalent, and Hydrogen Bonds

Crystals of some hydrated quarternary ammonium salts are related structurally to the gas hydrates. The similarity (11, 16) is so close that they have been described as clathrate hydrates, although in this instance there is no enclosed component which has *only* a van der Waals interaction with the surrounding cage. Examples of this type are a tetragonal series of tetra-n-butylammonium salts

$$[(n\text{-}C_4H_9)_4N^+]_nX^{n-}\cdot nyH_2O$$

where X is F$^-$, Cl$^-$, Br$^-$, CH$_3$CO$_2^-$, CrO$_4^{2-}$, WO$_4^{2-}$, C$_2$O$_4^{2-}$, HCO$_3^-$, HPO$_4^{2-}$, and y is approximately 32. A similar but orthorhombic series of tetraisoamylammonium salts of type

$$[(\text{iso-}C_5H_{11})_4N^+]_nX^{n-}\cdot ny'H_2O$$

has been prepared where X is F$^-$, Cl$^-$, CrO$_4^{2-}$ or WO$_4^{2-}$, and y' is approximately 40. The hydrate of tetra-n-butylammonium benzoate has the composition

$$[(n\text{-}C_4H_9)_4N^+]\cdot C_6H_5COO^-\cdot 39\tfrac{1}{2}H_2O$$

with approximately 40 water molecules but is tetragonal and structurally related to the other tetra-n-butyl compounds with about 32H$_2$O. In all these compounds the water structure is a hydrogen bonded clathrate framework in the cavities of which the tetraalkylammonium cations are located. A structural unit of the hydrogen bonded cage is the pentagonal dodecahedron of composition H$_{40}$O$_{20}$. Such dodecahedra share faces and therefore give rise to other larger polyhedra, tetrakaidecahedra and pentakaidecahedra, which form cages enclosing the cations. The anions are hydrogen bonded to the water framework, which is not necessarily the same for all compounds. The nitrogen of the cation is at a common vertex of four large water polyhedra. The radiating alkyl groups stretch into hydrogen bonded cages. Formation of such clathrate hydrates depends on the ability of the anions to link by hydrogen bonds to the water structure. Fluoride ion is therefore the most effective of the halides, and the oxygen-containing anions including acetate, carbonate, oxalate, benzoate, are suitable. The cations, which apart from their polar interaction, have a space occupying function similar to that of chemically inert gas molecules in the gas hydrates, should be such which do not form hydrogen bonds.

Of particular interest in relation to the stoichiometry (4) of these compounds is the structure of tetra-n-butylammonium benzoate hydrate. The clathrate framework is the same as that in the other tetra-n-butylammonium salts, but contains four tetra-n-butylammonium groups per unit cell, whereas many other members of this tetragonal series have five such groups. Owing to the need to accommodate the alkyl and benzyl groups, various distortions of the water framework occur and both positional and orientational disorders occur. The number of water molecules in the framework is affected by the incorporation of anion-oxygen atoms, and by some vacancies that are a result of the presence of other components in the structure. Evidence has been found also of water molecules within some of the pentagonal dodecahedra. There is a need for much detailed investigation here, before all the possible compositions, stoichiometric and non-stoichiometric, can be understood. In view of the nature of double gas hydrates, in which different inert molecules may occupy cavities of different kinds in the same structure, it seems possible that ionic structures, hydrated or similarly combined with other hydrogen bonded components, may be found capable of enclosing inert molecules as well as ions. If alkylamine molecules as well as alkylammonium ions could take part in clathrate hydrate formation, as is suggested by the observations of Waller (cf. Section III, B, 1), there seems a possibility here of forming a non-stoichiometric series by part substitution of one for the other.

From the empirical structural side the general conclusion concerning the relationship of clathrate formation to stoichiometry is therefore that each structure must be considered separately. Some structure determination, though not necessarily great detail, is required before the ideal numerical ratios of components can be established. Ordinary "simple" ratios are as likely as any others to imply non-stoichiometry. Owing to the complexities of structures in which more than one type of clathrate cavity is present, it may be necessary to consider several separate ratios between enclosed and enclosing components, the overall ratio resulting from the sum of these. All clathrates are potentially non-stoichiometric since some cavities may be unoccupied. When there are several cavity types the different ratios may differ in their closeness to the ideal. Particularly with water as the former of clathrate cages there is a possibility of non-stoichiometry through some of the cages being occupied by other molecules of the cage former. However the closed and limited nature of the clathrate cavity is itself a factor which favors a stoichiometric formula in whole groups of clathrates.

IV. EQUILIBRIUM RELATIONSHIPS AND NON-STOICHIOMETRY IN CLATHRATES

The equilibrium relationships in clathrates have been the subject of several investigations, and the conclusions are of special significance in relation to the stoichiometry of these compounds. Thermodynamically the clathrate is regarded as a solution of a gas in a solid, and there is in the β-hydroquinone series and the gas hydrates the complication that the solid solvent is metastable relative to the normal solid structure of the substance which forms the clathrate cage. The clathrate complex is stabilized by the interaction of the caged molecules with their surroundings which is similar to that between the adjacent molecules in a liquid. If all the cavities of the normal hydroquinone-type clathrate were empty the structure would be that of the metastable β-hydroquinone. Provided that a sufficient fraction of the cavities is occupied by enclosed molecules, the crystal is thermodynamically stable relative to the system consisting of the enclosed component as gas plus α-hydroquinone. α-Hydroquinone is the normal stable form of crystalline hydroquinone.

Experimentally the stability of clathrates presents a special problem concerning heterogeneous equilibria. Some direct experiments may not have achieved true decomposition pressures, but the difficulty was overcome by van der Waals and Platteeuw (23) who added a solvent to the system. Provided that the added liquid does not form a clathrate and is of low volatility the decomposition pressure measured should be the same as the true decomposition pressure. It was thus possible to make equilibrium measurements within a day or so. The variation with composition of the vapor pressures of argon–hydroquinone clathrates was found to obey a Langmuir-type isotherm. The heats of formation at constant pressure per three moles of hydroquinone can be derived from calorimetric measurements of the difference between heats of solution of clathrate compound and an equivalent amount of α-hydroquinone (9a). ΔH, the heat content change in the exothermic reaction

$$3C_6H_4(OH)_2 + xM = 3C_6H_4(OH)_2 \cdot xM$$

(solid α-hydroquinone) (gas)   (solid clathrate compound)

has been measured for various values of x, the fraction of spaces filled (9a). A linear relationship is obtained and this is in accordance with the assumption that the trapped molecules, which are widely separated, do not have an appreciable interaction with each other. The energy of interaction of a gaseous molecule and the β-hydroquinone cage can therefore be calculated. Allowance is made for the energy difference between α- and β-hydroquinone. The energy of interaction in kcal per mole of enclosed component, at 25°C, i.e. the heat evolved in the reaction

$$3C_6H_4(OH)_2 + M = 3C_6H_4(OH)_2 \cdot M$$

(solid   (gas)
β-hydroquinone)

is then found to be 6.0 for argon, which is considerably greater than the energy of interaction of argon atoms in the liquid and solid states; for argon the heat of vaporization at the boiling point in the same units is 1.56 and the heat of sublimation at absolute zero is 2.03. This may be attributed to the larger number of contacts made by an enclosed atom compared to the number it has in the liquid or solid. The large number of atoms required to form a clathrate cage has already been mentioned. Apart from this there is a second effect that in the liquid or solid each contact involves two like atoms and so the number of contacts must be divided by two when the total interatomic force in solid or liquid is considered, whereas this is not the case for the clathrate.

On the theoretical side the free energy function of the clathrate crystal has been derived (*33*, *33a*), by a statistical mechanical technique analogous to that used for describing ideal localized adsorption. Certain assumptions have to be made. (*a*) The enclosed molecules are taken to be nearly spherical; this should be valid for the inert gases. (*b*) There will never be more than one atom in a cage. This seems spatially a necessity in the case considered. (*c*) There is no interaction between the atoms enclosed in different cages. This cannot be completely true but the neglected effects must be small, and have in some cases been shown to be so (see Chapter 10, Section IV, C for the effect of neighboring N_2 molecules on the paramagnetic resonance of O_2 in the β-hydroquinone-O_2, N_2 clathrate). (*d*) The vibrational modes of the hydroquinone lattice are unaffected by the enclosed material. This is a reasonable assumption unless there is distortion of the cage to accommodate molecules of particular shapes. Such distortion can be found from crystal structure measurements and is practically absent for the hydroquinone–argon clathrate. Some of the characteristics of the nuclear quadrupole resonance spectrum of the nitrogen clathrate were attributed to slight distortions of the cavities (Chapter 10, Section IV, B).

Consider an assembly of Nm molecules of hydroquinone and $N\theta$ molecules of the enclosed component A, combined in a clathrate crystal having one cavity to every m hydroquinone molecules, and θ is the fraction of the total number, N, of these cavities occupied by A. The partition function for this assembly may be represented by

$$\exp\left(-\frac{G}{kT}\right) = \exp\left(-\frac{G^\circ}{kT}\right) \frac{N!}{[N\theta]![N(1-\theta)]!} Z_A(T)^{N\theta}$$

or, in terms of the free energy G

$$G/kT = G^\circ/kT + N\{\theta \ln \theta + (1-\theta)\ln(1-\theta)\} - N\theta \ln Z_A(T) \quad (1)$$

G° is the free energy of Nm molecules of hydroquinone in the empty β-hydroquinone modification at temperature T. The combinatorial factor in the first expression gives the number of distinct ways in which the A molecules can be distributed over the cavities and $Z_A(T)$ is the contribution of an encaged A molecule to the partition function. A similar form of partition function has been considered for the treatment of solubility of gases in water.

Before $Z_A(T)$ is evaluated some thermodynamic conclusions can be drawn from the general form of the partition function. The chemical potentials $\mu_A{}^\chi$ and $\mu_Q{}^\chi$ of the enclosed components A and hydroquinone Q in the clathrate crystal (χ) can be obtained from the free energy function.

For a change at constant temperature and volume in the assembly containing N_A molecules of A and N_Q molecules of Q

$$dG = \mu_A{}^\chi dN_A + \mu_Q{}^\chi dN_Q$$

Transformed to the variables N, θ instead of N_A, N_Q this equation becomes

$$dG = \mu_A{}^\chi (Nd\theta + \theta dN) + \mu_Q{}^\chi m dN$$

from which it follows that

$$\mu_A{}^\chi = (1/N)(\partial G/\partial \theta)_N$$

$$\mu_Q{}^\chi = (1/m)(\partial G/\partial N)_\theta - (\theta/mN)(\partial G/\partial \theta)_N$$

Substitution of Eq. (1) for G into these equations gives

$$\frac{\mu_A{}^\chi}{kT} = \ln \frac{\theta}{1 - \theta} - \ln Z_A(T)$$

$$\frac{\mu_Q{}^\chi}{kT} = \frac{\mu_Q{}^\beta}{kT} + \frac{1}{m} \ln (1 - \theta) \tag{2}$$

where $\mu_Q{}^\beta$ is equal to the chemical potential of solid β-hydroquinone. These two equations have implications for the phase behavior of systems involving Q and A.

Consider the equilibrium vapor pressure of the gas over a clathrate crystal. The chemical potential $\mu_A{}^g$ of the perfect gas A at temperature T is related to its partial pressure by

$$\frac{\mu_A{}^g}{kT} = \ln \frac{P_A}{kT} - \ln z_A(T)$$

where $z_A(T)$ is the partition function of a gaseous molecule of A with the volume factor removed. Thermodynamic equilibrium between clathrate and gas will exist if $\mu_A{}^\chi = \mu_A{}^g$ that is when

$$P_A = kT \frac{z_A(T)}{Z_A(T)} \cdot \frac{\theta}{1 - \theta} \tag{3}$$

Therefore at a given temperature the equilibrium pressure of A over the crystal depends on θ according to a Langmuir-type isotherm.

When the solid clathrate (S^x) is simultaneously in equilibrium with α-hydroquinone (S^α) and a gas phase (g) a second condition also applies,

$$\mu_Q{}^x = \mu_Q{}^\alpha$$

where $\mu_Q{}^\alpha$, is the chemical potential of α-hydroquinone. Substitution for $\mu_Q{}^x$ in Eq. (2) gives

$$\mu_Q{}^\alpha = \mu_Q{}^\beta + (kT/m) \ln (1 - \theta)$$

The difference ($\mu_Q{}^\beta - \mu_Q{}^\alpha$), 82 cal/mole, is determined by the properties of the two crystalline modifications, α and β, of hydroquinone and, as a function of temperature, may be denoted by $\delta(T)$. Then

$$\ln (1 - \theta) = -m\delta(T)/kT \qquad (4)$$

Equations (3) and (4) between the variables P_A, T, and θ together determine the three-phase equilibrium between α-hydroquinone, clathrate, and gas. A relationship between the pressure P_A of the gas and the temperature may be obtained by elimination of θ from these equations. This gives the position of the three-phase line in a temperature-pressure diagram.

Since the right hand side of Eq. (4) is a function of temperature but independent of the nature of the gas, the value of θ, and therefore the composition of the clathrate, it should vary with T along the three-phase line in an identical manner for all hydroquinone clathrates to which the starting assumptions apply. The variation of composition with temperature has been estimated. Equation (4) and the Gibbs-Helmholtz relation give

$$\frac{\partial \ln (1 - \theta)}{\partial T} = -m \frac{\partial [\delta(T)/kT]}{\partial T} = m \frac{H_Q{}^\beta - H_Q{}^\alpha}{RT^2}$$

where ($H_Q{}^\beta - H_Q{}^\alpha$) is the difference in molar enthalpy between β- and α-hydroquinone. A value 0.16 kcal/mole has been estimated for this difference and this leads to

$$\partial \ln (1 - \theta)/\partial T = 2.7 \times 10^{-3} \text{ deg}^{-1} \qquad (5)$$

For the argon-β-hydroquinone clathrate θ is about one-half along the three-phase line. The order of magnitude of the change with temperature may be obtained from $\theta = 0.34$ at $25°$ and 0.28 at $60°$ in agreement with Eq. (5).

Van der Waals (33) carried the calculation of the thermodynamic properties of these clathrates a stage further by evaluating the factor $Z_A(T)$ in Eq. (1).

Lennard-Jones and Devonshire had already developed a cell theory to explain the thermodynamic properties of the liquid states in a quantitative manner (see Chapter 2, Section III). Each molecule in the liquid is assumed to be contained within a space by neighboring molecules which move randomly around the central molecule. The potential within the cell is assumed to be spherically symmetrical, and the contributions to it of each molecule making up the cell are smeared over the surface of a sphere. In the hydroquinone clathrate crystal, the center of the cavity is surrounded by 12 oxygen atoms at 3.9 Å, 6 carbon atoms at 4.2 Å, and 6 carbon atoms at 3.8 Å. These with 18 adjacent hydrogen atoms are fairly evenly distributed therefore over the surface of a sphere of radius about 3.95 Å. The cell approximation made in the theory of Lennard-Jones and Devonshire is likely to be, if anything, more accurate for the hydroquinone clathrate cavity than for the more variable cells of a liquid structure. The energy of interaction $\phi(r)$ between pairs of molecules in the liquid was taken to be

$$\phi(r) = 4\epsilon \left[\left(\frac{\sigma}{r}\right)^{12} - \left(\frac{\sigma}{r}\right)^{6} \right]$$

where r is the distance between the centers of the two molecules and the constants ϵ and σ are obtained from measurements of pressure, volume, and temperature of appropriate gases. Van der Waals applied the model to clathrates by using intermolecular force parameters derived from the second virial coefficients of the gas concerned, together with reasonable values for the intermolecular force constants for the interaction between two elements of the cell wall. This gives good agreement with the values of heat of formation and with the three-phase point pressures and compositions.

It is thus established that the hydroquinone clathrates are necessarily non-stoichiometric, with a considerable and temperature-dependent deviation from the state in which every cavity is filled. From Eq. (4) it is seen that θ, whose limiting value is 1.0 when all cavities are occupied, is larger the larger $\delta(T)$. For hydroquinone $\delta(T)$ is relatively small and this accounts for the comparatively large numbers of unoccupied cavities. In simple terms the clathrate is stabilized relative to α-hydroquinone by a comparatively small amount of interaction between gas molecules and the cages. In the gas hydrates $\delta(T)$ may be relatively large and the values of θ should be closer to unity (see Chapter 6, Section IX, A), but there should still be departures from the strict stoichiometric formulas and these may be expected to vary with temperature along the three-phase line ice-hydrate-gas.

REFERENCES

1. Allen, K. W., *J. Chem. Soc.* p. 4131 (1959).
2. Baker, W., Gilbert, B., and Ollis, W. D., *J. Chem. Soc.* p. 1443 (1952).
3. Baker, W., and McOmie, J. F. W., *Chem. & Ind.* (*London*) p. 256 (1955).

4. Bonamico, M., Jeffrey, G. A., and McMullan, R., *J. Chem. Phys.* (in press).
5. Claussen, W. F., *J. Chem. Phys.* 19, 259, 662, 1425 (1951).
6. Clemm, A., *Ann. Chem. Liebigs*, 110, 357 (1859).
7. Cromer, D. T., and Larson, A. C., *Acta Cryst.* 15, 397 (1962).
8. Davy, Sir H., *Phil. Trans. Roy. Soc. London* 101, 30 (1811).
9. Dianin, A. P., *J. soc. phys.-chem. russe* 46, 1310 (1914).
9a. Evans, D. F., and Richards, R. E. *Proc. Roy Soc.* (*London*) A223, 238 (1954).
10. Faraday, M., *Quart. J. Sci. Lit. and Arts* 15, 71 (1823).
11. Feil, D., and Jeffrey, G. A., *J. Chem. Phys.* 35, 1863 (1961).
12. Hartley, H., and Thomas, N. G., *J. Chem. Soc.* 89, 1013 (1906).
13. Hofmann, K. A., and Arnoldi, H., *Ber.* 39, 339 (1906).
14. Hofmann, K. A., and Küspert, F., *Z. anorg. u. allgem. Chem.* 15, 204 (1897).
15. Lawton, D., and Powell, H. M., *J. Chem. Soc.* p. 2339 (1958).
16. McMullan, R., and Jeffrey, G. A., *J. Chem. Phys.* 31, 1231 (1959).
17. Mylius, F., *Ber.* 19, 999 (1886).
18. Nikitin, B. A., *Doklady Akad. Nauk. U.S.S.R.* 24, 567 (1939).
19. Nikitin, B. A., Kovalskaya, M. P., and Pushlenkov, M. F., *Izvest. Akad. Nauk U.S.S.R.* p. 661 (1951).
20. Palin, D. E., and Powell, H. M., *J. Chem. Soc.* p. 208 (1947).
21. Pauling, L., "The Nature of the Chemical Bond," 3rd ed. Cornell Univ. Press, Ithaca, New York, 1960.
22. Pauling, L., and Marsh, R. E., *Proc. Natl. Acad. Sci. U.S.* 38, 112 (1952).
23. Platteeuw, J. C., and van der Waals, J. H., *Mol. Phys.* 1, 91 (1958).
24. Powell, H. M., *J. Chem. Soc.* p. 61 (1948).
25. Powell, H. M., and Bartindale, G. W. R., *J. Chem. Soc.* p. 799 (1945).
26. Powell, H. M., and Wetters, B. P. D., *Chem. & Ind.* (*London*) p. 256 (1955).
27. Rayner, J. H., and Powell, H. M., *J. Chem. Soc.* p. 319 (1952); p. 3412 (1958).
28. Rheinboldt, H., *Liebigs Ann. Chem.* 451, 256 (1927).
29. Roozeboom, H. W. B., *Rec. trav. chim.* 3, 59 (1884); 4, 65 (1885).
30. Spallino, R., and Provenzal, G., *Gazz. chim. ital.* 39, (II) 325 (1909).
31. von Stackelberg, M., *Naturwissenschaften* 36, 327, 359 (1949).
32. Terres, E., and Vollmer, W., *Z. Petroleum* 31, 1 (1935).
33. van der Waals, J. H., *Trans. Faraday Soc.* 52, 184 (1956).
33a. van der Waals, J. H., and Platteeuw, J. C., *Advances in Chem. Phys.* 2, 1 (1959).
34. Waller, J. G., *Nature* 186, 429 (1960).
35. Wöhler, F., *Ann. Chem. Liebigs* 69, 297 (1849).

CHAPTER 8

Lloyd C. Fetterly
*Shell Development Co.,
Emeryville, California*

Organic Adducts

I. Introduction.. 491
II. Historical... 494
III. Urea Channel Adducts... 497
  A. Structure of Complexes.. 497
  B. Composition and Density... 503
  C. Stability of Urea Complexes..................................... 508
  D. Thermodynamics of Urea Complexes................................ 515
  E. Reaction Rate Studies—Inhibitors and Accelerators.............. 524
IV. Thiourea Channel Adducts... 530
  A. Crystal Structure... 531
  B. Properties of Thiourea Complexes................................ 534
V. Other Channel Inclusion Complexes................................. 538
  A. Carbohydrate and Protein Types.................................. 538
  B. Polynuclear Organic Channel Adducts............................. 538
  C. Mineral and Organometallic Complexes............................ 540
VI. Soluble "Complex" Phenomena...................................... 541
VII. Applications of Inclusion Complexes.............................. 551
  A. Selective Separation of Hydrocarbon Fractions................... 551
  B. Purification of Natural Products................................ 555
  C. "Molecular Packaging" of Chemicals............................. 556
  D. New Laboratory Techniques....................................... 558
  E. Stereospecific Polymerizations.................................. 560
  F. Channel Reactions.. 563
  References.. 563

I. INTRODUCTION

The words *complex* and *adduct* came into common use during the formative years of synthetic organic chemistry to designate substances which do not appear to be held together by classical chemical bonds. This group soon included a growing number of materials whose bonding was not well understood until the advent of new concepts regarding their structure.

491

Among them are the picrates of polynuclear hydrocarbons, which have long been familiar to the organic chemist. These substances, sometimes referred to as molecular compounds or adducts, appear to be binary complexes with no discrete bonds between the two components. They have sharp melting points and always show integral values for molecular ratios. The stability of their crystalline structure depends upon fairly strong interaction forces between oppositely charged permanent dipoles, dipole induction effects, and dispersion forces which cause the components to arrange in whole number ratios. Other complexes combined in whole number ratios which owe their stability to strong hydrogen bonding between the components are the urea-acetone, urea-hydrogen peroxide, and the urea or thiourea adducts of cholesterol. In many complexes the bonding forces are quite strong and vary widely in nature, including π bonded materials such as ferrocene, and Werner-type coordination compounds. All such complexes exist in an associated form in the solvent from which they are crystallized, with the same whole number ratio of components as in their crystallized form.

In contrast to the above compounds, we will describe in detail in this chapter a more recently discovered class of complexes known as channel or canal inclusion adducts. One of the most striking features first observed with this new class of materials was their lack of conformity to the classical law of simple multiple proportions. These tubular structures are related to the hydroquinones, hydrates, and other cage or *clathrate* (imprisoned) complexes named by Powell (*74, 75, 76*) who first investigated the crystal structures of several of these unique substances and, in fact, pointed out the importance of this whole new area of non-stoichiometric complexes. The most widely known examples of the channel adducts are the urea–*n*-paraffin, thiourea–branched-chain paraffin, and Schardinger cyclodextrin types. These substances were designated by early German investigators (*87*) as "Einschlussverbindungen" or inclusion compounds. In this class the molecules of one component are bound together, usually by hydrogen bonds, to give rise to large, cage-like or tubular intertwining polymer networks in which molecules of the second component may become trapped or stabilized through weak dispersion or van der Waals forces. The compound which traps or encloses another molecule has become known as the *host*, and molecules or atoms which become enclosed are often called *guest* molecules. Two unique properties of these substances are that they do not exist in solution in exactly the same form as they do in the crystalline state and their constituents do not exist as crystalline aggregates in ratios of exact whole numbers. They form only as continuous crystalline host lattices and not as molecules or complexes of the ordinary sense and sometimes appear to have no strong stabilizing forces. In spite of this lack of conventional bonding many of these complexes are quite stable.

An unusual property of the organic channel adducts is that their stability depends in part upon a very exact fit (according to van der Waals dimensions) within the cavity or cavities which the host molecule can form. For the first time we are dealing with substances which depend on *size and shape*, of the guest, for interaction and not on strong bonding forces of the classical type. In fact, materials with strong force fields of one sort or another do not form this new crystalline product. The channel and clathrate inclusion complexes have a somewhat related inorganic analogy in the continuous channel structures created by the three-dimensional arrays of the natural and synthetic zeolites such as faujasite which are now known as Barrer (*10*) molecular sieves and are discussed extensively in Chapter 6. In these and the organometallic ligand arrays of the Werner-type, as well as some hydroquinones, the host molecules can exist in their open network structures without the support of the guest molecules. In many other clathrates, such as the hydrocarbon hydrates and the channel urea and thiourea inclusion adducts, this is not possible.

The author and co-workers (*5*) have designated a new area of selective separations by such complex formation as *extractive crystallization.* by analogy to the nonideal *extractive distillation* separations. Extractive crystallization with urea, thiourea, water, Werner organometallic complexes, or other organic adduct forming host molecules is one of the newest commercial and laboratory separation techniques. Whereas well-known procedures such as adsorption and distillation separate molecules by class and size, adduct formation (adduction) permits segregation on the additional basis of shape of molecules. For example, complexes formed with agents such as urea, thiourea, 4,4'-dinitrodiphenyl, cyclodextrins, desoxycholic acid, spirochromans, tri-o-thymotide, triphenylmethanes, and others exist as extended channel configurations in which both the cross section and length of the extracted molecule are important variables determining the degree of reaction and selectivity of separation. In the clathrate group of hydrocarbon hydrates, hydroquinones, Werner ligand complexes, and related substances, smaller and more spherical molecules including the rare gases may be trapped. By employing extractive crystallization techniques, difficult separations of gases and liquids sometimes are possible which cannot be accomplished by usual methods. These inclusion complexes have the unique characteristic of permitting the isolation of gases, liquids, and waxy solids in a new and more easily handled form.

II. HISTORICAL

The discovery that urea forms crystalline adducts with long, straight-chain organic compounds was made accidentally by Bengen (11, 12) in 1940 while conducting tests with urea in a study of its action on proteins in pasteurized milk. He noted under certain conditions the fat separates out in such a form as to justify the use of urea in a method for determining the fat content in milk. When he was bothered by what appeared to be frothing and an emulsion, he added a small amount of n-octyl alcohol and set aside his samples. Later, he observed long crystals at the interface of the liquid layers. On attempting to reproduce these unexpected crystals, he made the classic discovery that they also form when saturated aqueous urea solution is mixed with n-octanol. From this point, investigation soon extended the adduct formation to include higher alcohols, acids, and finally n-paraffins and other straight-chain compounds.

After Bengen's discovery became known through the Technical Oil Mission publications (11), the author (26, 27, 64, 81, 94) discovered the complementary class of thiourea–branched-chain paraffin, naphthene, CCl₄, and ketone complexes while attempting to find a new complexing substance which would react more readily with the very low octane n-par-affins contained in gasolines than urea does. In France, Angla (1, 2) work-ing independently, reported similar complexes between thiourea and organic compounds of the terpene, camphene, cyclohexane, and chloro-paraffin classes. It remained for Smith (95, 96), Hermann and Lenné (43), and W. Schlenk (87) to clarify the puzzle these substances presented by determining their spatial array by x-ray analysis. They consist of the same type of channel inclusion complex as those involving urea but form a canal larger in diameter. The earliest studies of the thermodynamic properties, physical characteristics, uses, and other aspects of the urea and thiourea channel inclusion complexes were reported by W. Schlenk (13, 87, 88, 91), Redlich et al. (80, 81), Zimmerschied and co-workers (112), H. Schlenk (85), Fetterly (27, 28), Linstead (54), and other in-vestigators (21, 48, 100). Several reviews of this important field have been published by Kobe (49), W. Schlenk (91), H. Schlenk (86), Truter (103), McLaughlin (59), Mandelcorn (56), Swern (100), Fetterly (30), and Cramer (22).

The urea and thiourea inclusion complexes are not the first of the class of molecular complexes discovered wherein the partners are not united in whole number ratios. The chlorine hydrate, $6H_2O \cdot (\simeq)Cl_2$, was discovered by Davy (23) in 1811. A number of hydrates of the same type including the hydrocarbon hydrates have been prepared subsequently. It was not until 1949 that the true nature of these materials was accurately demonstrated by the x-ray studies of von Stackelberg (98, 99). Powell and co-workers (68, 74) were the first to describe these and related substances as clathrate inclusion structures. Their basic studies of the clathrates together with the analysis of the urea and thiourea complexes by Smith (96), Hermann and Lenné (43, 53) are landmarks among the successes of the x-ray technique. In fact, there is no other known method by which unequivocal identification of clathrates and inclusion compounds can be made.

The first channel inclusion complexes to be correctly identified appear to be those of the choleic acids. Cholic acid, $C_{24}H_{40}O_5$, a bile acid, was discovered by Strecker in 1848. Later, two more acids were isolated from bile; they were first named choleic acid and desoxycholic acid ($C_{24}H_{40}O_4$). Wieland and Sorge (109) were attempting to distill choleic acid under high vacuum and observed the appearance of palmitic, stearic, and oleic acids together with desoxycholic acid. Further investigation disclosed that many other straight-chain acids and even n-paraffins would give reversible complexes. The name *choleic acids* has now been broadened to include all types of complexes with the various bile acids including apocholic acid. In 1934 Go and Kratky (37) reported on their x-ray studies of these substances showing that the basic lattices of all the choleic acids, composed of desoxycholic acid and the separate members of the homologous series of aliphatic monobasic fatty acids, are the same. However, the ratio of the weight of the desoxycholic acid in the elementary cell to the weight of fatty acid is not always an integer. This evidence led Go and Kratky to postulate a channel inclusion complex structure. A number of, as yet unexplained, properties of these substances together with some controversy regarding the interpretation of results hindered early acceptance of these materials as actual clathrate complexes.

Gomberg (38) in 1930 reported unusual interaction between triphenylmethyl free radical and paraffins such as n-decane. These and the related triphenylmethane complexes described earlier by Hartley (42) were unexplainable by classical theories. We now know that no interaction stronger than dispersion forces can exist between a n-paraffin and another molecule (except where there is definite bond cleavage) so that any compound or complex which contains this inert material must be of the inclusion type. Barlow and Clamp (9) have recently discovered that paraffin molecular complexes based on derivatives of 4,4'-dihydroxytriphenylmethane do form inclusion channels 6 Å or more in diameter. Channel n-paraffin clathrates prepared from methylnaphthalene by Milgrom (62) are also related to those of triphenylmethane.

Another important group of channel complexes was first characterized by Mikus and co-workers (61) in 1946 when their work on the amylose–

fatty acid and alcohol inclusion complexes was reported. The purple starch–iodine indicator aqueous end point color has long been known but only recently has x-ray analysis by Cramer (*22, 33*) shown that it results from a complex similar to the amylose–fatty acid adducts. Cramer discovered a number of unique inclusion compounds using Schardinger (*83*) cyclodextrins, which are discussed in Chapter 9 and, briefly, in this chapter. These have been found to differ from the urea and thiourea complexes in

TABLE I

TYPICAL ORGANIC CHANNEL INCLUSION COMPLEXES[a]

Host molecule	Channel diameter	Example guests[b]	References
Urea	5.25 Å	*n*-p, *n*-f, *n*-derivatives	*11, 12*
Thiourea	6.1	iso-*p*, naph, *n*-p above C_{16}	*2, 26*
Desoxycholic acid	5–6	*n*-p, *n*-f, arom	*109*
4,4'-Dinitrodiphenyl	5	*n*-p, diphenyls	*22, 44, 91*
Tri-*o*-thymotide	4.8–6.9 (channel, cage)	*n*-p, naph, iso-p	*22, 52, 74,* Chapt. 7
α-Cyclodextrin	6.0	*n*-p, *n*-f	*22, 84,* Chapt. 9
β-Cyclodextrin	7–8	*n*-p, *n*-f, benzoic acid	*22, 84,* Chapt. 9
γ-Cyclodextrin	9–10	arom	*22, 84,* Chapt. 9
Amylose starch	6	*n*-f, I_2	*61,* Chapt. 9
4,4'-Dihydroxytriphenyl-methane	6.0–6.5	*n*-p, iso-p	*9*
Triphenylmethane	6	*n*-p, iso-p	*38, 42*
Methylnaphthalene	6.0–6.5 (channel, cage)	*n*-p to C_{16}, iso-p	*62*
Spirochromans	5.5 est. (channel, cage)	*n*-p, iso-p	*36*
Cellulose		*n*-p, I_2	*22*

[a] Some configurations shown in Fig. 14.

[b] *n*-p = *n*-paraffins; *n*-f = *n*-fatty acid or alcohol; iso-p = isoparaffin; naph = naphthalene; arom = aromatic molecules or compounds.

that the host molecules can exist in an open doughnut-shaped structure without the stabilizing support of the guest molecule.

Since it is impossible to predict molecular crystalline structure a priori, the discovery of a new clathrate has been and still is a matter of chance. There are some features common to several, such as the three-dimensional hydrogen bonding of some, and the bulky layer-like structure of others, which have led to stable complexes. Table I lists several of those substances known to form inclusion complexes with normal and branched-chain paraffins and fatty acids. The properties of these, especially the urea and thiourea adducts are the subject of this chapter. One major result from a study of these materials has been new insight into the theory of aqueous solutions that is also discussed in this chapter.

III. UREA CHANNEL ADDUCTS

A. Structure of Complexes

The urea and thiourea hydrocarbon molecular complexes differ from the clathrates in that they form channel rather than cage structures. X-ray investigations of the urea–n-paraffin hydrocarbon complexes by Smith (95, 96), Hermann and Lenné (43), W. Schlenk (87), and more recently by Lenné (53) and Kutzelnigg et al. (50) show that the urea molecules form a hollow channel just large enough to accommodate the planar zigzag hydrocarbon molecule. According to Smith, complete Weissenberg data were taken for single crystals of cetane–urea and 1,10-dibromodecane–urea complexes. Powder patterns were also taken of urea complexes of C_{10} to C_{50} normal paraffins and various straight-chain alcohols, acids, and esters. All gave essentially identical powder patterns. The unit cell is hexagonal, space group $P6_12$ or $P6_52$ with $a = 8.230 \pm 0.004$ Å and $c = 11.005 \pm 0.005$ Å. There are six urea molecules per unit cell. The urea molecules form large interpenetrating helical spirals with the hydrocarbon molecules situated at the center. The major portion of the hydrocarbon chains are not freely rotating around their long axis and on a statistical time average occupy fixed positions in the channel. According to the simplest analysis there are three such positions situated approximately 120° from each other which may be occupied in a random fashion (see Chapter 10, Section II,B).

The structure of the urea complex is illustrated in Figs. 1 and 2. The packing arrangement looking along the c axis is shown in Fig. 2 in which the nearly circular dimensions of the channel formed by van der Waals radii of the atoms of the urea molecules are indicated. There are three

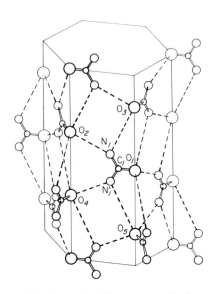

FIG. 1. Arrangement of hydrogen bonding in urea-n-hydrocarbon complexes (*96*).

interpenetrating spirals of urea molecules hydrogen bonded together to form the walls of the hexagonal channel lattice in the unit cell. These spirals are, by chance, in either the right- or the left-hand direction. Each oxygen is hydrogen bonded to four nitrogen atoms and each nitrogen to two oxygen atoms. The hydrogen bonds are essentially coplanar with the urea molecules and are of two types. The shorter bonds indicated by N_1—H$\cdots$O$_2$ and N_1'—H$\cdots$O$_4$ are about 2.93 Å in length. The longer bonds, N_1—H$\cdots$O$_3$ and N_1'—H$\cdots$O$_5$ are about 3.04 Å. Although the oxygen atoms of the urea molecules are each superimposed 3.7 Å apart along a vertical edge axis, the urea molecules are oriented 120° with respect to one another forming a helix spiral. The canal which forms has been called a *Hohlraum* by W. Schlenk (*87, 88*).

In order to more readily understand the nature of the binding forces involved in this very basic and theoretically important complex one must compare its structure and bonding with that of the individual urea and n-paraffin or fatty acid crystal lattices. The bond distance and intermolecular constants, including hydrogen bonds, for the urea-hydrocarbon complex and for tetragonal urea as determined by Wyckoff (*111*) are given in the following Table II.

In the tetragonal urea shown in Fig. 3 the hydrogen bonding between adjacent molecules results in a relatively open structure somewhat anal-

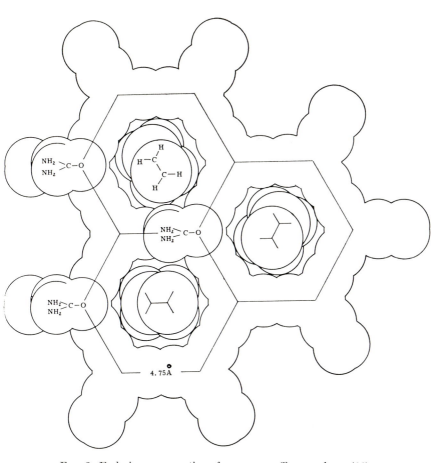

FIG. 2. End view cross section of urea-*n*-paraffin complexes (*96*).

ogous to the situation which occurs during ice formation. The maximum interaction between the urea molecules is therefore less than normal whereas in the urea-hydrocarbon complex they appear to be about normal through the added interaction with the *n*-paraffin chain. Although the urea crystals alone have a fairly open structure, inspection of Fig. 3 shows that the molecules are still too closely packed for a canal or other available free space in which guest molecules may be enclosed. Thus, there is a crystal transformation from the tetragonal to a hexagonal system when the adduct is formed. The simple experiment of reacting solid tetragonal urea with solid stearic acid or cetane, employing a trace of methanol as catalyst, readily demonstrates this transformation, with crystal structure

TABLE II

INTERATOMIC DISTANCES

Urea–hydrocarbon complexes		Tetragonal urea	
C—O	1.28 Å	C—O	1.26 Å
C—N	1.33 Å	C—N	1.33 Å
N_I—N_I'	2.30 Å	N—H···O	2.99 Å
N_I—H···O_2	2.93 Å	N—H···O	3.03 Å
N_I—H···O_3	3.04 Å		

change, evolution of heat, and change in density of the crystals taking place at room temperature.

Although some investigators (40, 57) have postulated the existence of an expanded channel urea structure without the n-paraffin being present, density measurements (27) indicate an immediate collapse of structure when the guest molecules are removed. As explained by Truter (103), the reason for the collapse of the clathrate-type structure on the removal of

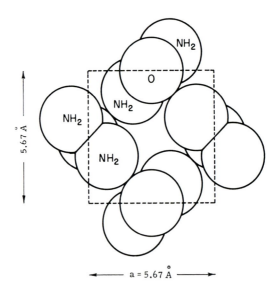

FIG. 3. Tetragonal urea structure (96, 111).

the endocytic (guest) component is best demonstrated by means of a mechanical analogy. Imagine an iris diaphragm which is being constrained to close down, but before it closes a rod is placed through it. The resistance of the rod to compression will then balance the forces tending to close the diaphragm, but if the rod is withdrawn, the diaphragm will close completely. In the same way the hydrogen bonds tends to make the urea honeycomb cells contract; while the endocytic component is present this force is resisted, but once it is removed, the contracting forces move the urea molecules from their alignment in the honeycomb walls and the structure collapses into the less open but now more stable tetragonal urea lattice.

The volume occupied by the n-paraffin or fatty acid in its pure crystalline state is essentially the same as that in the channel according to the x-ray structures, composition, and density measurements. There is little evidence normally of compression of the average van der Waals spacings which the C—H aliphatic bonds exhibit. X-ray and heats of reaction measurements (27, 28) show that the fatty acids and alcohols are aligned head-to-head through hydrogen bonding in the urea inclusion complex just as they are in their pure state. Smith (96) has noted that a certain amount of bending of longer paraffins into spaces created behind the shorter chains occurs in uncomplexed wax crystals. This cannot happen in the urea adduct. In their pure state and in a wide variety of inclusion complexes there is no evidence that forces of attraction exist between a paraffin chain and any similar adjacent molecule that is stronger than weak dispersion or van der Waals forces. Since these forces vary as the sixth power of the distance, they are extremely sensitive to configuration and do create zones of somewhat greater attraction depending on the fit between host and guest molecules. In the urea complex the closest possible approach between a carbon atom of the hydrocarbon and an oxygen atom of the urea is 4.1 Å which is larger than the normal van der Waals distances for these atoms. The packing distances between terminal paraffin chain methyl groups within the channel are about 4.1 Å which is normal for these substances in their solid states.

The higher stability hydrogen bonds which are created between the hydrogen atom of the NH_2 groups and oxygen of the adjacent urea molecules together with the increased van der Waals attraction through the additive interaction of the n-paraffin chain and the urea molecules are largely responsible for the stability of the urea and thiourea complexes. In these substances there is no need to assume any unusually strong interaction between the hydrocarbon and the urea molecules such as indicated by W. Schlenk (87) (about 2800 cal per CH_2 group) to explain the stability of the urea–n-paraffin complex. Similarly the presence of a strong coordination chemical bond as suggested by Angla (2) for the thiourea–CCl_4 complex is not necessary. The shorter N—H···O bonds in the urea complex and the tetragonal urea, 2.93 and 2.99 Å, respectively, differ by more than the probable error in the two structure determinations. An estimate (73) of the energy associated with a shortening of the N—H···O bond can be made by comparing known hydrogen bond distances as a function of known bond energies. Although data of this type are not available for N—H···O bonds, data for O—H···O systems, which are very similar in nature, indicate ΔH (shortening) of 0.3 kcal/mole for a change of bond distance of 0.01 Å. In Fig. 4 data of Huggins (45) shows this variation very clearly. Although the values will be slightly less for the N—H···O bond their variation in strength supports the conclusion that the observed shortening of the N—H···O bond together with the added van der Waals forces available are of the order of magnitude re-

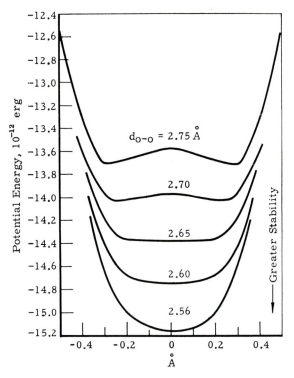

Fig. 4. Theoretical potential energy curves for OHO hydrogen bonds, assuming different O···O distances (45).

quired for the stabilization of the structure. In the urea–n-paraffin complexes these stabilization forces increase almost linearly with increasing chain length of the n-paraffin. They are sufficient to give only a weak n-heptane–urea complex, which readily decomposes at 25°C in the presence of other hydrocarbons, but very stable ones with n-hexadecane and higher n-paraffins which have stabilities approaching the melting point of urea (132.7°C).

An important point that is easily overlooked when considering the stabilizing forces of inclusion complexes of both the cage and channel types is that we have for the first time evidence of a new concept that a stronger hydrogen bond can exist *only* when it is supported by an otherwise inert surface capable of exerting only weak dispersion forces. Prior to the studies made on inclusion complexes this new driving force was unrecognized. Without the support of a paraffin, inert gas, or other fairly nonreactive molecule such substances as gas hydrates, urea, and thiourea complexes, and several other inclusion complexes just cannot exist. The author (*28*) has chosen to call attention to this fairly general phenomenon by naming these additionally stabilized bonds *supported hydrogen bonds*. If such bonds can exist to create stable crystalline arrays where the dimensions of the host and guest are very important, they must also exist in solutions, especially in water. In solutions the dimensions of the guest molecule need not be so critical and therefore the evidence for their formation is more general. Since the urea and thiourea complexes have a non-stoichiometric ratio between the guest and host molecules which is governed by crystalline dimensions, it is impossible for them to exist in solution in exactly the same form as they exist in the solid state. This phenomenon will be considered in more detail in Section VI.

B. Composition and Density

It is possible to calculate the composition of the urea-n-hydrocarbon complexes as a function of chain length of the n-hydrocarbon, directly from the crystal structure (*81, 88, 94, 96*). Taking 1.54 Å for the C—C bond distance, 109°28′ for the C—C—C bond angle (or 2.54 Å for the alternating bond distance) and 2.0 Å for the radius of a CH_3 group, the length of a hydrocarbon chain in the extended zigzag configuration is given by Smith (*94*) in the following equation:

$$\text{length (Å)} = 1.256\,(n - 1) + 4.0 \tag{1}$$

where n is the number of carbon atoms in the straight chain. Since the c-unit cell repeat distance in the urea–hydrocarbon complexes is 11.01 Å, and there are 6 urea molecules per unit cell, we may calculate that the urea/hydrocarbon mole ratio is

$$m = 0.684 \ (n - 1) + 2.175 \tag{2}$$

The measured values are in good agreement with the theoretical values as seen in Fig. 5 (27, 80). Redlich *et al.* (80) show agreement between the

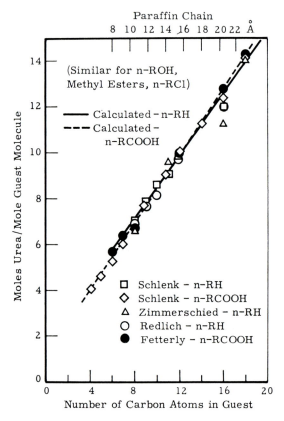

FIG. 5. Variation of molar ratio of urea complexes with number of carbon atoms in guest molecule (27, 80, 87, 112).

calculated composition of the complex and the experimentally determined values over the range *n* from 6 to 17 carbon atoms to be within experimental uncertainty as follows:

$$m = \text{mole ratio urea}/n\text{-paraffin} = 0.69n + 1.49 \text{ (calculated)} \tag{3}$$

$$m = \text{mole ratio urea}/n\text{-paraffin} = 0.65n + 1.51 \text{ (measured)} \tag{4}$$

These results clearly show the non-stoichiometric character of the urea inclusion compounds. Normally, it is by chance that an even numbered ratio occurs although Smith (96) finds that there is some tendency toward chain compression to provide an even ratio when the n-paraffin has a repeat spacing which matches that of the unit cell (see also Chapter 7, Section III,C for a similar effect in tri-o-thymotide channel complexes). For example, small deviations occur (96) when the chain length of the n-paraffin is slightly greater than a multiple of the height of a unit cell. In the case of C_7, $C_{16}C_{24}$, etc. the terminal methyl groups turn from the carbon plane so that the chain length is shortened to a multiple of 11.0 Å. It has been found that the height of the unit cell of the cetane complex is 22.0 Å rather than 11.0, confirming the expected turn of the methyl groups. The molar ratio, m, indeed, in this case is 12.0 instead of the value 12.57 which would be calculated from the usual spacings. The unusual agreement normally found between the calculated and measured ratios permits one to employ inclusion complexes as *molecular calipers* to measure questionable spacings in linear molecules. This is of more importance in the thiourea complex which has a larger channel dimension.

A study of the unit cell also shows that there are 1.83 Å of canal length per molecule of urea. If it were not for the larger end group packing spacing, the ratio of urea molecules to C atoms would be a constant 0.69. As the chain length of the n-paraffin increases, the end-group effects become negligible so that the complexes approach this constant ratio. The nearly linear relationship of many of the other properties with carbon number results from this fact. The composition of several urea complexes are given in Table III.

A number of other n-aliphatic organic compounds, besides the straight paraffinic chains, have been reacted with urea. Those of the fatty acid series have been studied by Redlich and co-workers (80), Truter (103), Fetterly (28), W. Schlenk (88), and others. Other series of complexes include those of the n-alcohols, esters, halides, diglycerides, dibasic acids, olefins, and many related normal aliphatic structures. Most recent studies have been carried out by Radell and co-workers who have reported several new homologous series involving maleate and fumarate esters (79), fluorinated esters (78), and organosilanes (77). Equations for the compositions of the n-fatty acids and alcohols formed at 25°C are given by Truter (104) as follows:

$$m \cong 0.71n + 1.08 \text{ for } n\text{-acids} \qquad (5)$$

$$m = 0.66n + 1.55 \text{ for } n\text{-alcohols} \qquad (6)$$

In Fig. 5 is shown a comparison of the experimentally measured values with those computed from the packing volume of the corresponding guest

506

TABLE III

COMPOSITION AND EQUILIBRIUM CONSTANTS OF UREA COMPLEXES AND INCREASE
OF HEAT CONTENT ON DECOMPOSITION (*80, 88*)

Reactant (guest)	Molal ratio urea/guest	Equilibrium constant (25°C) $(m.f.)_{Reactant}$	ΔH kcal/mole guest
Methyl ethyl ketone	3.78	0.64	4.7
Adipic acid	5.3	0.42	3.3
n-Heptane	6.1	0.57	7.3
n-Octane	6.73	0.28	9.7
1-Octene	6.3	0.51	7.3
trans-2-Octene	6.6	0.40	6.6
1-Octanol	6.7	0.34	7.3
2-Octanol	6.4	0.77	6.6
Di-*n*-butyl ether	6.5	0.64	9.3
n-Decane	8.1	0.09	13.1
1-Decene	7.8	0.15	11.6
1-Bromodecane	8.9	0.041	14.7
2-Bromodecane	7.6	—	—
n-Dodecane	9.3	0.022	16.1
Myristic acid	11.1	0.0029	22.5
n-Hexadecane (cetane)	11.95	0.0021	21.0

molecules. The agreement is excellent and demonstrates that the polar end groups of the *n*-alcohols and acids are hydrogen-bonded together in a head-to-head manner and that no hydrate or solvate exists between these groups as might be possible. Thus, materials having a functional terminal group (acids, alcohols, halides, etc.) have urea ratios which differ very slightly from those of substances of the same molecular length which have terminal methyl groups (e.g. esters and hydrocarbons).

Other long-chain molecules can be related to the *n*-paraffins not only for their urea reactivity but also their adduct properties such as composition and density. When the alkyl chains are of sufficient length, as shown in Table IV, hydrocarbons and organic materials with small side groups

TABLE IV

EFFECT OF PARAFFINIC CHAIN SUBSTITUENT GROUPS ON UREA REACTIVITY

(Lower complexing limit at 25°C—ref. 30)

Terminally substituted	No. min. unbranched C atoms[a]	Nonterminally substituted	No. min. unbranched C atoms
Side group = 2.3 Å	8	Side group = 2.3 Å	10
Side group = 2.3 Å + (1.5 Å)y	8 + 4y	Side group = 2.3 Å + (0.3 Å)y	10 + 3y
CH_3	6 (n-hexane)	2-Methyl	10–13
COOH	4	2-Ethyl (3.2 Å)	24
1-Bromo	5	2-Chloro (2-chlorooctane)	6
1-Phenyl	18	2-Bromo	8
α-Olefin	7–8	2-Hydroxy	6
Esters		β-Olefin (cis)	8
Methyl butyrate	6	2,2-Difluoro	6
n-Amyl acetate	8	Esters	
Phenyl octanoate	9	3-Methylbutyl hexanoate	9
Benzyl caprate	12	2-Methylbutyl decanoate	12
Cyclohexyl laurate	13	2-Ethylbutyl octanoate	10
β-Naphthyl palmitate	17	1-Methylheptyl butyrate	6
n-Decyl phenyl acetate	13	2-Ethylhexyl octanoate	10
Methyl adipate	10	Citronellyl octanoate	11
Ethyl succinate	10	Geranyl dodecanoate	15
Ethyl 3-methylundeca- noate	11		

[a] Minimum number of unbranched carbon atoms includes the O in COC groups.

such as a methyl group or a chlorine atom are also capable of adduct formation. The composition of these less stable complexes still may be calculated from their channel length realizing that the extra group is not contributing to the carbon ratio in a linear manner.

The densities of most urea complexes lie between 1.20 and 1.30 gm/cm³. This relative consistency results from the fact that the urea complexes are very constant in composition and contain close to 23% by weight of guest molecules (about 3.3 parts of urea per one part of guest molecule) which consist primarily of carbon and hydrogen. The adduct density, readily obtained experimentally using a pycnometer and suitable liquid, together with the component analyses provide simple clues to structural packing. For example, the densities of urea-stearic acid complex, tetragonal urea, and solid stearic acid densities are 1.235, 1.32, and 0.94, respectively. From an adduct analysis showing 22.8% weight stearic acid we calculate a density of 1.213 for the adduct assuming the same packing volumes as occupied by the pure component solids.

Densities may be accurately predicted from crystallographic data in a manner similar to that used for estimating compositions. The channel dimensions of the guest molecules may also be estimated from molecular models or prior measurements of the pure solids or films. Dimensions of the fatty acids, alcohols, and related compounds are listed by Moreno *et al.* (*63*). The calculated density of tetragonal urea agrees with the literature value of $d_4^{20} = 1.323$. Similarly, the density of the empty hexagonal urea structure as calculated from the cell constants by assuming a canal 5.25 Å in diameter is $d_4^{20} = 0.956$. (By substracting the volume of the channel, the density of the remaining urea structure becomes 1.34 which is approximately the same as that for tetragonal urea.) The weight of the host molecules contained in 1 cm³ of adduct, which is obtained by analysis, may be added to this value to obtain the density of the complex. In this way W. Schlenk (*87*) has found $d_4^{20} = 1.203$ for *n*-dodecane compared to a calculated value of 1.205. For 4,4′-dichlorodibutyl ether, a measured value of 1.310 compares to a computed d_4^{20} of 1.307.

Density measurements quickly show whether or not a complex is an existent interstitial clathrate unit or an induced open structure. For example, Mandelcorn *et al.* (*56a*) have found that Dianin's compound, 4-*p*-hydroxyphenyl-2,2,4-trimethylchroman, increases in density from 1.15 to 1.19 for the ethanol clathrate, $6C_{18}H_{20}O_2 \cdot 2C_2H_5OH$, and to 1.30 for a sulfur hexafluoride clathrate, $6C_{18}H_{20}O_2 \cdot 1.79SF_6$. The density measurements are evidence that the guest-free form of Dianin's compound possesses the open clathrate structure. A 1:1 rotenone–CCl₄ complex (*27*) also shows no volume change on formation suggesting a self-supporting clathrate structure. By comparison, density measurements on the urea, thiourea, gas hydrates, and other inclusion complexes show considerable expansion during complex formation.

C. Stability of Urea Complexes

Before considering the exact thermodynamic properties of some of these substances, it is well to discuss their qualitative stabilities. It became apparent to most early investigators in this field that a comparison of the end view and side view of a molecule to that of the ideal *n*-paraffin packing diameters and volume could be used to qualitatively predict the stability or complex forming ability of other molecules. If the end view, as determined by molecular models or drawings as shown in Fig. 2, shows the potential guest molecule to have a dimension more than marginally greater than the limiting dimension of the canal, the molecule cannot usually form an adduct.

As examples, iso-octane (2,2,4-trimethylpentane) and benzene have dimensions greater than the urea canal and will not react under any conditions. If the dimensions indicate a tight fit, the adduct may form with difficulty since considerable crystal lattice distortion is required to incorporate even a methyl side group. 3-Methylheptane and 3-methylnonane are of this type. Longer unbranched n-paraffin chains can act to balance this effect.

1. STRUCTURAL LIMITATIONS OF GUEST MOLECULES

The use of urea and thiourea complexes in laboratory and preparatory separation procedures and as analytical tools holds considerable promise. The methods involved are often convenient to use and have distinct advantages over previous ones for a number of specific applications. Although much of the original work in this field was directed towards petroleum hydrocarbon separation, many organic substances and mixtures such as natural products encountered in the chemical field can be hydrogenated or converted by other means to a hydrocarbon or reactive guest molecule before separation. Rules derived from a study of paraffins and waxes may be applied effectively to long-chain esters.

a. Effect of Chain Length. With each class of compounds or homologous series there is a minimum paraffin chain length which is required for adduct formation. Table IV lists these limiting values for several groups of compounds. As would be expected, those structures which in some way disrupt the urea lattice stability through bulkiness, lack of linearity, or polar nature will require a proportional amount of chain length to offset these influences. For n-paraffins, the minimum chain length is six carbons at room temperature and pressure, but at lower temperatures and under pressure even propane can be made to react. There is no theoretical upper limit to the length of paraffin chains which will complex with urea. This has been demonstrated by the reaction of poly(ethylene oxide) polymers as high as 4,000,000 in molecular weight (4). However, long-chain, high melting point paraffinic substances, such as a C_{50} normal paraffin wax or a beeswax (myricyl palmitate) react very slowly at 25°C. The rate of reaction of these materials is limited at this temperature by the rate of solution of their pure solids. Butyric acid is the shortest monobasic acid forming a true channel complex. The stability of the other linear saturated fatty acid-urea complexes increases rapidly with increasing chain length. For example, a molecule such as stearic acid can be extracted almost quantitatively from various mixtures since its equilibrium concentration is 0.05 gm/100 cm³ in benzene at 25°C.

b. Effect of Side Groups. It was first mistakenly believed that molecules with branching and irregularities of any sort on the paraffin chain would not permit reaction with urea. Now that the limitations of complex formation are becoming more defined, this group separation and identification is gaining in importance. When only a single 2-methyl side group (2.31 Å) is added to a paraffin hydrocarbon or ester a minimum of 10–13 straight-chain C atoms are required according to E. Gorin (*39*) before complexing will occur, whereas 2-ethyl branched molecules (3.19 Å) require over 24 C atoms (Table IV). Only considerably longer paraffins with short branches and occasional ring structures are efficiently removed from a mixture such as petroleum wax and lubricating oil distillate (*29b*). Geiser (*36*) and Schiessler and Flitter (*93*) have reviewed these effects on the reactivity of such branched hydrocarbons. Similar separations have been made of naturally occurring long-chain ester mixtures. For example, methyl-2-methyloctanoate does not react with urea at room temperature whereas methyl-12-methyltetradecanoate and 3-methylbutyloctanoate do react. Although all triglycerides are completely unreactive, many diglcyerides or monoglycerides will complex (*27, 90*). Similar reactivities are noted in other classes of guest compounds which are related.

c. Effect of End Groups. A bulky group, such as halide, carboxyl, phenyl, ester, double bond, or other substituent, usually distorts the urea lattice less when located at the end of the paraffin chain than if the same group is attached along the side of a chain (Table IV). For example, 1-phenyloctadecane and 1-cyclohexyleicosane react readily, but the corresponding hydrocarbons of the same chain length with these groups located along the middle of the chain will not react under any conditions. Schiessler and Flitter (*93*) have pointed out that the two structurally similar hydrocarbons, 1-cyclopentylheneicosane, and 2-ethyltetracosane, have 5 carbon atoms attached to the end of a straight-chain of 21 carbon atoms. Here the rigid cyclic arrangement does not completely inhibit reaction whereas the ethyl group prevents urea adduction. Among the alkyl halides, 1-bromohexane forms a complex but 2-bromooctane does not; the bromine atom behaves in a manner analogous to a methyl group. 2-Bromodecane is the first member of this series which forms an adduct. The extreme sensitivity of inclusion in urea to the configuration of end groups was demonstrated by W. Schlenk (*90*) when he accomplished the separation of the optical isomers of racemic 2-chlorooctane. Zimmerschied *et al.* (*112*) found that 2,2-difluorooctane still reacts. Here the small fluorine atoms resemble hydrogen in size and both are located near the end of the chain. Although perfluoroparaffins are too hindered to form an adduct, Radell and Connolly (*78*) found that partially fluorinated long-chain esters complex readily with urea.

d. Effect of Unsaturated Groups. The presence of a rigid nonrotating *cis* double bond along a paraffin chain creates a kink which interferes with its linearity and in this way produces a urea lattice of reduced stability. A *trans* double bond as found in elaidic acid produces only a minor deviation in the lattice structure. Such variations in the C_{18} fatty acids series are reflected in the relative concentrations of these components in equilibrium with a saturated urea solution (Table V). Purified saturated, oleic, linoleic, linolenic, and more highly unsaturated fatty acids and their methyl esters have been separated, and several natural products have been upgraded by taking advantage of these differences. Hanson (*41*) has demonstrated that successive urea complex fractionation of marine animal oils used in drying oil and resin formulations gives the same analysis as that achieved by low temperature crystallization followed by molecular distillation. In this application, when the chain length of the fatty acids may vary from 14 to 22, the urea additive is more sensitive to the degree of unsaturation of the ester than is direct crystallization.

e. Accessory Reactions. The successful use of complexes as a separation technique is often improved by combination with accessory "reactions." Several methods have been used to modify and amplify the structural differences and reactivities of a molecule: (i) the attachment of a "handle" or stabilizing group; (ii) introduction of a bulky group to decrease the reactivity; and (iii) the formation of solid solutions in the channel of the complex to induce an unreactive species to enter the channel and to improve the stability of others.

Certain branched-chain and relatively unreactive substances can be made to adduct readily with urea by lengthening the straight-chain. This technique is most effectively applied by utilizing esters with a long-chain alcohol or fatty acid stabilizing group which can be readily removed. Although the methyl- and ethylbutanols and hexanols do not form urea complexes, the corresponding longer chained esters such as 3-methylbutyl hexanoate, 2-methylbutyl decanoate, 2-ethylhexyl octanoate, and 2-ethylbutyl decanoate do react.

The added group is more frequently selected to decrease reactivity. A hydroxyl group located near the center of a paraffin chain—as in secondary alcohols such as decanol-5, tridecanol-6, and tetradecanol-7, or in ricinoleic acid, 12-hydroxy-Δ^9-octadecenoic acid, from castor oil—does not completely inhibit urea complex formation. Thus, further fractionation of alcohols or hydroxy acids can be accomplished by acetylation of the hydroxyl groups followed by recomplexing. This operation permits the separation of primary and secondary alcohols by increasing the length of the straight-chain in the primary alcohols and at the same time enlarging

TABLE V

PROPERTIES OF C_{18} FATTY ACID AND METHYL ESTER UREA COMPLEXES

Fatty acid	Equilibrium at 25°C		Adduct dissociation temperature (°C) (102)	Melting point of the solid acid (°C)	Urea-acid mole ratio (11)	Length of dimeric acid (67)
	Methyl ester constant K (m.f.)Reactant (5, 80, 102)	Conc gm/100 cm³ in benzene over saturated urea solution^a (27, 28)				
Stearic	0.0001	0.05	126 Acid / 132 Ester	70.0	14.3	50.11 Å
Elaidic (trans)	—	0.10	116 Acid / 125 Ester	43.7	13.7	49.75 Å
Oleic (cis)	0.0019	0.80	110 Acid / 110 Ester	13.4, 16.2	13.1	48.15 Å
Linoleic (cis-cis)	0.013	2.7	—	−5.0 to −12.0	13.6	46.65 Å
Linolenic (cis)	0.023	25 est.	—	−11.0	—	—

^a In the presence of the urea adduct.

the size of the side group of the secondary alcohols. Meade (cf. Fetterly, *30*) has used boric acid to esterify the hydroxyl-containing moiety. These procedures have been very successful in studies on wool wax and alcohols (*82, 105*). Oxime formation can be used to block the reactivity of ketones (*35*). Other useful accessory reactions can be carried out on various types of unsaturation found in fatty molecules. Bromination of a molecule such as oleic acid will convert it to an unreactive form. Similarly, formation of Diels-Alder addition products, coupling of acids and esters through the use of di-*tert*-butylperoxide, treatment with peracetic acid, oxidation, and polymerization, all give various means of modifying the reactivities of unsaturated groups or the molecules containing them.

Molecules having borderline reactivities also can be made to react through solid solution formation in the channel when a considerable amount of another more reactive adduct former is present. Pure 3-methylheptane cannot adduct directly with urea but will adduct in the presence of *n*-decane. When hexadecane is used in place of *n*-decane in the above example or when stearic acid is reacted in the presence of oleic acid (*27*) their tendency to form such solid solutions is reduced. This results from too large a difference in the relative rates of reaction of the components in each of these pairs. The ability to *draw in* a less reactive component into solid solution within the channel is more important when using the less stable thiourea adducts.

2. DISSOCIATION OF UREA ADDUCTS

Urea complexes form excellent hexagonal needle crystals of variable stability depending on the guest component. They exhibit definite vapor pressure-temperature relationships as do other types of crystals, but usually do not have definite melting points. The melting points are indefinite when measured in a capillary tube because the guest molecules usually escape from the channel before the complex appears to melt. Complexes which do not dissociate below 132.7°C, the melting point of tetragonal urea, finally dissociate at this point. An exception to this rule has been recently discovered with long-chain polyether adducts which dissociate near 140°C (*4, 31*). If a few dry transparent crystals are examined under a microscope fitted with a hot stage, it is found that there is a transition at a reproducible *dissociation temperature* from transparency to opaqueness before any sign of melting is detectable. This temperature usually lies above the thermodynamic decomposition temperature and depends upon the rate of heating of the sample. Thus, when heated at the rate of 1°C/5 min, lauric acid-urea transforms at 94°C, but when heated at the rate of 1°C/min, the transformation takes place at 115–120°C (*103*).

The reason for this effect is that the decomposition of urea complexes in the dry state has a rather appreciable activation energy and therefore proceeds at a relatively slow rate at the decomposition temperature.

Urea and thiourea adducts are definitely not pure adsorbates but are of a true chemical nature from a thermodynamic standpoint as is $CuSO_4 \cdot 5H_2O$. For this reason they obey classical laws such as the Clausius-Clapeyron equations (7) and (8) when the guest molecule is volatile. The heat of dissociation, ΔH_{diss} of adducts is obtained from these relationships as follows:

$$\frac{d \ln P}{d(1/T)} = \frac{-\Delta H_{diss}}{R} \tag{7}$$

$$\Delta H_{diss} = \frac{(2.303) R T_1 T_2 (\log P_2 - \log P_1)}{(T_2 - T_1)} \tag{8}$$

where P is the equilibrium vapor pressure of the guest component. W. Schlenk (87) observed that for a n-heptane-urea system the equilibrium vapor pressures of heptane at 0°, 10°, and 20°C are 3.3, 8.0, and 19 mm Hg, respectively. These results give an average heat of dissociation of 14.35 kcal/mole of heptane which checks closely a value of 14.37 kcal obtained by calculation from the lattice energy of adduct formation. These measurements also agree with the equilibrium values of the n-heptane complex in isooctane and show that heptane cannot be removed quantitatively from a solvent mixture by adduct formation under any normal conditions. For the latter system at 10°C, the heptane content of the remaining mixture was found to be 40%; at 5°C, 30%; and at -10°C, 20%. In a similar manner Morrish (64) has measured the heats of dissociation and reactivity at several thiourea complexes. The validity of the Clausius-Clapeyron equation for clathrate adducts has been investigated by van der Waals and Platteeuw (107).

Solvents (49) which may be used to dissociate either urea or thiourea adducts are of three general classes: (i) those which dissolve only the guest component; (ii) those which dissolve only urea; and (iii) those which are solvents for both. In the case of solvents of type (i) several systems have been studied: urea-cetane, urea-cetyl alcohol, and urea-lauric acid with benzene, carbon tetrachloride, isooctane, cyclohexane, and chloroform solvents. In all cases the concentration of the guest in the solvent at 25°C reached an equilibrium level of 0.1% or less which favors the undissociated adduct at that temperature. Water is an example of the type (ii) solvent. Since water has a very high solvent capacity for urea, a moderate amount is sufficient for virtually complete adduct dissociation. When a mole of cetane adduct (1 mole cetane and 12 moles urea) was dissolved in 72 moles of water at 31°C, the adduct dissociated to the extent of 97.5%. This represents the best laboratory method for separating the components of the adduct, since two readily separable layers are produced. The use of an inert solvent of the type (i) such as benzene and a higher solution temperature improves the decomposition and separation still further. An example of type (iii) solvent is methanol which brings about rapid dissociation. The more stable complexes still may not completely decompose even in this solution. For example, for decane-urea complex in methanol at 26°C the following equilibrium resulted: 1 mole of adduct (1 mole decane and 8.1 moles urea) dissociated to the extent of 69% in 90 moles of methanol. The solubilities of the decane and urea components in this amount of methanol are 2.6 and 13.5 moles, respectively.

Experimental techniques for the formation of urea or thiourea complexes involve the same three systems described above, for their decomposition, with the exception that the equilibria are shifted in a favorable direction by the use of saturated solutions and an excess of the solid urea or thiourea reactant. Methanol or water in trace or larger amounts are favored laboratory solvents. Experimental procedures have been extensively described in various reviews (*30, 49, 91, 101, 103*).

D. Thermodynamics of Urea Complexes

1. EQUILIBRIUM CONSTANTS OF SINGLE REACTANTS IN SOLUTION

Chemical equilibrium is established in the formation of urea complexes just as in more conventional chemical reactions. In the separation of *n*-paraffins, fatty acids, or long-chain alcohols the equilibrium on reaction with solid urea or a saturated urea solution shifts towards the adduction of more reactant as the chain length increases. The thermal stability of the complexes increases concurrently with chain length. The chemical equilibrium of the pure complex, of complexes in the presence of various solvents, and of mixed complex systems can all be accurately ascertained by classical free energy and equilibrium relationships.

For the dissociation of a complex containing one species of reactant molecules the reaction may be written:

$$\text{complex}_{(solid)} \rightleftharpoons \text{reactant (R)} + m \cdot \text{urea (U)} \tag{9}$$

where m, the moles of urea per mole of reactant in the complex, may be a fractional number because of the non-stoichiometry involved. The free energy change ΔG and equilibrium constant K are represented in terms of the activities of the constituents as follows:

$$\Delta G = -RT \ln a_R \cdot a_U{}^m \tag{10}$$

$$K = a_R \cdot a_U{}^m \tag{11}$$

Thus the value of K is equal to the mole fraction, X_R, of the reactant in a perfect solution which is in equilibrium with the complex ($a_C = 1$) and solid urea (or its saturated solution where $a_U = 1$). Under these conditions the reciprocal of K (i.e., $K_{reaction}$) is a direct measure of the stability of the complex. In these systems it may be assumed that the solutions of the reactant are ideal. In other systems when the reactant is present as a separate pure liquid phase $a_R = 1$, only the activity of urea in aqueous solution must be determined. The activities of urea in aqueous solutions were presented by Redlich (80) and Fetterly (27) for this purpose.

The measurement of the equilibrium constant K, which may also be regarded as a partition coefficient between the liquid phases and the complex, is accomplished in several ways (80, 103):

(1) *Aqueous urea solution method.* When equilibrium is established between a pure reactant, aqueous urea, and a complex, it may be assumed that the solution is ideal. Since the reactant is present as a separate liquid phase, $a_R = 1$. It follows that $K = a_U{}^m$, and from the relation between the activity of urea in water and its concentration the value of K can readily be determined when the equilibrium aqueous urea concentration is known. If a saturated urea solution containing an excess of solid urea is employed ($a_U = 1$), then decomposition of the complex into an inert solvent (ideal solution) will provide a direct measure of K. In this case the activity of the reactant (a_R) is essentially equal to the concentration in the inert solvent phase, C_R, so that

$$K = a_R = C_R = kC_{soln} \tag{12}$$

The interphase distribution coefficient for the reactive solute is $k = C_R/C_{soln}$.

(2) *Nonaqueous urea solution method.* If a solution of the reactant in a neutral solvent such as benzene is allowed to equilibrate with an excess of powdered urea moistened with traces of water or methanol to catalyze the transformation of crystal structure, then the concentration, C_R, can often be measured by refractive index or other means. As in the last procedure, the dissociation equilibrium constant is given here by (Eq. 12).

(3) *Two phase concentration change method.* Sometimes for reasons of reactivity it is best to interact both a solution of the reactant in a neutral solvent and an aqueous urea solution. From the concentration of the

guest and host molecules in their respective phases the equilibrium constant may be calculated. In these methods involving a change in concentration of the urea solution it is necessary to know the composition of the complex.

(4) *Dew point method.* When investigating the more volatile reactants, a dew point method is most convenient. In this system the equilibrium constant is given by the relation

$$K = P/P°$$ (13)

where $P°$ is the vapor pressure of the pure reactant, and P is the equilibrium decomposition pressure. The data are obtained by using a dew point apparatus described by Redlich *et al.* (*80*).

All four of the above methods are equally reliable for thiourea complex systems. With thiourea the reactants are often volatile so that the dew point method is particularly useful.

Equilibrium constants have been obtained for a number of systems (*28, 80, 87, 103, 112*). The relationship between K and temperature for n-paraffins up to hexadecane is shown in Fig. 6. In Fig. 7, K is plotted as

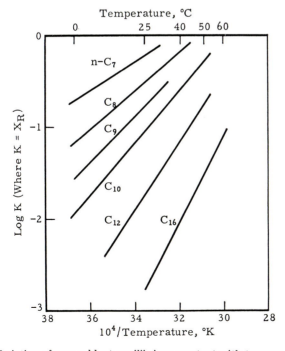

Fig. 6. Variation of urea adduct equilibrium constant with temperature (*80*).

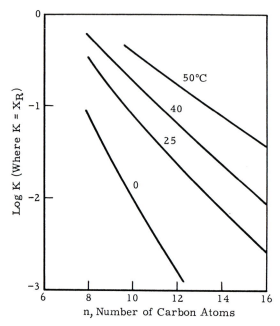

Fig. 7. Variation of urea adduct equilibrium constant with chain length in saturated urea solution ($a_U = 1$).

a function of the number of carbon atoms in the n-paraffin chain at various temperatures. It can be seen that the increase in stability (a decrease in K value) with chain length is much more rapid at lower than at higher temperatures.

Equilibrium constants and their variation with temperature have been reported for n-paraffins, olefins, halides, alcohols, acids, esters, and related substances. A plot of log K as a function of m gives essentially a straight line (note Fig. 7) which can be generalized at 25°C for these long-chain reactants. Data for the n-paraffins (80) and for acids and alcohols (103) are as follows.

n-paraffins: $\log K = 2.20 - 0.403\,m$ where $m = 0.69\,n + 1.50$ (14)

n-acids: $\log K = 1.9 - 0.4\,m$ where $m = 0.71\,n + 1.08$ (15)

n-alcohols: $\log K = 2.5 - 0.43\,m$ where $m = 0.66\,n + 1.55$ (16)

In these equations m represents the moles of urea per mole of reactant and n is the number of carbon atoms in the guest molecule. The author (27, 28) determined the equilibrium concentrations for n-fatty acid reactants in benzene solution, and these are plotted in Fig. 8 as a function of

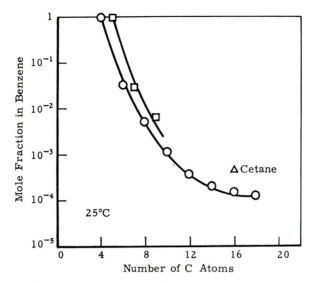

FIG. 8. Equilibrium concentration of *n*-fatty acids in benzene over saturated urea solutions at 25°C (*27*, *28*).

the number of carbon atoms. Here can be noted an unusual variation for odd and even number acids. A complete solubility-equilibrium diagram for *n*-caproic acid is presented in Section VI. When equilibrium constants are not available for a paraffinic reactant, a correlation (*80*) of the ratio $K/K_{n\text{-paraffin}}$ as a function of the chain length of a series is useful for interpolation and extrapolation from a single known or estimated value since the relationship is very general and approaches unity for chain lengths above $n = 16$.

2. Equilibria for Mixtures of Reacting Substances

Mixtures of *n*-paraffins as found in petroleum products and many other naturally occurring reactants often do not behave on complexing with urea like independent pure reactants in an inert solvent but, instead, form a single solid phase (solid solution) within the channel (*80*). For example, if similar *n*-paraffins, such as *n*-heptane and *n*-octane dissolved in decalin, acted independently of each other on reaction with solid urea at 0°C, their equilibrium distribution would follow from the relationships and equations previously given for the adduction of single substances in solution and would not fall below their respective equilibrium values of K_{C_7} and K_{C_8}. Thus for systems employing solid urea:

$$K_{C_7} = a_{C_7} = X_{C_7} \tag{17}$$

where X_{C_7} is the mole fraction of heptane in decalin, at equilibrium. Similarly, $K_{C_8} = X_{C_8}$ so that if the components of the mixture acted independently of one another, then

$$\frac{X_{C_7}}{K_{C_7}} = \frac{X_{C_8}}{X_{C_8}} = 1 \tag{18}$$

Actually it was found that they approach much lower values which satisfy the relation

$$\frac{X_{C_7}}{K_{C_7}} + \frac{X_{C_8}}{K_{C_8}} = 1 \tag{19}$$

This is further evidence the adduct forms a single solid solution from the mixture.

In developing more general relationships which apply to mixtures we shall consider the following definitions:

Z_i = mole fraction of any individual reactant in the feed;

$$Z = \sum Z_i \tag{20}$$

$(1 - Z)$ = mole fraction of all nonreactants in the feed.

X_i = mole fraction of individual reactants in the mother liquor at equilibrium;

$$X = \sum X_i \tag{21}$$

Y_i = mole fraction of reactants in the solid complex at equilibrium on an urea-free basis;

$$\sum Y_i = 1 \tag{22}$$

The equilibrium constants may now be represented as follows:

$$\text{complex}_i \text{ (s)} \rightleftharpoons R_i + m_i \text{ (urea)} \tag{23}$$

$$K_i = \frac{(a_i)(a_U)^{m_i}}{Y_i} = \frac{X_i(a_U)^{m_i}}{Y_i} \tag{24}$$

where the activity a_i of a reactant in the mother liquor is taken equal to its mole fraction; that is, the activity coefficients γ_i, defined by $a = \gamma X$, are assumed to be unity.

Equation (24) may be used to obtain the value of K for a substance which does not normally form a complex by itself ($K > 1$). As an example, since 3-methylheptane does not form a complex with urea, its K value cannot be evaluated directly. On the other hand, 3-methylheptane can be induced to react with urea in the presence of n-heptane. Knowing the values of a, Y, and m obtained from the solid solution mixed complex and the equilibrium constant K_7 for pure n-heptane, one can solve for $K_{unknown}$, which is here the equilibrium constant for 3-methylheptane.

It follows from this enhancement of reactivity that the concentration of the individual reactants in the mother liquor can differ from the equilibrium concentrations for pure reactants and that sharp separations in the mixture may not always be obtained. Considerable enrichment can usually be achieved by controlling the value a_u or by employing successive treatments with an amount of urea insufficient to complex with all the reactive components. Determination of relative reaction rates is another important consideration discussed later. The degree of separation obtainable by a single treatment of a binary mixture can be deduced from the ratio of two equilibrium constants

$$\frac{K_1}{K_2} = [(a_1 Y_2/a_2 Y_1)]a_U{}^{(m_1-m_2)} \tag{25}$$

if $m_1 = m_2$ or if solid urea is present. This separation ratio plays the same role in urea separations as the relative volatility does in distillation calculations.

The main problem in calculations for multicomponent reactant systems in an extractive crystallization separation is the determination of mole fractions X_i in the mother liquor and Y_i in the solid complex. Their derivation can be made from a material balance by employing Eqs. (20), (21), (22) and by expressing the quantities of reactants relative to one mole of nonreacting solvent $(1 - Z)$ moles in the feed as the tie element since it moves unchanged through the process. The material balance for each component is then expressed by the equation

$$\frac{Z}{(1 - Z)} = \frac{X_i}{(1 - X)} + Y_i \left[\frac{Z}{(1 - Z)} - \frac{X}{(1 - X)} \right] \tag{26}$$

By eliminating Y_i, simplifying, and solving for X_i one obtains

$$X_i = \frac{K_i Z_i(1 - X)}{K_i(1 - Z) + a_U{}^{mi}(Z - X)} \tag{27}$$

The problem is reduced to the determination of X so that the individual values of X_i can be calculated. The other terms are known or can be determined and with solid urea present, $a_U = 1$. As a good approximation, the following expression may be substituted for X in Eq. (17):

$$\bar{X} = \frac{\sum Z_i K_i}{Z} \tag{28}$$

Solving Eq. (27) graphically, the results obtained by Truter for the sepa-

TABLE VI

CALCULATED EQUILIBRIUM SEPARATION OF ALCOHOL MIXTURES (103)

	Initially in mole benzene		Mother liquor			Complex[a]			Distribution of individual components		Equilibrium constant
	mol	%	mol	%		mol	%		mother liquor	complex	$K^{25°C}$—m.f.
n-Octanol	0.2	33.3	0.0901	66.6		0.1099	23.7		45.0%	55.0%	0.341
n-Decanol	0.2	33.3	0.0345	25.4		0.1655	35.3		17.5	83.5	0.089
n-Dodecanol	0.2	33.3	0.0108	8.0		0.1892	41.0		5.4	94.6	0.022

[a] In equilibrium at 25°C with an aqueous slurry of urea (500 gm urea, 200 cm³ water).

ration of equimolecular proportions of three n-alcohols in benzene are summarized in Table VI.

3. HEATS OF FORMATION OF UREA ADDUCTS

The formation of urea complexes is an exothermic process which for liquid paraffins is of approximately the same order of magnitude as the heat of vaporization of the guest molecule. Three general methods can be employed for determining the heat of formation, ΔH, which is equal and opposite in sign to the heat of dissociation, ΔH_{diss}: (i) estimation from equilibrium vapor pressures by the Clausius-Clapeyron equation or from the variation of the equilibrium constant with temperature utilizing the van't Hoff relation; (ii) direct measurement using a calorimeter; and (iii) calculation from lattice energy correlations. The heat of formation derived from the van't Hoff relationship,

$$\Delta H = R \left[\frac{\partial \ln K}{\partial (1/T)} \right]_P \tag{29}$$

is not linear with chain length because of van der Waals end group effects, and a lack of linearity of the heat of fusion and vaporization with chain length. For the shorter chain n-paraffin liquids, the results (80) derived from Fig. 6 are approximated by the following equation:

$$\Delta H_{liquid} = -6.5 + 2.37m \text{ (kcal/mole reactant)} \tag{30}$$

A more meaningful comparison is made with reference to the solid states of the reactants and product. Here the heat of fusion or solution is deducted from the reaction. Equation (30) for n-paraffins now becomes

$$\Delta H_{solid} = 1.5 + 0.51m \text{ (kcal/mole)} \tag{31}$$

These results show that the heat of reaction of a paraffin chain compound increases linearly by about 0.5 kcal/mole of urea in the adduct or 0.3 kcal for one CH_2 group. This is the order of magnitude of the energy resulting from a shortening of the hydrogen bonds in urea by means of the *supporting* mechanism, plus a very small contribution from the increased van der Waals interaction. These results agree well with those determined by calorimetric means. In the case of fatty acid and alcohol complexes the heats of formation show that the polar groups are hydrogen bonded together, which is in agreement with other evidences such as x-ray spacings, infrared, and NMR measurements.

The estimation of the heat of formation from lattice energy considerations may be done by considering that adduction results from the following hypothetical steps: (1) the overcoming of molecular adhesion of the reactant molecules in the solid state to form isolated single molecules, e.g. ΔH sublimation; (2) the transformation of urea from a tetragonal lattice to a hexagonal lattice; (3) the addition of the isolated reactant to the open channel to form an adduct. Although the energy change involved in step 1 is accurately known, it cannot be obtained directly for steps 2 and 3. The calorimetric measurements (27) for solid stearic acid reacting with solid urea indicates that $\Delta H_{step\ 3} \cong \Delta H_{subl}$. Data gained from a consideration of liquids and solutions interacting often give inaccurate results for the calculation of lattice energies, but again may be estimated assuming $\Delta H_{step\ 1} = \Delta H_{vap}$ or $-\Delta H_{solution}$, and $\Delta H_{step\ 3} \cong \Delta H_{subl}$.

E. Reaction Rate Studies—Inhibitors and Accelerators

Most early investigators experienced difficulties while carrying out adduction reactions with aqueous urea solutions, especially on treating crude heavy petroleum distillates. Zimmerschied et al. (112) isolated sulfur compounds which were effective in the complete inhibition of complex formation with the n-paraffins in petroleum fractions. Fetterly (28) reviewed the role of various crystallization rate-controlling effects in the reaction of n-fatty acid solutions with aqueous urea solutions. For the moment, let us consider several rate barriers which influence the rate of adduct formation in the fatty acid system.

The interaction between urea and a paraffinic compound in aqueous urea solutions to produce a solid complex product is essentially a crystallization process and not a classical chemical reaction in the usual sense; however, it does follow the thermodynamic relationships of true classical compounds. From the fractional combining ratios it is obvious that the complexes cannot exist in solution with the same composition and structure as in the solid state. However, a related complex monomer unit of the guest component covered with a crystalline husk is believed to exist in solution as will be discussed in more detail in Section VI. The movement of the respective reactants from two separate phases into this pseudo-liquid complex form in the aqueous urea solution and finally to cluster together into a true solid crystal will involve all the following possible mechanisms:

(1) crystal nuclei formation;
(2) interphase mass transfer of reactants;
(3) bulk phase mass transfer of reactants;
(4) crystal growth.

1. NUCLEATION

Urea complex formation exhibits all the peculiarities associated with crystal nucleation. Adequate supersaturation, agitation, and seeding are all required to insure initiation of a possible adduction reaction. A lack of nucleation from the absence of seed crystals and the existence of one to one or more of the other processes often creates an effect reminiscent of induction periods in oxidative chemical reactions. Freshly prepared urea solutions appear to provide a less favorable medium for nucleation than do solutions which have been aged for several days. No explanation was ever found for this as experiments testing this point were not always reproducible. Seeds from stearic, oleic, or linoleic acid complexes will nucleate the complex of any other acid; solid urea will not do this, as would be expected from its tetragonal crystal structure. Nucleation is of concern only in starting the adduction process and providing a crystal product of desired size; it usually does not control the over-all reaction rates, has no influence on selectivity, and is of minor importance in a continuously operating reactor unit.

2. INTERPHASE AND BULK PHASE MASS TRANSFER

Interphase diffusion or mass transfer was found to be an important rate-controlling step in the movement of the complexing agents to the crystal nuclei in the bulk urea-water phase. A barrier of interphase films between the oil phase and an aqueous urea solution may be the controlling resistance to complex formation in many instances, particularly in starting a reaction. In systems involving solutions of n-paraffin or fatty acid in benzene or other inert solvent, reaction with urea occurs in the immiscible aqueous solution phase as various evidences indicate that it is necessary for the paraffinic substance to pass from the oil phase to the urea phase before crystal nuclei can form or complex crystals grow. It can be shown that a negligible amount of urea dissolves in the hydrocarbon layer for reaction to occur in that phase. Similarly, studies show that forces at the interphase film are sufficient to orient urea contrary to its disposition in the complex and to prevent adduct formation in this region. Complex crystals were observed under a microscope to grow exclusively in the aqueous layer near the surface. Rapid stirring creates a very large interphase surface, and aids both the rate of mass transfer and nuclei formation.

Pure cetane (n-C_{16}) or its solution in a hydrocarbon will give a very slow reaction with a saturated aqueous urea solution at 25°C despite a very favorable equilibrium. Alcoholic (methanol) urea solutions do not present this difficulty. The addition of methyl isobutyl ketone, a slightly water soluble solvent, to the cetane-oil layer will permit a very rapid interaction with an aqueous urea solution. This does not result from solubilization or a favorable shift in the equilibria, but is associated with the existence of a rather impervious monomolecular water or water-urea layer at the surface of the solution, which is strongly hydrogen bonded. This layer is oriented differently from the bulk solution and provides many of the surface tension and interphase phenomena noted for water and aqueous solutions. It also forms an effective barrier against the mass transfer of high molecular weight molecules into the water phase. The polar groups in the ketone solvent effectively disrupt this strong film by interaction, probably by hydrogen bonding, with the surface layer molecules. The addition of alcohols and other water soluble agents to the urea phase may be similarly effective. Also, long-chain fatty acids, alcohols, and other substances having terminal polar groups serve as their own rate enhancing agents and are capable of reducing this barrier without the need of an auxiliary solvent.

One would reason that soap-like molecules should also provide improved mass transfer since they are known to disrupt the surface film of aqueous solutions. Quite the reverse is observed. Ammonium oleate or stearate soaps strongly inhibit the urea reaction. In this system although the surface tension of the aqueous phase is effectively decreased by the soap molecules, a new layer of bulky molecules forms at the interphase which still bars the transverse movement of the paraffin or fatty acid molecules from one phase to another. It is for this reason that the pH of the aqueous phase must be 6–7 for rapid reactivity and proper growth in many separations. In pilot or commercial units ammonium salts from urea hydrolysis will form soaps and other rate-limiting by-products unless neutralized. This rate effect in fatty acid systems is reversible, and the rate is very slow at a pH of 9 and fast at a pH of 6.

In many undistilled fatty acid stocks or petroleum fractions, small amounts of foreign oxygenated or polar impurity such as hydroperoxides or sulfur compounds can act in the same manner to markedly inhibit complex formation. Other examples (27) of materials giving this type of interphase barrier are unreactive long-chain polar molecules, strongly ionic soaps, octadecyl sulfate and sulfite acids, and aerosols. Since these substances cannot react in either the salt or acid form, they should inhibit the reaction over all pH ranges. This was observed. The same is true for nonionic surface agents, and many large molecular weight salts such as sodium 2,4-dinitrobenzene, and sodium naphthalene sulfonates. Sometimes wax or another insoluble foreign material can collect at the interphase and form an effective barrier. Occasionally, certain long-chain molecules with configurations which make them unreactive can stop the formation of nuclei by blocking the growth of clusters. The mechanism is similar to that involved in the addition of wax suppressants to reduce the pour point of an oil.

Other agents, besides alcohols and ketones, which improve the reaction rate are low molecular weight alkane salts such as the C_4–C_8 alkyl sulfonates. These reduce the interfacial barrier without substituting another in its place. A few liquids and solids having low solubility in either phase improve reaction rates. Examples are nitrobenzene, dinitrobenzene, and oxalic, adipic, and salicyclic acids.

3. CRYSTAL GROWTH

The tremendous selectivity in separations utilizing urea channel complexes results from the stability of the crystal lattice and is reflected in the equilibrium reactivities previously described. Superimposed on this equilibrium condition is a rate effect which can be utilized to obtain separation selectivities that are not possible under equilibrium conditions. In a study of the equilibria (Fig. 9) and reaction rates of individual stearic, oleic, linoleic, and linolenic acids and their mixtures dissolved in benzene, Fetterly (28) noted marked differences in the reaction rate ratios of mixtures when compared to their equilibrium reaction ratios. In general, stearic acid reacts almost 100-fold faster than linoleic acid and about 10–20 times as fast as oleic acid if equilibrium is not reached. Over the temperature range from 0°C to 50°C it was found that the reaction rates in these systems increase slightly when the temperature is lowered, an effect opposite to that observed in most reactions. These observations were made after adequate nucleation was provided and the interphase resistances were reduced to a minimum leaving only the barrier on the crystal surface to control the different rates.

As an example (Fig. 10), in a batch separation of a stearic-oleic acid mixture dissolved in benzene, reaction was initiated with a nearly saturated solution of urea in water at 26.6°C. After only 5 minutes, 40% of the stearic acid had reacted, yielding a complex whose stearic acid content was 97.5% of the guest composition. This represents a separation ratio of 37. After 2 hours, the near equilibrium purity of the stearic acid derived from the urea complex was only 88% giving a separation ratio of only 4.5. The oleic acid phase had a 92% purity, with respect to stearic acid, at this point. A favorable balance of products and purity occurred after 20 minutes when the ratio was 10.5. If the two reactants had reacted

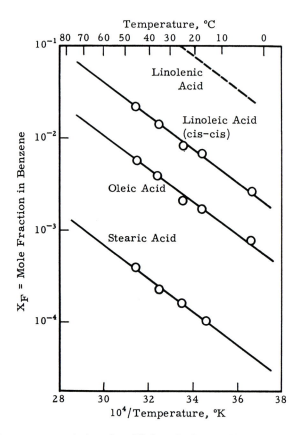

FIG. 9. Temperature variation of equilibrium C_{18} fatty acid concentrations in benzene over saturated urea solutions (*27*, *28*).

independently, equilibrium data (Fig. 9) would have predicted a ratio of 15.5, showing that some induction of oleic by solid solution into the stearic acid complex occurs in this system.

Relative rates (*27*, *28*) of reactions of several C_{18} fatty acids in saturated and unsaturated aqueous urea solutions are shown in Fig. 11. These measurements predict that the split between stearic and oleic acids would be greatest with unsaturated urea solutions; whereas the separation of oleic acid from linoleic and other polyenic acids should be best when saturated urea solutions or solid urea are used. This was demonstrated on natural mixtures such as cottonseed, soybean, and linseed fatty acid mixtures. As in the synthetic mixtures, optimum separations were obtained by using filtration to quench the reaction after short periods rather than to allow equilibrium to be approached. In this way linseed acids

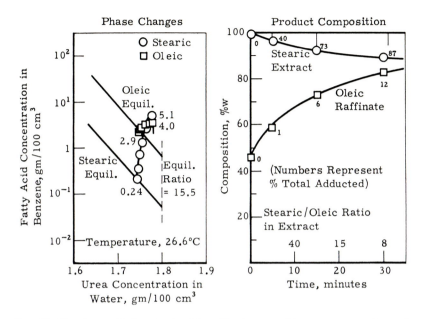

FIG. 10. Reaction path for stearic-oleic acid mixtures with aqueous urea (27, 28).

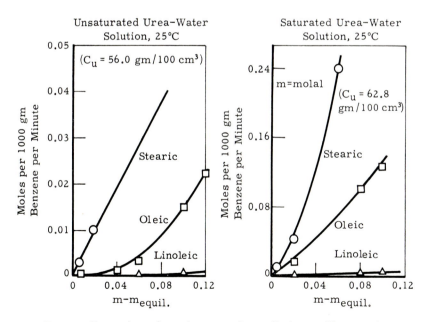

FIG. 11. Comparison of reaction rates of pure C_{18} fatty acids (27, 28).

were raised from 166 to 215 iodine number, soybean acids from 122 to about 175, and cottonseed acids from 99 to 151.

Up to this point we have been discussing the reactivities of urea solutions. Some of these rate principles also apply to reactions involving solid urea promoted by very small amounts of water or methanol. Absolutely dry cetane and solid urea do not appear to react until an *activator* is added. Trace amounts of methanol will permit a slow reaction. Zimmerschied *et al.* (*112*) have demonstrated that cetane containing 0.25% of added sulfur compounds extracted from a petroleum fraction can completely inhibit the reaction until 0.4% methanol was added. Gorin and Rosenstein (*40*) suggested that prereacted solid urea retains some open structure and promotes solid urea reactions with hydrocarbon systems. Density measurements, however, show that no open canal structure remains after the complex has been warmed in a solvent such as toluene but the increased fineness of the crystals and number of seeds after prereaction certainly enhance the rates of reaction.

Another related form of rate barrier, inhibiting complex formation, is exhibited by very long-chain substances. This is the added resistance of the rate of solution of the pure reactant (or competitive precipitation if it has been dissolved). Long-chain petroleum waxes (n-C_{55}) and vegetable or animal waxes such as beeswax, myricyl palmitate, do not appear to react with solid urea or urea solutions at 25°C since the solubility of these materials is very low at this temperature. When the temperature is raised to 50° or 60°C, rapid crystallization does result with urea-saturated solutions. When a long-chain guest molecule readily dissolves, as in the case of long-chain polyethers, then the reaction rate is rapid and not limited in any way by the chain length of the reactant.

IV. THIOUREA CHANNEL ADDUCTS

The thiourea inclusion channel compounds, discovered independently by Fetterly (*26*; cf. *64*, *81*, *94*) and Angla (*1*, *2*) in the middle 1940's, are similar to the urea–n-paraffin type complexes in substantially every respect. It has now been well established that the cross-sectional dimensions of the lumens formed by both urea and thiourea molecules, together with the spatial configuration of the reactant or potential guest molecules, largely determine whether specific adducts can be formed. Whereas, the principal requirement for adduction with urea is a long, unbranched paraffin chain; the thiourea adducts, having a channel of larger diameter resulting from the larger sulfur molecules, will react readily with various branched-chain hydrocarbons, cycloaliphatic compounds and other organic substances of similar molecular diameters which are too large to be accommodated in the urea channel. For this reason, the urea and thiourea separation techniques often complement each other in their selectivity. Thiourea is usually not so specific as urea in its action, and its complexes derived from smaller but wider molecules such as cyclohexane or isooctane are usually not as stable.

In general molecules which react with thiourea have similar cross-sectional dimensions rather than chemical similarities. Knowing the bond angles and van der Waals packing radii one can predict whether a given molecular series will complex. Schiessler and Flitter (93) described the use of molecular models in predicting the adductibility of a substance, and showed the average cross-sectional dimensions of adducting structures to be 5.8 by 6.8 Å. As a rule, compounds which adduct with urea do not adduct with thiourea, but exceptions are being found among the longer chain compounds. For example, it was originally thought that thiourea would not complex with any straight-chain compounds but it was reported by McLaughlin and McClenahan (58) that n-paraffins with 16 or more, and not less, carbon atoms will form weak complexes at 0°C, but not at 25°C. In these complexes the packing dimensions show that the n-paraffin chain becomes coiled into a multiturn helix such that the dimensions meet the spatial requirements for thiourea adduction. Also, fatty acids are linearly compressed in β-dextrin channels (Chapter 9, Section IV,B).

A. Crystal Structure

Angla (1, 2) recognized the difficulty of explaining the structure of the several thiourea complexes, which he had discovered, on the basis of the classical theory of valence. His interpretations were made without the aid of x-ray data, and they involve hydrogen bonding and coordination between the atom of sulfur in thiourea and an atom in the reacting molecule. He reported that adducts he prepared consist primarily of three moles of thiourea to one of reactant, $3CS(NH_2)_2 \cdot M$. Using this concept he was unable to recognize the non-stoichiometric and inclusion character of these substances. Their true nature was conclusively determined by Smith (95) using x-ray diffraction. Redlich and co-workers (81), W. Schlenk (88), and others (64) have explored the thermodynamics and various properties of these materials thoroughly. Hermann and Lenné (43, 53) have extended Smith's early x-ray work by an extensive survey of several typical adducts as well as two classes of compounds of increasing chain length (Table VII, Fig. 12).

The arrangement of thiourea molecules in the adduct is rhombohedral, forming a smaller pseudo-hexagonal but similar cell to that of the urea

TABLE VII

COMPOSITION OF THIOUREA ADDUCT SERIES SHOWING COMPRESSIBLE GUEST MOLECULES (53, 88)

n-Alkyl cyclohexane series[a]		Dicyclohexyl series[a]			
No. C atoms in n-alkyl group	Mole ratio thiourea/guest	No. C atoms in ω,ω'-methylene bridge	Mole ratio exp. (88)	Thiourea/guest unit cell (53)	Channel length used (Å)
0 Cyclohexane	3.1	0 Dicyclohexyl	5.2	5.24	10.9
1 Methylcyclohexane	3.3	1 Dicyclohexylmethane	6.0	6.00	12.4
2	4.3	2	6.0	6.00	12.5
3	4.7	3	6.1	6.46	13.5
4	5.1	4	7.3	7.37	15.4
5	6.0	5	8.2	7.89	16.4
6	5.9	6	8.9	8.96	18.6
7	6.1	7	9.2	8.97	18.7
8	7.1	8	9.1	8.95	18.8
9	7.7	9 1,9-Dicyclohexylnonane	9.6	9.97	20.8
10	8.4				
11	8.9				
12	8.8				
13	9.6				
14 n-Tetradecylcyclohexane	10.1				

[a] Average weight ratio for alkylcyclohexanes = 2.8, and for dicyclohexyls = 2.5.

complex. There are six molecules of thiourea in the unit cell (space group $R\bar{3}2/C$ with $a \approx 15.8$ Å, $c \approx 12.5$ Å along tube length); however, the arrangement of these molecules is not so simple as is the case for urea (Fig. 1). The larger size of the sulfur atom in thiourea, compared with the oxygen in urea, results in a canal of larger cross section. The distance between two molecules lying one above another is 4.2 Å, and the edge

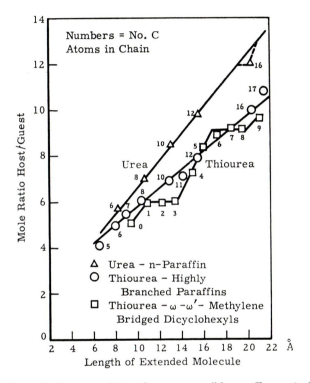

FIG. 12. Example of compressible and noncompressible paraffin guests (*53, 88*).

length of the cell is 5.37 Å; these values compare with 3.7 and 4.8 Å respectively, for the urea adduct. As in the urea complex, the host molecules may spiral in either a right-hand or left-hand direction, depending on chance.

An x-ray diffraction pattern can readily distinguish an enclosed or guest component and determine the position and canal length which is occupied by each molecule. In this way Lenné determined that cyclohexane is situated near the sulfur atoms within the thiourea channel in a zone of maximum attraction or fit. In a like manner a series of dicyclohexyl derivatives having a linear polymethylene bridge was examined. These substances were found by W. Schlenk to be most unusual for non-stoichiometric inclusion complexes since they show an almost constant mole ratio of 6:1 for the series: dicyclohexylmethane, 1,2-dicyclohexylethane, and 1,3-dicyclohexylpropane. These results together with measurements on similar adducts are shown in Table VII. Their x-ray patterns show a compression of the slender paraffinic portion of the dumbbell-shaped reactant molecules within the canal. In this way several ω,ω'-dicyclohexyl derivatives can fit into the same channel space. As soon as a paraffin chain length and channel period become comparable, e.g. their ratio may be expressed as an exact whole number, then anchoring (coupling) between channel and hydrocarbon chain with periodically occurring members at preferred channel positions may be assumed with certainty. Thus, if the fully extended length of the guest molecule exceeds an integral multiple of half the length of the unit cell only slightly, there is a tendency for the enclosed molecule to take up a somewhat less extended form whenever possible to fit the repeating half unit of the thiourea complex. In this way the terminal cyclohexyl rings coincide with zones of maximum attraction determined by the unit cell length as exhibited by individual cyclohexane molecules. Dicyclohexyl cannot occupy these preferred positions and thus a distortion of the basic lattice superstructure occurs. Such "space economy" through compression is also recognized for other reactants which contain unbranched paraffinic sections. Zones of maximum attraction are not encountered to any appreciable degree in the case of urea adducts because of the relatively small diameter of the adduct canal, but choleic acids show very strong channel localization attractions.

B. Properties of Thiourea Complexes

The most stable thiourea adducts are obtained if the organic component has a branched-chain or a saturated ring system. Typical guest substances which may have wide chemical differences, including such compounds as carbon tetrachloride, cyclohexane, isooctane, triptane, *tert*-butyl iodide, camphane, carvone, cyclopentanone, *p*-methylphenyl *tert*-butyl ketone, and other molecules of similar cross-sectional dimensions are listed in Table VIII. None of these materials reacts with urea. Normally benzenoid compounds do not readily form complexes with thiourea. When they are alkylated with a side group having a proper adducting structure (e.g. 3-benzyl cyclohexane or *tert*-butylbenzene) or with methyl groups to provide the necessary diameter (e.g. durene), then stable thiourea complexes form readily. Simple straight-chain substances, such as the *n*-acids or alcohols, do not form adducts unless they have sufficient chain length. A methyl group along a chain is usually not sufficient to provide

TABLE VIII

COMPARISON OF COMPOUNDS FORMING THIOUREA COMPLEXES

| | Adducting with thiourea at 25°C | | | |
| | thiourea/reactant | | | |
Reactant	molal ratio	weight ratio	ΔH formation (kcal/mole)	Nonadducting with thiourea at 25°C
2,2-Dimethylbutane	2.6	2.3	4.4	n-Hexane
2,2,3-Trimethylbutane	—	—	3.7	
2,2,4-Trimethylpentane	3.3	2.2	3.4	n-Dodecane
2,2,4,4-Tetramethylpentane	4.0	2.6	3.4	3-Methylheptane
2,6,9,11-Tetramethyldodecane	7.9	2.6	—	5-n-Butylnonane
Cyclopentane	2.4	2.6	2.2	Benzene
Cyclohexane	3.0	2.7	3.6	Toluene
Cyclohexadiene-1,4	2.9	2.76	—	1-Phenyloctane
Methylcyclohexane	2.9	2.3	—	1,2-Diphenylethane
Isopropylcyclohexane	—	—	1.5	
n-Hexylcyclohexane	5.9	2.7	—	9-Cyclohexyleicosane
1,2-Dicyclohexylethane	6.0	2.5	—	Tricyclohexylmethane
Carbon tetrachloride	3.0	1.5	3.3	Methyl iodide
Cyclohexanol	3.0	2.3	—	Methanol
Cyclooctane	3.1	2.1	—	Isopropanol
Decahydronaphthalene	4.0	2.2	—	n-Butanol
2,6,9,12,15-Pentamethylheptadecane	11.0	2.7	—	Amyl acetate

a stable complex. W. Schlenk (88; cf. 53) has prepared a series of n-alkyl-α-cyclohexanes (Table VII) which do react. These show chain compression with the straight-chain portion not fully extended just as in the previously described examples of dicyclohexyl derivatives. The compression effect is exhibited by steps similar to those shown in Fig. 12. By comparison a groups of highly branched paraffins does give good agreement between the calculated extended length of the molecule and the length of inclusion channel.

In a manner similar to mixed complex formation with urea, some compounds which are nonadducting by themselves often can be induced to form a thiourea complex when mixed with certain adduct formers. The equilibrium relationships for such solid solutions have been reviewed in Section III, D. Examples of inductors, arranged in order of decreasing activity, are: diisobutylene > 2,2,4-trimethylpentane > triisobutylene > 2,2,2-trimethylbutane > decahydronaphthalene > cyclohexane > dicyclohexyl. Some examples of inducted compounds, arranged in decreasing ease of induction, include 1,3-dimethylcyclohexane > dipentene > benzene > 3-methylheptane > heptane > decane > octene-1 > toluene > m-xylene > o-xylene > p-xylene. From these series it can be seen that the larger diameter thiourea adducts are more complicated than the urea complexes. Very large polycyclic substances do not react under any conditions. However, cholesterol forms complexes with both urea and thiourea, but these are not of the inclusion type.

The two most striking new thiourea complex discoveries are the stereospecific polymerization of 2,3-dimethylbutadiene-1,3 by Clasen (18), and Brown and White (14), within the thiourea channel, as described later in Section VII, and the formation of crystalline thiourea (and urea) inclusion complexes with linear poly(ethylene oxide) of extremely high molecular weights by Bailey and France (4). While both urea and thiourea form low molecular weight complexes with poly(ethylene glycols) (8, 69), it is most unusual that high molecular weight polymers also form readily. The reactions were carried out by dissolving the water soluble resins in benzene to 1–3% concentration and reacting this solution with finely ground urea or thiourea. The presence of the complex product was confirmed by x-ray analysis, melting point determinations, and mechanical behavior. The initial rate of complex formation from solution was approximately 50% greater for thiourea than for urea, and quantitative removal of the polymer from solution occurred to form a channel product of about 2 moles of thiourea to each oxyethylene structural unit. Quantitative removal with urea occurred only in the presence of an excess of urea. This product requires a similar ratio of host to guest monomer unit and had a melting point of 143°C. This is the highest melting point ever shown for urea complexes and indicates that the stability range of the inclusion complexes is not limited to the melting point of the host molecule, which is 132.7°C for urea. The thiourea complex was found to have a higher stability with a melting point near 180°C, the melting point of thiourea. These polymer complexes showed a marked increase in stiffness when molded and caused a change in viscosity to occur in solutions.

The thermodynamics of thiourea complexes are essentially the same as for urea complexes. Redlich *et al.* (*81*) have obtained equilibrium constants for the decomposition of a number of these complexes. Selected examples, as shown in Fig. 13, are as defined by Eqs. (11) and (29) for urea complexes. The equilibrium constants are generally higher, and the heats of adduction, or complex formation, given by the temperature coefficient of K, are lower for thiourea than for urea complexes [Table VIII, and Eq. (30)]. The low temperature coefficient of K, however, reflects the high melting point of thiourea (180°C) and a lower heat of adduction (lesser stability) of thiourea complexes. It is interesting that the heat of formation of the dimethylbutane complex is greater than that for tri-methylbutane, and both of these are greater than that for the trimethyl-pentane complex (Table VIII). Relationships for free energy, molal ratio, and heat of formation cannot be expected to have the general application

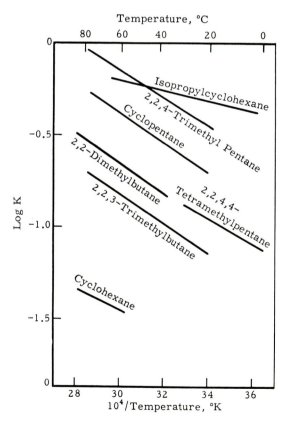

FIG. 13. Equilibrium constants for typical thiourea complexes (*81*).

that is achieved with urea complexes because thiourea complexes form with such a wide variety of reactants of differing chemical structure. Nonetheless, correlations on the basis of reactant length for a series of similar compounds do provide useful information (Fig. 12).

Complex densities range from 1.1 to 1.2 gm/cm³ and are considerably lower than the value of 1.405 for thiourea itself. These may be calculated from crystallographic data. Molal ratios and weight ratios are usually lower than the ratios for the urea product which is in agreement with their structural differences (Fig. 12, Table VII). Methods of preparation, isolation, analysis, and decomposition of thiourea inclusion compounds are essentially the same as for urea inclusion compounds. Their lower stability with most guest molecules requires that added precautions be taken in their handling and storage.

V. OTHER CHANNEL INCLUSION COMPLEXES

A. Carbohydrate and Protein Types

The cyclodextrins are a theoretically important group of solid complexes having unsupported channels as large as 9–10 Å in diameter. These will be briefly reviewed relative to their unusual solution phenomena in Section VI. These complexing agents and the related amylose starches, cellulose, and various carbohydrates have been considered as interrelated by Cramer (22). Together with the other complexing agents mentioned briefly in this section these substances are reviewed in detail in Chapter 9. Some proteins and nitrogen containing polymers are also capable of forming large hydrogen bonding layers and helical networks ideal for inclusion complex formation. Cramer (22) has reviewed the properties of protein agents such as the layer complexes exhibited by horse hemoglobin and serum albumins. It is but a short extension of these classifications to the antibody and antigen complexes of the blood proteins (22, 27) and the unusual nucleic acids.

B. Polynuclear Organic Channel Adducts

Another large and growing group of channel forming inclusion complexes is derived from widely differing polynuclear organic chemicals (Fig. 14) such as choleic acids (22, 37, 109); the chromans (76), spirochromans (36), and 2'-oxyflavones (22); tri-o-thymotide (22, 52); 4,4'-dinitrodiphenyl (22, 44, 91); triphenylmethane and its derivatives (9, 38, 42); methylnaphthalenes (62); and related systems. Several of these are capa-

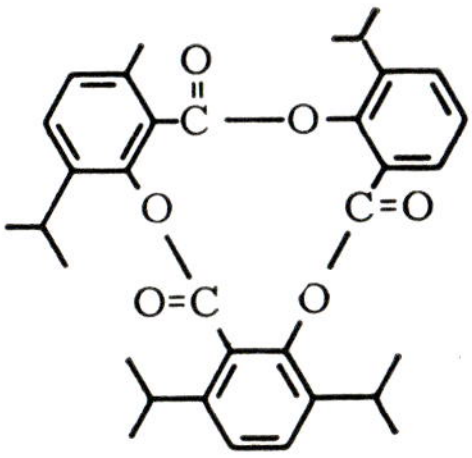

Tri-o-Thymotide

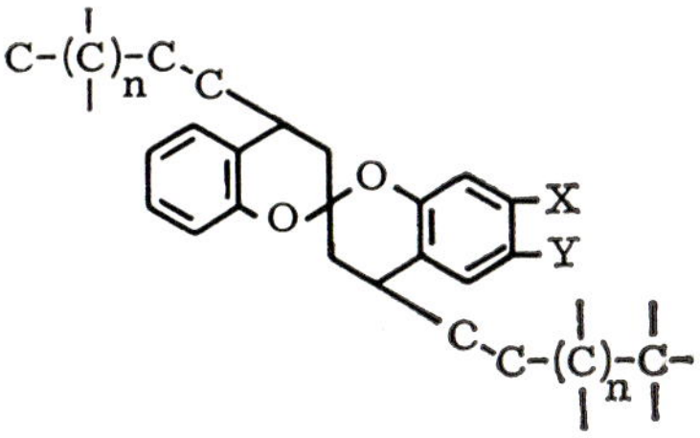

Spirochromans

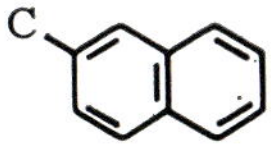

2-Methylnaphthalene

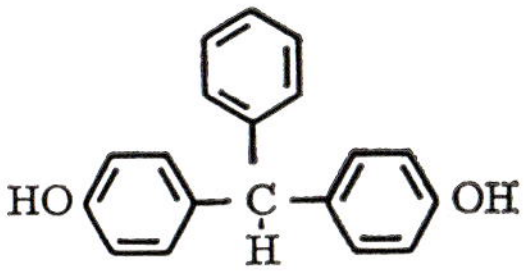

4,4′-Dihydroxy-
triphenylmethane

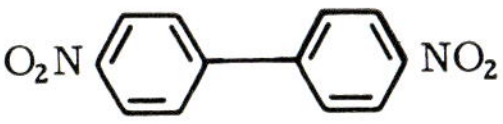

4,4′-Dinitrodiphenyl

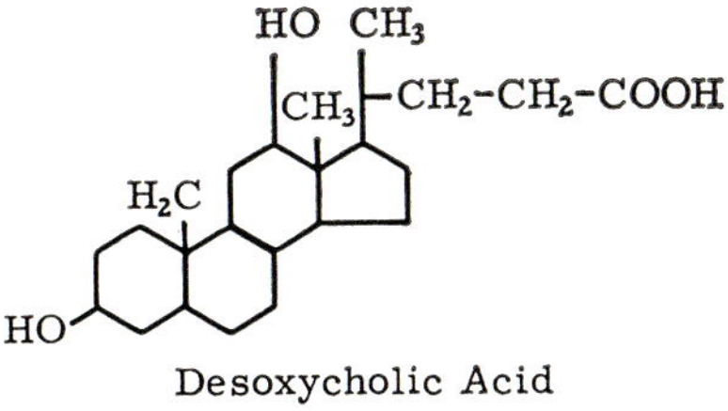

Desoxycholic Acid

FIG. 14. Channel and clathrate cage forming polynuclear organic substances.

ble of forming both closed cage and channel inclusion compounds. One of their characteristic properties is the ability to form layer-like crystal arrays with sufficient interaction or steric hindrance from side groups between the layers to produce localized clathrate pockets or extended inclusion channels. On the basis of x-ray diffraction studies, Powell (9) has suggested that substituted 4,4′-dihydroxytriphenylmethanes form layer structures whereby each hydroxyl group is hydrogen bonded to hydroxyl groups from two other molecules; the substituent such as a nitro or chloro on the third phenyl group is *sterically linked* to the corresponding group in another molecule forming an interlocking assembly. These form channels about 6.0–6.5 Å diameter capable of nonselective complexing with *n*-alkanes, *n*-alkenes, and branched-chain materials like 2,2,4-trimethylpentane, diisobutene, squalene, isoprene, and dipentene. By comparison, 4,4′-dinitrodiphenyl (*44*) produces layer-like plates with channels slightly smaller (~5.0 Å) than those exhibited by urea complexes. According to Hess (*44*) this substance is capable of separating a purer *n*-paraffinic wax from a crude wax mixture than will urea under equilibrium separation conditions.

The spirochromans (*36*) will also extract the predominantly *n*-paraffinic materials from a mixture by complex formation. Normally, the chromans and related flavones tend to produce clathrates. The crystal structure of methylnaphthalene (*62*) at room temperature provides a channel-like cavity which will accommodate guest molecules of both straight- and branched-chain hydrocarbons. These are not exactly similar to the urea and thiourea classes since molecules longer than *n*-hexadecane will not fit and hence do not react. The intensities of the cohesive forces in urea and methylnaphthalene complexes can be compared by measurement of their respective dissociation pressures. At 0°C, the dissociation pressure of *n*-heptane–urea is 3.3 mm; that of *n*-heptane-2-methylnaphthalene is 9.0 mm. These complexes often contain an integral number of molecules suggesting that they are more like graphite layer intercalation compounds and the hallosite clays (Chapter 6).

Tri-*o*-thymotide has been employed by Powell (*74g*) to separate optical isomers. This material proved to have available spaces in trigonal crystals capable of accommodating carbon chains up to five or six carbon atoms in length and one methyl side group in width. The adduct with *n*-hexane melts at 174°C and shows a 1:2 combining ratio more characteristic of the clathrates. This substance is also capable of forming a hexagonal structure which contains extremely long channels. Paraffin chains containing 18 carbon atoms have been adducted in this configuration (*74g*). The two tri-*o*-thymotide systems are discussed in detail in Chapter 7, Sections II,A,7 and III,B,3.

C. Mineral and Organometallic Complexes

Several layer-like minerals or clays such as hallosite (*22*, *27*) or montmorillonite are capable of swelling and interaction with many organic molecules giving complex-like products. These are nonselective and often depend on hydrogen bonding for stability. Graphite also will form non-selective layer complexes sometimes called intercalation compounds. When the minerals form a three-dimensional array as in the case of the molecular sieves, then the configuration and length of the included molecules become important. These products are more comparable to the cage clathrates than they are to the channel structures but since diffusion into the preformed pores is usually rate-controlling these cannot be considered as the same class of complexes as the many organic substances discussed in detail in this chapter. Another group of clathrating substances intermediate between the mineral and purely organic types are those of the Werner complex class (56). Ligand containing organometallic compounds such as monoamine nickel(II) dicyanide or tetra(alkylpyridine)nickel(II) dithiocyanate are capable of selectively reacting with and separating certain aromatic molecules from mixtures. Other ligands with metals such as iron, nickel, copper, and cobalt may form comparable structures providing complexing cavities. These host substances, like the mineral structure, exist without the guest molecule being present. Future studies may provide clues to the ready formation of channel as well as cavity structures from these materials. Their important characteristics and properties are reviewed in Chapter 6.

VI. SOLUBLE "COMPLEX" PHENOMENA

If a urea, thiourea, or other clathrate complex could exist as such in a dissolved state in sufficient amounts, a solution containing these host species might have very selective properties and a separation process based on them could be greatly simplified by avoiding the steps of handling of solids, filtration, and washing. This was the hope of several early investigators but measurements soon indicated that if such a complex state can exist, it is not sufficiently stable to be of practical significance in liquid-liquid extraction processes. However, a detailed study of thermodynamics, stoichiometry, and probable mechanism of complex formation has led more recently to the proposal (27, 28, 88) of a pseudo-complex "swarm" or "husk" crystalline state of host and guest molecules existing in aqueous solutions. One of the most important results of these findings may be the new light which they will shed on the theory of solutions in general and aqueous solutions in particular. For example, in the case of aqueous urea solutions we are dealing with the dissolved state of the long-chain reactant such as a n-paraffin or fatty acid just prior to adduction and following complex formation. This state is essentially the same as that which has received much theoretical study over the years in the fields of micelle formation, surface tension (Traube's rule), interphase film tension, solubility phenomena, and vapor pressures (Henry's law) and related properties. Similarly, homogeneous stereospecific polymerization and catalysis with clathrating organometallic ligand complexes may be controlled by the holes occupied by the reactants in solution.

An important outgrowth of these studies on the dissolved state of channel and clathrate compounds (27, 28) has been the support they give to Franks and Evans' proposals (32) of "iceberg" formation around small inert gases dissolved in water. The related data and evidences cast considerable doubt on the mechanism of paraffin solubility in water at 0°–50°C as proposed by Langmuir (51) in his theory of "independent surface action" and more recently refined by Ward and Tordai (108). Some of these evidences and findings will be reviewed briefly.

If we are to explain the formation of a urea complex such as that of stearic acid in an aqueous solution, we must account for the mechanism by which a minimum of 28.4 molecules of urea and 2 stearic acid monomers collect together and start the first unit of a linearly aligned swarm of crystallites which ultimately grow into visible crystal nuclei. Energetics of the urea lattice system as discussed earlier indicate it is highly improbable that the metastable adduct channel is "preformed" and that somehow the n-paraffinic compound slips into it. Instead, we are forced to assume that the urea molecules "grow" spiralwise around the hydrocarbon chain. According to the Langmuir-Ward theory, it is assumed that little affinity exists between water and the paraffin chain and that a very strong interaction exists between the water molecules resembling liquid water in its surface phase. Using surface tension measurements and this model they concluded that the long paraffin chain compounds remain tightly coiled in water and water solutions of this type. The same argument would hold for urea-water solutions. Since it is nearly impossible that an uncoiling and sudden alignment of the paraffin chain with so many urea molecules can occur simultaneously, one is forced to look for another explanation, namely the existence of long, extended, partially adducted, non-stoichiometric species in solution.

A powerful argument in favor of the existence of the dissolved complex is that the formation of strong "supported hydrogen bonds", which is the driving force for solid complex formation, must also occur in aqueous solutions of urea, thiourea, and other clathrate-forming substances, and also in water itself. Dimensional restrictions are less exacting for the dissolved complex than in the solid state. Thus there is a great tendency for three-dimensional hydrogen bonding molecules to wrap around the surface of dissolved substances which exhibit only van der Waals surface attractive forces. As will be shown, this wrapping effect is still restricted dimensionally to configurations of the solute just as in the solid state, but other noncrystallizing configurations may exist in solutions which differ markedly from those in the solid states of urea, thiourea, water, and other host species which produce known non-stoichiometric complexes. In the case of channel-forming substances this wrapping phenomenon would produce an essentially linear rod-like configuration of the paraffin group in solution. The linear variation of solubilities (log X) with chain length (Fig. 15) together with other measurements suggest this is also true for aqueous solutions. Substances such as glucose and bile acids may interact with the solute without ever producing a solid crystalline complex.

On the assumption that the same driving force for complex formation exists in aqueous solutions for many hydrogen bonding substances and for water itself, we may inspect a large amount of accurately measured data in the literature and make new interpretations based on this concept. Butler (15) noted (1933) that dissolving a normal paraffinic substance in water is associated with a very high negative entropy change ($\Delta S°$). This effect, rather than the heat content ($\Delta H°$) as predicted by other theories, contributes the most to the solubilizing process. Butler also observed a linear increase in both the $\Delta S°$ and $\Delta H°$ with chain length and calculated a value of $\Delta H°$ per CH_2 group of 3.4 kcal which is far higher than the 0.3 kcal per CH_2 group estimated for the van der Waals

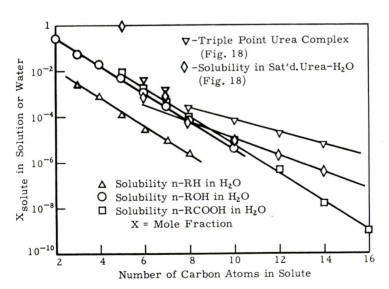

FIG. 15. Solubilities of linear paraffin chain homologues in water and urea-water solutions at 25°C (21).

attraction in water hydrates and urea complexes. These thermodynamic functions for solution of a vapor product are interrelated by the following well-known equations:

$$\Delta G^{\circ}{}_{hyd} = \Delta H^{\circ}{}_{hyd} - T\Delta S^{\circ}{}_{hyd} = RT \ln (P/X) \qquad (32)$$

where X is the mole fraction of solute and P is the pressure of saturated solute vapor. These observations were enlarged upon by Butler and Barclay (15) but no attempt was ever made to explain the unusual results. Later, Frank and Evans (32) made an extensive study of thermodynamic functions related to the solution in water of rare gases and light hydrocarbons. He noted that not only is the solution entropy change highly negative per mole of solute and the heats of solution exothermic, but the slope of a plot of $\Delta H^{\circ}{}_{vap}$ versus $\Delta S^{\circ}{}_{vap}$ is very different for water solutions when compared to normal solutions. Further, they observed enormous partial molar heat capacities which exceed 60 cal/°C-mole for xenon in water. Many of these measurements have been confirmed by Morrison and Johnstone (65). These and other evidences led Frank and Evans to propose an iceberg effect or water husk of greater crystallinity around the surface of these inert dissolved gases at temperatures near 25°C. In this manner the variations in the entropy term and partial molar heat capacities could all be accounted for on the basis of the formation and melting of this iceberg husk. Frank and Evans, however, were dealing with small spherical molecules dissolved in water so did not acknowledge the configuration effects posed by the dissolved longer chain paraffinic substances.

Claussen and Polglase (19, 20) proposed that the iceberg shells described by Frank and Evans have the same configurations in solution as the solid gas hydrates which are discussed in Chapters 6 and 7. These, they concluded from the x-ray work of von Stackelberg and Müller (98, 99), and Pauling and Marsh (70) consist of either of two cubic structures (I and II) in which the hydrated molecules are situated in clathrate cavities formed by a framework of water molecules linked together by hydrogen bonds. This view appears to be supported by the fact that similar water soluble tetra-n-butyl and tetra-$tert$-amyl quaternary ammonium salts were noted to form both water soluble hydrates and solid hydrate complexes which Jeffrey and co-workers (60) indicate are of the same clathrate type but with $ions$ instead of inert molecules occupying the cavities. Glew (36a) has found direct evidence for the existence of a three-dimensionally hydrogen bonded liquid hydrate of ethanol in water at 0–30°C having a cage structure and composition $17H_2O \cdot C_2H_5OH$.

We are confronted with a problem when we consider the solution in water of n-paraffins and related substances which are too large to fit into even the largest possible solid hydrate cavities. The author (27, 28) has searched for a discontinuity in the water solubilities and related properties such as heats of solution, entropy change, and partial molar heat capacities of several homologous n-paraffinic series and found no inflection at the C_3 or C_4 point which are the limiting water hydrate guest sizes. In fact the plot of log X (mole fraction) versus number of carbon atoms for several homologous n-aliphatic series at constant temperature, as shown in Fig. 15, is so very linear one is forced to assume some other, perhaps spiralling, water configuration must be present. Since Pauling (72) suggested that unfilled pentagonal dodecahedra probably exist in liquid water and that these aggregates may arrange relative to one another in a large number of ways, it is possible that these also arrange to form channels as well as the usual gas hydrate structures much in the same manner that tri-o-thymotide forms both types of configurations. This agrees with the observation of Baker (6) who has found a 10% increase in the solubility of n-octadecane when smaller hydrate forming paraffins are present. The existence of channel soluble structures (27) in water is further confirmed by a comparison of the solubilities of twenty-three isomeric octanols and methyl heptanols measured by Dorough (24). If these were contained in any sort of spherical cavity, their solubilities would not be influenced by the location of the OH group or chain configuration. Instead, these meas-

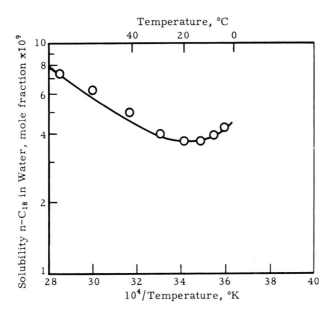

Fig. 16. Solubilities of n-octadecane in water (6).

urements, when corrected to a common basis by adjusting for variations in vapor pressure, show a very regular additive variation of solubilities with configuration and position of the OH group. Separate additive effects from the presence of polar groups, chain branching, and an extended unbranched-chain suggests areas of differing solubilization phenomena. These considerations carry over into the urea-water systems.

Baker (6) has recently measured the solubility of tritiated n-octadecane (n-$C_{18}H_{38}$) in water while gathering evidence for his new theory of the migration of petroleum oils in microporous rock and found it to be 28 parts per billion. He also measured the over-all entropy change of solution, $\Delta S°_{soln}$, to be a large negative number (-31.5 cal/°C-mole at 25°C) rather than the positive value previous theories would predict. From this he concluded that the solution of a hydrocarbon molecule in water modifies the structure in the direction of greater crystallinity; from measurements of the heats of solution which show a minimum in the log X versus $1/T$ curve (Fig. 16 and Table IX) Baker also proposed a rod-like structure below 18°C and an increasingly random structure above this temperature. At this point the energy gained from the increased clathration in water in the vicinity of the dissolved hydrocarbon molecule exactly cancels the energy necessary to separate the hydrocarbon molecule from its neighbors in the condensed state.

The entropy data indicate 17 molecules of water per molecule of n-$C_{18}H_{38}$ are induced into a new hydrogen bonding ice structure. This number is estimated in the following manner. The solution process is considered to involve two steps: (a) the vaporization of the pure solute; and (b) the

TABLE IX

THERMODYNAMIC QUANTITIES OF AQUEOUS OCTADECANE SOLUTIONS (6)

Temp. (°K)	$\Delta S°_{soln}$ cal/°C/mole	$\Delta H°_{soln}$ cal/mole	$\Delta S°_{hyd}$ cal/°C/mole	n (moles of H_2O per HC mole)
278	-49.4	-3110	-85.2	16.2
286	-43.3	-1650	-79.7	15.1
292	-38.8	0	-73.6	14.0
294	-32.1	1900	-66.9	12.7
303	-30.6	2340	-64.5	12.4
328	-29.6	2610	-61.8	12.1
352	-29.7	2610	-60.0	11.4

solution or hydration of the gaseous solute. Thus, we may write the free energy change

$$\Delta G'^{\circ}_{soln} = \Delta G'^{\circ}_{vap} + \Delta G'^{\circ}_{hyd} \tag{33}$$

The standard free energy of vaporization is given by the conventional equation

$$\Delta G'^{\circ}_{vap} = -RT \ln P \tag{34}$$

and the free energy of hydration of the gaseous solute, ΔG°_{hyd}, by Eq. (32). Similarly, the entropy changes for these processes may be written:

$$\Delta S^{\circ}_{soln} = R \ln X + \frac{\Delta H^{\circ}_{soln}}{T} \tag{35}$$

$$-\Delta S^{\circ}_{hyd} = \frac{\Delta H^{\circ}_{vap}}{T} - \frac{\Delta H^{\circ}_{soln}}{T} + R \ln P - R \ln X \tag{36}$$

Since the ΔH°_{soln} is readily obtained from the slopes of the solubility curve with temperature change (Fig. 16), Baker (6) calculated the entropy changes over a range of temperature as is given in Table IX. Knowing the entropy change upon freezing water to the common form of ice at 0°C is −5.26 e.u. and is nearly independent of the temperature, one obtains the number, n, of ice molecules which would have to form per molecule of dissolved hydrocarbon in order to account for the over-all observed entropy change of solution.

In the urea-water system it was observed by both W. Schlenk (87) and the author (27, 28) that the formation of a dissolved form of channel adduct, which from the foregoing may be reasonably assumed, results in a large increase in the solubility of a long-chain substance relative to its water solubility. For example, the solubility of stearic acid, although very low in aqueous urea solutions (Fig. 17), is increased almost 1000-fold before urea complex formation begins. Similarly, at 25°C, 100 parts of water will dissolve 12 parts of n-valeric acid; in a saturated solution of urea in water, n-valeric acid is miscible in all proportions. To show that this is not a case of interaction of the carboxyl group with urea, the isomeric α-methylbutyric acid, which has too large a diameter to be an adduct former, was dissolved in the same concentration urea-water solution and found to be no more soluble than in water. The full equilibrium diagram for the solution of caproic acid, the first n-fatty acid which produces a complex at 25°C, is shown in Fig. 18. It is interesting that a metastable region of supersaturation from increasing complex solubility can exist up to the urea-water saturation point if solid complex seed crystals

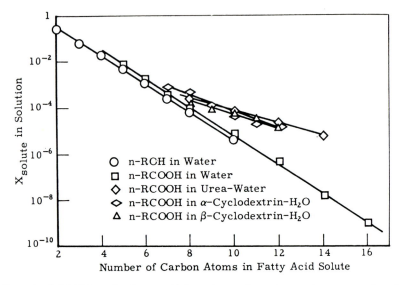

Fig. 17. Solubilities of *n*-fatty acid homologues in water, water-urea, and water-dextrin solution.

are absent. In this region a large increase in solubility is noted, but it does not reach a point of complete miscibility as in the case of *n*-valeric acid. The author (27) also noted (Fig. 18) that *n*-caproic acid is capable of being solubilized in a similar manner by thiourea, which normally produces a channel complex of larger diameter than that of urea. In this case the crystal lattice never reaches a stability that will produce a solid phase. Later, the discovery by McLaughlin (59) that long-chain *n*-paraffins form solid thiourea complexes at low temperatures by drawing the chain into a helical spiral within the channel demonstrated that complexing of thiourea with a *n*-paraffinic structure is not restricted to the liquid phase. Very recently, Bailey and France (4) have shown that both urea and thiourea form stable water soluble solid complexes of poly(ethylene oxide) polymer. The author (31) has noted similar complexes with polyethers of 1,3-propanediol.

In a plot of the water solubilities and increased urea-water solubilities for the homologous series of fatty acids as a function of chain length, as shown in Figs. 15 and 17, we again see evidence of increased complex stability with increasing chain length just as in the solid state. It was also observed (47) that there is a regular variation in the onset of complex formation (triple points) with the odd and even carbon number of these acids. No other explanation than a variation in the stabilities of the dissolved and solid complex appears possible to account for this. Similar

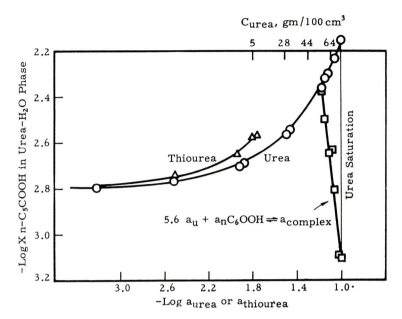

Fig. 18. Solubility of n-caproic acid in urea-water solutions at 25°C (27).

effects as the solubilization of long-chain soaps by urea may be attributed in part to this same phenomenon.

Emulsification, micelle formation, and hydrotropic action have all been proposed to account for some of the results observed in the solubilization of fatty acids and the mono- and diglyceride esters into the blood stream by the action of salts of desoxycholic and taurodesoxycholic acids. Here again we may be dealing with large soluble channel complexes although no one has yet proven this conclusively. Sobotka and Kahn (97) claim, however, that these materials completely dissociate in solution.

More recently, association phenomena in aqueous solutions have been studied utilizing the so-called Schardinger dextrins α-, β-, and γ-cyclodextrins (or in more significant nomenclature, cyclohexa-, cyclohepta-, and cyclooctaamylose). While several host molecules are needed to provide the encasing structure, one molecule of cyclodextrin provides the geometry necessary for inclusion. Unlike the urea and thiourea host molecules, the doughnut-shaped cyclodextrin molecule which is discussed in detail in Chapter 9 contains a preformed cavity so that inclusion is not necessarily restricted to the crystalline phase, but may take place in solution. Cramer and co-workers (22) investigated reactions inducing optical asymmetry, rates of dehydrogenation, enzymatic processes, spectra of dyestuffs, and oxidation, reduction potentials in solutions of cyclodextrins with primary reference to the mode of enzyme action. It remained for H. Schlenk and Sand (84) to study the steric conditions which influence the association of cyclodextrins with guest molecules in aqueous solutions such as the n-fatty acids and various benzoic acids. They found that the solubility of benzoic acid and the n-fatty acids is definitely increased by the presence of α- and β-cyclodextrins. Figure 17 shows the increase in solubility of the longer-chained fatty acids in the cyclodextrin solutions in a manner very similar to that noted by the author for urea and thiourea solutions. The concentration of cyclodextrin was, however, only 3 gm/100 cm³ in these experiments.

A mechanism for increasing the solubility of a substance having normally a low solubility in water by means of co-solutes is ordinarily classed either as hydrotropy or micelle solubilization. Hydrotropy, however, involves salts of organic acids that, at high concentration, increase the solubility of other compounds by associating with them. Solubilization by cyclodextrins and related channel inclusion complexes does not involve hydrotropy since dilute solutions are usually involved. Micelle solubilization involves a multitude of molecules organized to form a colloidal system which provides a solubilizing environment. Cyclodextrins and other channel complexes, however, provide this environment without micelle-type aggregations or colloid formation. The phenomenon involved here must be molecular or *inclusion* solubilization. An example familiar to most chemists is the blue starch-iodine end point. Both α-cyclodextrin and starch have the unique role of associating with iodide (I⁻) ion. When these interact with I₂, a soluble blue channel complex forms. The color results from a resonance hybrid of I₃⁻ wherein the iodine atoms are at equal intervals along the channel (see Chapter 9).

Important additional evidence (84) that the solutions of cyclodextrins do involve inclusion has been the specification of solubilization due to steric interference of the solute (or potential guest molecule), as was shown for urea. Again we find configuration governing solubilization and, as in the case of other host molecules, the steric requirements in solution are more liberal than in crystals. This is observed in the interaction of benzoic acid with α-cyclodextrin even though great difficulty is encountered with this system in crystallization of the solid complex from solution. Tests on iodobenzoic acid isomers, durylcarboxylic acid, and homologous substances corroborate this. p-Iodobenzoic acid is the only isomer which forms a stable soluble complex readily with α-cyclodextrin, whereas all three iodobenzoic acid isomers crystallize as complexes without difficulty and are solubilized by β-cyclodextrin; apparently their diameters do not exceed the limit which still permits association to a considerable extent (see Chapter 9, Section IV, 2). On the other hand, acids containing a tetramethylphenyl group exceed the dimensions permissible for proper inclusion even in solution and only with difficulty do they become associated.

Based upon the many evidences presented there seems to be little doubt that water soluble channel and clathrate complexes of many kinds can exist in the aqueous phase. This phenomenon may serve an important role in the solutions of long-chained proteins, celluloses, sugars, and synthetic polar polymers. Stereospecific reactions and polymerization within solvent or reactant cages and channels will become increasingly important especially in the field of soluble Werner complexes and other organometallic ligand systems. These may include interactions with trapped ions, radicals, and neutral molecules. Increasing discussions of "cage" effects of organic reactions indicate a growing concern for the role of the solvent in rapid reactions. Very recently Pauling (71) proposed a new molecular theory of general anesthesia which he attributed to the formation in the brain of minute solid hydrate crystals of the clathrate type. This may actually involve the same soluble forms of the clathrate types discussed in this section.

Attention is called to the theory of liquids, presented in Chapter 2, Section III, which may be applied to the various liquid state models cited in this section.

VII. APPLICATIONS OF INCLUSION COMPLEXES

A. Selective Separation of Hydrocarbon Fractions

Extractive crystallization with urea is one of the more recent commercially successful separation techniques. The urea process provides a practical means for selectively removing the straight-chain hydrocarbon components from fractions ranging from gasoline to heavy distillates. Some of the more important applications which have been tested on pilot plant scale are the production of pure n-paraffins, α-olefins from cracked stocks, low pour-point diesel and jet fuels, lubricating oil bases, straight-chain and specialty waxes, gasoline of improved octane number, and diesel oil of high quality. A single cyclic urea process unit could be sufficiently flexible to be used in all of the above applications.

Each of the various cyclic continuous processes which has been proposed (5, 29) involves four steps of varying complexity: (i) formation of the crystalline adduct by agitation of the hydrocarbon with either dissolved or solid urea; (ii) separation of the reaction product into crystalline adduct and liquid phases; (iii) decomposition of the adduct into the urea solution and hydrocarbon; and (iv) purification of the product streams and recovery of urea and solvents. The principal difficulty inherent in most urea processes results from the voluminous character of the inclusion complexes which crystallize into small hexagonal needles giving a very porous mass of low bulk density. The successful processes control the crystal growth for better separations. The most characteristic feature of

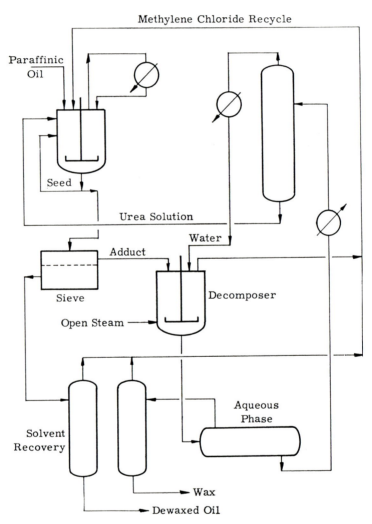

FIG. 19. Deutsche Erdol A.G. uses a process that employs several unique operational techniques.

a cyclic process is the solvent used for urea. Water with suitable additives and auxiliary solvents competes mainly with the methanol system originally suggested by Bengen.

The aqueous urea processes have been the more promising since very little solubilization of urea in the hydrocarbon phase occurs. The aqueous solution not only minimizes the problem of urea recovery but serves alternately to convey, wash, and decompose the complex. In the first process of this class, reported by Bailey *et al.* (*5*), a hydrocarbon soluble solvent such as methyl isobutyl ketone facilitates the rate of complex formation by increasing the rate of transfer of the *n*-paraffins between phases (*28*), and also provides additional wash of the complex during filtration. A successful commercial urea dewaxing plant employing water as a urea solvent has been operated by Deutsche Erdol A. G. since 1955 on a 320 barrel/day scale for producing low pour-point diesel and spindle oils from a feed having a pour-point of $+17°C$ and containing about 15% wax. Much larger plants for purifying wax are currently under construction employing this system. The flow scheme (Fig. 19) involves several unique operational techniques which are claimed to improve the economics of the process. Methylene chloride is used as an oil phase diluent to reduce the viscosity of the oil, thus improving the rate of reaction, and to provide auto-refrigeration by removing the heat of reaction at its boiling point of $41°C$. In the process cycle equal volumes of the feed hydrocarbon, dichloromethane solvent, and seeded aqueous urea solution are violently agitated together at $40°C$ before transfer to a filter. By utilizing a urea solution containing no more than 40 weight per cent water (saturated at $70°C$) a second aqueous phase does not form and the product readily settles from the lower density raffinate and is separated by sieves of the simplest design.

In a like manner, complex formation can serve as a means of purifying the host molecules such as urea, thiourea, and cyclodextrin by a reversal of the complexing processes. This approach has lead to one (*7*) of the more promising methods for the desalination of sea water.

1. PURE *n*-PARAFFINS AND OLEFINS

These processes are capable of producing enormous amounts of *n*-paraffins from *n*-C_7 to C_{24} and even as high as *n*-C_{50} depending on the starting material. The *n*-paraffins can be isolated free from branched or cyclic compounds and the usual sulfur, oxygen, and nitrogen contaminants found in crude oils. Product purities above 99% have been obtained. Fractional distillation of the mixed *n*-paraffins yields substantially pure individual compounds. Although no other single class of compounds in petroleum has the same degree of similarity in structure and chemical properties, there is at present little demand for the purified n-paraffin. When n-paraffins and mixed waxes are thermally cracked, they provide high yields of straight-chain olefins with the double bond predominantly in the alpha position. Garner and co-workers (34) describe the separation of these products from the branched-chain components with urea. These products are of current interest in Ziegler-type polymerizations and chemical synthesis.

2. Hydrocarbon Treating

When gasolines were lower in octane rating, some improvement was made by removing the n-paraffins which had ratings of -20 (ASTM) or lower octane number in reference to an arbitrary rating of 0 for n-heptane and 100 for isooctane. In the kerosene range urea treatment has been found to be a very effective means for lowering the freezing point below $-76°F$ for use as JP–4 jet fuels. Since pure n-hexadecane (cetane) has a cetane number of 100, by definition on the Diesel fuel performance reference scale relative to methylnaphthalenes rating 0, the urea technique can be used to provide special arctic Diesel fuels (29) of nearly 100 cetane rating. Similarly, urea is effective for dehazing potential lubricating oils and producing very high quality refrigeration oils. The first commercial application of the urea process utilized promoted solid urea in a batch cycle to dewax a premium water-clear white mineral oil (29).

3. Dewaxing

During the early stages of investigation of urea-extractive crystallization, the possibility of dewaxing most lubricating oil stocks without refrigeration appeared promising. Research soon demonstrated, however, that sorting molecules according to shape does not give the same results as does conventional low temperature solvent dewaxing based upon freezing points. The melting point of a long-chain branched or cyclic paraffin often corresponds to that of the n-paraffin equal in length to the longest unbranched chain in the molecule (29). On the other hand, many branched and naphthenic waxes of high melting point may have average cross sections too large for inclusion in the urea complex and would not permit complete dewaxing of certain crude stocks. As would be expected, natural and synthetic waxes and lubrication oils separated by urea often have properties and applications which differ from the conventional products (29).

B. Purification of Natural Products

1. SEPARATION OF UNSATURATES

Urea not only affords fractionation according to structural differences of molecules such as the branched- and straight-chain paraffins in petroleum, but it also serves as a tool for the segregation of straight-chain mixtures having different chain lengths and different degrees of unsaturation. The advantage of separating vegetable and marine oils or their fatty acids into at least two fractions having different degrees of unsaturation has long been recognized. The more unsaturated fraction is valuable for drying properties imparted to the polyol esters by acid radicals having two or more double bonds. The more saturated fraction of a mixture is in itself a valuable product. This separation is possible because the double bonds (especially the *cis* configurations) cause the chain to deviate from a linear form sufficiently to no longer fit easily into the urea channel structure. The optimum separation is made on the basis of both equilibrium (Fig. 9) and reaction rate differences (Fig. 11) as previously discussed.

Separation according to unsaturation permits the isolation of certain acids such as oleic and linoleic in highly enriched or purified forms. In the C_{18} series the gradient of separation is best between oleic and linoleic acid. Even these two fatty acids, however, can be prepared in pure state by urea fractionation only when low temperature crystallization or high vacuum distillation is used as an accessory step. The preparation of linoleic acid is most advantageous when safflower oil is used since it contains about 75% linoleic acid and only a small amount of linolenic acid. After a urea treatment and low temperature crystallization of the esters, the quality of the product is better than 98% *cis*-linoleic acid. The conventional preparation involving bromination and debromination is cumbersome and produces appreciable amounts of the *trans* isomer. Purified oleic acid has been isolated (*30, 86*) similarly from corn oil acid and various edible fats.

2. STRAIGHT CHAINS FROM BRANCHED CHAINS

Although a considerable number of branched-chain fatty acids occur in nature, the separation of fatty acids and monoglycerides from triglycerides is of greater importance. Deacidification of fats or natural oils is often a necessary refining step before further use. Marine oils, olive oil, and cottonseed oil have been treated in this manner. In typical experiments, low grade cottonseed oil containing 41.8% free acids was reacted with aqueous urea to yield a fraction containing 80% acids and a triglyceride fraction containing 3% or less acids. The concentration of tall oil acids is a related problem. Alkaline treatments are seldom undertaken because of the likelihood of the formation of emulsions that are difficult to handle. In a similar manner unreacted unsaturated fatty acids and monomer vinyl esters of fatty acids from partial polymerizations can be separated by urea. Truter (*103*) described the concentration of cholesterol from wool wax by urea removal of long-chain alcohols.

At times an auxiliary reaction can be employed to aid a particular separation. An elegant procedure for the preparation of pure ricinoleic acid from castor oil fatty acids is accomplished by first reacting the mixture with boric acid which interacts only with the unsaturated hydroxylated fatty acid of the ricinoleic, and then adducting the impurities with urea. The highly branched orthoborate is separated and easily reconverted into ricinoleic acid.

$$(CH_2)_5CH_3$$

Orthoborate of methyl ricinoleate: $B(OCH)_3$

$$CH_2—CH=CH—(CH_2)_7COOCH_3$$

Swern and co-workers (*101–102*) used urea to concentrate methyloleate peroxides to a purity of 80–90%. Bromination, epoxidation, and other accessory reactions can be employed to add bulky groups to a substance and permit new separations. In some areas the fractionation of fatty acids by thiourea, employing cyclohexyl esters as anchors to facilitate inclusion has been considered. The reactivities of fatty acid esters containing methyl and ethyl side chains have been studied by Truter (*103*) and are reviewed earlier in Table IV. A naturally occurring cyclopropene derivative, sterculic acid, is very unstable and polymerizes at 0°C. This substance can best be isolated as a urea complex. These principles apply to separation of a wide variety of other fatty materials such as nitriles, alcohols, amides, and peroxides. H. Schlenk (*86*) and Truter (*103*) have reviewed this general field.

C. "Molecular Packaging" of Chemicals

A remarkable property of the urea inclusion compounds is that the guest molecules are protected from attack by oxygen. H. Schlenk and Holman (*85*) and Fetterly (*27*) observed that unsaturated fatty acids, esters, and related compounds are perfectly stable against autoxidation when held within the inclusion lattice. The stability has been demonstrated by following the peroxide values of soybean acids and esters over a period of several weeks in both the free and urea bound states. The oxygen uptake of pure linoleic and linolenic acids and their adducts (Fig.

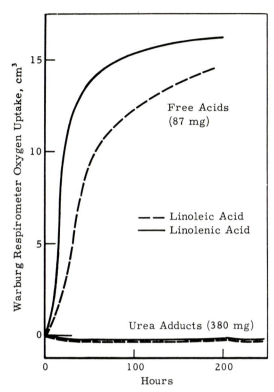

FIG. 20. Oxygen absorption of linoleic and linolenic acids and their urea adducts at 37°C under oxygen (*86*).

20) shows a very rapid peroxidation and rancidity development of the free acids but no reaction of the complex. It is known that autoxidation of unsaturated substances proceeds by a chain reaction mechanism, which is completely suppressed in the crystals. In effect, the urea lattice is a barrier against the free penetration of oxygen, or may prevent the chain reaction by immobilizing the oxidizable molecules as noted in Chapter 9, Section IV, 2 for α- and β-dextrins. An ideal storage form is thereby achieved, especially on a laboratory scale. In this form such complexes have been used directly for the preparation of feed rations in nutritional studies on essential fatty acids where the presence of urea did not interfere. Attempts (*27*) have been made to incorporate oxygen sensitive materials such as vitamin A by promoting adduction through reactive ester formation. Although the author was unsuccessful with urea, H. Schlenk (*84a*) formed vitamin A-cyclodextrin adducts. Similarly, highly unsaturated cod-liver fatty esters and long-chain terminal hydroperoxides have been

packaged in urea. Experiments with thiourea, desoxycholic acid, and cyclo-dextrins as host components together with unsaturated acids, aldehydes, and alcohols as guest molecules showed the same effect of stabilization, indicating that inclusion stabilization is valid for most inclusion compounds.

As indicated, this new approach is not limited to urea channel complexes and the protection of materials from oxidation. The larger thiourea channel has been employed by the author to stabilize and package peroxides (31) such as tert-butyl hydroperoxide, di-tert-butyl peroxide, and other similar materials of proper cross section. Doubly active fungicides (31) of thiourea and tetrachloroethylene and novel fumigants of thiourea and chloropicrin (40) have been prepared. The protection of sterculic acid (103) from spontaneous polymerization within the urea channel has previously been mentioned. The packaging of long-chain polyethers within both urea and thiourea will not only provide protection against oxidation but will facilitate their use in dry powder mixes. This is true of many mono- and diglyceride formulations. The inclusion of radioactive substances such as Kr^{85} in hydroquinone clathrates (3, 17) has led to novel detection devices and applications where radioactivity is desired. The storage and transportation of the low molecular weight paraffins as water hydrates has been considered. Similarly, Mandelcorn et al. (56a) have conveniently stored sulfur hexafluoride within the clathrate structure of Dianin's compound for later controlled release.

D. New Laboratory Techniques

1. SEPARATION OF OPTICAL ISOMERS

The phenomenon of optical activity associated with an asymmetric atom, usually carbon, is very important in theoretical organic problems and the resolution of racemic mixtures has been a useful technique. This is usually achieved by the destruction of one form by means of stereospecific enzymes, or by hand-sorting of the anantiomorphic crystals of a mixture which resolves on crystallization. Often the mixture is combined with an optically active substance to form a product containing two asymmetric centers having different physical properties, which are separable. An entirely new approach to the problem has been developed by W. Schlenk (90) who, starting with a racemic mixture of 2-chlorooctane, successfully obtained the d isomer in 95.6% purity using the symmetrical urea molecule and channel inclusion compound formation. When a racemic mixture can be made to crystallize in one of the different crystal classes by association with a suitable carrier which gives rise to optically active solids, then spontaneous resolution should occur on crystallization. This condition is fulfilled in the urea adduct but not with thiourea. The triple helix formed by urea molecules in a complex will have either a left-hand or right-hand screw axis, so that when the guest component is a racemic mixture, two sets of mirror images are possible. Thus, by cooling a solution of a racemic mixture and urea, the first seed crystal which forms must have either screw axis. By controlling the conditions so that there is no interference by secondary seeds, half of the racemic mixture can be precipitated as a complex in which the urea has a screw axis determined by the first chance seed crystal leaving a mother liquor that is also partially resolved. Several urea treatments are necessary to obtain high optical purity. This technique has the advantages that separations are very easy to carry out and the possibility of a change in configuration is eliminated.

Another inclusion complexing substance which will separate optical isomers is tri-o-thymotide. This molecule (see Chapter 7) is nonplanar and lacks both a mirror plane and a center of symmetry. It forms two stereochemical configurations which resemble a three-bladed propeller, and are optically active and interconvertible by heating. Slow crystallization will provide the chance formation of either the l or d form. These have inclusion cavities which are mirror images. Thus, crystallization of trithymotide from a reactive solvent which is also a racemic mixture results in the preferential inclusion of either the l or d form of the solvent. This agent has been used to achieve the optical resolution of sec-butyl bromide (75). Although tri-o-thymotide forms both the small clathrate chamber and the long channel structures, it is not entirely analogous to urea for resolutions since it is also asymmetric.

2. Molecular Calipers and Structure Proof

A very useful application of adduction as an analytical tool has been devised by reversing the usual procedure of treating the complex as an unknown. Since spacing between the urea or thiourea molecules is uniform and known, then the length and configuration of unknown materials which are placed within the channel can be accurately estimated from x-ray measurements and analysis and compared with known configurations. Nicolaides and Laves (67) showed that x-ray diffraction patterns of single adduct crystals give continuous layer lines which are a function of the length of the guest molecule. By measuring the length of aliphatic molecules and their corresponding olefinic derivatives the shortening effect of a cis or trans double bond on the length of the molecule is measured. Information gained from the series of C_{18} fatty acid-urea adducts clearly indicates that an isolated trans double bond shortens the molecule by 0.19 Å and an isolated *cis* bond shortens it by 0.88 Å. Check values can be derived from measurements on natural and balata forms of rubber. Applications of this technique to the thiourea adducts of squalene, which contains six isoprene units and six double bonds, and squalane, its hydrogenated analog, shows a chain length difference of 0.73 ± 0.3 Å. This demonstrates that natural squalene must be the all-*trans* isomer, and is a structure proof which is an important clue to the biosynthetic mechanism by which plants and animals apparently synthesize cholesterol from squalene. Although we have only discussed how to differentiate *cis* from *trans* isomers, this technique could be applied to any structural problem in which the length of an adducted molecule is discriminating.

3. Separations by Gas and Partition Chromatography

The very efficient separations currently being achieved by the several forms of laboratory analytical and preparative chromatography systems are made even more selective by incorporating inclusion compounds and clathrate forming components in the separation train. In a manner similar to the successful use of molecular sieves in the quantitative determination of *n*-paraffins in hydrocarbons (*25*), many of the previously described channel and clathrate forming compounds have demonstrated high degrees of selective retardation, and in some instances quantitative separations, of a particular component or class of material passed over them. In one example (*47*), the *ortho* isomers of nitrophenol, nitroaniline, chloronitrobenzene, and nitrotoluene have all been quantitatively separated by partition chromatography on a tetra–(alkylpyridine)-nickel dithiocyanate Werner clathrating complex column. In a similar manner, the other isomers as well as mixed nitroaliphatic compounds were effectively separated over another modification of this same complex. Urea (*46*) and spirochromans (*36*) have been employed similarly to remove *n*-paraffins. Tri-*o*-thymotide columns (*55*) have shown a high degree of selective retardation of the unbranched *n*-paraffins and alcohols from mixtures by a factor of 1.3 relative to the branched components of mixtures. Gas chromatographic techniques can serve as a useful tool in the search for new types of inclusion agents and to measure some of the thermodynamic separation properties of known systems.

E. Stereospecific Polymerizations

Clasen (*18*) in 1956 was the first to use urea and thiourea complexes as molecular templates for carrying out selective and stereospecific polymerization reactions. Thic technique has been studied extensively and extended by Brown and White (14). These investigators have developed a polymerization technique which involves forming a canal complex from a monomer and thiourea or urea, and irradiating this product with high energy electrons to initiate polymerization. After extracting the host molecule with solvent, pseudomorphic hexagonal needles of the stereoregular polymers formed which had the same alignment and shape as the complex crystals. From thiourea adducts, high melting crystalline *trans* 1,4-addition polymers were obtained from 2,3-dimethylbutadiene, 2,3-dichlorobutadiene, 1,3-cyclohexadiene, and cyclohexadiene monoxide. Isobutylene and vinylidene chloride were also polymerized but gave the expected normal polymers. Cyclopentadiene and cyclooctatetraene were polymerized only as co-polymers. The main product from cyclopentadiene was the ordinary *endo* dimer which supports the idea of a high degree of overlapping in the thiourea canals by the smaller molecules. It was further noted that small flat guest molecules, such as isobutylene and vinylidene chloride, may lie directly on top of each other as in a stack of coins. Only those molecules which are capable of at least partial overlapping were able to be polymerized.

The poly(2,3-dimethylbutadiene) obtained by the canal complex polymerization was a high melting (267–270°C) crystalline polymer soluble in tetralin. The infrared spectrum and x-ray diffraction patterns of this material have been shown to be identical to those of the *trans*-1,4-poly(2,3-dimethylbutadiene), m.p. 253–259°C, obtained by the use of a Ziegler catalyst system. The x-ray identity period of 4.68 Å for the 2,3-dichlorobutadiene polymer product agrees with that of the all *trans* polymer. The relative position of the molecules before and after polymerization can be estimated from the complexing ratio and the known dimensions of the monomer, canal, and polymer repeating unit. Their schematic scale representation of a 2,3-dimethylbutadiene polymerization in a thiourea channel is shown in Fig. 21. Since the van der Waals packing spacing disappears during polymerization, considerable movement of monomer along the channel is indicated as polymerization nears completion.

Stereospecific polymerization in the smaller diameter urea canal complexes has also been accomplished by the ionization radiation of 1,3-butadiene, vinyl chloride, acrylonitrile, acrolein, and a mixture of vinyl chloride and acrylonitrile guest monomers. Two products which are of particular interest are the polybutadiene which proved to be the all-*trans*-1,4-polybutadiene and the polyvinyl chloride which was an insoluble crystalline solid. The presence of a solid solution of solvent or impurity such as *n*-butene together with the butadiene monomer within the channel markedly restricts the degree of polymerization and yield of product, as would be expected. This particular irradiation test was carried out at

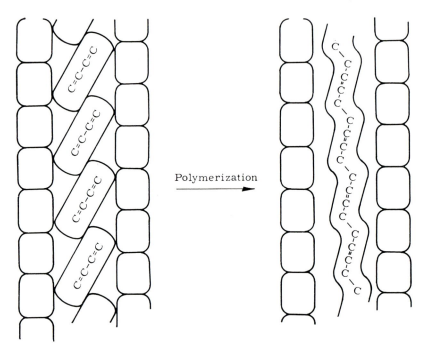

FIG. 21. Schematic representation of a 2,3-dimethylbutadiene polymerization in a thiourea canal (drawn approximately to scale) (14).

−55°C where the complex is stable. It is of interest that uncomplexed monomers such as acrylonitrile often did not polymerize under these low temperature reaction conditions using short bursts of electrons, 25 sec or less, of 2×10^5 rps intensity.

The main limitation to the scope of canal complex polymerization appears to be one which is inherent in any type of template synthesis: namely, substrate specificity. Using urea and thiourea canals as the template, only a small number of monomers are capable of entering the template at all and even fewer of these will react. Apparently, a rather delicate matching between the size and shape of the substrate molecules and the size and shape of the canals must be achieved if polymerization is to occur. It is possible that other channel complexing agents, such as the cyclodextrins and tri-o-thymotide may be capable of providing model polymer products which have sufficiently desirable properties to be reproduced by more practical methods. For this reason Barlow and Clamp (9) attempted, without success, to polymerize isoprene stereospecifically in several channel forming systems including 4,4'-dihydroxytriphenyl-methane. Stereoregular homogeneous solution catalysis in all probability involves similar inclusion configurations with some organometallic systems.

F. Channel Reactions

The utilization of inclusion complexes to study the properties or reactions of a guest or combination of guest molecules is just beginning. With a somewhat different objective than the channel polymerization experiments previously discussed, Chipault *et al.* (*16*) studied gamma radiation (5 × 10⁶ rep at 25°C) of the methyl linoleate-urea inclusion compounds in a study of the preservation of fats. They noted that the channel complex retards but does not completely prevent oxidation as it does when the material is not irradiated. About 3% polymer was also isolated from this complex after a 2 megarep radiation dose. The polymer level increased to 6% by increasing the length of irradiation to 10 megarep and there appeared to be interreaction to some degree with the urea host molecules. Considerable isomerization of the *cis* double bonds to *trans* was also observed. In a like manner other substances may be reacted, isomerized, or irradiated within the channel or cage clathrate structures.

Van der Waals and Platteeuw (*106, 107*) have recently shown that certain hydroquinone and hydrate clathrate compounds follow the idealized Lennard-Jones and Devonshire cell model for solution thermodynamics. Accordingly, many of the inclusion compounds will serve for various theoretical studies of isolated molecules trapped within cages or channels. For example, the *molecular packaging* of radioactive molecules such as rare gas radioisotopes (*17*) and other tracer organic substances may not only serve as a more convenient method for their storage, shipment, and handling, but the radioactive complexes may also be utilized as sources of radiation for various applications, including the activation of other guest molecules in mixed systems. Kr⁸⁵ contained in the hydroquinone clathrate structure has served as a beta ray source and has proven to be a form of chemical amplifier (*3*) in the detection of small amounts of gaseous impurity with decompose the inclusion compound. A study of the Mössbauer effect in Kr⁸³ (a gamma emitter) utilizes this cage structure as the solid matrix for the individual radiating atoms (*42a*). The results of this work should be related to the nature of the cages and their interaction with the included atoms.

REFERENCES

1. Angla, B., *Ann. chim. (Paris)* [12] 4, 639 (1949).
2. Angla, B., *Compt. rend. acad. sci.* 224, 402, 1166 (1947).
3. Anonymous, *Chem. Eng. News* 68, 51 (Jan. 23, 1961).
4. Bailey, F. E.. Jr.. and France. H. G.. *J. Polymer Sci.* 49, 397 (1961).

5. Bailey, W. A., Jr., Bannerot, R. A., Fetterly, L. C., and Smith, A. G., *Ind. Eng. Chem.* **43**, 2125 (1951); *Proc. World Petrol. Congr.*, Sect. III, p. 11 (1951).

6. Baker, E. G., Am. Chem. Soc. Div. Petrol. Chem., Dallas Meeting, Symposium on Chemistry in the Exploration and Production of Petroleum. Preprint 1, No. 2, Pt. 2, p. 5 (April, 1956).

7. Barduhn, A. J., Towlson, H. E., and Hu, Y. C., *U. S. Dept. of Interior, Research and Development Rept. No.* 44, Syracuse Univ. Research Inst. (September, 1960).

8. Barker, G. E., and Rananto, H. J., *J. Am. Oil Chemists' Soc.* **32**, 249 (1955).

9. Barlow, G. B., and Clamp, A. C., *J. Chem. Soc.* p. 393 (1961).

10. Barrer, R. M., *J. Chem. Soc.* p. 127 (1948); *J. Soc. Chem. Ind. (London)* **64**, 130 (1945).

11. Bengen, M. F., German Patent Appl. OZ 123438 (Mar. 18, 1940); German Patent 869,070 (1953); *Tech. Oil Mission Reel* **143**, 135 (1946).

12. Bengen, M. F., *Angew. Chem.* **63**, 207 (1951).

13. Bengen, M. F., and Schlenk, W., Jr., *Experientia* **5**, 200 (1949).

14. Brown, J. F., and White, D. M., *J. Am. Chem. Soc.* **82**, 5671, 5678 (1960).

15. Butler, I. M., and Barclay, J. A. V., *Trans. Faraday Soc.* **34**, 1445 (1938).

16. Chipault, J. R., Privett, O. S., Mizuno, G. R., Nickell, E. C., and Lundberg, W. O., *Ind. Eng. Chem.* **49**, 1713 (1957).

17. Chleck, D. L., and Ziegler, C. A., *Nucleonics* **17** (9), 130 (1959).

18. Clasen, H., *Z. Electrochem.* **60**, 982 (1956).

19. Claussen, W. F., and Polglase, M. F., *J. Am. Chem. Soc.* **74**, 4817, (1952); **73**, 1571 (1951).

20. Claussen, W. F., *J. Am. Chem. Soc.* **74**, 3937 (1952).

21. Coleman, J. E., Knight, H. B., and Swern, D., *J. Am. Chem. Soc.* **74**, 4886 (1952).

22. Cramer, F., "Einschluss-Verbindungen." Springer, Berlin, 1954.

23. Davy, H., *Phil. Trans. Roy. Soc. London Ser.* **A101**, 30 (1811); *Ann. chim. (Paris)* **79**, 26 (1811).

24. Dorough, G. L., Glass, H. B., Gresham, T. L., Malone, G. B., and Reid, E. E., *J. Am. Chem. Soc.* **63**, 3102 (1941).

25. Eggertsen, F. T., and Groennings, S., *Anal. Chem.* **33**, 1147 (1961).

26. Fetterly, L. C., U. S. Patent 2,499,820 (filed February 21, 1947); German Patent 865,141 (filed March 29, 1947); U. S. Patents 2,520,715 and 2,520,716 (1950); 2,569,984 and 2,569,986 (1951) assigned to Shell Development Co.

27. Fetterly, L. C., "Study of Kinetics and Equilibria of Urea-Fatty Acid and Related Complexes." Ph.D. Thesis, Univ. of Washington, Seattle, 1950.

28. Fetterly, L. C., "Study of Kinetics of Equilibria of Urea-Fatty Acid and Related Complexes." Presented at 26th Fall Meeting, Am. Oil Chemists' Soc., Cincinnati, Ohio, 1952.

29. Fetterly, L. C., *Petrol. Refiner* (a) **34**, 134 (1955); (b) **36**, 145 (1957).

30. Fetterly, L. C., in "Resins Analysis" (C. P. A. Kappelmeier, ed.), Chapter XV-B. Wiley (Interscience), New York, 1959.

31. Fetterly, L. C., unpublished observations.

32. Frank, H. S., and Evans, M. W., *J. Chem. Phys.* **13**, 507 (1945).

33. Freudenberg, K., and Cramer, F., *Ber.* 83, 296 (1950).
34. Garner, P. J., Goldsbrough, L. N., and Byers, T. B., U. S. Patent 2,518,-677 (1950) assigned to Shell Development Co.
35. Geiseler, G., and Richter, P., *Ber.* 93, 2511 (1960).
36. Geiser, E. M., U. S. Patent 2,851,500 assigned to Universal Oil Products Co.
36a. Glew, D. N., *Nature* 195, 698 (1962).
37. Go, Y., and Kratky, O., *Z. physik. Chem.* (*Leipzig*) B26, 439 (1934).
38. Gomberg, M., *J. Am. Chem. Soc.* 37, 2569 (1915).
39. Gorin, E., U. S. Patents 2,681,332, -3, -4, -6 (1954) assigned to Socony-Vacuum Oil Co.
40. Gorin, M. H., and Rosenstein, L., U. S. Patents 2,600,431; 2,750,361; 2,773,853, and 2,801,993.
41. Hanson, N. W., *J. Oil & Colour Chemists' Assoc.* 37, 143 (1954).
42. Hartley, H., and Thomas, N. G., *J. Chem. Soc.* p. 1013 (1906).
42a. Hazoni, Y., Hillman, P., Pasternak, M., and Ruby, S., *Physics Letters* 2, 337 (1962).
43. Hermann, C., and Lenné, H. U. von, *Naturwissenschaften* 39, 234 (1952).
44. Hess, H. V., Arnold, G. B., and Truitt, J. K., U. S. Patent 2,589,380, assigned to The Texas Co.
45. Huggins, M. L., *J. Chem. Educ.* 34, 480 (1957).
46. Karr, C., U. S. Patent 2,912,426 (1959) assigned to Gulf Research and Development Co.
47. Kemula, W., and Sybilska, D., *Nature* 185, 237 (1960).
48. Knight, H. B., Witnauer, L. P., Coleman, J. E., Noble, W. R., Jr., and Swern, D., *Anal. Chem.* 24, 1331 (1952).
49. Kobe, K. A., and Domask, W. G., *Petrol. Refiner* 31 (3), 106; (5), 125 (1952); 34 (4), 128 (1955).
50. Kutzelnigg, W., and Mecke, R., *Z. Electrochem.* 65, 109 (1961).
51. Langmuir, I., *J. Am. Chem. Soc.* 39, 1883 (1917).
52. Lawton, D., and Powell, H. M., *J. Chem. Soc.* p. 2339 (1958).
53. Lenné, H. U. von, *Acta Cryst.* 7, 1 (1954).
54. Linstead, R. P., and Whalley, M., *J. Chem. Soc.* p. 2987 (1950).
55. Maczek, A. O. S., and Phillip, C. S. G., *in* "Gas Chromatography: Proceedings of the Third Symposium" (R. P. W. Scott, ed.), Paper No. 19, p. 284. Butterworths, London, 1960.
56. Mandelcorn, L., *Chem. Revs.* 59, 827 (1959).
56a. Mandelcorn, L., Goldberg, N. N., and Hoff, R. E., *J. Am. Chem. Soc.* 82, 3297 (1960).
57. McAdie, H. G., and Frost, G. B., *Can. J. Chem.* 33, 1275 (1955).
58. McLaughlin, R. L., and McClenahan, W. S., *J. Am. Chem. Soc.* 74, 5804 (1952).
59. McLaughlin, R. L., *in* "The Chemistry of Petroleum Hydrocarbons" (B. T. Brooks, C. E. Boord, S. S. Kurtz, and L. Schmerling, eds.), Vol. 1, Chapter 10, p. 241. Reinhold, New York, 1954.
60. McMullan, R., and Jeffrey, G. A., *J. Chem. Phys.* 31, 1231 (1959). Feil, D., and Jeffrey, G. A., *J. Chem. Phys.* 35, 1863 (1961).
61. Mikus, F. F., Hixon, R. M., and Rundle, R. E., *J. Am. Chem. Soc.* 63, 1115 (1946).
62. Milgrom, J., *J. Phys. Chem.* 63, 1843 (1959).

63. Moreno, J. M. M., Mazuelos, F., and Janer, C., *Fette u. Seifen* **57**, 652 (1955).
64. Morrish, J. A., "Study of Molecular Complexes of Thiourea," M. S. Thesis, Univ. of Washington, Seattle, 1949.
65. Morrison, T. J., and Johnstone, N. B., *J. Chem. Soc.* p. 3441 (1954).
66. Newey, H. A., Shokal, E. C., Mueller, A. C., Bradley, T. F., and Fetterly, L. C., *Ind. Eng. Chem.* **42**, 2538 (1950).
67. Nicolaides, H., and Laves, F., *J. Am. Chem. Soc.* **76**, 2596 (1954).
68. Palin, D. E., and Powell, H. M., *Nature* **156**, 334 (1945).
69. Parrof, J., and Kohler, A., *Compt. rend. acad. sci.* **246**, 1046 (1958).
70. Pauling, L., and Marsh, R. E., *Proc. Natl. Acad. Sci. U. S.* **38**, 112 (1952).
71. Pauling, L., *Science* **134**, 15 (1961).
72. Pauling, L., "Nature of the Chemical Bond," 3rd ed., p. 473. Cornell Univ. Press, Ithaca, New York, 1960.
73. Pimentel, C., and McClellan, A. L., "The Hydrogen Bond," p. 255. Freeman, San Francisco, California, 1960.
74. Powell, H. M., *et al.*, *J. Chem. Soc.* (a) p. 61 (1948); (b) p. 571 (1948); (c) p. 815 (1948); (d) p. 298 (1950); (e) p. 468 (1950); (f) p. 319 (1952); (g) p. 3747 (1952); (h) p. 2658 (1954).
75. Powell, H. M., *Nature* **170**, 155 (1952).
76. Powell, H. M., *Rec. tran. chim.* **75**, 885 (1956).
77. Radell, J., and Hunt, P. D., *J. Am. Chem. Soc.* **80**, 2683 (1958).
78. Radell, J., and Connolly, J. W., *J. Org. Chem.* **25**, 1202 (1960).
79. Radell, J., Connolly, J. W., and Cosgrove, W. R., Jr., *J. Org. Chem.* **26**, 2960 (1961).
80. Redlich, O., Gable, C. M., Dunlop, A. K., and Millar, R. W., *J. Am. Chem. Soc.* **72**, 4153 (1950).
81. Redlich, O., Gable, C. M., Beason, L. R., and Millar, R. W., *J. Am. Chem. Soc.* **72**, 4161 (1950).
82. Rudloff, E. von, *Chem. & Ind. (London)* p. 338 (1951).
83. Schardinger, F., *Z. Untersuch. Nahr. u. Genussm.* **6**, 874 (1903).
84. Schlenk, H., and Sand, D. M., *J. Am. Chem. Soc.* **83**, 2312 (1961).
84a. Schlenk, H., personal communication.
85. Schlenk, H., and Holman, R. T., *Science* **112**, 19 (1950); *J. Am. Chem. Soc.* **74**, 1720 (1952).
86. Schlenk, H., *in* "Progress in the Chemistry of Fats and Other Lipids" (R. T. Holman, W. O. Lundberg, and T. Malkin, eds.), Vol. II, Chapter 5, p. 243. Academic Press, New York, 1954.
87. Schlenk, W., Jr., *Ann.* **565**, 204 (1949).
88. Schlenk, W., Jr., *Ann.* **573**, 142 (1951).
89. Schlenk, W., Jr., *Angew. Chem.* **61**, 447 (1949).
90. Schlenk, W., Jr., *Analyst* **77**, 867 (1952).
91. Schlenk, W., Jr., *Fortschr. chem. Forsch.* **2**, 92 (1951).
92. Schlenk, W., Jr., *Chemie e industrie* **69**, 454 (1953).
93. Schiessler, R. W., and Flitter, D., *J. Am. Chem. Soc.* **74**, 1720 (1952).
94. Smith, A. E., *J. Chem. Phys.* **18**, 150 (1950).
95. Smith, A. E., *J. Chem. Soc.* p. 2416 (1951).
96. Smith, A. E., *Acta Cryst.* **5**, 224 (1952); and personal communication.

97. Sobotka, H., and Kahn, S., *Biochem. J.* **26**, 898 (1932).

98. Stackelberg, M. von, Jahns, W., and Müller, H. R., *Z. Electrochem.* **58**, 25, 162 (1954).

99. Stackelberg, M. von, and Müller, H. R., *Naturwissenschaften* **36**, 327, 359 (1949); **39**, 20 (1952).

100. Swern, D., and Port, W. S., *J. Am. Chem. Soc.* **74**, 1738 (1952).

101. Swern, D., Inclusion compounds. *In* "Encyclopedia of Chemistry and Technology" (R. E. Kirk and D. F. Othmer, eds.), 1st Suppl. Vol. Wiley (Interscience), New York, 1957.

102. Swern, D., *Ind. Eng. Chem.* **47**, 216 (1955).

103. Truter, E. V., "Wool Wax: Chemistry and Technology," Vol. I, p. 195. Wiley (Interscience), New York, 1956.

104. Truter, E. V., *J. Chem. Soc.* p. 2416 (1951).

105. Truter, E. V., *Chem. & Process Eng.* **35**, 75 (1954).

106. Van der Waals, J. H., and Platteeuw, J. C., *Advances in Chem. Phys.* **2**, 1 (1959).

107. Van der Waals, J. H., and Platteeuw, J. C., *Nature* **183**, 462 (1959).

108. Ward, A. F. H., and Tordai, L., *Trans. Faraday Soc.* **42**, 408, 413 (1956).

109. Wieland, H., and Sorge, H., *Z. physiol. Chem. Hoppe-Seyler's* **97**, 1 (1916).

110. Wood, P. D. S., and Aylward, F., *Chem. & Ind. (London)* p. 1479 (1955).

111. Wyckoff, R. W. G., and Corey, R. B., *Z. Kryst.* **89**, 102 (1934).

112. Zimmerschied, W. J., Dinerstein, R. A., Weitkamp, A. W., and Marschner, R. F., *Ind. Eng. Chem.* **42**, 1300 (1950); *J. Am. Chem. Soc.* **71**, 2947 (1949).

CHAPTER 9

Frederic R. Senti and Stig R. Erlander

Northern Regional Research Laboratory,*
Peoria, Illinois

Carbohydrates

I. Introduction. 568
II. Amylose Inclusion Compounds. 569
   A. Solid Complexes of Amylose. 569
   B. Formation of Amylose-Iodine Complexes in Solution. 577
III. Iodine-Iodide Complexes of Glycogen and Amylopectin. 587
IV. Schardinger Dextrin Complexes. 588
   A. Complexes with Iodine and Iodide. 591
   B. Insoluble Complexes with Organic Compounds. 594
   C. Dye Binding by the Schardinger Dextrins. 596
   D. Catalytic Action of the Cyclodextrins. 599
   E. Stereospecific Effects of the Cyclodextrins. 600
   F. Inclusion Compounds of Cyclodextrins with Gases. 600
V. Adsorption and Addition Complexes of Polysaccharides. 601
   References. 602

I. INTRODUCTION

Carbohydrates as a class of organic compounds provide examples of non-stoichiometric compounds of two general types. One has channel or cage structure, as exemplified by the complexes of amylose and the cyclodextrins; the other involves formation of compounds or complexes as a result of the multiplicity of binding sites in the amorphous regions of solid polysaccharides. Non-stoichiometric compounds of the second type include solvates as well as a number of addition compounds whose formation is generally accompanied by hydration or solvation of the polysaccharide.

In contrast to the clathrates, which exist only in the solid state and in

* This is a laboratory of the Northern Utilization Research and Development Division, Agricultural Research Service, U. S. Department of Agriculture.

which guest molecules are included in cavities or cages provided by the crystalline structure of the host, both amylose and the cyclodextrins form inclusion compounds that are stable in solution as well as in solid form. In solution, a single molecule provides the cavity in which guest molecules are bound. The helical configuration of the high polymeric amylose molecule which gives rise to the cavity structure is stabilized only by secondary bonds as contrasted to the primary bonded cyclic structure of the cyclodextrins. For this reason amylose complexes may be expected to be less stable in solution than the cyclodextrin complexes.

In the crystalline state both amylose and the cyclodextrins form channel structures; the cyclodextrins also adopt crystalline structures in which the axial holes formed by the cyclic molecules are blocked on each end by noncoaxial alignment of adjacent dextrin molecules, thus forming a set of crystallographically related cages in the structure. Occupancy of each of these cages by a guest molecule results in integral molar ratio of host and guest as observed in many complexes of the cyclodextrins. Channel structures place no restriction on the long dimension of the guest molecule provided its lateral dimensions are compatible with the diameter of the tunnel. Mole ratios of host and guest then depend on the length of the guest molecule and on the extent to which the tunnels are filled.

Non-stoichiometry of adsorption and addition complexes formed by polysaccharides is associated with the presence of amorphous regions in the solid state of these high polymeric substances. The loose packing and disordered arrangement of polymer chains in these regions allow the entrance of small polar molecules and their binding to exposed polar groups of the polymer chain. At low levels of sorption there may be a maximum stoichiometric relationship between polar groups of the polysaccharide and sorbed molecules, but binding can continue on less energetic sites, and the process becomes essentially one of solution with loss of stoichiometric relations. Concurrent sorption may occur in crystalline regions of the polysaccharide, but here the ordered arrangement determines the location and maximum number of molecules which can be accommodated.

II. AMYLOSE INCLUSION COMPOUNDS

A. Solid Complexes of Amylose

1. COMPOSITION AND PROPERTIES OF AMYLOSE

Amylose is a linear, high polymeric carbohydrate consisting of glucose units joined through 1,4-α-glucosidic linkages. It comprises 20–30% of all common starches, except the waxy starches, which contain little or no amylose but are essentially all amylopectin. The latter is a branched polymer and is the major component of all common starches. The molecular weight of amylose varies with the starch from which it is isolated. Corn starch amylose, for example, has a weight-average molecular weight of about 300,000 (*79*), the corresponding value for potato amylose is about 1 million (*29*). Intrinsic viscosity measurements indicate that amyloses from other starches fall within this range of molecular weights. Ultracentrifugal sedimentation patterns (*10, 12, 25, 79*) and fractionation studies (*29*) show that amyloses contain a distribution of chain lengths; the distribution for corn amylose (*79*) approximates that expected for a condensation-type polymerization.

The configurations that the amylose chain can assume depend on the conformation of its constituent glucose units, i.e. the arrangement of the carbon, oxygen, and hydrogen atoms of a glucose unit in space. Eight strainless forms of the glucose units are possible, two chair forms and six boat forms. Holló *et al.* (*44*) concluded from models that only the C1 chair and B1 boat glucose conformations (Reeves' (*66*) nomenclature for ring conformation) are suited for the formation of a helical structure in the amylose molecule. Infrared studies (*36, 68*) of the solid amylose-iodine complex provide evidence for the C1 conformation in the helix. The conformation of the amylose chain in aqueous solution is not established. From results on cuprammonium complex formation, Reeves (*65*) concluded that both the B1 and B3 boat forms exist in the amylose chain in aqueous solution. However, combination of the B1 and C1 forms would also satisfy his experimental results and from these considerations alone, the helix could exist in aqueous solution. Intrinsic viscosity and radii of gyration measurements (*28*) on amylose fractions clearly rule out a rigid, helical, amylose molecule in aqueous solution. Helical segments interrupted by more extended chain sections about which rotation could occur to give an overall randomly coiled configuration, however, would be consistent with these properties. This chain configuration has been proposed (*43*) to explain the observation that the viscosity of amylose-iodine-iodide solutions does not change as a function of bound iodine. Griffin *et al.* (*37*) found that the effective kinetic segment length of the amylose molecule as derived from viscosity and light-scattering measurements is consistent with the presence of helical loops in neutral solution and with their destruction in alkali. Based on the thermodynamic properties of amylose in aqueous solutions, Rao and Foster (*64*) also suggested the possibility of some helical coiling. However, absorption spectra (*87*) show that if such helical segments exist, they are not sufficiently well-formed to bind iodine in the absence of iodide ion.

2. PREPARATION OF AMYLOSE INCLUSION COMPOUNDS

Amylose combines with a variety of organic compounds to form inclusion compounds which are insoluble at room temperature, whereas amylopectin does not. These compounds can be prepared by addition of the guest molecule to a molecularly dispersed solution of starch. If the complex is formed from a hot solution by slow cooling, it separates in characteristic crystalline forms visible under the microscope. Schoch (76) was the first to recognize that complex formation with butanol or isoamyl alcohol fractionates starch into distinct molecular species. His procedure, still widely used, was either to autoclave starch for 2–3 hours at 18–20 lb/inch² pressure or to stir vigorously for 5–6 hours under reflux in the presence of excess butanol. On slow cooling in a jacketed container, the amylose complex separated and was purified by recrystallizations from hot butanol-saturated solution. Other investigators have followed Schoch's procedure in preparing amylose complexes with other organic compounds.

Amylose solutions useful for complex formation can be obtained by selective leaching (84) of starch at temperatures just below the gelatinization point; the granule residues are removed by centrifugation. Kerr and Severson (49) observed that about half the amylose in defatted corn starch can be extracted in this manner with a purity of 85–90%. Complexes separated from these extracts by adding butanol to the hot liquors are remarkable for their well-formed crystals, which are rectangular plates. Montgomery and Senti (57) found that pretreatment of starches in hot aqueous glycerol, dioxane, 1-butanol, Cellosolve, or Pentasol improves both the yield and purity of amylose extracted at 98°C. Principal advantage of using leached amylose in the preparation of complexes is that the product is relatively free from amylopectin without recrystallization.

Amylose complexes which precipitate from solution are microcrystalline and give powder x-ray diffraction patterns. Oriented crystalline complexes with normal and branched chain alcohols have been prepared by deacetylating oriented filaments of amylose triacetate in alcoholic alkali, which produces oriented alkali amyloses (81), followed by conversion of the alkali amylose to the desired complex by soaking in an aqueous solution of the appropriate alcohol (80).

Amylose-iodine complexes can be prepared by adding iodine-potassium iodide solutions either to starch dispersions or to solutions of amylose. At amylose concentrations of 0.01%, or less, as used in the potentiometric (6) or spectrophotometric methods (4) for titrating amylose with iodine, the complex formed remains in solution several days. Complete molecular dispersion before complex formation appears to increase solution stability of the complex (30). At higher concentrations of amylose, precipitation occurs on complex formation and is more rapid at higher concentrations of iodide ion.

Although amylose-iodine complexes precipitated from solution give the the V-type x-ray powder pattern (7) characteristic of the helical amylose structure, superior patterns are given by complexes in which iodine is introduced into crystalline butanol-precipitated amylose. Preparations from which the butanol has been removed by drying absorb iodine vapor to form complexes containing up to 26% iodine by weight (72). Kerr (48) reports, however, that at least 2% moisture in the amylose is necessary for iodine absorption to occur at an appreciable rate. The iodine complex is formed when butanol-precipitated amylose is stained with iodine-potassium iodide solutions (71). Similarly, fatty acids can be introduced into dried, butanol-precipitated amylose by treating the amylose with methanolic solutions of the desired fatty acid.

3. Structure of Butanol and Iodine Complexes of Amylose

Most complete structural investigations have been made on the butanol and the iodine complexes. Unit cell dimensions of the butanol complex determined from powder patterns are given in Table I. These were confirmed by indexing of fiber patterns (80) which provides an unambiguous determination of c and also identifies this direction in the structure with the length of the amylose molecules. With the exception of the *wet* butanol complex, i.e., wet with water saturated with butanol, $b = \sqrt{3}a$ for all butanol and iodine complexes listed in Table I and their x-ray patterns

TABLE I

Unit Cell Dimensions of Amylose Complexes

Complex	Orthorhombic cell dimensions, Å			Reference
	a	b	c	
Butanol, *wet*	13.7	25.6	7.8	(70)
Butanol, hydrated	13.7	23.8	8.05	(70)
Butanol, anhydrous	12.97	22.46	7.91	(69)
Iodine, hydrated	13.7	23.8	8.05	(92)
Iodine, anhydrous	12.97	22.46	7.91	(72)
Fatty acid, hydrated	13.7	23.8	8.05	(56)
Fatty acid, anhydrous	13.0	23.0	8.05	(56)

can be indexed equally well on a hexagonal cell having $A = 2a$ and $C = c$. The pattern of the iodine complex can be indexed on an even smaller hexagonal cell having $A = a$ and $C = c$. The apparent hexagonal symmetry of these complexes led Rundle and co-workers (70, 72) to propose a helical structure for the amylose molecules in these complexes; packing of the helices approximates the closest packing of cylinders and accounts for the hexagonal cell. Six glucose units comprise one turn of the helix. The absence of change in unit cell dimensions when the anhydrous butanol complex was treated with iodine vapors, after all butanol and water were removed, provides strong evidence that iodine entered the channels of the amylose helices.

Since the anhydrous butanol precipitate and the iodine complex appeared to have isomorphous structures, differing only in the kind of guest molecules in the channels, Fourier analyses of the structures of the complexes could be made in which the high scattering power of the iodine atoms determines the signs of the terms entering the Fourier series. Projections of the structures of the anhydrous butanol precipitate and the iodine complex* as given by Rundle (69) are presented in Fig. 1. These projections are consistent with an amylose helix of nearly circular cross section with the iodine molecules occupying the helix channel.

Within the helices, the iodines pack to form a one-dimensional lattice as evidenced by a pair of continuous layer lines on x-ray patterns of oriented filaments (78) and by a diffuse halo on patterns of unoriented preparations (90). Similar layer lines were observed on patterns of other polymers complexed with iodine, iodine bromide, and bromine (90). West (90) interpreted the spacing, 3.10 Å, in the iodine complexes as the interatomic distance in a linear polyiodine chain. This distance is intermediate between the covalent bond spacing in I_2, 2.67 Å, and the nonbonded separations of iodine atoms in crystalline I_2, which are 3.55 and 4.0 Å. Rundle (69a) pointed out that the x-ray evidence, which was limited to the observation of three orders of the one-dimensional lattice spacing, does not

---

* Rundle (69) points out that the peak appearing at the center of the helix on the projection of the anhydrous butanol precipitate is probably spurious, resulting from early termination of the Fourier series due to the inability to measure intensities of the very weak diffraction maxima at large angles. Senti and Witnauer (unpublished work) obtained an improved projection from intensity data obtained from microdensitometer traces of the amylose-iodine complex (23.8% I_2) and anhydrous butanol precipitate. By comparison with fiber patterns of the anhydrous butanol structure, they were able to correct the powder pattern data for superpositions of (hkl) forms on the $(hk0)$ forms which enter the projection. Their projection of the amylose-iodine complex showed no peak at the center of the helix, but there was a ring of scattering matter at 1.6 Å from the center. The height of this peak, however, was much less than that of the projection of the helix, rather than the opposite as shown on Rundle's projection.

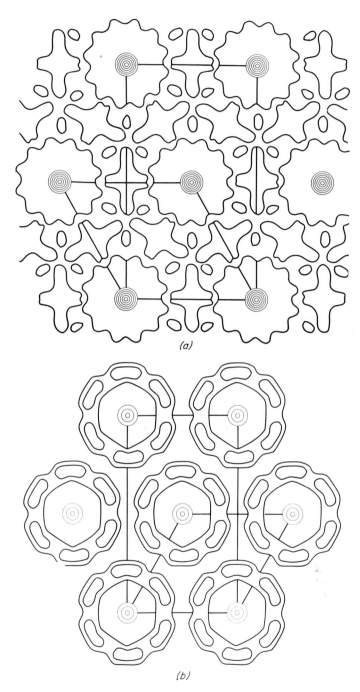

Fig. 1. Fourier projection of the structure of the amylose-iodine complex (a) and the anhydrous butanol complex (b) on a section perpendicular to the helix axis (69).

make certain that the halogen atoms in the one-dimensional array are equally spaced. In the I–Br complexes, the first order spacing, corresponding to the bromine-bromine separation (—Br—I—Br—) along the chain, should have been observed regardless of whether the atoms were evenly spaced. The absence of this reflection casts doubt on the assignment of the 3.10 Å spacing as a first order reflection in the iodine complex. If the iodine atoms were unequally spaced, the first order spacing, 6.2 Å, corresponding to the distance I—I···I would be weak and difficult to observe.

The wet butanol complex, as precipitated, contains both water and butanol in its structure. Its pattern can be indexed on an orthorhombic unit cell but not on a hexagonal cell. The complex loses volatiles in two stages. On brief drying the unit cell contracts along the a and b directions to give the *hydrated* form; the structure contracts further on prolonged vacuum drying at 50°, and the anhydrous form is obtained. On humidification at 60% R.H. or higher, the anhydrous form sorbs water and the unit cell dimensions return to those of hydrated form (*92*). Exposed to iodine vapor the hydrated form absorbs iodine without change in lattice dimensions which indicates that the water of hydration lies on the exterior of the helix.

The structure of the complexes formed with other linear alcohols is the same as that of the butanol complex. X-ray powder patterns of amylose precipitated with 1-propanol and 1-pentanol, as well as 1-butanol are identical (*8*). Amylose precipitated with ethanol, and especially methanol, gives poor powder diffraction diagrams, but both alcohols convert oriented filaments of alkali amylose into structures giving excellent x-ray fiber diagrams (*80*) identical with those of the butanol complex structure. Both 1-hexanol and 1-octanol precipitate amylose, but the x-ray patterns of these complexes have not been reported.

4. AMYLOSE-FATTY ACID COMPLEXES

Amylose complexes formed by precipitation (*77*) with long-chain fatty acids are microcrystalline. Mikus *et al.* (*56*) have determined unit cells from powder patterns of the lauric, palmitic, stearic, and oleic acid complexes. Unit cell dimensions (Table I) of the hydrated fatty acid complex are the same as those of hydrated butanol-precipitated amylose; those of the anhydrous form differ only slightly from dimensions of the anhydrous butanol precipitate or the corresponding iodine complex. That the fatty acid is located within the amylose helix is strengthened by two further observations: (i) fatty acids can be introduced into dried butanol-precipitated amylose by suspension in either alcoholic or carbon tetrachloride solutions of fatty acids; (ii) on exposure to iodine vapor, most of the fatty acid is displaced from the complex.

Approximate constancy of composition of the long-chain fatty acid complexes on a weight basis is expected if the fatty acid molecules are packed end to end in the helices, since the fatty acids have about the same weight per unit length. From the data of Mikus *et al.*, amylose binds 6.5% of lauric, palmitic, or oleic acid (a similar effect was observed for urea long-chain adducts; see Chapter 8). This binding is about 20% less than the capacity of the helix as calculated from the helix length (8 Å per six glucose residues) and the dimensions of the fatty acid molecules. At least part of this discrepancy can be attributed to the presence of 10% amylopectin, as pointed out by Mikus *et al.*, which does not form inclusion complexes with fatty acids.

The short-chain fatty acids, *n*-valeric, *n*-butyric, and α-bromopropionic, also precipitate (*8*) amylose from solution in the form of iodine-staining, two- to six-lobed spherocrystals similar to those formed by the long-chain acids.

5. Complexes with Branched Chain Alcohols

Branched chain alcohols precipitate amylose from solution in microcrystalline form. X-ray powder patterns (*8*) of the complexes formed with iso-, *sec*-, and *tert*-butyl alcohols are indistinguishable among themselves but are different from those of complexes with linear alcohols in that the spacings are larger and they cannot be indexed on a hexagonal lattice. Fiber patterns (*80*) show that the repeat distance along the amylose chain of the *tert*-butyl alcohol complex is 7.92 Å, nearly identical with this spacing in the 1-butanol and iodine complexes. As on fiber patterns of linear alcohol complexes, intensities of diffraction maxima on the second and higher layer lines are very weak or absent. These features of the fiber pattern thus indicate that the amylose molecules in the *tert*-butyl alcohol complex also have a helical configuration. Lateral spacings of the *tert*-butyl alcohol complex, however, are larger and the pattern was indexed on a unit cell having $a = 33.7$, b (fiber axis) $= 7.92$, $c = 19.4$ Å and $\beta = 130°$ for a filament containing also 10% moisture. Two helices pass through the unit cell, but deviation from closest packing of cylindrical helices must occur in this nonhexagonal cell or, possibly, the helices are not circular in cross section. Along the a axis the helices have a packing diameter of 16.8 Å; along the c axis, a diameter of 19.4 Å, as compared to 13.7 Å for the hydrated butanol complex and 12.97 Å for the anhydrous complex. Expansion of the butanol helix to eight glucose residues per turn should give a hydrated diameter of 12.97 Å $\times \frac{8}{6} + 0.8$ Å $= 18.1$ Å, which is in agreement with the average diameter, 18.0 Å of the *tert*-butyl alcohol helix. If the carbohydrate density of the crystalline regions of the filaments is assumed to be the same, 1.23 gm/cm³, as that of the anhydrous butanol complex (70), the calculated number of glucose residues in the unit cell of the *tert*-butyl alcohol complex is 18.2 corresponding to 9 residues per turn. This, however, is an upper limit since the expanded helix, if approximately circular in section, should give a structure with a density less than 1.23. A helix with 8 residues per turn, as deduced from dimensions of the unit cell, thus appears to be a better estimate.

2-Pentanol and 4-methyl-2-pentanol (8) precipitate amylose as iodine-staining, two- to six-lobed spherocrystals indicating that these, too, are inclusion compounds. No x-ray data have been reported, however, in support of a helical structure.

6. COMPLEXES WITH OTHER ORGANIC COMPOUNDS

Selective precipitation of amylose from starch solutions occurs with the following compounds:

Ketones (8). Methyl ethyl and methyl *n*-propyl ketones, and diacetone alcohols.

Phenols (8). o-, m-, and p-cresol.

Terpene alcohols (38). Thymol, menthol, borneol, and terpene hydrate.

Nitro compounds (91). Nitroethane, 1-nitropropane, 2-nitropropane, and nitrobenzene.

Miscellaneous. Pyridine (91), benzaldehyde (8), amyl acetate (91), butyl mercaptan (91), aniline (8), cyclohexanol (38), benzyl alcohol (8), and 1-hexanol (8).

In most cases, the precipitates are described as iodine-staining, micro-crystalline products. X-ray powder patterns have been reported only for complexes with the nitroparaffins, nitrobenzene, *n*-amyl methyl ketone, and *n*-amyl acetate (26). These patterns are different from the patterns of either the linear or branched alcohol complexes; hence, similarity of structure cannot be established by comparison of patterns.

B. Formation of Amylose-Iodine Complexes in Solution

The inclusion compounds formed by amylose with organic compounds do not have properties that permit easy study of their formation in solution. In contrast, formation of amylose-iodine complexes is accompanied by an intense blue color; moreover, change in the activity of iodine in equilibrium with the complex during its formation can be measured electrometrically from the potential of the iodine-iodide electrode. Both properties of the complex are measurable at very low amylose concentrations

(0.01% or less) at which the complex remains in solution. As a result, many investigators have applied spectrophotometric and potentiometric methods to determine the composition of the complex, to evaluate the equilibrium constant and associated thermodynamic quantities of the formation reaction, and to study the influence of such factors as polysaccharide chain length and structure, e.g., branching, salt concentration, and temperature, on the reaction.

1. Composition of the Complex

Bates *et al.* (*6*) determined the uptake of iodine by starch and its components by potentiometric titration, measuring the potential of a half-cell containing polysaccharide, iodine, and iodide ion against a calomel electrode. Equilibrium free iodine concentrations at various points in the titration were determined by comparison with titration curves of reagent blanks not containing polysaccharide. More recently, the differential titration method has been introduced (*1, 24, 34*), which makes the blank titration an integral part of the system and is a more accurate method for determining low iodine concentrations in equilibrium with the complex.

Titration of amylose with dilute iodine solution at constant iodide concentration increases the activity of iodine up to a certain value, after which the iodine activity remains essentially constant until the amylose has absorbed about one-fifth its weight of iodine. On further addition of iodine, its activity increases and approaches that obtained in the absence of amylose. Bates *et al.* (*6*) also report that crystalline corn amylose, prepared by the procedure of Kerr (*49*), binds about 19% iodine in 0.05 M and 0.10 M potassium iodide, corresponding to about eight glucose residues per molecule of iodine in the complex. This value was confirmed by Dube (*24*) using 3-times crystallized corn amylose prepared by Schoch's procedure.

Spectrophotometric measurements (*5*) on the binding of iodine by amylose at concentrations of iodide between 0.5 M and 0.001 M showed that the percentage of iodine in the complex decreases as the concentration of iodide increases. The number of glucose residues per iodine bound varies linearly with the fourth root of the iodide concentration, and on extrapolation of the data to zero iodide concentration, a composition corresponding to six glucose residues per iodine molecule was obtained.

Increasing the temperature in the range of 0–50°C has little effect on maximum iodine uptake of amylose (*24*) in complex formation, but the activity at which the iodine is bound increases (*50*).

In none of these experiments was a distinction made between iodine molecules bound as molecular iodine and as triiodide ions, which exist in equilibrium in the titration solutions. The spectrophotometric measurements, however, indicate that iodide ions are bound along with iodine and reduce the capacity of the helix for iodine. That iodide ions are necessary for formation of colored complexes has been shown (50, 87); no blue color developed when solutions of amylose and iodine were made 0.2 M in HIO_3 to repress iodide formation by hydrolysis of I_2.

By differential potentiometric titration Gilbert and Marriott (34) demonstrated the incorporation of iodide ions in the complex and determined the number of iodide ions and iodine molecules which combine with amylose in the initial stage of complex formation. They concluded that at low iodine binding (up to 2% of maximum binding) and at iodide concentrations of about 10^{-3} M, amylose is associated with I_8^{2-} ions formed by the absorption of three iodine molecules and two iodide ions. The characteristic blue of the amylose complex was developed when the complex had this composition; at higher iodine concentrations, the number of iodine molecules in the complex increased from three to four and higher, while on increasing the iodide concentration the complex tended toward $(I_3^-)_n$ and its color shifted toward purple.

2. Effect of Chain Length on Complex Formation

The first potentiometric titration experiments (6) on starches and their separated amylose components showed that the iodine activity for complex formation decreases as the molecular weight of the amylose increases. Thus, potato amylose, DP_W 6100 (DP_W is the average degree of polymerization based on weight-average molecular weight), absorbed iodine at a slightly lower concentration of free iodine than corn amylose, DP_W 1850. In mixtures of the two amyloses, potato amylose bound iodine first showing that the longer helices bind iodine more firmly. Bates et al. (6) also observed that when excess potassium iodide was added to a solution containing sufficient iodine to half saturate an amylose, only half the amylose precipitated leaving an uncolored supernatant free from iodine. These experiments demonstrated that not only do the longer chains in the amylose sample absorb iodine first, but they fill completely before the shorter chains begin complex formation.

Degradation of amylose by acid hydrolysis considerably increases the iodine activity needed for complex formation (26) as measured by potentiometric titration. Mould (58) measured the minimum iodine concentration required for complete complex formation of maltodextrin fractions separated from amylose hydrolyzates by zone electrophoresis in the presence of iodine-iodide. For fractions of DP 10–25 (orange staining), 25–40 (red staining), and 40–90 (blue staining), the respective iodine concentrations for complex formation in 0.001 M potassium iodide were 15×10^{-5}, 3.2×10^{-5}, and 1.0×10^{-5} M as compared to about 1×10^{-6} M for an undegraded amylose. The composition of the complex first formed by maltodextrin (DP 40–90) was $2I_2 \cdot yI^-$, which changed to $3I_2 \cdot yI^-$ (y was not determined) as sufficient iodine was added to develop the blue color. Gilbert and Marriott (*34*) also found that the minimal ionic grouping for blue coloration of amylose contains three iodine molecules.

Thoma and French (*88*) have provided the most complete information on iodine binding by the low DP maltodextrins. Using the potentiometric titration method, they determined the equilibrium constants for complex formation for maltodextrins, ranging in DP from 4 through 15, that had been separated from amylose hydrolyzates by column chromatography. All maltodextrins bound iodine in 0.25 M potassium iodide at I_2 concentrations ranging from 10^{-4} to 10^{-2} M. Iodine exists predominantly as triiodide ion in such solutions, and Thoma and French interpreted their results as binding of I_3^- according to the equations

$$G_n + I_3^- = G_n I_3^-; \qquad K_1 = \frac{(G_n I_3^-)}{(G_n)(I_3^-)} \tag{1}$$

$$G_n I_3^- + I_3^- = G_n I_6^{2-}; \qquad K_2 = \frac{(G_n I_6^{2-})}{(G_n I_3^-)(I_3^-)} \tag{2}$$

where G_n represents a dextrin of n glucose units. Distinction was not made between I_2 and I_3^- in the potentiometric titration and total *free iodine* ($I_2 + I_3^-$) was used instead of (I_3^-) in calculating the data. Hence, apparent equilibrium constants for reactions (1) and (2) were obtained which differ from K_1 and K_2 by the factor $(1 + 1/K_I[I^-])$ where K_I is the formation constant for triiodide ion.

For dextrins G_4 through G_9, the complex contained one triiodide ion per dextrin molecule. Dextrins G_{10} through G_{15}, however, appeared to bind 2 moles of triiodide at higher free iodine concentrations, and both first and second equilibrium constants for these dextrins could be determined (Fig. 2). Thoma and French also reported that iodine binding by G_3 could be detected at 25°C, and by both G_3 and G_2, but not glucose, at 0.2°C.

Formation constants for the triiodide complexes of the maltodextrins are presented in Fig. 2. Most interesting is the discontinuity in the plot of the first apparent formation constants between G_6 and G_7. As Thoma and French point out, this can be interpreted as a configurational transformation from a *loop* arrangement to a *helical* arrangement, maintaining an essentially constant radius of the coiled dextrin molecules. That is, in the G_7 dextrin there is an overlap or superposition of the two terminal

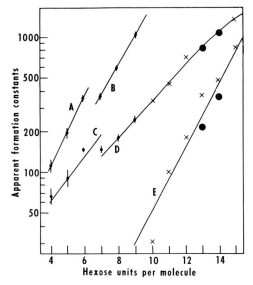

FIG. 2. Equilibrium constants (mole/liter)$^{-1}$ for the reaction of maltodextrins, G_4 through G_{15}, with triiodide ion. Curves A and B are the formation constants for $G_nI_3^-$ at 0°; curves C and D are at 25°. Curve E represents the formation constants for $G_nI_6^{2-}$ at 25° (88).

glucose units, rather than the formation of an expanded loop similar to the seven-membered cyclic dextrin, cycloheptaamylose. In support, Thoma and French cite the equality of the first formation constants of G_6 and G_7 triiodide complexes, whereas the corresponding constant for cycloheptaamylose is 100 times less than that for cyclohexaamylose; the larger radius in the cycloheptaamylose is less favorable for binding iodine.

3. EFFECT OF CHAIN LENGTH ON THE ABSORPTION SPECTRUM OF THE IODINE COMPLEX

From the foregoing discussion, it is evident that dextrins of very short chain length bind iodine if the iodine activity is sufficiently high. A definite absorption peak in the visible region does not develop in iodine-iodide solutions until a chain length of 18 glucose units (3, 58, 87) is reached. At relatively high I_2 and KI concentrations, however, the G_{16} dextrin (87) showed absorption in the region 400–440 mμ which has been attributed to the probable formation of a diiodide complex, I_6^{2-}. Spectrophotometric absorption curves of dextrins G_6 through G_{12} showed an enhancement of the ultraviolet triiodide ion spectrum which has peaks at 287 and 353 mμ.

The chain length of an amylose thus needs to be long enough to form three turns of the helix in order to stabilize a polyiodide ion of length sufficient to give enhanced absorption in the visible region. As the chain length is further increased, the absorption maximum shifts toward longer wavelengths and the color changes progressively from red through purple to the blue characteristic of native amyloses. From the work of Bailey and Whelan (3) it appears that 12 turns of the helix (DP about 72) are required to stabilize a linear polyiodide ion of length sufficient to give a blue color. However, a number-average DP of 350–400 in synthetic amyloses was required to shift the absorption maximum to 645 mμ, the wavelength observed for potato amylose which has a number-average DP of 1000–4000 according to osmotic pressure measurements (35). The potentiometric measurements on corn and potato amylose discussed in the preceding section show that cooperative effects associated with increasing turns of the helix which reduce the activity of bound iodine extend beyond DP 350–400.

4. THERMODYNAMIC ASPECTS OF THE AMYLOSE-IODINE-IODIDE REACTION

The reaction between amylose, iodine, and iodide ion can be written:

$$Am + nI_2 + rnI^- \rightleftarrows Am(I_2 \cdot rI^-)n$$

where Am = amylose and r = ratio of iodide to iodine in the complex. From the potentiometric titration results of Dube (24), the complex appears to behave as a solid phase, and the equilibrium constant can be expressed as

$$K^{1/n} = \frac{1}{(Am)^{1/n}(I_2)(I^-)^r} = \frac{1}{(I_2)(I^-)^r}$$

if it is assumed for large values of n that $(Am)^{1/n} = 1$. Dube reported $K^{1/n} = 1.0 \times 10^9$ at 25°C in 0.05 M KI (concentrations being expressed as mole/liter), where r was assumed to be unity; the same value is obtained by extrapolating Kuge and Ono's (50) plot of K versus $(1/T)$ to 25°C. They also assumed $r = 1$ in 0.05 M KI. Values reported for the enthalpy of the reaction, obtained from the temperature coefficient of the equilibrium constant, are not in good agreement. Gilbert and Mariott (34) reported $\Delta H° = -11.2$ kcal for each mole of iodine bound in the temperature range 3°–20°C, Dube found -19.6 kcal at 25°C, whereas Kuge and Ono reported -15.5 kcal at 16°C. Gilbert and Marriott, however, determined their values at very low levels of iodine binding (less than 2% of maximum) and at 10^{-3} M KI.

Equilibrium constants for the reaction of maltodextrins with triiodide ion at 0° and 25°C are presented in Fig. 2. On the assumption that $\Delta H°$ is constant over this temperature range, $\Delta H°$ values can be calculated and compared for the formation of loop and helical complexes which are represented by lines A and C, and B and D, respectively (Fig. 2) as discussed in the preceding section. By extrapolating lines A and C to higher DP, $\Delta H°$ for the two types of complex can be compared at the same DP. $\Delta H°$ values in calories per mole of iodine bound are listed in Table II. The

TABLE II

Thermodynamic Constants of the Amylose–Iodine Reaction for Maltodextrins[a]

Glucose units	Loop complex[b]			Helical complex[b]		
	$\Delta G°$	$\Delta H°$	$\Delta S°$	$\Delta G°$	$\Delta H°$	$\Delta S°$
6	-3000	-5800	-9.6	-2700	-6300	-12.8
7	-3200	-7100	-13.1	-2900	-7000	-13.7
8	-3400	-8400	-16.6	-3100	-8300	-17.4
9	-3700	-9600	-19.9	-3300	-9500	-21.8
10	-3900	$-10,800$	-23.2	-3500	$-10,800$	-24.7
11	-4100	$-12,000$	-26.6	-3600	$-12,200$	-28.7
$n = \infty$ [c]	—	—	—	$-12,000$	$-19,600$	-25.6

[a] Calculated from the data of Thoma and French (88).
[b] Values given in this table are based on calories per mole of iodine.
[c] Obtained by Dube (24).

small difference in $\Delta H°$ for the loop and the helical complexes shows that hydrogen bonding, which would be expected between adjacent turns of the helix, but which cannot occur in the loop complex, contributes little to the enthalpy of the reaction. In formation of the helix, hydrogen bonds between glucose hydroxyls and water would be exchanged for glucose-glucose hydrogen bonds, and there appears to be little difference in energy between the two.

The enthalpy increases regularly per mole of iodine (as I_3^-) in the helical complex for each additional glucose unit added to the maltodextrin chain. If a linear increase of 1.2–1.3 kcal/glucose unit (Table II) is assumed, the limiting value of $-\Delta H°$ (15.5–19.6 kcal) found for the amylose complex would be reached in the maltodextrin series at DP of about 14–17. Apparently the lowest DP at which maximal interaction occurs for the first triiodide ion that enters the amylose helix is the same as that required for color formation in solutions of the complex. Moreover, the enthalpy per mole of triiodide ion would appear to be the same for all subsequent iodine entering the complex, indicating that resonance in the polyiodine chain contributes little to the stability of the complex.

The discontinuity in $\Delta G°$ which occurs at DP 6–7 (Fig. 2) for the formation reaction has been associated with the transition from a loop to a helical complex. Since the enthalpy change per iodine molecule for each glucose unit in the chain appears to be the same for the two types of complex, the difference in $\Delta G°$ must be ascribed to a difference in $\Delta S°$ of reaction. The values listed in Table II show that $\Delta S°$ for the formation of the loop complex is 1–2 e.u. larger (more positive) than for the helical complex. Helix formation therefore appears to be more restrictive on the number of configurations of the maltodextrin molecule than loop formation. In the helix, the seventh glucose unit in the dextrin chain is probably hydrogen bonded to the first glucose unit, the eighth glucose unit to the second, and so on, thereby reducing the flexibility of the molecule as compared to a loop. The seven-membered helix should have approximately the same number of possible configurations as the six-membered loop and it is interesting to note that the equilibrium constants for formation of these two complexes are about the same (Fig. 2).

5. THEORETICAL TREATMENT OF THE AMYLOSE-IODINE REACTION

Several theories have been proposed to explain the formation and properties of the amylose-iodine complex. Stein and Rundle (*83*) suggested that the complex can be attributed to the cumulative dipolar forces of the amylose helix which increase with helix length and polarize the included iodine molecules, thereby producing electrostatic iodine-iodine interactions. Additional stabilization is achieved in this model by assuming that iodine exists in the helix as a resonating polyiodine chain. An important aspect of the theory is that it predicts that the stability of the complex should increase with helix length, which is consistent with experimental observations. The theory applies, however, only to the formation of the complex of dry amylose with iodine in the vapor phase. In aqueous solutions polarization of water would reduce the electrostatic fields of the amylose helix; moreover, the solution complex includes iodide ions as essential components. Indeed, iodide ions may be involved in complex formation in the solid state. A small amount of water is necessary in the preparation of the complex from dry amylose and iodine vapor; therefore, iodide ions may be present as a result of hydrolysis of iodine or its reduction by amylose.

Stein and Rundle's proposal of a resonating polyiodine chain in the amylose helix has been the basis for application of Kuhn's equation (51) relating chain length of a resonating polyene chain to its absorption spectrum. Ono and co-workers (61) assumed that the polyiodine chain has two π orbitals arising from the two pairs of p electrons of each iodine atom and that these p electrons are responsible for the light absorption of the complex. Shifts of λ_{max} to shorter wavelengths with increasing iodide concentration were explained by assuming that when iodide enters the polyiodine chain, the resonating units are broken into shorter units. Ono et al. calculated that a resonating chain length of 52 iodine atoms gives an absorption maximum at λ = 600 mμ while 160 atoms in the resonating chain corresponds to λ_{max} of 628 mμ. Experimentally, however, no more than 12 iodine molecules or 24 iodine atoms were needed to give an absorption maximum at 600–610 mμ, as shown by the results of Bailey and Whelan (3) on amylose of DP 72, corresponding to a helix with, at most, 12 turns. The discrepancy may result, in part, from incorrect evaluation by Ono et al. of the perturbation parameter in Kuhn's equation. To evaluate this parameter knowledge is required of the length of the resonating unit in the complex under some condition of formation. Ono et al. assumed that no iodide enters the amylose complex at low iodide concentration; this, however, is unlikely and doubtless contributes to the discrepancy.

Cramer and Herbst (23) calculated λ_{max} on the assumption that all seven electrons of each iodine atom are involved in resonance, that is, the polyiodine chain behaves as a one-dimensional electron gas. They found λ_{max} = 435 mμ corresponds to ten atoms in the polyiodine chain. Experimentally, however, a λ_{max} of 440 mμ was observed (87) for an amylodextrin of DP 18 which can form a helix of 3 turns and should accomodate a maximum of 3 iodine molecules or 6 iodine atoms.

Hsieh and Hsu (45) extended the one-dimensional free electron model of Cramer and Herbst to a three-dimensional free electron model. They assumed the electron gas is free to move in a cylindrical volume defined by the inner radius and length of the helix. Solving Schrödinger's wave equation with these boundary conditions, they calculated energy levels related to the radius and length of the helix. Their results predict four absorption maxima in the visible and ultraviolet, but the wavelengths of these maxima are related only to the effective inner radius of the helix and not to the length of the polyiodine chain (Table III). Although this model predicts the absorption spectrum of the iodine complex in more detail than other proposed models, it fails to account for the dependence

TABLE III

CALCULATED ABSORPTION MAXIMA OF AMYLOSE-IODINE COMPLEX BASED ON A
THREE-DIMENSIONAL FREE ELECTRON MODEL (60)

Effective radius of helix, Å	Absorption maxima, Å			
	λ_1	λ_2	λ_3	λ_4
3.8	5328	3004	2529	1847
4.0	5904	3328	2802	2047
4.1	6203	3496	2944	2151
4.3	6823	3846	3238	2365
Observed spectrum	5700	3440	2240	2000

of λ_{max} on iodide concentration and chain length of amylose. The observed shift of λ_{max} to longer wavelength with increasing amylose chain length might be ascribed to a concurrent expansion of the radius of the helix, but no evidence for this expansion has been reported.

Murakami (60) proposed that the amylose-iodine complex is stabilized by charge transfer (59) interaction through weak covalent bond formation between iodine and the oxygen atoms of the glucosidic linkage or hydroxyl groups of the helix. The covalent bond is not localized but was assumed to resonate over all oxygen atoms surrounding an iodine molecule. Support for such bonding has been given by infrared studies of Greenwood and Rossotti (36) and of Rossotti (68) on complexes of dry amylose with iodine vapor. They concluded that the iodine molecule interacts with the glucosidic ether oxygens but not with hydroxyl groups. According to Murakami, charge transfer from amylose oxygen to iodine results in the formation of I_4^{2-} ions, which are considered to be the elemental units of the polyiodide chain. Applying Kuhn's equation to the I_4^{2-} ion considered a one-dimensional gas, λ_{max} was calculated to be 5214 Å, which is in the range observed for iodine complexes with amyloses of short chain length. Potentiometric and spectrophotometric studies on complex formation in solution, however, indicate that I_6^{2-}, I_8^{2-}, or I_3^{-} ions are bound by amylose; λ_{max} calculated for the first two ions by Murakami's method would be much larger than observed values. It is also likely that charge transfer would contribute much less to the stability of solution complexes than to the dry amylose-iodine vapor complex since polyiodide ions are already present in solution.

Recently, Bersohn and Isenberg (11) proposed that the $(I_3^{-})_n$ complex behaves as a metallic complex. They proposed that the iodine and iodide are covalently linked together in a polyiodide chain. The stability of this amylose-triiodide complex is ascribed to the dispersion forces between the helix and the iodine atoms and the strength of the covalent bonds between iodine atoms. The absorption at 6250 Å was explained as a transition from a π band to the σ band. The σ band is only partially occupied and, hence, resembles a metallic structure. The filling of this σ band accounts for the increase in λ_{max} with an increase in triiodide chain length. As pointed out by Bersohn and Isenberg, the stability of this polytriiodide chain cannot be explained on the basis of interaction between the iodine atoms, that is, the expansion of interatomic distance from 2.90 Å in the isolated I_3^- ion to 3.10 Å in the $(I_3^-)_n$ polymer cancels any possible superior resonance energy. In addition, it destroys a small amount of the original resonance energy associated with the isolated I_3^- complex. Experimental observation of electron spin resonance provided evidence of the metallic nature of the complex, but the measured electron spin resonance was about one-fifth the predicted value. Hence, this observation plus the inability to explain the stability of the polytriiodide chain suggests that this model needs further refinement.

Apparently none of the proposed theories accounts for all the properties of the amylose-iodine-iodide complex. The theories of Stein and Rundle, and Murakami provide explanations for the stability of the dry amylose complex, but are of doubtful validity for solution complex formation. The remaining theories predict the optical properties of the complex but are not concerned with the energetics of formation.

III. IODINE-IODIDE COMPLEXES OF GLYCOGEN AND AMYLOPECTIN

Branching in amylopectins and glycogens greatly reduces the chain length effective for helix formation and inclusion of iodine. Both poly-saccharides have high molecular weights (*35*) (ca. 10^7 for glycogens to 10^8 for amylopectins) and a ramified, treelike structure (*55*). Exterior branches of the molecules are longer than the interior branches, which are chain segments lying between branch points. In amylopectin the exterior branches range from 14 to 17 glucose units in average length depending on the plant source, whereas those in the more highly branched glycogen range (*2*, *55*) from 4 to 11 glucose units, and their average length varies with origin of the glycogen. Interior branches range from 5 to 8 glucose units in the amylopectins and from 2 to 7 in the glycogens. Since amylopectin and glycogen can be considered as statistical polymers (*27*), considerable variation about their average branch lengths would be expected, and some of the branches in glycogen as well as amylopectin exceed the 18 glucose units required for color formation in helical complexes.

The wavelength of maximum absorbance observed (2) for glycogens in iodine-iodide solution is in the range 420–490 mμ, whereas λ_{max} for amylopectins is 530–540 mμ; the longer wavelengths for the amylopectins are consistent with their greater average branch length and their ability to form longer helices. Archibald et al. (2), however, found no linear relation between average branch length and λ_{max} of the iodine complexes in water solution.

Formation of the iodine-iodide complex in half saturated ammonium sulfate greatly enhances the absorbance of the glycogen complex (73) and also shifts λ_{max} to longer wavelengths (10–55 mμ shift) (2); the ammonium sulfate apparently stabilizes the shorter helices. Lesser effect was observed for amylopectins in ammonium sulfate solution. Under these conditions λ_{max} determined for amylopectins and glycogens was approximately linearly related to degree of branching, and Archibald et al. suggest that the relationship may be used to deduce average chain length from measurements of λ_{max}.

At high iodine concentrations Higgenbotham (42) found that amylopectin binds as much iodine as amylose which suggests that the binding occurs by surface adsorption as well as through inclusion in helices. The results of Thoma and French (88) on the maltodextrins show that short chain segments in amylopectins would be expected to bind iodine at high triiodide concentration. Segments long enough to form 1–2 turns of a helix would bind iodine and iodide ions, but these amylopectin complexes would only exhibit an enhanced triiodide spectrum and no color change in the visible.

No evidence has been reported for inclusion compound formation of amylopectins or glycogens with alcohols, fatty acids, or other organic molecules that complex with amylose. Like the iodine complexes, these complexes with the branched polysaccharides would be expected to be soluble, and evidence for their formation might be found either by increased solubility of the organic compound in the presence of polysaccharide (see Chapter 8, Section VI) or by diminished iodine binding of the polysaccharide.

IV. SCHARDINGER DEXTRIN COMPLEXES

The Schardinger dextrins are cyclic glucose polymers formed from starch by the action of *Bacillus macerans* amylase. As in amylose, the glucose units in the Schardinger dextrins are joined through 1,4-α-linkages. Although evidence has been presented for the existence of seven cyclic dextrins, DP 6 through 12, in enzymic digests of starch (63) properties of only three have been investigated extensively. These are the α-, β-, and γ-dextrins consisting of 6, 7, and 8 glucose residues, respectively. Details for preparing Schardinger dextrins are given in an excellent article by French (32), who also reviews the literature through 1956 on the chemical structure and the physical and biochemical properties of the Schardinger dextrins and their derivatives. Only the molecular complexes formed by the cyclic dextrins are considered here.

The cyclic dextrins are unique in that a single molecule provides space on its interior for the inclusion of guest molecules. Unlike the amylose helix, which is stabilized by secondary bonding between adjacent turns of the helix and the guest molecule, the annular structure of the cyclic dextrins is formed by primary bonds between glucose units and is therefore pre-existent in solution before complex formation occurs. Photographs of scale models (74) of α-cyclodextrin are shown in Fig. 3. The model in Fig. 3a was constructed with the glucose units in the C1 chair form, whereas the B1 boat conformation was used for the model in Fig. 3b. Both models have an interior diameter of about 6 Å, and a channel length of 7–8 Å. Both have an upper layer of six CH_2OH groups (removed in Fig. 3); the center layers differ in that the chair form at the left presents CH groups of carbons 3 and 5 of each glucose unit and the glucosidic oxygen to the interior, whereas the boat form presents only the CH groups of carbons 1 and 4 of each glucose unit. The lowest layer of the chair form consists of the secondary hydroxyls on carbons 2 and 3; that of the boat form is made up of the secondary hydroxyl on carbon 3 and the CH of carbon 2. The cyclic dextrins made from glucose in the boat form thus have a more hydrophobic lining than do those from glucose units in the chair form; however, both have a multiplicity of hydroxyl groups available for hydrogen bonding.

Models of the β- and γ-cyclodextrins indicate internal diameters of about 8 and 10 Å, respectively, for these molecules. One may therefore expect differences in complex formation with the three cyclodextrins depending on the size of the guest molecule, and these differences have been demonstrated experimentally. Complexes having greatest stability appear to be formed when the guest molecule can adopt an orientation in the cyclodextrin which allows maximal interaction with the groups lining the interior of the ring. Thus the γ-dextrin appears to be too large (13) to form stable complexes with small molecules with which the α- and β-dextrins complex readily, and the α-dextrin excludes large molecules.

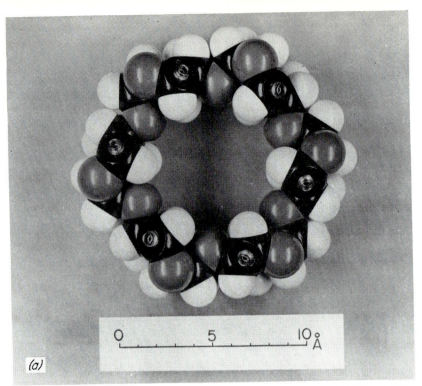

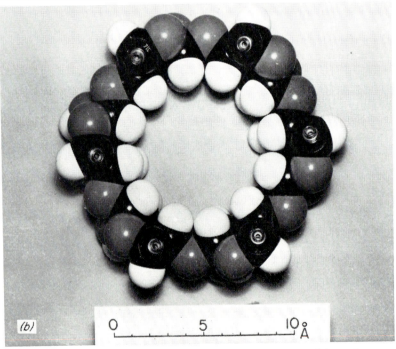

Fig. 3. Photographs (74) of models of α-cyclodextrins constructed from glucose units in the C1 chair form (a), and in the B1 boat form (b). Upper layer of CH₂OH groups have been removed. [Courtesy Dr. Hermann Schlenk, The Hormel Institute, University of Minnesota].

A. Complexes with Iodine and Iodide

α-Cyclodextrin forms a series of crystalline compounds with iodine and potassium iodide (Table IV). In the absence of iodide, orange-yellow crystals are formed having the composition $\alpha \cdot I_2 \cdot 14H_2O$. X-ray analysis (46) of these crystals showed that the cyclodextrin and iodine molecules are arranged as represented by the projection of the structure given in Fig. 4. Each iodine molecule lies in a cage formed by a cyclodextrin molecule, which has its ends blocked by adjacent cyclodextrin molecules. Iodine molecules are thus prevented from interacting strongly with each other to give highly colored crystals as observed in amylose-iodine complexes.

TABLE IV

IODINE-POTASSIUM IODIDE COMPLEXES OF α-CYCLODEXTRIN

Composition	Unit cell dimensions			Crystal system	Crystal color
	a	b	c		
$\alpha \cdot I_2 \cdot 14H_2O$	14.38	36.07	9.43	Orthorhombic	Orange-yellow
$\alpha \cdot I_2 \cdot KI$	16.0	—	39.7	Hexagonal	Blue-black
$\alpha_2 \cdot 2I_2 \cdot KI$	13.8	—	15.4	Pseudohexagonal	Green
$\alpha \cdot KI$	—	—	—		

In solutions containing both iodine and iodide, α-dextrin forms two crystalline compounds, $\alpha \cdot I_2 \cdot KI$ and $\alpha_2 \cdot 2I_2 \cdot KI$ (31). From the unit cell dimensions, symmetry, optical properties of the crystals, and dimensions of the α-cyclodextrin molecules, both compounds appear to have extended channel structures formed by coaxial packing of the cyclodextrin molecules. The second compound, $\alpha_2 \cdot 2I_2 \cdot KI$, gives an x-ray pattern with essentially the same spacings and intensities as the amylose-iodine complex (32) and, hence, should have a similar structure. The iodine molecules in the cyclodextrin complexes appear to lie in the channels of the structure. Composition of the $\alpha_2 \cdot 2I_2 \cdot KI$ crystals suggests the unit of structure is the I_5^- ion enclosed by a pair of α-dextrin molecules. Cramer (14), however, has reported that the α-dextrin forms crystals containing variable amounts of iodine (15.4–20.9%) and potassium iodide (4.2–6.5%) in the range of composition represented by the formula $\alpha_2 \cdot 2I_2 \cdot KI$. X-ray patterns of these crystals showed sharp, continuous layer lines, which were identified with a one-dimensional lattice of polyiodine chains lying in

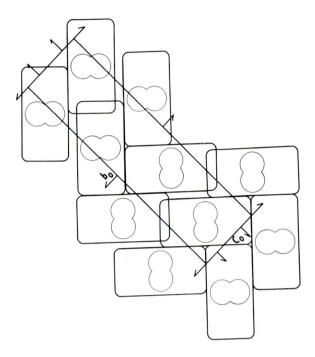

FIG. 4. Projection of the structure of cyclohexaamylose-iodine complex, $(C_6H_{10}O_5)_6 \cdot I_2 \cdot 14H_2O$, showing the cage structure formed by noncoaxial packing of the cyclodextrin molecules. Iodine molecules lie on the axis of the dextrin rings (46).

channels. The spacing, 3.06 Å, corresponding to these layer lines was interpreted as a uniform separation of the iodine atoms in a resonating polyiodine chain. As pointed out in the discussion of the amylose-iodine complex, the observation of a single layer line is not definitive evidence of equally spaced iodine atoms, but it does show that they lie in a linear array in the structure with a spacing unrelated to that of the dextrin molecules. Although French did not observe continuous layer lines for the $\alpha_2 \cdot 2I_2 \cdot KI$ complex, he reported (32) their appearance on x-ray patterns of the sodium iodide-iodine complex having comparable composition.

The composition of $\alpha \cdot I_2 \cdot KI$ suggests I_3^- ions are present in the crystals, but the blue color of the crystals indicates polyiodide ions of greater length since the $\alpha \cdot I_3^-$ complex in solution exhibits (86) only absorption maxima in the ultraviolet. In not one of the iodine-iodide complexes has the position of the cation been determined. Some cations must lie outside the channels in order that polyiodide ions of length greater than I_3^- can be formed in $\alpha \cdot I_2 \cdot KI$.

The compound $\alpha \cdot KI$ has been crystallized from potassium iodide solution (34), but its properties have not been reported.

Both β- and γ-dextrin form crystalline complexes in I_2–KI solutions (*21, 31*). Only the composition of the γ-dextrin complex has been reported. According to Cramer and Henglein (*21*), the mole ratio of I_2:dextrin is 2:1 for this complex; analysis for potassium iodide in the crystals was not reported. If this complex has a channel or cage structure there must be two iodine molecules packed side by side in each dextrin ring and, in addition, an undetermined number of iodide ions. Packing diameters of iodine would permit this structure; indeed, from spatial considerations alone, three iodine molecules might be expected to pack side by side in the γ-dextrin ring, which is about 10 Å in diameter.

Chlorine and bromine also form adducts with the Schardinger dextrins (*21*). α-Dextrin complexes with Cl_2 and Br_2 as well as with I_2; β-dextrin, only with Br_2 and I_2; and γ-dextrin with I_2 alone. These results illustrate the size relationship between guest and host molecules for inclusion compound formation; all halogens can enter the α-dextrin ring but the γ-dextrin is too large to bind the smaller halogens, Br_2 and Cl_2.

Binding of iodine and iodide ions by cyclic dextrins in solution has been measured by potentiometric and spectrophotometric methods. The absorption spectrum of α-dextrin in iodine solutions to which iodic acid has been added to repress iodide formation has a peak at 420 mμ characteristic of the $\alpha \cdot I_2$ complex (*86*). In the absence of α-dextrin, iodine exhibits a peak at 460 mμ. By applying the method of continuous variation to the optical densities obtained when the ratio of I_2:α was varied, Thoma and French (*85*) determined that α and I_2 react in 1:1 ratio. The dissociation constant of the $\alpha \cdot I_2$ complex was found to be 1.07×10^{-4}. Applying the same methodology, these investigators determined that in the presence of I_2 and I^-, α-dextrin forms the $\alpha \cdot I_3^-$ complex. This complex exhibits peaks at the same wavelengths at which the triiodide ion absorbs, 288 and 353 mμ, but the absorbance is greatly enhanced as compared to free I_3^- ion.

From potentiometric measurements of the equilibria of the α- and β-dextrins with iodine in potassium iodide solution Dube (*34*) obtained equilibrium constants for the following reactions:

$$\alpha + I^- \rightleftarrows \alpha \cdot I^- \qquad K = 13.5 \qquad \text{(mole/liter)}^{-1}$$

$$\alpha \cdot I^- + I_2 \rightleftarrows \alpha \cdot I_3^- \qquad K = 2.0 \times 10^7 \ \text{(mole/liter)}^{-1}$$

$$\beta + I^- \rightleftarrows \beta \cdot I^- \qquad K = 1.45 \qquad \text{(mole/liter)}^{-1}$$

$$\beta \cdot I^- + I_2 \rightleftarrows \beta \cdot I_3^- \qquad K = 1 \times 10^6 \quad \text{(mole/liter)}^{-1}$$

Affinity of the dextrins for triiodide ion is much stronger than for iodide ion, and the α-dextrin binds both ions more strongly than does the β-dextrin.

B. Insoluble Complexes with Organic Compounds

Many organic compounds which selectively precipitate amylose from aqueous solution also form insoluble complexes with the Schardinger dextrins. Thus, the α- and β-dextrins were reported to form complexes with the linear alcohols (*13*, *46*), C_1 through C_{12}; the fatty acids (*21*, *74*, *75*), C_2 through C_{18}; and benzaldehyde and nitrobenzene (*33*). In addition, β-dextrin is precipitated from dilute water solutions by thymol, benzyl alcohol, aniline, and cyclohexanol (*33*), which also selectively precipitate amylose from starch solutions.

The Schardinger dextrins differ from amylose in that they complex organic molecules that contain no polar functional groups. All three cyclic dextrins are precipitated from water solutions saturated with cyclohexane, toluene, *p*-xylene, *p*-cymene, diphenyl, or terphenyl (*14*, *33*). Anthracene precipitates only the γ-dextrin, naphthalene the β- and γ-dextrins, whereas benzene forms insoluble inclusion compounds with all three dextrins. These observations suggest that unsubstituted aromatic compounds tend to be bound with the plane of their molecules perpendicular to the axis of the cyclodextrin ring since naphthalene and anthracene could enter α-dextrin if the aromatic rings were parallel to the axis of the dextrin. β-Dextrin, which appears to have the greatest tendency for complex formation, is precipitated from water solutions covered with a layer of mineral oil.

Halogenated hydrocarbons (*33*) are excellent precipitants for the Schardinger dextrins; trichloro- and tetrachloroethylene and tetrachloroethane precipitate all three dextrins; the complexes of the β- and γ-dextrins are generally less soluble than those of the α-dextrin. Chlorobenzene forms a 1:1 insoluble complex with α- and β-dextrins; bromobenzene, a 1:1 complex with β- and γ-dextrins; but a complex of this molar composition with iodobenzene occurs only with the γ-dextrin (*21*). Each of the halogenated benzenes also forms complexes with the other dextrins, but less halogenated benzene is present in the complex, indicating less favorable dimensional relationships for inclusion.

Schlenk and Sand's (*74*) experiments on complex formation of the α- and β-dextrins with benzoic and substituted benzoic acid provide further examples of the effect of size of the guest molecule. β-Dextrin readily formed solid complexes in 1:1 molar ratio with benzoic acid and its *o*-, *m*-, and *p*-iodo derivatives. In contrast, α-dextrin yielded a crystalline complex only with benzoic and *p*-iodobenzoic acid; these had a component ratio of 2 dextrin:1 acid and were formed only at high dextrin concentrations. Models (*74*) of the α-cyclodextrin accept *o*- and *m*-iodobenzoic acids with difficulty but these can be inserted easily in the β-dextrin ring. Benzoic acid and p-iodobenzoic acids can both enter the α-cyclo-dextrin ring, but the fit is so close that the carboxyl and iodine groups are constrained to be near the axis of the ring, minimizing their interaction with cyclodextrin oxygens.

Crystalline inclusion compounds of the cyclic dextrins with n-alcohols and fatty acids above C_4 would be expected to form channel structures in which the dextrin molecules are aligned coaxially. X-ray data have been reported for the α-dextrin complexes of the lower alcohols, methanol, ethanol, and 1-propanol, and these appear to be isomorphous (46) with the $\alpha \cdot I_2$ complex whose structure is given in Fig. 4. This structure, however, has cages rather than channels and would not be expected to accommodate the higher alcohols. Cramer (13) reported unit cell dimensions for complexes of 1-hexanol, 1-octanol, and 1-dodecanol with α- and β-dextrin and stated that these are the same as for the pure cyclodextrins. For Cramer's α-dextrin complexes, the cell dimensions were reported as $a = 14.95$, $b = 31.1$, and $c = 9.5$ Å. These differ slightly from the cell dimensions, $a = 14.78$, $b = 33.96$, and $c = 9.51$ reported by James, et al. (46) for α-dextrin hydrate which, they suggested, has the cage structure as in the α-dextrin complexes with iodine and the lower alcohols. Differences in cell dimensions might result from differences in hydration but it is more likely that the higher alcohols have a channel structure rather than the cage structure shown in Fig. 4. Further investigation of these structures is needed.

Composition of the solid complexes of α- and β-dextrins with linear fatty acids, caproic through stearic, was reported by Schlenk and Sand (74). Their results are presented in Fig. 5. From the slope of the broken line in Fig. 5, one cyclodextrin molecule is required on the average to accomodate five CH_2 groups in the fatty acid chain. If the acid molecule is extended, this corresponds to 6.3 Å, rather smaller than the 7 Å width of the dextrin ring measured on models, and indicates interpenetration of rings in the complexes. Extrapolation of the line, composition versus number of carbon atoms, to zero cyclodextrin intercepts the abscissa at zero CH_2 groups (two carbon atoms in the acid) and gives a measure of the space occupied by the terminal groups of the fatty acid molecule. As shown in Fig. 5, the intercept corresponds to about 6 Å which is consistent with the packing dimensions of the CH_3 and COOH groups. All fatty acids are not extended to their maximum chain length in the complexes; because the C_{13}, C_{14}, and C_{15} acids occupy the same length in the β-dextrin complex as the C_{12} acid, these acids assume a spiral or some contracted configuration. A similar effect has been noted for thiourea adducts (Chapter 8, Section IV).

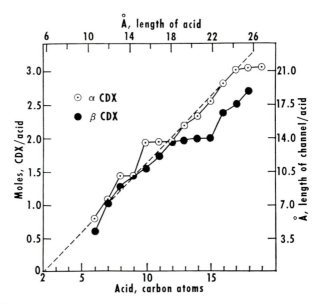

Fɪɢ. 5. Composition of solid fatty acid complexes of α- and β-cyclodextrins. Broken line has the slope of 1 cyclodextrin/5 CH₂ groups. Upper and right hand scales were derived from measurements on models of the cyclodextrins and extended fatty acid chains (74).

Linoleic and linolenic acids, cinnamaldehyde (75), and benzaldehyde (15) autoxidize at a greatly reduced rate when complexed with the α- and β-dextrins. For the adducts to be stable it was necessary to remove all excess lipid from the crystals by heating in vacuum. Prevention of a chain mechanism for oxidation by immobilizing the oxidizable molecules, rather than complete exclusion of oxygen from the structure (which has been suggested in the case of urea adducts; see Chapter 8, Section VII, C), has been proposed (75) to explain the reduced rate of oxidation.

C. Dye Binding by the Schardinger Dextrins

Cramer (13, 17) observed that malachite green, crystal violet, methylene blue, and dichlorophenolindophenol in β-dextrin solution give stronger blue color than solutions at the same dye concentration in either water or glucose solution. Absorption spectra of these dyes in ½–1% β-dextrin solution showed an enhancement of the peak near 600 mμ and, for crystal violet and dichlorophenolindophenol, a 10–20 mμ shift of the maximum toward longer wavelengths. Cramer attributed the spectral changes to the high electron density of the interior surface of the cyclic dextrin,

which acts as a Lewis base toward the included dye molecule. Consideration of the molecular structure of these dyes shows that only part of the
molecule can enter the cyclodextrin ring. Crystal violet, for example, has

$$(CH_3)_2N-\underset{}{\bigcirc}-C=\underset{}{\bigcirc}=N(CH_3)_2Cl$$

$$\underset{N(CH_3)_2}{\bigcirc}$$

(I)

the structure (I) which is much too large to be completely included in the
β-cyclodextrin ring.

More extensive spectrophotometric studies of the dye complexes have
been made by Lautsch and co-workers (53), who used cyclodextrins as
models for investigations of the role of inclusion complexes in enzyme action.
They showed that binding of methyl orange by β-dextrin and bovine
serum albumin produces similar changes in the absorption spectrum of the
dye. From optical density measurements as a function of dye:dextrin
ratio at a wavelength showing increased absorbance on complex formation, the extent of complex formation was calculated and the equilibrium
constant for the reaction determined. Values of the equilibrium constant
for the reaction of the dextrins with different dyes as determined by
Lautsch et al. (53) are listed in Table V. These formation constants are

TABLE V

EQUILIBRIUM CONSTANTS, K_F, FOR FORMATION OF SCHARDINGER DEXTRIN
COMPLEXES AND ACID DISSOCIATION CONSTANTS, K_D (MOLES/LITER), OF
INCLUDED MOLECULES (53)

Complex	K_F	K_D without dextrin	K_D with dextrin
β-Dextrin and crystal violet	1.41×10^{-4}		
β-Dextrin and fuchsine	1.26×10^{-3}	3.3×10^{-2}	7.4×10^{-2}
β-Dextrin and marine blue	3.55×10^{-4}	7.9×10^{-6}	7.9×10^{-5}
β-Dextrin and methyl orange	2.51×10^{-4}		
α-Dextrin and methyl orange	1.12×10^{-4}		

several orders of magnitude lower than those for the iodine-iodide com-

$$(CH_3)_2N - \langle \underline{\quad} \rangle - N{=}N - \langle \underline{\quad} \rangle - SO_3H$$

(II)

plexes. Methyl orange, a linear molecule with the structure (II) has only slightly more affinity for the dextrin than crystal violet, suggesting that only one of the substituted phenyl groups enters the dextrin ring in either case.

Prototropic equilibria of cyclodextrin inclusion compounds with molecules which dissociate protons are shifted in the direction that dissociation to the proton is made easier. Acid dissociation constants of fuchsine and marine blue (Table V) are shifted about one unit in pK.

An alkaline environment in the β-dextrin molecule is also indicated in its inclusion compound with uridine-5′-phosphate; the ultraviolet spectrum of the included nucleotide shows an alkaline reaction in β-dextrin solutions buffered at pH 7 (89). These complexes were studied as models for the adenosine triphosphate enzyme systems. Inclusion compound formation may provide an explanation for the stronger phosphorylating activity of ATP *in vivo* as compared to its weak activity *in vitro*.

The potential of redox equilibria of dye/leuco compounds are changed by inclusion compound formation (17). Thus, the redox potential of methylene blue/leucomethylene blue is increased 0.048 volt at pH 7.0 in the presence of β-dextrin, corresponding to a weakening of the reducing power of the system. Decrease in the effective concentration of the reduced form of the dye by preferential inclusion would increase the redox potential; however, the effect might also be attributed to the change in electronic structure of the included dye molecule, which is shown by the shift in the absorption spectrum. Similar shifts in redox potential have been observed for 2,6-dichloroindophenol and crystal violet. The results are again of interest in relation to the role of inclusion in enzyme action. In the case of lactoflavin, for example, the redox potential is -0.185 volt, but when the flavin mononucleotide combines with the apoenzyme to form "yellow enzyme," the redox potential rises to -0.06 volt (85). Lautsch *et al.* (53) observed that redox active groups chemically bound to high polymer molecules show a change in reduction potential as compared to the free active groups. Existence of inclusion regions in the high polymers may account for this change.

These physicochemical effects and the one that follows are also discussed in Chapter 10, Section VI.

D. Catalytic Action of the Cyclodextrins

The alkaline action of the cyclic dextrins, manifest in their complexes with indicator dyes, suggests that the dextrins may increase the rate of base-catalyzed reactions. Increased rate of oxidation of α-hydroxyketones in the presence of cyclic dextrins illustrates this effect. Absorption spectra show that on complex formation with β-dextrin, acetylacetone, furoin, and dioxindol are shifted (16) to the easily oxidizable endiol form. The rate constant for the oxidation of dioxindol (16) at pH 8.4 was found to increase twofold in the presence of α-dextrin, threefold by β-dextrin, and twofold by γ-dextrin. β-Dextrin also increases the rate of oxidation of furoin.

Adduct formation with the cyclodextrin can retard acid-catalyzed reaction of the included molecule, presumably because of the alkaline environment. Thus, hydrolysis of indican (15), the β-glucoside of indoxyl, is retarded by β-cyclodextrin in 0.1 N HCl at 30°. The rate constant of the reaction is reduced 40% in the presence of β-dextrin as compared to the rate constant in the presence of α-methyl glucoside.

β-dextrin also inhibits the splitting of indican by the enzyme emulsin (15); the rate constant at pH 5 is reduced about 50% in solutions containing β-dextrin. Whether the reduced rate results from the basic environment of the included molecule or steric factors hindering the attack of hydrolytic agent may be questioned. It seems likely that even partial inclusion of indican in β-dextrin would retard the action of a large enzyme molecule that needs to make contact with the substrate for activation.

The Schardinger dextrins also act as a microheterogenous catalyst in the splitting of the P—O—P bond in symmetrical diesters of pyrophosphoric acid (18). The magnitude of the catalytic effect depends on the R group in the diester,

$$
\begin{array}{ccc}
\text{O} & & \text{O} \\
\parallel & & \parallel \\
\text{RO—P—O—POR} \\
\mid & & \mid \\
\text{O} & & \text{O}
\end{array}
$$

and on the cyclic dextrin.

Cramer (18) compared reaction rates for the diphenyl, di-p-chlorophenyl, and di-p-tolyl esters at pH 12 with and without cyclodextrin. The catalytic effect of each dextrin varies with the R group and, as with enzyme action, there is substrate specificity. Thus, α-dextrin has little influence on the rate of splitting of the p-tolyl ester, but increases the rate of the p-chloro ester more than fifteen-fold. The β-dextrin has maximum effect on all three esters and illustrates again the importance of size relationships. The dextrins, however, do not act as true catalysts; in the splitting of P^1-ethyl-P^2(4-chlorophenyl)pyrophosphate by β-dextrin (39), the ethyl phosphoric acid half of the molecule is liberated into solution, whereas the other half is chemically bound to the carbohydrate. From this it appeared that the more lipophilic end of the molecule is bound preferentially to the dextrin and subjected to the influence of the carbohydrate hydroxyls, which are partially ionized at high pH.

E. Stereospecific Effects of the Cyclodextrins

The cyclodextrins are optically active compounds, composed of D-glucose units, and preferential inclusion of one of the antipodes of a racemic mixture might be expected. Cramer and Dietsche (19) showed that insoluble β-dextrin inclusion compounds formed with several racemates are enriched 3–12% in one of the stereoisomers. Racemates, for which partial separation was achieved, included ethyl esters of mandelic, o-chloromandelic, phenylchloroacetic, phenylbromoacetic, and atrolactic acids, menthyl esters of acetic and monochloroacetic acids, dichlorosuccinic and cinnamic acids, and 4,4′- and 2,2′-dichlorobenzoin.

Cyclodextrins have a directing effect on asymmetric reactions (20) of molecules with which inclusion compounds are formed. Addition of hydrogen cyanide to 2- and 4-chlorobenzaldehyde in the presence of α-dextrin gives optically active α-hydroxy nitriles which, on saponification, produce optically active mandelic acids. Inclusion compound formation of β-dextrin with racemic 2-chloromandelic acid ethyl ester results in stereospecific saponification of the ester to yield optically active 2-chloromandelic acid. The ester remaining at 50% saponification was also found to be optically active; a slight enrichment in one of the enantiomorphs occurred. Cramer and Dietsche (20) pointed out the parallelism between inclusion compound specificity of the cyclodextrins and that of certain enzyme systems, which suggests the use of cyclodextrin systems as models for study of mechanism of enzyme action.

F. Inclusion Compounds of Cyclodextrins with Gases

The solubility of α-dextrin is reduced in solutions saturated with certain gases at high pressure and dextrin crystals formed from such solutions include gas in their structure. Cramer and Henglein (22) observed the formation of inclusion compounds of α-dextrin with krypton, xenon, oxygen, carbon dioxide, ethylene, methane, ethane, propane, and butane. Nitrogen and argon, which have smaller molecular diameters, did not form compounds. Propane and butane formed crystals with β-dextrin, but only in trace amounts. Analysis of the α-dextrin crystals showed molar ratios of gas:α-dextrin ranged from 0.3 to 1.375; ratios of unity or above were attained with the saturated hydrocarbons and carbon dioxide. A cage structure (Fig. 4) which James, French, and Rundle (46) proposed for α-dextrin hydrate, would be expected also for the gas inclusion compounds.

V. ADSORPTION AND ADDITION COMPLEXES OF POLYSACCHARIDES

Non-stoichiometric adsorption and addition complexes are not limited to the polysaccharides but are common to almost all organic high polymers, particularly those containing polar groups. Hydrate formation is a familiar example. Exposed to water vapor, native cellulose sorbs increasing amounts of water as the vapor pressure is increased; a limit is reached, however, in saturated atmospheres since cellulose is insoluble in water. X-ray diffraction patterns show that the crystalline regions of cellulose are unchanged irrespective of moisture content, and the water must therefore be taken up by the amorphous regions. It is therefore apparent that the water content of a cellulose sample will depend not only on the relative humidity but also on its percentage crystallinity. Indeed, regenerated cellulose sorbs twice as much water as native cellulose at 65% relative humidity and has about twice as much amorphous structure.

Measurement of the heat of sorption at low moisture levels shows that the first water to enter the amorphous regions of cellulose is tightly bound, probably through hydrogen bonding to cellulosic hydroxyl groups, and thus can be considered to form a true hydrate. Beyond this region of true hydrate formation, which is difficult to determine experimentally but which is considered to correspond up to 2–2.5 molecules of water per glucose residue (40, 52), additional water is loosely bound, and hydration in this region appears to be a solution process. No stoichiometric relationship can be expected; the limit of water uptake is the physical constraint which limits swelling of the structure.

In some cases, as for example regenerated cellulose (40) and native starches (9), water enters the crystalline as well as the amorphous regions in the sorption process. X-ray evidence indicates that the crystalline regions reach their hydration limit at relatively low water vapor pressures and form hydrates of definite composition. The stoichiometry may, however, be difficult to determine because it is obscured by the non-stoichiometric hydration in the amorphous regions.

A similar situation holds in the formation of addition compounds of polysaccharides with alkali metal hydroxides, salts, and acids. Such compounds have been most studied in the case of cellulose and starch. Alkali addition compounds of cellulose are formed when cellulose is soaked in concentrated solutions of the alkali metal hydroxides (62). X-ray patterns show that new structures are formed and that both crystalline and amorphous regions are present. Above and below certain limits of alkali concentration in the solution, the amorphous regions contain either an excess or a deficiency of alkali as compared to the stoichiometry of the compound formed in the crystalline regions, with the result that the overall composition is variable. Starch sorbs alkalies from solution, but crystalline regions with a definite stoichiometry are not formed, and uptake of alkali follows Freundlich's sorption isotherm (54).

Polysaccharides form solvates of indefinite composition with many organic molecules. In contrast to water, organic liquids are difficult to remove completely by ordinary drying procedures. Mechanical entrapment or inclusion likely contributes to their retention in the polysaccharide structure. Polysaccharides such as pectin (47) precipitated from aqueous solution with alcohol, for example, retain alcohol even after vacuum drying at 100°C for long periods. Cotton (82), washed successively with water, acetone, and cyclohexane, may contain up to 10% cyclohexane after drying to constant weight at 0.1 mm and 100°C. Benzene can be introduced similarly into cellulose (67), and, like cyclohexane, apparently replaces water in the amorphous regions. Neither can escape, however, unless displaced by a liquid or vapor which swells the cellulose structure. Even larger amounts of organic liquids are held in viscose cellulose if the water in freshly regenerated cellulose gels is replaced by alcohol and then by a miscible liquid, such as ether or benzene. After drying 3 hours at 105°C, regenerated cellulose fibers prepared this way were found to contain 40% ether (41). In this case the outer layers of the fibers formed a barrier to the escape of ether included in the interconnected gel structure within, since the odor of ether was apparent when the fibers were chopped up.

REFERENCES

1. Anderson, D. M. W., and Greenwood, C. T., J. Chem. Soc., p. 3016 (1955).
2. Archibald, A. R., Fleming, I. D., Liddle, A. M., Manners, D. J., Mercer, G. A., and Wright, A., J. Chem. Soc., p. 1183 (1961).
3. Bailey, J. M., and Whelan, W. J., J. Biol. Chem. 236, 969 (1961).
4. Baldwin, R. R., Bear, R. S., and Rundle, R. E., J. Am. Chem. Soc. 66, 111 (1944); McCready, R. M., and Hassid, W. Z., ibid. 65, 1154 (1943); Kerr, R. W., and Trubell, O. R., Paper Trade J. 117, 25 (1943); Bourne,

E. J., Haworth, W. N., Macey, A., and Peat, S., *J. Chem. Soc.*, p. 924 (1948).

5. Baldwin, R. R., Bear, R. S., and Rundle, R. E., *J. Am. Chem. Soc.* **66**, 111 (1944).
6. Bates, F. L., French, D., and Rundle, R. E., *J. Am. Chem. Soc.* **65**, 142 (1943).
7. Bear, R. S., *J. Am. Chem. Soc.* **64**, 1388 (1942).
8. Bear, R. S., *J. Am. Chem. Soc.* **66**, 2122 (1944).
9. Bear, R. S., and French, D., *J. Am. Chem. Soc.* **63**, 2298 (1941).
10. Beckmann, C. O., and Landis, Q., *J. Am. Chem. Soc.* **61**, 1495, 1504 (1939).
11. Bersohn, R., and Isenberg, I., *J. Chem. Phys.* **35**, 1640 (1961).
12. Coles, J. S., Doctoral Dissertation, Columbia University, New York, 1941.
13. Cramer, F., *Chem. Ber.* **84**, 851 (1951).
14. Cramer, F., *Chem. Ber.* **84**, 855 (1951).
15. Cramer, F., *Ann.* **579**, 17 (1953).
16. Cramer, F., *Chem. Ber.* **86**, 1576 (1953).
17. Cramer, F., *Chem. Ber.* **86**, 1582 (1953).
18. Cramer, F., *Angew. Chem.* **73**, 49 (1961).
19. Cramer, F., and Dietsche, W., *Chem. Ber.* **92**, 378 (1959).
20. Cramer, F., and Dietsche, W., *Chem. Ber.* **92**, 1739 (1959); *Chem. & Ind. (London)* p. 892 (1958).
21. Cramer, F., and Henglein, F. M., *Chem. Ber.* **90**, 2561 (1957).
22. Cramer, F., and Henglein, F. M., *Chem. Ber.* **90**, 2573 (1957).
23. Cramer, F., and Herbst, W., *Naturwissenschaften* **11**, 256 (1952).
24. Dube, H. A., Doctoral Dissertation, Iowa State College, Ames, 1947.
25. Dumbrow, B. A., and Beckmann, C. O., *J. Physik. Colloid Chem.* **51**, 107 (1947).
26. Dvonch, W., Yearian, H. J., and Whistler, R. L., *J. Am. Chem. Soc.* **72**, 1748 (1950).
27. Erlander, S. R., and French, D., *J. Polymer Sci.* **30**, 7 (1956); **32**, 291 (1958); Erlander, S. R., *ibid.* **37**, 91 (1959).
28. Everett, W. W., and Foster, J. F., *J. Am. Chem. Soc.* **81**, 3464 (1959).
29. Everett, W. W., and Foster, J. F., *J. Am. Chem. Soc.* **81**, 3459 (1959).
30. Foster, J. F., and Paschall, E. F., *J. Am. Chem. Soc.* **75**, 1181 (1953).
31. French, D., Doctoral Dissertation, Iowa State College, Ames, 1942.
32. French, D., *Advances in Carbohydrate Chem.* **12**, 189 (1957).
33. French, D., Levine, M. L., Pazur, J. H., and Norberg, E., *J. Am. Chem. Soc.* **71**, 353 (1949).
34. Gilbert, G. A., and Marriott, J. V. R., *Trans. Faraday Soc.* **44**, 84 (1948).
35. Greenwood, C. T., *Advances in Carbohydrate Chem.* **2**, 363 (1956); Jorgensen, B. B., and Jorgensen, O. B., *Acta Chem. Scand.* **14**, 2135 (1960).
36. Greenwood, C. T., and Rossotti, H., *J. Polymer Sci.* **27**, 481 (1958).
37. Griffin, H. L., Erlander, S. R., and Senti, F. R., *Abstr. Papers, Div. Carbohydrate Chem., 137th Meeting, Am. Chem. Soc., Cleveland, Ohio* p. 7D (1960).
38. Haworth, W. N., Peat, S., and Sagrott, P. E., *Nature* **157**, 19 (1946).
39. Hennrich, N., and Cramer, F., *Chem. & Ind. (London)* p. 1224 (1961).
40. Hermans, P. H., "Physics and Chemistry of Cellulose Fibers," p. 189. Elsevier, Amsterdam, 1949.

41. Hermans, P. H., and deLeeuw, A. J., *Kolloid-Z.* **82**, 58 (1938).
42. Higgenbotham, R. S., *Shirley Inst. Mem.* **23**, 171 (1944).
43. Holló, J., and Szejtlé, *Periodica Polytech.* **2**, 25 (1958).
44. Holló, J., Szejtlé, J., and Toth, J., *Stärke* **13**, 222 (1961).
45. Hsieh, Y. C., and Hsu, K. H., K'o Hsüeh T'ung Pao, p. 107 (1958).
46. James, W. J., and French, D., *Proc. Iowa Acad. Sci.* **58**, 197 (1952) ; James, W. J., French, D., and Rundle, R. E., *Acta Cryst.* **12**, 385 (1959).
47. Jansen, E. F., Waistbrot, S. W., and Rietz, E., *Ind. Eng. Chem., Anal. Ed.* **16**, 523 (1944) ; Jansen, E. F., MacDonnell, L. R., and Ward, W. H., *Arch. Biochem. Biophys.* **21**, 149 (1949) ; Percival, E. G. V., and Ross, A. G., *J. Chem. Soc.,* p. 717 (1950).
48. Kerr, R. W., "Chemistry and Industry of Starch," 2nd ed., p. 466. Academic Press, New York, 1950.
49. Kerr, R. W., and Severson, G. M., *J. Am. Chem. Soc.* **65**, 193 (1943).
50. Kuge, T., and Ono, S., *Bull. Chem. Soc. Japan* **33**, 1269 (1960).
51. Kuhn, H., *J. Chem. Phys.* **17**, 1198 (1949).
52. Lauer, K., and Ayer, J. E., *J. Polymer Sci.* **24**, 67 (1957).
53. Lautsch, W., Broser, W., Biedermann, W., and Gnichtel, H., *J. Polymer Sci.* **17**, 479 (1955).
54. Leach, H. W., Schoch, T. J., and Chessman, E. F., *Stärke* **13**, 200 (1961).
55. Manners, D. J., *Advances in Carbohydrate Chem.* **12**, 261 (1957).
56. Mikus, F. F., Hixon, R. M., and Rundle, R. E., *J. Am. Chem. Soc.* **68**, 1115 (1946).
57. Montgomery, E. M., and Senti, F. R., *J. Polymer Sci.* **28**, 1 (1958).
58. Mould, D. L., *Biochem. J.* **58**, 593 (1954).
59. Mulliken, R. S., *J. Am. Chem. Soc.* **72**, 600 (1950).
60. Murakami, H., *J. Chem. Phys.* **22**, 367 (1954).
61. Ono, S., Tsuchihashi, S., and Kuge, T., *J. Am. Chem. Soc.* **75**, 3601 (1953).
62. Ott, E., and Spurlin, H., "Cellulose and Cellulose Derivatives," Part II, 2nd ed., Wiley (Interscience), New York, 1954.
63. Pulley, A. O., and French, D., *Biochem. Biophys. Research Communs.* **5**, 11 (1961).
64. Rao, V. S. R., and Foster, J. F., *Abstr. Papers, Div. Carbohydrate Chem., 140th Meeting. Am. Chem. Soc., Chicago, Illinois,* p. 9D (1960).
65. Reeves, R. E., *J. Am. Chem. Soc.* **76**, 4595 (1954).
66. Reeves, R. E., *J. Am. Chem. Soc.* **72**, 1499 (1950).
67. Richter, G. A., Herdle, L. E., and Wahtera, W. E., *Ind. Eng. Chem.* **49**, 907 (1957).
68. Rossotti, H., *J. Polymer Sci.* **36**, 557 (1959).
69. Rundle, R. E., *J. Am. Chem. Soc.* **69**, 1769 (1947).
69a. Rundle, R. E., *J. Chem. Phys.* **15**, 880 (1947).
70. Rundle, R. E., and Edwards, F. C., *J. Am. Chem. Soc.* **65**, 2200 (1943).
71. Rundle, R. E., and French, D., *J. Am. Chem. Soc.* **65**, 558 (1943).
72. Rundle, R. E., and French, D., *J. Am. Chem. Soc.* **65**, 1707 (1943).
73. Schlamowitz, M., *J. Biol. Chem.* **190**, 519 (1951).
74. Schlenk, H., and Sand, D. M., *J. Am. Chem. Soc.* **83**, 2312 (1961).
75. Schlenk, H., Sand, D. M., and Tillotson, J. A., *J. Am. Chem. Soc.* **77**, 3587 (1955).

76. Schoch, T. J., *Cereal Chem.* **18**, 121 (1941); *J. Am. Chem. Soc.* **64**, 2957 (1942).
77. Schoch, T., and Williams, C., *J. Am. Chem. Soc.* **66**, 1232 (1944).
78. Senti, F. R., unpublished work.
79. Senti, F. R., and Babcock, G. E., *Abstr. Papers, Div. Carbohydrate Chem., 138th Meeting Am. Chem. Soc., New York* p. 16D (1960).
80. Senti, F. R., and Witnauer, L. P., *J. Am. Chem. Soc.* **68**, 2407 (1946); and unpublished work.
81. Senti, F. R., and Witnauer, L. P., *J. Am. Chem. Soc.* **70**, 1438 (1948).
82. Staudinger, H., *Angew. Chem.* **64**, 149 (1952).
83. Stein, R. S., and Rundle, R. E., *J. Chem. Phys.* **16**, 195 (1948).
84. Tauret, M. C., *Compt. rend. acad. sci.* **158**, 1353 (1914); **159**, 530 (1914).
85. Thoma, J. A., and French, D., *J. Phys. Chem.* **62**, 1603 (1958).
86. Thoma, J. A., and French, D., *J. Am. Chem. Soc.* **80**, 6142 (1958).
87. Thoma, J. A., and French, D., *J. Am. Chem. Soc.* **82**, 4144 (1960).
88. Thoma, J. A., and French, D., *J. Phys. Chem.* **65**, 1825 (1961).
89. Todd, A. R., *Chem. & Ind. (London)* p. 802 (1956).
90. West, C. D., *J. Chem. Phys.* **15**, 689 (1947).
91. Whistler, R., and Hilbert, G. E., *J. Am. Chem. Soc.* **67**, 1161 (1945).
92. Zaslow, B., and Miller, R. L., *J. Am. Chem. Soc.* **83**, 4378 (1961).

CHAPTER 10

L. A. K. Staveley

Inorganic Chemistry Laboratory,
Oxford University, England

Physics and Chemistry
of Inclusion Complexes

I. Introduction.. 606
II. Dielectric Properties... 608
  A. Hydroquinone Clathrates.. 608
  B. Urea Inclusion Complexes... 610
  C. Other Inclusion Complexes.. 615
III. Magnetic Susceptibility Studies... 616
  A. The Oxygen-Hydroquinone Clathrate...................................... 616
  B. The Nitric Oxide-Hydroquinone Clathrate................................. 619
IV. Spectroscopic Studies... 620
  A. Infrared Spectra... 620
  B. Nuclear Quadrupole Resonance Spectra.................................... 622
  C. Paramagnetic Resonance Studies... 624
  D. Nuclear Magnetic Resonance Studies...................................... 626
V. Thermodynamic Studies of the Movement of the Guest Molecules in
  Hydroquinone Clathrates.. 626
VI. Changes in the Chemical Behavior of Guest Molecules............... 629
  A. Inclusion Complexes Containing Iodine................................... 629
  B. Inclusion Complexes Containing Organic Molecules........................ 630
VII. The Stability and Decomposition of Inclusion Complexes............. 632
  References... 634

I. INTRODUCTION

Non-stoichiometric compounds in which the interaction between host and guest is relatively weak have been the subject of a number of interesting physicochemical studies primarily intended to throw light on the movement of the guest molecules and on the nature and degree of the host-guest interaction. These two matters are necessarily related. Thus if, for example, it is found that a guest molecule is unable to rotate freely, the energy barrier preventing its rotation will probably be derived primarily from its interaction with the host. Of particular importance are those systems in which any one guest molecule is virtually isolated from any other, as exemplified by the β-hydroquinone clathrates. In the adducts of urea with straight-chain aliphatic compounds, each molecule of the latter is likewise essentially independent of any other guest molecule, apart from the no doubt minor interaction between the ends of the chains of adjacent molecules lying in the same channel. In systems such as these, any one guest molecule has an environment which is usually of relatively high symmetry, which is not much altered by temperature changes, and which is almost unaffected by any variation in the movement of the guest molecule itself. It is this last factor which gives these systems their particular physicochemical interest. What complicates the study of molecular movement and behavior in the liquid and solid forms of a pure compound is that one is dealing with a cooperative phenomenon, in that the movement of any one molecule affects, and is affected by, the movement of its neighbors. Clearly the situation in a solid such as a β-hydroquinone clathrate is altogether simpler. Since the guest molecules here are enclosed in almost spherical cages of almost fixed dimensions, these systems in fact provide examples in an idealized form of the so-called 'cell model' which has played such an important part in the development of molecular theories of solids, pure liquids, and solutions.

The existence of inclusion complexes can also make it possible to study down to much lower temperatures than would otherwise be the case, certain properties of individual molecules when almost isolated from each other. Thus, by using the oxygen and nitric oxide β-hydroquinone clathrates, the magnetic susceptibilities of these diatomic molecules can be investigated down to the lowest attainable temperatures, which cannot of course be done with the pure substances themselves owing to intermolecular magnetic coupling.

Since we are concerned only with those systems in which the host-guest interaction is relatively weak, the inclusion of the guest molecules cannot be expected to have striking effects on their chemical properties. Nevertheless, these effects can be large enough to be interesting. They may, for example, take the form of significant changes in oxidation-reduction potential, or in the susceptibility of the guest molecule to oxidation or photolysis.

Finally, we shall briefly review the evidence bearing on the thermal stability of non-stoichiometric compounds with weak host-guest interaction. This evidence is at present admittedly rather fragmentary.

II. DIELECTRIC PROPERTIES

A. Hydroquinone Clathrates

The first dielectric studies of inclusion compounds seem to be those carried out by Dryden (11) and by Meakins (24) on the hydroquinone clathrates and urea inclusion compounds respectively. Dryden measured the dielectric constant ϵ' at low frequencies (50 kc/sec) of the hydroquinone clathrates of H_2S, HCN, SO_2, CH_3OH, CH_3CN, and C_2H_2 (the last being studied to permit comparison with a clathrate containing a nonpolar molecule). The values obtained for ϵ' were as follows (μ being the dipole moment of the trapped molecule): acetylene, 3.2 ($\mu = 0$); hydrogen sulfide, 3.85 ($\mu = 1.1$); methanol, 5.0 ($\mu = 1.66$); sulfur dioxide, 4.4 ($\mu = 1.7$); hydrogen cyanide, 9.2 ($\mu = 2.6$–3.0); methyl cyanide, 3.55 ($\mu = 3.4$). The increase in the dielectric constant is roughly proportional to μ^2, except for the methyl cyanide clathrate where the dielectric constant is relatively low in spite of the high dipole moment of CH_3CN. The reason for this will appear in due course.

The measurements of the dielectric loss factor made by Dryden on the methanol and methyl cyanide clathrates are particularly illuminating. It will be recalled that if an alternating field is applied to a dielectric at frequencies low enough for polar molecules within it to keep pace with the variations in field, the displacement current in the dielectric is exactly 90° out of phase with the voltage and so has no current component in step with it. But at higher frequencies at which the rotation of the molecules lags behind the voltage oscillations, the current has a component in step with the voltage and consequently energy is dissipated in the medium by Joule heating. The magnitude of this dielectric loss is expressed by the loss factor ϵ''. The variation of ϵ'' with frequency f can often be expressed by the Debye equation

$$\epsilon'' = \frac{2\pi f \tau(\epsilon_0 - \epsilon_\infty)}{1 + (2\pi f \tau)^2}, \tag{1}$$

where ϵ_0 is the value of the static dielectric constant (i.e., its value when $f = 0$), ϵ_∞ the limiting value approached on the high frequency side of the dispersion region, and τ a relaxation time characteristic of the medium, such that if the medium is polarized in a field which is suddenly removed at the time $t = 0$, the subsequent decrease of polarization P with time t is given by the equation $P = P_0 e^{-t/\tau}$. If Eq. (1) adequately represents the observed dependence of ϵ'' on f (as it does for the methanol and methyl cyanide-hydroquinone clathrates) it means that there is a single relaxation time for any one system, and this in turn implies that each polar molecule has effectively the same environment and that the rotation of each molecule is hindered by one and the same energy barrier. It is readily shown that the curve of ϵ'' against f will pass through a maximum at a frequency f_{max} such that $2\pi f_{max}\tau = 1$, and that $\epsilon_{max}'' = \frac{1}{2}(\epsilon_0 - \epsilon_\infty)$. Thus from the dependence of dielectric loss factors on frequency the corresponding values of the relaxation time τ can be obtained. τ decreases exponentially with temperature according to the equation $\tau = Ae^{E/RT}$, where E is the height of the energy barrier opposing rotation of the polar molecule. From measurements of ϵ'' made on polycrystalline samples of the hydroquinone-methanol clathrate, Dryden obtained for E a value of 2.3 kcal/mole, which is much lower than the activation energy usually associated with the rotation of a polar molecule in a solid.

It had already appeared from the crystallographic work of Palin and Powell (29) that although the C—O bonds of the methanol molecules are on the average directed along the c axis, there is considerable movement on the part of the methanol molecule in its cavity. Measurements of the dielectric constant of single crystals of the methanol clathrate in fact gave the same results both perpendicular and parallel to the c axis.

Similar measurements of the dielectric loss and dielectric constant of the methyl cyanide clathrate gave strikingly different results. Whereas for the methanol clathrate ϵ'' reaches its maximum at room temperature

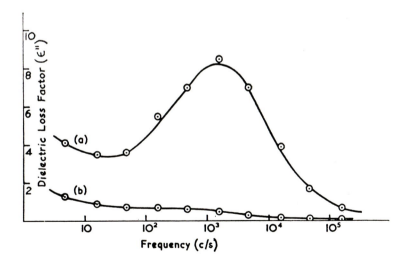

Fig. 1. Dielectric loss of a single crystal of the β-hydroquinone-methyl cyanide clathrate. (a) Section cut perpendicular to the c axis, i.e., measured with field parallel to the c axis; (b) Section cut parallel to the c axis (11).

at a frequency of $\sim 10^{11}$ cycles/sec, for the methyl cyanide system the corresponding frequency is only $\sim 3 \times 10^3$ cycles/sec, so that the restriction on the orientational freedom of the methyl cyanide molecules is altogether greater. This is why the dielectric constant of this particular clathrate at 50 kc/sec is comparatively low. From the temperature dependence of the relaxation time the activation energy of the reorientation process was found to be about 18 kcal/mole. This relatively high figure is not surprising since the inclusion of methyl cyanide in the hydroquinone lattice is known definitely to distort it, making the cavities ellipsoidal by elongating them in the c direction. Studies of the dielectric loss on single crystals showed that dielectric absorption only occurs when the field is parallel to the c axis (Fig. 1). Thus reorientation takes place between two equilibrium positions in which the C–C–N axes of the molecules in the holes lie on the c axis of the crystal.

B. Urea Inclusion Complexes

Meakins (24) has carried out a similar experimental study of the dielectric properties of the urea inclusion complexes formed from the following long-chain substances: 9-heptadecanone; 16-hentriacontanone; 18-pentatriacontanone; methyl palmitate; cetyl acetate; didodecyl ether; 12-bromotricosane; 16-bromohentriacontane; n-octadecyl bromide; and 1,10-dibromodecane. With all of these adducts there was pronounced dielectric absorption at microwave frequencies, the absorption maxima at room temperature occurring at frequencies between $\sim 10^9$ and 3×10^{11} cycles/sec. No dielectric absorption was obtained, however, with the adduct derived from the nonpolar hydrocarbon n-docosane, $CH_3—(CH_2)_{20}—CH_3$, so that the dielectric loss for the inclusion compounds with polar molecules must be due to dipolar reorientation. The high frequencies at which this loss occurs show that this reorientation is a relatively facile process. It is of particular interest that dielectric absorption is displayed by the 1,10-dibromodecane adduct, since it is known (35) from the x-ray examination of this solid that the occluded molecules are fully extended in the tunnels in the urea lattice, so that the terminal dipoles are opposed to each other and the overall dipole moment is zero. The occurrence of dielectric absorption therefore means that the C—Br dipoles can rotate independently of the intervening hydrocarbon chain. It also appears that the polar groups in the three ketones in the above list can also rotate in the urea lattice without the molecule rotating as a whole, since f_{max} proved to be virtually the same for all three adducts in spite of the considerable variation in length of the guest molecules. The most interesting feature of Meakins's results, however, is that the dielectric absorption occurs over rather a wide range of frequencies, implying that there is more than one relaxation time. This was confirmed by studying the dielectric loss for some of the adducts over a range of temperature. The results obtained for one of these, the urea adduct with 16-hentriacontanone, CH_3—$(CH_2)_{14}$—CO—$(CH_2)_{14}$—CH_3, are shown in Fig. 2, in which the composite character of

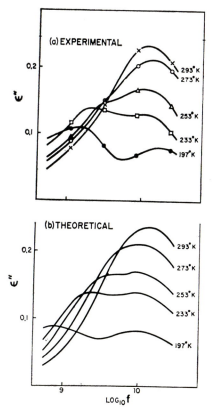

FIG. 2. Comparison of the experimental and theoretical dielectric loss curves for 16-hentriacontanone at various temperatures. (*a*) Experimental curves [Meakins (*24*)]. (*b*) Calculated curves [Lauritzen (*21*)].

the curve of loss against frequency is obvious. By analyzing the curve for 12-bromotriacosane, CH_3—$(CH_2)_{10}$—$CHBr$—$(CH_2)_{10}$—CH_3, Meakins concluded that the overall curve is composed of three simple Debye curves and that three separate relaxation mechanisms are involved. He estimated the activation energy associated with the lower frequency part of the absorption for several adducts from the temperature dependence of f_{max} and obtained values ranging from 1.0 to 2.3 kcal/mole.

More recently, Lauritzen (*21*) has carried out a detailed analysis of Meakins's dielectric results for the 12-bromotricosane and 16-hentria-contanone adducts. This appears to be the first attempt to relate quanti-tatively the crystalline field within a solid to its dielectric properties (namely the static dielectric constant and the dielectric loss), and it there-fore provides an elegant demonstration of the value which inclusion com-plexes can have in testing and developing physicochemical theories. For what makes Lauritzen's analysis possible is that (*a*) the polar molecule in the urea lattice is in a known, symmetrical environment which is virtually unaffected by changes of orientation of the dipoles, and that (*b*) the inter-action between different polar molecules is negligible. It will be recalled that the long-chain molecules lie in channels which are roughly hexagonal

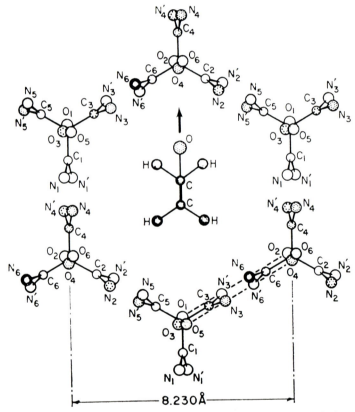

Fig. 3. Crystal structure of the urea lattice with an included long-chain ketone mole-cule, viewed along the negative *z* axis. Carbon, oxygen, and nitrogen atoms with the same indices belong to the same urea molecule (*21*).

in cross-section. Figure 3 shows the environment of an included ketone molecule viewed along the z axis along which the long-chain molecule lies. If this molecule is rotated in a plane normal to the z axis it would be expected that it would pass through six positions approximately 60° apart for which the potential energy would be a minimum. These minima determine the possible orientational sites. To investigate the potential energy relationships more fully, Lauritzen assumed either that the potential energy $V(r)$ of a pair of atoms at a distance r (one atom being in the guest molecule and the other in the urea lattice), can be represented by the well-known Lennard-Jones (12–6) potential as

$$V(r) = C[\tfrac{1}{2}(r_0/r)^{12} - (r_0/r)^6] \tag{2}$$

or alternatively that $V(r)$ is proportional to the overlap of the van der Waals spheres associated with the two atoms. On either assumption, the potential energy of the polar group in 16-hentriacontanone proves to pass through a minimum at each of the sites numbered 1 to 6 in Fig. 4. The energy barriers between these positions of minimum potential energy arise chiefly from the electronic overlap on the close approach of the polar group to a nitrogen atom in the urea lattice; purely electrostatic interaction between the polar group and the urea molecules is small.

The dielectric properties are of course intimately connected with the rate of passage of the polar group from one site to another. Lauritzen assumed that the probability of reorientation between nonadjacent sites

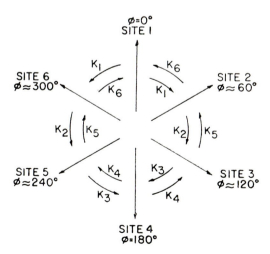

FIG. 4. Possible orientational sites for the C=O bond of a long-chain ketone molecule in the urea inclusion complex; cf. Fig. 3, (21).

is negligible (the "single-jump hypothesis"). However, as it appeared from the potential energy considerations that site 4 (Fig. 4) is a very shallow site—a result confirmed by the application of the theory to the experimental data, which also showed that site 4 is in any case a 'high' site and therefore only sparsely occupied (cf. Fig. 6)—it was disregarded, and the problem treated as one of *five* sites, which would then, of course, give rise to only *four* relaxation modes. The values of k_1, k_2, etc. (Fig. 4), which are the probabilities of reorientation between adjacent sites, are then determined by the energy barriers separating these sites. Thus, if W_1 is the barrier which must be surmounted for the polar group to proceed from site 1 to site 2, then $k_1 = Ae^{-W_1/kT}$. If N_1, N_2, etc. are the occupation numbers of each site, a set of differential equations can then be written down for the change of the occupation numbers with time. Thus, for N_1,

$$dN_1/dt = -2k_1N_1 + k_6(N_2 + N_6) \qquad (3)$$

By applying to these equations a procedure developed by Hoffman *et al.* (*16, 17, 18*) the four molecular relaxation times τ_1, τ_2, etc. can be expressed in terms of the k_1, k_2, etc. The corresponding polarizabilities can be evaluated in terms of the appropriate τ and k values. The dielectric loss can then be derived from the molecular relaxation times and the static dielectric constant from the polarizabilities. (In dealing with the static dielectric constant it is important that the interaction between the dipoles of the long-chain molecules in the solid is very small.)

Of the two urea addition compounds considered by Lauritzen, only for

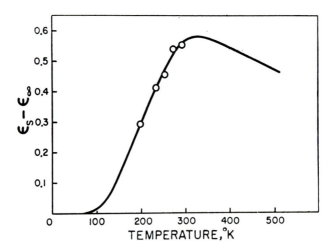

FIG. 5. Calculated temperature dependence of the static dielectric constant of 16-hentriacontanone in urea (*21*). The circles represent Meakins's experimental points (*24*).

the 16-hentriacontanone adduct were dielectric loss data available at more than one temperature. To fit these data at all temperatures it was necessary to assume that there is some variation in the energy barriers (and to a lesser extent in the site energies) with temperature. This is not unreasonable in view of the change of the lattice dimensions with temperature, though admittedly allowance for the variation has to be made on a rather arbitrary basis. Lauritzen's calculated curves of the dielectric loss as a function of frequency are compared with Meakins's experimental results in Fig. 2. The results for the static dielectric constant are shown in Fig. 5. Finally, the potential energy of the polar group in the guest ketone molecule as a function of its orientation, as derived from the experimental

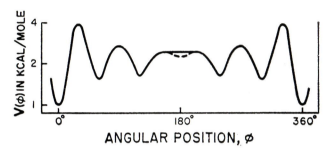

FIG. 6. The potential energy $V(\phi)$ of the polar group of 16-hentriacontanone in urea as a function of its angular position ϕ in the $z=0$ plane, as deduced from the experimental dielectric data at 293°K (*21*).

dielectric results, is given in Fig. 6. For the 12-bromotricosane adduct the loss curve at 20°C was fitted by four relaxation times (the fit being rather better than that obtained by Meakins with three modes of relaxation), and predictions were made of the shape of the curves at other temperatures. As already mentioned, the barrier heights for the reorientation of the polar substituent on the long-chain molecules in the urea lattice are not large, being about the same as those found for dipole reorientation for similar molecules in the liquid state, and smaller by a factor of ten or so than the barriers of 10–30 kcal/mole which restrict reorientation in the pure crystalline long-chain compounds.

C. Other Inclusion Complexes

Meakins (*25*) has made a preliminary study of some clathrates of Dianin's compound (4-*p*-hydroxylphenyl-2,2,4-trimethylchroman, Chapter 7, Secs. II,3, and III,C) and also of biuret hydrate. Dielectric constant measurements were made at about 50 kc/sec on Dianin clathrates with methanol, nitromethane, acetone, and o-dichlorobenzene as the guest, and showed that the apparent dipole moments of the guest molecules are effectively the same as the moments of these molecules when orientationally free. Measurements at higher frequencies gave evidence of dielectric loss which would probably reach a maximum in the microwave region.

Biuret hydrate is an interesting inclusion complex the structure of which has recently been determined by Hughes et al. (19). The water molecules form zigzag chains in tunnels in the biuret lattice. They are bound to each other by hydrogen bonds, and also form much weaker hydrogen bonds with oxygen atoms in the walls of the tunnel. Meakins found that this hydrate shows pronounced dielectric absorption with a rather broad peak which becomes wider on cooling. The derived value for the activation energy of the reorientation process is between 4 and 5 kcal/mole. This is about the same as the value for liquid water and presumably represents the rupture of one hydrogen bond.

III. MAGNETIC SUSCEPTIBILITY STUDIES

A. The Oxygen–Hydroquinone Clathrate

Two investigations of the temperature dependence of the magnetic susceptibility of oxygen in the β-hydroquinone clathrate have been carried out. Cooke et al. (5) made measurements from 1 to 20°K, and Meyer et al. (27) from 0.25° to 4°K. The results of these investigations, which were originally undertaken to test predictions about the magnetic behavior of effectively free oxygen molecules at low temperatures, have in fact given interesting information about the restriction on the rotation of the oxygen molecules in the β-hydroquinone lattice.

The electronic ground state of the oxygen molecule is $^3\Sigma$, and it would be expected that from about 10°K upwards the paramagnetic susceptibility χ of free oxygen molecules would closely obey Curie's law, ($\chi \propto 1/T$). At low temperatures where quantization of molecular rotation becomes important departures from Curie's law are to be expected. Measurements cannot be made on the gas below about 70°K, but the β-hydroquinone-oxygen clathrate offers the possibility of studying oxygen molecules down to very low temperatures under conditions where the magnetic interaction of these molecules and the effect of the immediate environment of an oxygen molecule on its magnetic properties are both very small. Cooke et al. determined the susceptibility of a clathrate with about 60% of the holes filled by measuring the change of mutual inductance of a pair of coils round the cryostat containing the specimen as the temperature of the

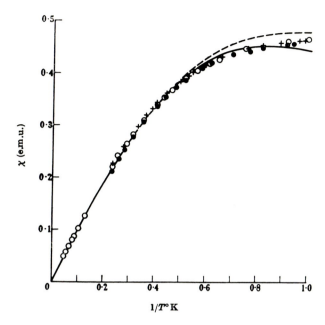

FIG. 7. The molar susceptibility of oxygen in the β-hydroquinone clathrate as a function of temperature. The circles show the values obtained with normal oxygen, the crosses those obtained with oxygen enriched to 11% in $O^{16}O^{18}$. Full line, calculated susceptibility of an ideal gas of normal oxygen. Broken line, calculated susceptibility of an ideal gas containing 11% of $O^{16}O^{18}$ molecules (5).

latter was varied, the apparatus being calibrated by experiments on substances of known magnetic properties. Their results (Fig. 7) show that Curie's law is in fact obeyed down to 10°K. Between 2° and 10°K, the susceptibility agrees with that calculated for freely rotating oxygen molecules taking into account the available energy levels. But below 2°K this agreement ceases. To investigate whether the behavior at very low temperatures is due to some suppression of the rotational freedom of the oxygen molecules, measurements were also made on a sample of the oxygen clathrate enriched to the extent of about 11% in $O^{16}O^{18}$. Since the O^{16} nucleus has no spin, the $O^{16}O^{16}$ molecules which almost completely make up normal oxygen are limited to odd values of the rotational quantum numbers K, whereas for the $O^{16}O^{18}$ molecules all values of K are possible. A particular difference between the two isotopic species is that for $O^{16}O^{16}$ molecules the coupling between the rotation and the spin is such that in the lowest possible energy level ($K = 1$) the molecule is diamagnetic, whereas the ground state of the $O^{16}O^{18}$ molecule ($K = 0$) is paramagnetic. In consequence of this, χ for freely rotating $O^{16}O^{16}$ molecules should become temperature-independent at very low temperatures, while χ for $O^{16}O^{18}$ should conform to Curie's law. For freely rotating molecules, therefore, there should be a demonstrable difference at very low temperatures in the relation between susceptibility and temperature for the normal oxygen clathrate on the one hand and that enriched in the O^{18} isotope on the other. In fact, as may be seen from Fig. 7, this difference was not observed.

The matter was carried further by Meyer *et al.* (*27*) on the experimental side by extending the susceptibility measurements to lower temperatures, and on the theoretical side by a quantitative treatment of the restriction of the rotation of the oxygen molecules in the cavities. In making the measurements, the clathrate sample was joined by silver ribbons to a sample of chromium methyl ammonium alum situated vertically above it, the clathrate and the paramagnetic salt each lying within coils (situated outside the cryostat) with which susceptibility measurements could be made. The alum was cooled by adiabatic demagnetization to 0.25°K, whereupon the clathrate was cooled by conduction by the silver ribbons. The susceptibilities of both clathrate and salt were then measured, that of the salt being used to give the temperature of the measurements. The

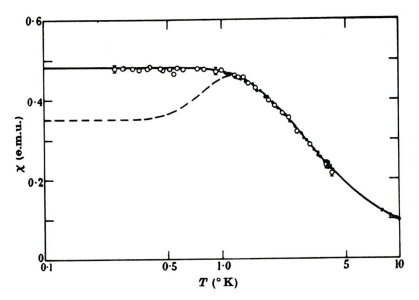

Fig. 8. Comparison of the theoretical and experimental values of the susceptibility of oxygen in the β-hydroquinone clathrate at low temperatures (*27*). Full circles, Cooke *et al.* (*5*); open circles, Meyer *et al.* (*27*). Full line, calculated curve for $D/k = 4.15°K$ (corresponding to a potential barrier of 128 cal/mole); broken line, calculated susceptibility of free $O^{16}O^{16}$.

samples were then heated and the measurements repeated at suitable temperature intervals. The results are shown in Fig. 8.

If the oxygen molecules were rigidly fixed in the lattice, the susceptibility χ would be given by the following equation

$$\chi = \frac{A}{T} \frac{\left[e^{-x} + (2/x)(1 - e^{-x}) \right]}{1 + 2e^{-x}} \tag{4}$$

where A is a known coefficient and $x = D/kT$. The terms in D arise from the coupling of the spin to the axis of the oxygen molecule. D is virtually identical with the energy separation of the outlying spin components of the free molecule in its ground state ($K = 1$). While Eq. (4) leads to correct values of the free-spin susceptibility at high temperatures, it does not, of course, fit the data at very low temperatures since the oxygen molecules are not rigidly bound in the lattice. The effect, however, of a partial hindrance to free rotation is to reduce the effective value of D to some value D', and with $D' = 0.73D = 4.15k$ there would be agreement between the experimental values of χ and those derived from Eq. (4) with D' replacing D. The hindrance to free rotation was expressed quantitatively by writing for the potential energy V of an oxygen molecule

$$V = V_0(1 - \cos 2\theta), \tag{5}$$

where θ is the angle between the axis of the oxygen molecule and that of minimum energy. Equation (5) is similar to that commonly used in treating the problem of restricted rotation about single bonds in molecules. The relation between D', D, and θ is

$$D' = D(\tfrac{3}{2}\langle \cos^2 \theta \rangle_{Av} - \tfrac{1}{2}) \tag{6}$$

If the Eq. (5) for V is inserted in the Schrödinger equation, then depending on the value of V_0 the energy values must lie somewhere between the extremes of those for a free rotator and those for a two-dimensional harmonic oscillator. It proves that the reduction of D to $0.73D$ needed to fit the susceptibility data is achieved if $V_0/k = 32°$ (see Fig. 8). (The lowest energy levels then approximate closely to those of the harmonic oscillator.) Thus the height of the barrier ($2V_0$) opposing rotation of the oxygen molecule in its cavity is 128 cal/mole. For a molecule in a crystalline lattice this barrier is undoubtedly exceptionally small.

B. The Nitric Oxide–Hydroquinone Clathrate

Detailed experimental and theoretical studies have also been made of the magnetic susceptibility of nitric oxide in its β-hydroquinone clathrate. The susceptibility measurements were more difficult to make than those on the oxygen clathrate, since the nitric oxide clathrate is rather unstable, and if allowed to decompose in the presence of air it produces nitrogen dioxide which then attacks the lattice. Moreover, above 100°K the diamagnetic susceptibility of the clathrate and its container is comparable with the paramagnetic susceptibility of the nitric oxide, which reduces the accuracy of the measurements of the latter quantity. The theoretical analysis of the results for nitric oxide is altogether less simple than for the oxygen clathrate, since the nitric oxide molecule is unsymmetrical and has a spin multiplet separation of the same order of magnitude as the potential barrier to rotation.

The first susceptibility measurements were made down to 10°K by Cooke and Duffus (6), and showed that below about 200°K the susceptibility becomes progressively greater than that predicted by Van Vleck (38) for the free gas. Meyer (26) has recently remeasured the susceptibility from 1°K to 300°K, using the Gouy method above 20°K and a mutual inductance bridge below this temperature. His values below 100°K are lower than those of Cooke and Duffus, and instead of increasing continuously with falling temperature tend to a limiting value, becoming constant from 20°K downwards within the experimental error of about 5%. Meyer considers that the difference in the two sets of results may perhaps have been due to paramagnetic impurities in the sample used by Cooke and Duffus.

Van Vleck (38) has discussed the magnetic properties of the nitric oxide clathrate using the hindered rotation model described above (Section III A). There is difficulty in explaining why the susceptibility is almost temperature-independent below about 20°K, since for most crystalline potentials the susceptibility should contain a term in $1/T$ arising from the Kramers doublet. Use of a crystalline potential having the trigonal symmetry consistent with the crystallographic symmetry of the hydroquinone clathrate can be made to account for the observed susceptibility increase over that of the free gas. But it would then be expected that the term in $1/T$ would amount to about 6% of the main term at 1°K, unless the spin-lattice relaxation time happens to be so long that this term could not be detected at the frequencies used in Meyer's experiments.

IV. SPECTROSCOPIC STUDIES

A. Infrared Spectra

The first study of this kind on the hydroquinone clathrates was carried out by Hexter and Goldfarb (15) in the hope that the presence or absence of rotational fine structure in those regions of the spectra attributable to the molecules in the cavities would show whether or not these molecules were rotating. In the absence of any fine structure some information on the hindrance to molecular rotation might be obtained from the breadth of the vibration bands. They examined samples of the hydrogen chloride, hydrogen sulfide, carbon dioxide, and sulfur dioxide clathrates suspended in potassium bromide pellets. The spectra obtained with the hydrogen chloride and hydrogen sulfide clathrates, while confirming that the hydroquinone lattice is definitely different from that of α-hydroquinone, were disappointing in that it was not possible to recognize bands due to the hydrogen chloride or hydrogen sulfide molecules themselves. (These molecules do not absorb strongly in the infrared and their fundamentals tend to overlap the strong hydroquinone bands.) More informative results, however, were obtained with the sulfur dioxide clathrate and especially with that containing carbon dioxide, the absorption in the spectrum of the latter in the region of 2350 cm^{-1} and between 600 and 700 cm^{-1} being due respectively to the parallel and perpendicular bands of the guest molecule. The parallel band of carbon dioxide gas at room temperature consists of P and R branches but has no Q branch. The corresponding band for the clathrate is rather broad, and owing to the absence of maxima which might be associated with P and R branches it was instead assigned as the Q branch, which is no longer forbidden for a restricted rotator. The conclusion that the carbon dioxide molecules in the holes do not rotate freely is not surprising in view of the length of the linear carbon dioxide molecule in relation to the diameter of the hole. It would in fact be expected that there would be some distortion of the holes and hence of the crystal structure, and indeed the spectra of both the sulfur dioxide and carbon dioxide clathrates showed that the host lattices in these solids are not identical with that in the clathrate containing the smaller hydrogen chloride molecule.

McKean (23) has made a careful examination of the infrared spectrum of the carbon monoxide clathrate (dispersed in a potassium bromide pellet). Observations were made over a considerable range of temperature and the spectra of krypton and nitrogen clathrates were used for comparison. The carbon monoxide molecules give rise to a main peak in the absorption spectrum at about 2135 cm^{-1} with a satellite peak on either side of it. At room temperature the separation of the two satellite peaks from each other is about 86 cm^{-1}. The peaks become broader and less pronounced with rising temperature, so much so that at about 150°C they have almost disappeared. (This disappearance is not, however, due to thermal decomposition of the clathrate since the room temperature spectrum could be obtained again on cooling the sample.) The central peak is almost certainly a Q branch, showing that the carbon monoxide molecules are unable to rotate freely. The side bands at lower temperatures can probably be attributed to combination with the frequencies with which the guest molecules 'rattle' and undergo torsional oscillations within their cells. When the details of the spectrum are considered, however, it becomes evident that even in a system such as this where there is virtually no interaction between the carbon monoxide molecules themselves and where each has the same environment, there are still a number of factors which may affect that part of the spectrum due to the guest molecules. A complete analysis of these factors will probably only be possible if use is made of all the information obtainable from a variety of experimental techniques.

An investigation of the infrared spectrum of benzene monoammino–nickel cyanide, $Ni(CN)_2 \cdot NH_3 \cdot C_6H_6$, by Aynsley et al. (1) has shown that the absorption due to the benzene molecules differs notably from that for crystalline benzene, although the benzene molecules in the two solids have the same site symmetry. Thus, in the clathrate there is a marked reduction in the intensity of the C–H stretching modes, while bands appear at 1573 and 1166 cm^{-1} corresponding to vibrations at 1595 and 1178 cm^{-1} which, while active in the Raman spectrum of the vapor, are absent from the infrared spectrum of crystalline benzene.

B. Nuclear Quadrupole Resonance Spectra

Meyer and Scott (28) have made a study of the pure quadrupole resonance of nitrogen in the β-hydroquinone clathrate which gave interesting information about the movement of the nitrogen molecules in the cavities and about the interaction of these molecules with the lattice.

If an atomic nucleus has a spin I which exceeds $\frac{1}{2}$, then the distribution of the positive charge on the nucleus is nonspherical and the nucleus possesses a quadrupole moment. An example is the nucleus of N^{14}, for which $I = 1$. In a homogeneous electric field such a nucleus will have no tendency to adopt any particular orientation, but in an *inhomogeneous* field the situation is different since the energy of the nucleus now depends on the orientation of the quadrupole with respect to the electric field. The possible orientations will be quantized and will in general correspond to different energy states. Transitions between these states give rise to a pure quadrupole resonance spectrum in the radiofrequency region. The energy of interaction of the nuclear quadrupole with the surrounding field is proportional to eQq, where e is the charge on the proton, Q is the nuclear quadrupole moment, and q is the field gradient, $\partial^2 V / \partial x^2$, V being the potential at the nucleus due to the charges outside it while x refers to some fixed axis. In a spherically symmetrical field q is zero and no pure quadrupole spectrum will be observed. In a molecule such as N_2^{14}, the field gradient at any one nucleus is determined by the disposition of the other charges in the molecule, notably by the p electrons. In the liquid and gaseous states, owing to the rapid and random molecular movement, the value of q at the nucleus changes rapidly and its average is zero. In the solid at sufficiently low temperatures, however, the molecules must have more or less fixed orientations, and the field gradient at a nucleus will no longer have an average value of zero. Solid nitrogen at 4.2°K does in fact give rise to a single pure quadrupole resonance line at a frequency of 3.5 Mc/sec. The experimental technique with a solid consists essentially of supplying radiofrequency power to a sample of the solid which forms one arm of a bridge circuit. The frequency of the power supplied is varied and when the solid absorbs radiofrequency energy the bridge becomes unbalanced.

Meyer and Scott examined the pure quadrupole resonance spectrum of N_2^{14} in the β-hydroquinone clathrate from $\sim 1.5°$ to $\sim 25°$K, using samples in which the proportion of the holes filled ranged from 0.2 to 0.8. Here the field gradient at a nucleus is still mainly due to the nitrogen molecule itself, and indeed the pure quadrupole resonance was again observed at about 3.6 Mc/sec. But the spectrum now consists not of just one line, but of at least seven lines with frequencies varying from 3580.2 ± 0.2 to 3594.0 ± 0.3 kc/sec. These frequencies are independent of the proportion of the holes filled. The complexity of the resonance spectrum is believed to arise from slight variations in the electric field from one hole to another. It will be recalled that the x-ray studies of β-hydroquinone clathrates have shown that the inclusion in the cavities of sufficiently large molecules (such as sulfur dioxide or acetonitrile) causes the holes to be distorted, and it is therefore plausible that some slight distortion is produced by diatomic molecules even though it is too small to be detected by x-ray analysis. Any one cavity has two holes as nearest neighbors at a distance of 5.6 Å, six at a distance of 9.5 Å, and six at 10.1 Å. If the inclusion of a nitrogen molecule in a hole slightly distorts the surrounding lattice, it is reasonable to suppose that the electrical field gradient acting on a nucleus in any one particular nitrogen molecule can take various values depending on which of the neighboring cavities happen to be filled. The interesting observation was made that after the clathrate had been stored at room temperature for some time or annealed at 65°C, the relative intensities of the resonance lines (but not the frequencies) changed considerably. This alteration may arise from the relieving of strains by the movement of nitrogen molecules, the ability of which to diffuse was indicated by the partial loss of nitrogen from the clathrate during the annealing process.

From a study of the Zeeman splitting, briefly described below, Meyer and Scott concluded that the field gradient tensor is parallel to the crystal axis of the clathrate, so that the nitrogen molecules rock about this axis with a frequency ν_0. As the temperature rises, the amplitude of this oscillation increases, and since such movement tends to reduce the inhomogeneity of the field there will be a decrease in the field gradient q and hence in the quadrupole resonance frequency $\nu(T)$. To the observed temperature dependence of the resonance frequency between 1.5° and 25°K Meyer and Scott applied the theoretical relation between $\nu(T)$, ν_0 and T derived by Bayer (3), and so estimated ν_0, obtaining a value of 1.55×10^{12} sec^{-1}.

In order to examine the relation between the field gradient symmetry axis and the crystalline axis, the Zeeman splitting of the quadrupole lines at 1.5°K was measured by imposing on the crystals a d-c magnetic field H at an angle of θ to the crystalline axis. The quadrupole resonance should then be split by an amount $\Delta\nu = 2\mu H \cos \theta / h$, where $\mu = 0.4036$ nuclear magnetons. In agreement with this equation, $\Delta\nu$ was in fact found to vary linearly with $\cos \theta$ and to have its maximum value for $\theta = 0°$ (within experimental error), thus showing that the field gradient tensor has axial symmetry and lies in the same direction as the crystalline axis of the clathrate.

C. Paramagnetic Resonance Studies

Foner et al. (12) have investigated the paramagnetic resonance of oxygen in the β-hydroquinone clathrate at low temperatures. Besides confirming the conclusion reached from the magnetic susceptibility studies (Section III A) about the barrier height hindering molecular rotation, their results also give some information on the interaction of molecules in different cavities. It will be recalled that the ground level of the oxygen molecule in the clathrate is split by the coupling of the spin with the molecular axis. The magnitude of this splitting ($\sim 4°K$) is such that to produce a paramagnetic absorption spectrum it is necessary to use relatively high fields and high frequencies. Foner et al. worked with single crystals so that they could study the effect of the orientation of the crystal with respect to the direction of the applied field. Observations were made at $\sim 1.5°K$ and 4.2°K using radiation of wavelength 4 mm and 8 mm and both d-c and pulsed magnetic fields. The oxygen clathrate at 4.2°K gave a resonance spectrum which could be successfully interpreted on the model used to account for the magnetic susceptibility, so confirming the belief that the potential energy of the oxygen molecule is a minimum when its molecular axis coincides with the c axis of the lattice. The resonance line for samples with about 40% of the holes filled is unusually broad ($\sim 2\text{kG}$). The value of the parameter D' (see Section III A) derived from the position of the center of the line is 4.43°K, in reasonable agreement with the figure of 4.15°K required to fit the susceptibility results. Improved resolution was obtained by reducing the temperature and decreasing the oxygen concentration. Owing to the difficulty of getting suitable single crystals of the oxygen clathrate with only a small proportion of the holes filled, crystals were therefore prepared in which more than half of the holes were occupied by nitrogen molecules and less than 5% by oxygen molecules. These crystals were studied at ~ 1.6°K, and gave absorption spectra consisting of three well-resolved lines, corresponding to values of D' of 4.36, 4.48, and 4.58°K. The most striking feature of the spectra was that the relative intensities of the components were markedly affected by the nitrogen content of the clathrate.

This last fact can be interpreted as arising from the interaction of an oxygen molecule with nitrogen molecules in nearby cavities. In the β-hydroquinone clathrate, any one cavity has two nearest neighbors at a distance of 5.6 Å along the c axis. The next six cavities are much further away (9.5 Å). In a clathrate which is dilute in oxygen and much richer in nitrogen, the two cavities nearest to any one oxygen molecule may between them contain 0, 1, or 2 nitrogen molecules. The van der Waals forces which must operate between this oxygen molecule and one of its nitrogen neighbors will be London dispersion forces. There may also be some contribution from quadrupole-quadrupole forces, but the short-range repulsion forces will be negligible at 5.5 Å. Since the polarizability of a diatomic molecule is anisotropic, the London interaction of a pair of diatomic molecules at a given distance apart is a function of their mutual orientation. Consequently the energy barrier hindering the rotation of the oxygen molecule in its cavity will be different according to whether it has 0, 1, or 2 nitrogen molecules in the adjacent holes. To these three slightly different values of the barrier height there correspond three different values of the parameter D', thus accounting for the triplet character of the absorption spectrum and the effect of the nitrogen concentration on the relative intensities of the three components. Foner et $al.$ treated the London interaction between the diatomic molecules quantitatively and found that its anisotropic character could account for the order of magnitude of the observed splitting. There is, however, a discrepancy between the observed and calculated splittings which they attributed to the inadequacy of the theory of intermolecular forces in its present form rather than to that of their model.

D. Nuclear Magnetic Resonance Studies

An attempt has been made to investigate the rotational movement of methane molecules in the hydroquinone clathrate by an NMR study (*34*). The methane signal was very broad. This does not necessarily mean, however, that the methane molecules are not rotating. A heat capacity analysis (*30*) has in fact shown that the methane molecules are rotating almost freely at ordinary temperatures, and the broad signal probably arises because the magnetic fields of the fixed protons in the walls of the cavity do not average to zero.

V. THERMODYNAMIC STUDIES OF THE MOVEMENT OF THE GUEST MOLECULES IN HYDROQUINONE CLATHRATES

Another source of information about the movement of the small molecules trapped in the holes of a β-hydroquinone clathrate is the heat capacity of the system. In these clathrates there is one hole to three hydroquinone molecules, and for the smaller guest molecules at least it is seldom possible to fill all the holes. Different samples of any one clathrate can, however, usually be made in which the fraction of the holes filled varies over a range of at least one-half. If heat capacity measurements are made from low temperatures up to room temperature on a series of such samples, it is generally found that at any one temperature the heat capacity is a linear function of the fraction of the holes filled, so that an estimate can be made of the contribution C_G to the heat capacity at that temperature made by a mole of guest molecules. The variation of C_G with temperature can give information about the movement of the molecules in the cavities. For all molecules there will be a contribution C_{vib} from the vibration or 'rattling' of the molecule as a whole. C_{vib} can be measured experimentally for the rare gas clathrates since for monatomic molecules $C_{vib} = C_G$. It can also be calculated by the statistical mechanical theory of clathrates of the kind developed by J. H. van der Waals (*37*) on the basis of the so-called "cell model" used by Lennard-Jones and Devonshire in their theoretical treatment of the condensed states of matter (see Chapter 2, Section III, and Chapter 7, Section IV). Van der Waals' theory uses classical statistics and cannot therefore be expected to apply at low temperatures, but comparison with experiment shows that for the argon (*31*) and krypton (*13*) clathrates it is valid from about 60° and 120°K respec-

tively.* From the experimental results for argon and krypton two parameters characteristic of the hydroquinone lattice can be evaluated which
partly determine the potential energy of the molecule in the cavity. Knowing these parameters it is then possible to calculate the value of C_{vib} for
diatomic and polyatomic guest molecules. (The only facts about these
molecules which are necessary for the evaluation of C_{vib} are the values
of the parameters of the Lennard-Jones potential for the interaction of a
pair of guest molecules.) The difference, C_{rot}, between the experimental
values of C_G and the calculated values of C_{vib} gives information about
the rotational movement of the molecules in the cavities. For nonlinear
polyatomic molecules the limiting values of C_{rot} at high temperatures
will be $(3/2)R$ for free rotation and $3R$ for simple harmonic torsional
oscillations; for diatomic or linear molecules the corresponding quantities
will be R and $2R$. For partially restricted rotation, C_{rot} will rise to a maximum with increasing temperature and then decrease asymptotically to
the appropriate value for free rotation.

Parsonage and Staveley (30) studied the methane clathrate in this way
and found that from about 150°K upwards C_{rot} is $3R/2$ within experimental error, showing that above this temperature, at least, the rotation
of the methane molecules is almost free. A similar investigation of the
oxygen, nitrogen, and carbon monoxide clathrates by Grey and Staveley
(14) showed that the restriction on the rotation of these molecules is
greater than for methane, since for all three systems C_{rot}, even at room
temperature, is still appreciably greater than R. From the experimental
values of C_{rot} over a range of temperature it should be possible, with the
aid of the well-known tables of Pitzer and Gwinn (32) relating to the
thermodynamic properties of restricted rotators, to evaluate the corresponding barrier height. A number of factors, however, limit the accuracy
with which this can be done. In particular, C_G only contributes a few per
cent to the measured heat capacity of the clathrate, and C_{rot} is only a
part of C_G; while the range over which C_{rot} can be reliably assessed is
limited by uncertainty in the calculated values of C_{vib} at lower temperatures where van der Waals' theory is no longer applicable. Nevertheless,
the heat capacity analysis shows that the oxygen molecules have undoubtedly a much smaller energy barrier to overcome than the nitrogen
or carbon monoxide molecules. The values of C_{rot} for the oxygen clathrate
are in fact consistent with a barrier of 200–250 cal/mole. The figure obtained from the magnetic susceptibility data (cf. Section III, A) is 128

---

* Hazoni et al. (14a) have recently studied the Mössbauer effect in Kr[83] trapped in
the hydroquinone clathrate. They found that whereas the Mössbauer efficiency has
only a small temperature dependence above ∼125°K, below this temperature there is
a rapid rise to higher efficiency.

cal/mole, while the paramagnetic resonance investigation would suggest a rather higher value of $\sim$250 cal/mole for an oxygen molecule for which the two nearest cavities are also occupied. For the nitrogen clathrate Grey and Staveley's heat capacity results gave a barrier height of $\sim$1000 cal/mole. Coulter (7), also by a heat capacity study, has independently obtained a value of 820 cal/mole. For the frequency, ν_0, with which the nitrogen molecules vibrate at low temperatures, Meyer and Scott (28) found 1.55 $\times$ 10^{12} sec^{-1}. At low temperatures where the amplitude of the oscillations is small ν_0 can be related to the moment of inertia I and the quantity V_0 (half the barrier height) by the equation

$$\nu_0 = \frac{1}{\pi} \left(\frac{V_0}{I}\right)^{\frac{1}{2}} \tag{7}$$

The value of $2V_0$ corresponding to $\nu_0 = 1.55 \times 10^{12}$ is 940 cal/mole, in good agreement with the thermodynamic estimates. For carbon monoxide, the heat capacity study gives a slightly higher barrier than for nitrogen of about 1200 cal/mole.

It is worth noting that even if the barrier heights could be more precisely estimated, the values obtained by the techniques described in previous sections which depend on measurements made at very low temperatures need not necessarily agree with the estimates made from heat capacity data covering a range of higher temperatures. The magnitude of the energy barrier opposing rotation of a guest molecule must depend on its position within the cavity. At very low temperatures the guest molecules will be in the lowest vibrational level, but occupancy of higher levels as the temperature rises will bring them for part of the time into closer contact with the walls of the cavity, and the average effective barrier height must change. There must moreover be a change in the size of the cavity with rising temperature owing to the expansion of the lattice.

It is interesting that the barrier should be so much less for an oxygen molecule in a hydroquinone clathrate than for a nitrogen or carbon monoxide molecule. Two possible reasons for this may be mentioned. Although of the three diatomic molecules the bond length of oxygen is the greatest, its intermolecular (van der Waals) diameter appears to be the smallest. Also, although oxygen and nitrogen molecules are nonpolar and that of carbon monoxide only has a dipole moment which is very small, all three are quadrupoles which must interact with the polar groups of the cavity wall. This electrostatic interaction, however, is least for the oxygen molecule, since its quadrupole moment is much less than those of the other two. That of nitrogen seems to be rather smaller than that of carbon monoxide, which may be why the energy barrier for nitrogen is apparently less than that for carbon monoxide.

VI. CHANGES IN THE CHEMICAL BEHAVIOR OF GUEST MOLECULES

A. Inclusion Complexes Containing Iodine*

It has long been known that iodine can give rise to intensely blue complexes with a wide variety of organic substances. Of these complexes, that formed with α-dextrin is particularly suitable for experimental study. Here the iodine atoms lie in a straight line in cylindrical cavities in the dextrin molecule (8). The chains of iodine atoms can be of considerable length, and the distance between adjacent atoms in the chain, 3.06 Å, is greater than the bond length in the diatomic iodine molecule, 2.66 Å. The iodine atoms in the complex, in fact, form a delocalized electronic system. Such a fundamental alteration of the electronic structure of the guest molecules is admittedly an unusual occurrence. Generally the mutual influence of the host and guest electronic systems is slight, as we shall see, though other cases are known in which the complex formation can give rise to visible color changes. Thus, the sulfur dioxide–hydroquinone clathrate is yellow at ordinary temperatures, and becomes colorless on heating (39). Consequent on the delocalization of the electrons in the iodine complexes there is a pronounced shift in the absorption bands towards longer wavelengths, as may be seen in Fig. 9 in which some of the spectra obtained by Cramer (9) are compared with that of iodine vapor. Cramer also carried out potentiometric titrations of solutions of potassium iodide containing different proportions of dextrin with a solution of iodine in potassium iodide, and found that the presence of α-dextrin could alter the redox potential of the $I_2/2I^-$ system by as much as 0.059 volt, the direction of the change being such that the iodine is a weaker oxidizing agent in the presence of dextrin than in its absence. Such a change in potential corresponds to an alteration of the order of 1 kcal/mole in the associated free energy change, and to a factor of the order of ten in an equilibrium constant in which iodine and the iodide ion are involved. The comparison of the α-dextrin and β-dextrin iodine complexes is interesting. β-Dextrin is similar to α-dextrin but its cylindrical holes have a greater diameter. It forms a brown complex with iodine which does *not* contain linear chains of equally spaced iodine atoms. Changes in the $I_2/2I^-$ redox potential due to β-dextrin, though observable, are much smaller than those brought about by the same amount of α-dextrin (18). Thus the host-guest interaction in the β-dextrin complexes must be altogether weaker than that in the α-dextrin complexes.

* A detailed discussion of these may be found in Chapter 9.

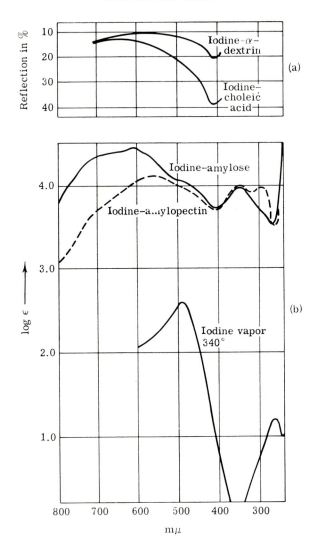

Fig. 9. The spectra of some iodine inclusion complexes compared with that of iodine vapor. (a) Reflection spectra of the complexes with α-dextrin and choleic acid. (b) Absorption spectra of iodine vapor and of the complexes of iodine with amylose and amylopectin (9).

B. Inclusion Complexes Containing Organic Molecules

Some interesting observations have been made, especially by Cramer and his co-workers (Chapter 7 in ref. 8), on the spectroscopic changes and alterations in chemical reactivity which can follow on the inclusion of an organic substance in a suitable host (see Chapter 9). In general, the absorption bands of the organic molecule tend to be displaced towards longer wavelengths. Typical of the shifts observed are the displacements of 5 and 10 mμ of the absorption maxima in the visible spectrum of methylene blue on complexing with β-dextrin. Moreover, there are changes in the redox potential of the systems involving the organic substance which may amount to as much as 0.05 volt, the reduced form of the organic guest being stabilized by formation of the inclusion complex. Cramer considers that the cavity of an inclusion complex is to be regarded as a region of high electron density, so that the cavity behaves as an electron donor, that is, as a base in the Brönsted-Lewis sense. Hence a cavity will encourage the formation within it of an anion, or of the enol form of a substance if it is tautomeric. As long ago as 1932, Sobotka and Kahn (*36*) reported that tautomeric substances were often completely enolized when bound in the choleic acid complex. Studies of the ultraviolet spectrum of furoin in the presence and absence of β-dextrin (*10*) show clearly that at higher pH values the tautomeric equilibrium

$$\begin{array}{ccc} \diagdown & & \diagdown \\ \text{CH(OH)} & & \text{C(OH)} \\ | & \rightleftharpoons & \| \\ \text{CO} & & \text{C(OH)} \\ \diagup & & \diagup \end{array}$$

is shifted towards the endiol side by addition of β-dextrin. Since furoin in the latter form is much more prone to oxidation than when in the α-ketol form, the susceptibility to oxidation in alkaline solution is increased by forming its β-dextrin inclusion complex.

In contrast to this example of the enhancement of chemical reactivity due to inclusion complex formation, there also exist inclusion complexes in which the stability of a somewhat unstable or reactive guest molecule is increased simply because the host lattice affords it protection, as it were, on a molecular scale. Thus, Bähr and Meier (*2*) reported that the adducts of urea with mercury dialkyls are much more resistant to photolysis than the free alkyls. Radell and Hunt (*33*) have suggested that alkylsilanes which form inclusion complexes may be stored in this form, since protection is thereby given to the reactive silicon hydride part of the molecule which otherwise tends to be decomposed slowly by the alkali present in glass. Also, autoxidation of organic compounds is suppressed by inclusion in urea (Chapter 8, Section VII, C) and in dextrins (Chapter 9, Section IV, B).

632 L. A. K. STAVELEY

VII. THE STABILITY AND DECOMPOSITION OF INCLUSION COMPLEXES

The inclusion complexes with which we have been concerned in this chapter are not particularly stable systems, and indeed some of them under ordinary conditions are in a metastable state. A detailed theoretical and experimental study of the thermodynamic relationships involved in the formation of hydroquinone clathrates and rare gas hydrates has been carried out by J. H. van der Waals and his collaborators (37), an account of which will be found in Chapter 7, Section IV. This has shown, for example, that the equilibrium pressure of argon for the argon β-hydroquinone clathrate at 25°C is 3.4 atm. Since this clathrate is stable for periods of months and perhaps years, the decomposition process, whatever it may be, must involve a considerable activation energy.

A number of observations have been reported from time to time which bear on the stability of the adducts of urea or thiourea with long-chain compounds. For these, the reader is referred to Chapter 8. We shall here summarize the comparatively meager information on the stability and decomposition of inclusion complexes where the guest molecule is small or else roughly spherical. It must first be pointed out that, as in other kinetic studies of the decomposition or reactions of solids, factors are involved which cannot be exactly specified or controlled. It is only to be expected, and it is in fact found, that the decomposition of clathrates is affected by the size of the crystals and the tightness with which they have been packed together in the sample. Nevertheless studies of the decomposition of inclusion complexes can give interesting qualitative information about the process. Of such studies, perhaps the most detailed is that of Mandelcorn et al. (22) on the sulfur hexafluoride clathrate of Dianin's compound, 4-p-hydroxyphenyl-2,2,4-trimethylchroman. As these authors point out, the decomposition of a clathrate (without the intervention of a liquid phase) could occur by one or more of the following processes: (a) sublimation of the host; (b) a change of structure of the host lattice; (c) diffusion of the guest molecules through the host lattice; (d) surface desorption of the guest molecules. For the sulfur hexafluoride clathrate of Diamin's compound, the evidence strongly suggests that decomposition occurs by sublimation of the host. The decomposition was investigated between 100° and 160°C and at pressures which ranged from that generated by the escaping sulfur hexafluoride down to 10^{-5} mm, and it was found that the gas is evolved more rapidly the lower the external pressure and the smaller the sample size. Moreover, while loss of sulfur hexafluoride was invariably accompanied by loss of Dianin's compound, the ratio of the weights of sulfur hexafluoride and Dianin's compound lost from the crystals was always higher than the weight ratio in the original sample. This is understandable, for whereas experiments showed that once sulfur hexafluoride molecules have left the lattice they are not taken up again by guest-free Dianin's compound, the host molecules which sublime can recondense on the sample.

On the other hand, Lahr and Williams (20) concluded that decomposition of the β-hydroquinone-argon clathrate is a diffusion-controlled process. Their samples were prepared not by crystallization from solution in the presence of argon, but by subjecting solid α-hydroquinone to high pressures of argon, whereupon much of the solid could be transformed into the β-form. When, however, the β-hydroquinone clathrate decomposed, the β-structure was retained. In calorimetric experiments on the argon-hydroquinone clathrate, Parsonage and Staveley (31) observed that loss of argon took place as a result of cooling and warming the sample between room temperature and the temperature of liquid oxygen, but the loss could be much reduced if care was taken to remove from the crystals the last traces of the solvent from which the clathrate had been crystallized. Subsequent work (14) has shown that some of the hydroquinone clathrates (e.g. oxygen, carbon monoxide) are more prone to decomposition when subjected to temperature changes than the argon clathrate, while others (e.g. the methane clathrate) are less so. The oxygen and carbon monoxide clathrates which seem to be least affected by temperature changes are those where about half the available holes are filled. But while clathrates richer than this in the guest molecules seem to retain the β-structure on partial decomposition, there are indications that a clathrate with, say, only one-fifth of the cavities filled will tend, on breaking down, to change into the α-form.

Aynsley et al. (1) studied the decomposition of the benzene clathrate of monoammino-nickel cyanide and found that the benzene could be removed in vacuo slowly at room temperature and rapidly between 40° and 60°C. Since for the removal of most of the benzene the decomposition was of zero order, they concluded that the rate-determining step (for which the activation energy is approximately 11 kcal/mole) is escape of the benzene from the surface. Migration of the benzene within the lattice must therefore be a comparatively facile process. Thus, of the four possibilities cited above for the process determining the rate of decomposition of a clathrate, it seems likely that examples of three of them have already been discovered.

Chleck and Ziegler (4) prepared clathrates of β-hydroquinone and krypton containing the radioactive Kr^{85} isotope. These were found to be resistant to radiation damage and so could be used as convenient solid sources of Kr^{85}.

REFERENCES

1. Aynsley, E. E., Campbell, W. A., and Dodd, R. E., *Proc. Chem. Soc.* p. 210 (1957).
2. Bähr, G., and Meier, G., *Z. anorg. u. allgem. Chem.* **294**, 22 (1958).
3. Bayer, H., *Z. Physik* **130**, 227 (1951).
4. Chleck, D. J., and Ziegler, C. A., *Intern. J. Appl. Radiation and Isotopes* **7**, 141 (1959).
5. Cooke, A. H., Meyer, H., Wolf, W. P., Evans, D. F., and Richards, R. E., *Proc. Roy. Soc.* **A225**, 112 (1954).
6. Cooke, A. H., and Duffus, H. J., *Proc. Phys. Soc.* (*London*) **A67**, 525 (1954).
7. Coulter, L. V., private communication.
8. Cramer, F., "Einschlussverbindungen," Chapter III. Springer, Berlin, 1954.
9. Cramer, F., *Chem. Ber.* **84**, 855 (1951).
10. Cramer, F., *Chem. Ber.* **86**, 1576 (1953).
11. Dryden, J. S., *Trans. Faraday Soc.* **49**, 1333 (1953).
12. Foner, S., Meyer, H., and Kleiner, W. H., *J. Phys. and Chem. Solids* **18**, 273 (1961).
13. Grey, N. R., Parsonage, N. G., and Staveley, L. A. K., *Mol. Phys.* **4**, 153 (1961).
14. Grey, N. R., and Staveley, L. A. K., *Mol. Phys.* (in press).
14a. Hazoni, Y., Hillman, P., Pasternak, M., and Ruby, S., *Physics Letters*, **2**, 337 (1962).
15. Hexter, R. M., and Goldfarb, T. D., *J. Inorg. & Nuclear Chem.* **4**, 171 (1957).
16. Hoffmann, J. D., *J. Chem. Phys.* **23**, 1331 (1954).
17. Hoffmann, J. D., and Axilrod, B. M., *J. Research Natl. Bur. Standards* **54**, 357 (1955).
18. Hoffmann, J. D., and Pfeiffer, H. G., *J. Chem. Phys.* **22**, 132 (1954).
19. Hughes, E. W., Yakel, H. L., and Freeman, H. C., *Acta Cryst.* **14**, 345 (1961).
20. Lahr, P. H., and Williams, H. L., *J. Phys. Chem.* **63**, 1432 (1959).
21. Lauritzen, J. I., *J. Chem. Phys.* **28**, 118 (1958).
22. Mandelcorn, L., Goldberg, N. N., and Hoff, R. E., *J. Am. Chem. Soc.* **82**, 3297 (1960).
23. McKean, D. C., private communication.
24. Meakins, R. J., *Trans. Faraday Soc.* **51**, 953 (1955).
25. Meakins, R. J., private communication.
26. Meyer, H., *J. Phys. Chem. Solids* **20**, 238 (1961).
27. Meyer, H., O'Brien, M. C. M., and Van Vleck, J. H., *Proc. Roy. Soc.* **A243**, 414 (1957).
28. Meyer, H., and Scott, T. A., *J. Phys. Chem. Solids* **11**, 215 (1959).
29. Palin, D. E., and Powell, H. M., *J. Chem. Soc.* p. 571 (1948).
30. Parsonage, N. G., and Staveley, L. A. K., *Mol. Phys.* **3**, 59 (1960).
31. Parsonage, N. G., and Staveley, L. A. K., *Mol. Phys.* **2**, 212 (1959).
32. Pitzer, K. S., and Gwinn, W. D., *J. Chem. Phys.* **10**, 428 (1942).
33. Radell, J., and Hunt, P. D., *J. Am. Chem. Soc.* **80**, 2683 (1958).

34. Schneider, W. G., private communication.
35. Smith, A. E., *Acta Cryst.* 5, 224 (1952).
36. Sobotka, H., and Kahn, S., *Biochem. J.* 26, 898 (1932).
37. van der Waals, J. H., and Platteeuw, J. C., *Advances in Chem.* 2, 1 (1959).
38. Van Vleck, J. H., *J. Phys. Chem. Solids* 20, 241 (1961).
39. Wynne-Jones, W. F. K., and Anderson, A. R., *Soc. chim. phys., Compt. rend. deuxième réunion annuelle* p. 246 (1952).

Author Index

Numbers in parentheses are reference numbers and indicate that an author's work is referred to although his name is not cited in the text. Numbers in italic show the page on which the complete reference is listed.

A

Abraham, B. M., *265*
Abrikosov, N. Kh., *201*
Acosta, R. S., *262*
Adam, N. K., 348, *430*
Adamson, G. M., Jr., *267*
Adelsköld, V., 149, *201*
Aellen, M., 373(195), *435*
Aftandilian, V. O., 153(45), *202*
Agranovskaya, A. I., 134(292), 143(293), (114), 296(115), *208*, 295, *308*
Alberman, K. B., 116(3), *201*
Albrecht, W. M., 225(62), 248(1), *258*, *260*, *263*, *264*, *265*
Alder, B. J., 78(34), *96*
Allen, K. W., 318, *430*, 461(1), *489*
Amberg, C. H., 420(3), *430*
Ames, L. L., Jr., 367(4), 395(5), *430*
Amiot, P., *262*
Anderko, K., 183(4), *201*
Anderson, A. R., 629(39), *635*
Anderson, D. M. W., 578(1), *602*
Anderson, J. S., 99, 100, 116(3, 7), 121(8), 122(6), 197, *201*, 326(113), 327(114), 398(113), *432*, *433*
Anderson, P. W., 300(1), *305*
Andersson, G., 107(10), 110(9), *201*
Andersson, S., 106(15), 109(13), 110(11, 14, 16), 111(16), 112(320), 131(20), 135(17, 18, 19, 20), 152(20), 153(18, 19), *201*, *209*, 347(6), *430*,
Andreini, A., 310, *430*
Andresen, A., 124(21), *201*
Andrew, K. F., 211(27, 28, 29, 30), 216(27, 31), 219(29), 220(28), 222(27), 227(29), 233(27, 28, 29, 30), 239(28), 257, *259*
Angier, R. P., *266*
Angla, B., 494, 496(2), 502, 530, 531, *563*
Appel, J., 292(2), *305*
Appleman, D. E., 373(8), *430*

Aragon, F., 354, *430*
Arata, H., *263*
Archibald, A. R., 587(2), 588(2), *602*
Arkharov, V. J., *262*
Arnold, G. B., 496(44), 538(44), 540(44), *565*
Arnoldi, H., 443, *490*
Aroeste, H., 77(40), *96*
Aronson, S., 123, *201*
Aronsson, B., 100, 177(25), *201*
Asbrink, S., 153(26), *201*
Aselius, J., 177(25), *201*
Ash, R., *263*
Asher, R. C., 355, 358(10), *430*
Aston, J. G., *263*, *264*, 420(11), *430*
Atoji, M., 132(27), *201*, 282(3), 284, *305*
Aurivillius, B., 122(33), 134(28), 142, 144(29, 30, 31, 32, 32a),
Axilrod, B. M., 614(17), *634*
Ayer, J. E., 601(52), *604*
Aylward, F., *567*
Aynsley, E. E., 622, 633, *634*
Azou, P., 236(18), *259*, *261*, *266*

B

Babcock, G. E., 570(79), *605*
Bachman, C. H., *264*
Bacon, G. E., 42(1), 44(1), 45(3), *47*
Bähr, G., 631, *634*
Baenziger, N. C., 119(34), 120(34, 140), 124(276), 125(276), *201*, *204*, *208*, 292(4), *305*
Bailey, F. E., Jr., 509(4), 513(4), 536, 548, *563*
Bailey, J. M., 581(3), 582, 585, *602*
Bailey, W. A., Jr., 493(5), 512(5), 551(5), 553, *564*
Baker, E. G., 545, 546, 547, *564*
Baker, G. S., *264*
Baker, W., 447, 469(2), *489*
Baldwin, R. R., 571(4), 578(5), *602*, *603*
Banege-Nia, A., *262*

637

Bangert, L., *265*

Bankina, V. F., *201*

Banks, E., 108(338), 132(62, 265), 133(62), 185(35), *201, 202, 207, 209*, 282(12, 13, 96), 283(96), 284, 285, *305, 307*.

Bannerot, R. A., 493(5), 512(5), 551(5), 553(5), *564*

Bannister, F. A., 373(147, 148, 149), *433*

Barclay, J. A. V., 543(15), 544, *564*

Barduhn, A. J., 553(7), *564*

Barker, D. B., 282(56), 286(56), *306*

Barker, G. E., 536(8), *564*

Barlow, G. B., 495, 496(9), 538(9), 562, *564*

Barnes, R. G., 288(68), *307*

Baron, M., 394(12), *430*

Barrer, R. M., 224(2), *258, 263*, 310(27), 312(28), 315(22), 318, 319, 320, 325(25, 75), 326(58, 75), 327(28, 34, 54, 75), 328(75), 330(50), 332, 337(51), 338(51), 339(46, 52, 59), 341(52, 59, 60), 342(52, 56, 57, 59), 343(46, 52, 57), 344(46), 356(45), 365(42), 366(42), 367(23, 24, 32, 40), 370(39, 68), 371(37, 47, 55), 372(37), 373(37), 374(31, 37), 375(37), 376(32, 47), 377(47), 378(47), 379(25, 72, 73), 380(25, 40), 383(23, 63), 384(25), 385(58), 386(25, 47), 387(47), 388(15, 16, 20, 27, 33), 389(19), 390(27, 35, 44), 392(25, 73), 393(25, 35, 38, 54, 65, 71, 72), 394(25), 395(23), 396(17, 30, 32, 37, 40, 41, 49, 53, 75), 397(18, 30, 31, 32, 49, 74), 398(19, 40), 399(22, 75), 400(42, 65), 401(21), 402(21), 403(69), 404, 406(38, 65, 71), 407(62), 408(38), 409, 410(46), 415, 416, 418(64, 66, 70), 419(48, 71), 420(14, 69, 70), 421(26), 422(43), 423(43), 424(43), 425(19, 36), 426, 427(36, 63), 428, 429(19), *430, 431*, 493, *564*

Barth, V. D., *263*

Bartindale, G. W. R., 364(207), *435*, 463(25), *490*

Bartram, S. F., 174(36), 175(36), *201*

Bastien, P., 215(3), 236(18), *258, 259, 261, 262, 266*

Bates, F. L., 571(6), 578, 579(6), *603*

Baumback, H. H., 269(5), *305*

Baur, R., 352, *431*

Baur, W. H., 371(79), 373(79), *431*

Bayer, H., 624, *634*

Baynham, J. W., 367(32), 374(31), 376(32), 396(30, 32), 397(30, 31, 32), *430*

Bear, R. S., 571(4), 572(7), 575(8), 576(8), 577(8), 578(5), 601(9), *602, 603*

Beason, L. R., 494(81), 503(81), 530(81), 531(81), 537(81), *566*

Beck, R. L., *266*

Beckmann, C. O., 570(10, 25), *603*

Bedworth, R. E., 90(50), *96*

Beebe, R. A., 420(3, 77, 78), *430, 431*

Belbeoch, B., 123(37), *202*

Belchetz, L., 388(33), *430*

Belle, J., 123, *201, 266*

Belyaev, I. N., 295(6), *305*

Belyakov, Y. I., *263*

Bénard, J., 100, 108(38), 173(184), *202, 205, 258*

Bengen, N. F., 494(13), 496(11, 12), 512(11), *564*

Bennaceraff, A., 185(41), *202*

Benson, E., 189(331), *209*

Berg, T. G. O., 215(5), 227(5), *258*

Bergerhoff, G., 371(79), 373(79, 80), *431, 432*

Bergsma, J., *261*

Berman, H., 189(251), *207*

Bernoff, R. A., 137(42), *202*

Bernstein, R. B., *266*

Berry, K. L., 153(45), *202*

Berry, W. E., *266*

Bersohn, R., 586, *603*

Bertaut, E. F., 37(4), *47*, 135(44), 167, 170(43), *202*, 304(7), *305*

Bevan, D. J. M., 119(46), 120(46), *202*

Bickel, R. W., 242(6), *258*

Biedermann, W., 597(537, 598(53), *604*

Bijvoet, J. M., 40, *47*

Biltz, W., 167, *202*. 304(71), *307*

Birchenall, C. E., *264*, 289(51), 290(51), 300(51), *306*

Bird, R. B., 69(29), *96*, 404(151), *434*

Bishop, D., 325(126), *433*

Bizette, H., 298(8), *305*

Blakey, R. C., 116(3), *201*

Blanchard, P. A., *262*

Blanchard, R., *262*

Blankenship, F. F., 317(81), 318, 319(81), *432*

Blatter, F., 352(118), *433*
Block, S., 162(98), *203*
Blomberg, B., 126(48), 133(231), 139(231), 140(231), *202, 206*
Blomberg-Hansson, B., 126(232), *206*
Blomgrem, G., 77, *95*
Blum, P., 135(44), *202*
Boggs, E. M., 78(33), *96*
Boghen, J., *263*
Bogotskaia, I. A., *262*
Bokii, G. B., 195(48a), *202*
Bokros, J. C., *266*
Bonamico, M., 483(4), *490*
Bonatti, S., 372(82), *432*
Borchert, W., 182(49), *202*
Born, L., 195(50), 197(50), *202*
Born, M., 78(5), *95*
Bornkessel, K., *263*
Bose, S. N., 61, *95*
Boullé, A., 124(51), *202*
Bourne, E. J., 571(4), *602*
Bowman, M. G., *265*
Boyle, R. F., *266*
Bradley, T. F., *566*
Bradley, W. F., 329(83, 186), 356(84), *432, 434*
Brantley, J. C., 137(60), 140(60), *202*, 282(10), *305*
Bratt, G. C., 327(34), 370, *430*
Brauer, G., 105(52), 107(52), 111(55), 115(54), 119(53), 123(56), 159, 174, 175(187), 179(187), *202, 205*, 213(8), *259*
Braun, P. B., 147(57), 150, 151(59), *202*
Brauner, K., 329(85), *432*
Breck, D. W., 370(86), 371(210), 388(86), 393(86), 395(86), *432, 435*
Breckenridge, R. G., 280, *305*
Brennan, D., *265*
Bretschneider, O., 359(228), *435*
Bridge, J. R., 213(86), *261*
Brimm, E. O., 137(60), 140(60), *202*, 282(10), *305*
Brindley, G. W., 148(61), *202*, 287(11), *305*, 333(87, 88) 334(88), 335(88), 372(143), *432, 433*
Britton, J. D., 115(218), *206*
Brook, D. W., 390(35), 393(35), 425(36), 427(36), *430*

Broser, W., 597(53), 598(53), *604*
Broussard, L., 371(89), 374(89), *432*
Brown, A., *266*
Brown, B. W., 132(62), 133(62), *202*, 282(12, 13), 283, 284, 285, *305*
Brown, F. H., Jr., 271(14, 26, 27), 272(27), 273(27), *305*
Brown, J. F., 536, 561, 562(14), *564*
Brunauer, S., 343(90), *432*
Budnik, J. L., *264*
Buehler, R. H., 75(63), 77(63), *97*
Buehler, R. J., 406(150), *433*
Buerger, M. J., 25(12), 38(6), *47*, 182(64), 190(63), 195(237), 197(65, 236, 237), *202, 207*
Buerger, N. W., 182(64), *202*
Bürki, H., 195(240), 197(240), *207*
Buhrer, C., 296(15), *305*
Bultitude, F. W., 367(32), 371(37), 372(37), 373(37), 374(37), 375(37), 376(32), 393(38), 396(32, 37), 397(32), 406(38), 408(38), *430, 431*
Burk, B. I., *265*
Burki, H., 352(119, 120, 121, 122, 123), *433*
Burton, W. K., 20(13), *48*
Buser, W., 112(66), *202*, 370(39), *431*
Butler, G., 112(68), 119, *202*
Butler, I. M., 543, 544, *564*
Byers, T. B., 554(34), *565*
Byström, A., 112(70), 121(69), *202*
Byström, A. M., 112(70), *202*

C

Cabane, G., *266*
Cabrera, N., 20(13), *48*
Cadenbach, G., 355(129), *433*
Calmon, C., 395(211), *435*
Cameron, A., 109, *202*
Campbell, I. E., *264*
Campbell, W. A., 622(1), 633(1), *634*
Campos, F. P., *261*
Careri, G., 77(40), *96*
Carlson, O. N., *266*
Carmichael, D. C., *262*
Carslaw, H. S., 219, 220(9), *259*
Carson, A. W., *263*
Carter, F. L., 292(16, 102), *305, 308*
Casey, J. J., 118(72), *202*
Castellan, G. W., *263, 264*

Cernuschi, F., 72(8), 77, *95*
Chang, R., *266*
Chapoorian, J. A., *264*
Chatelain, P., 372(290), *437*
Cheselske, F. J., *264*
Chessman, E. F., 602(54), *604*
Chipault, J. R., 563, *564*
Chleck, D. J., 558(17), 563(17), *564*, 633, *634*
Choain, C., 126(73), *202*
Christian, C. G., 352(231), *436*
Clamp, A. C., 495, 496(9), 538(9), 562, *564*
Clarke, W., 325(126), *433*
Clasen, H., 536, 560, *564*
Clauss, A., *264*, 354(91), *432*
Claussen, W. F., 313, 315(92), *432*, 460(5), *490*, 544, *564*
Cleland, B. B., *266*
Clemm, A., 439(6), *490*
Cochran, C. N., *261*, *263*
Cochran, W., 37(7), *47*
Codd, I., 216(10), 223(10), *259*
Cohen, E. G. D., 77(4), *95*
Cohen, M. H., 161(74), *202*
Cohn, E., 271(28), *306*
Cole, W. F., 112(75), *202*
Coleman, J. E., 494(21, 48), 543(21), *564*, *565*
Coles, J. S., 570(12), *603*
Collén, B., 109(13), *201*
Collongues, R., 118(76, 254), *203*, *207*
Condit, R. H., 290(17), *305*
Connolly, J. W., 505(78, 79), 510, *566*
Conroy, L. E., 133(77), 137(42), *202*, *203*, 288, *305*
Coogan, C. E., 242(80), *261*
Coogan, C. K., *265*
Cooke, A. H., 616, 617(5), 618, 620, *634*
Coombs, D. S., 372(94), 373(95), 395(96), *432*
Copp, J. L., 119, *202*
Corey, R. B., 498(111), 500(111), *567*
Cosgrove, W. R., Jr., 505(79), *566*
Coster, D., 40(8), *47*
Cotterill, P., 211(11), 243(11), *259*
Coucoulas, A., *265*
Coughanour, L. W., 142(78), 161(269), *203*, *207*

Cowley, J. M., *48*, 148(79), *203*, 362(97), *432*
Cox, B., *266*
Cox, D. E., 303(106), *308*
Craig, R. S., *264*
Craighead, C. M., *265*
Cramer, F., 394(98), *432*, 494, 496(22), 538(22), 540(22), 549, *564*, *565*, 585, 589(13), 591, 593(21), 594(13, 14, 21), 595, 596(15), 598(17), 599(15, 16, 18), 600(20, 39), *603*, 629(8), 630(9), 631(10), *634*
Crank, J., 421(144), 422(144), *433*
Croatto, U., 115(344), 123(80), *203*, *209*
Croft, R. C., 353, 354(102), 360(102), 363(99), *432*
Cromer, D. T., 115(81), *203*, 465(7), *490*
Cubicciotti, D. D., *266*
Cupp, C. R., 211(12), *259*
Curry, N. A., 45(2), *47*
Curtis, C. E., 278, *305*, *307*
Curtiss, C. F., 69(29), 72(53), 75(63), 77(63), *96*, *97*, 404(151), *434*
Custers, J. F. H., 419, *432*
Cynarski, J., 420(77), *431*

D

Dachs, H., 115(82), *203*
Dahler, J. S., 77(4), *95*
Dalgaard, S. B., *266*
Dana, J. D., 367, 370, *432*
Danielson, G. C., 282(36, 56), 283, 284(29), 285(29, 36, 113), 286(29, 36, 56), *306*, *308*
Darange, L., 292(94), *307*
Darken, L. S., *262*, 275(20), 288(20), 289(20), *305*
Darling, A. S., *263*
Darwin, C. G., 18, 34(9), *47*
Dasgupta, D. R., 165(83), *203*
David, I., 147(84), *203*
Davidson, W. L., 43(32), *48*
Davis, H. M., 215(56, 90), 216(90), *260*, *261*
Davis, W. D., *263*, *265*
Davy, Sir H., 313, *432*, 461, *490*, 494, *564*
Dawson, I. M., 18, 34(10), *47*
Day, D. L., *265*

Dearing, B. E., *266*
Deaton, W. M., 317(105), *432*
de Boer, J. H., 71(3), 77, 78, 87, *95*, *96*, 147(309), *209*, 217(7), *259*, 352, 354(108), 419, *432*
Debye, P., 29, *47*
de Jager, W. G. R., *261*
de Jong, W. F., 282(21), *305*
de Kazincy, F., *262*
Dekker, A. J., 270, *305*
de Leeuw, A. J., 602(41), *604*
Denny, P. J., 367(40), 380(40), 396(40, 41), 397(40), 398(40), *431*
Dent, L. S., 371(109), 373(109), 376(109), 386(109), *432*
Deprosse, V. A., 142(78), *203*
Deryabina, V. I., *262*
Devonshire, A. F., 72, 73, 75(36), *96*, 404(172), 415, *434*
De Vries, R. C., 132(180), *205*, 282(63), 283(63), 295, *305*, *306*
Dianin, A. P., 442, 481(9), *490*
Dickerson, R. F., *267*
Dickinson, J. G., 134(194), *206*
Dickson, J. G., 147(85), *203*
Diepen, G. A. M., 316(257), *436*
Dietsche, W., 600(20), *603*
Dietzel, A., 118(86), 272(24), *203*, *305*
Dioler, K., 213(13), *259*
Dirac, P. A. M., 60, *95*
Diverstein, R. A., 494(112), 504(112), 510(112), 517(112), 524(112), 530(112), *567*
Dixon, J. M., 211(57), 233(57), 240(57), 251(57), *260*
Dodd, R. E., 622(1), 633(1), *634*
Doi, H., 125(278), *208*
Domange, L., 171(104), *203*
Domask, W. G., 494(49), 514(49), 515(49), *565*
Dominé-Bergès, M., 124(51), *202*
Donnay, G., 182(87), 191(88), *203*
Donnay, J. D. H., 182(87), 191(88), *203*
Dorough, G. L., 545, *564*
Dorsey, W. S., 352(231), *436*
Dosdat, J., *263*
Doty, M. E., 275(75), 276(75), 277(75), 278(75), 290(75), *307*
Douglas, T. B., *266*

Douglass, D. L., *266*
Drain, L. E., 420(110), *432*
Drake, J., 365(42), 366(42), 400(42), *431*
Draley, J. E., *261*
Dravnieks, A., 282(116), *308*
Dryden, J. S., 113(89), 141(89), *203*, 304(25), *305*, 608, 609(11), *634*
Dube, H. A., 578(24), 582, 583, 593, *603*
Ducros, P., 425, *432*
Dürrwächter, W., 278(61), 279(61), *306*
Duffus, H. J., 620, *634*
Dumbrow, B. A., 570(25), *603*
Dunlop, A. K., 494(80), 504(80), 505(80), 506(80), 512(80), 516(80), 517(80), 518(80), 519(80), 523(80), *566*
Dunwald, H., 89(10), *95*
Dushman, S., 211(14), *259*
Duwez, P., 161(199), *206*, 271(14, 26, 27), 272(77), 373, *305*
Dvonch, W., 577(26), 579(26), *603*
Dykstra, L. J., 211(57), 233(57), 240(57), 251(37), *260*

E

Earley, J. W., 183(90), *203*
Ebert, F., 271(28, 101), 272(101), *306*, *307*
Eborall, R., 215(15), *259*
Eckerlin, P., 184(258), *207*
Edwards, A. B., 190(91), *203*
Edwards, F. C., 572(70), 573(70), 577(70), *604*
Edwards, R. K., 240(16), *259*, *261*
Eggertsen, F. F., 560(25), *564*
Ehrlich, P., 105(92), 109(92), 166(93), 173(93), *203*
Eick, H. A., 119(34), 120(34), *201*, 292(4), *305*
Einstein, A., 61, *95*
Ejima, T., 109(295), *208*
Ellerbeck, L. D., 284(29), 285(29), 286, *306*
Ellinger, F. H., 213(42), *260*, *262*
Ellis, A. J., 395(96, 112), *432*
Ells, C. E., 211(17), 233(17), *259*
Emeleus, H. J., 326(113), 327(114), 398(113), *432*, *433*
Erchak, M., 146(94), *203*

Erd, R. C., 170(95), 172(95), *203*
Erlander, S. R., 570(37), 587(27), *603*
Espogna, L., 236(18), *259, 261, 266*
Eucken, A., 412, *432*
Euler, R., 189(96), 195(96), *203*
Eustice, A. L., *266*
Evans, C. T., Jr., 215(19), *259*
Evans, D. F., 412(116), *433*, 485(9a), *490*, 616(5), 617(5), 618(5), *634*
Evans, H. T., 161, 162(97, 98, 99), 170(95), 172(95), *203*
Evans, M. W., 542, 544, *564*
Evans, R. C., 213(20), *259*
Evans, U. R., *262*
Everett, D. H., *263*
Everett, W. W., 570(28, 29), *603*
Evers, M., *265*
Eversole, W. G., 370(86), 388(86), 393(86), 395(86), *432*
Ewald, P. P., 25(12), *47*
Ewell, R. H., 398(117), *433*
Eyring, H., 50(15), 56(15), 57(15), 59(16), 60(16), 61(48), 64(13, 22), 72(8), 77, 78(17), 94(12, 22), *95, 96, 264*
Eyring, L., 119(34, 103), 120(34, 103, 140), *201, 203, 204*, 292, *305*

F

Fallon, R. J., *263*
Fang, P. H., 142(32a), 144(32a), *201*, 297, *306*
Fankuchen, I., 109(284), 146(94, 297), *203, 208*
Faraday, M., 461, *490*
Farr, J. D., *265*
Fassel, V. A., 215(21), *259*
Feil, D., 318(157), *434*, 482(11), *490*, 544(60), *565*
Feitknecht, W., 112(66), 161(102), *202, 203*, 352(118, 119, 120, 121, 122, 123), *433*
Feitknecht-Steinmann, V., 161(102), *203*
Fender, B. E. F., 422(43), 423(43), 424(43), 426, *431*
Fergason, L. A., *265*
Ferguson, R. E., 119(103), 120(103), *203*
Fermi, E., 60, *95*
Fesenko, E. G., 295(6), *305*

Fetterly, L. C., 493(5), 494(26, 27), 496(26), 500(27), 501(27, 28), 503(28), 504(27), 505, 508(27), 510(27, 29b), 512(5, 27, 28), 513(27), 515(30), 516, 517(28), 518(27, 28), 519(27, 28), 524(27), 526(27), 527, 528(27, 28), 529(27, 28), 530, 538(27), 540(27), 541(27, 28), 542(27, 28), 545(27, 28), 547(27, 28), 548(27), 549(27), 551(5, 29), 553(5, 28), 554(29), 555(30), 556, 557(27), *564, 566*
Fillnow, R. H., 216(84), *261*
Fischer, K., 372(125), *433*
Flahaut, J., 105(105), 171(104, 106), *203*, 292(94), *307*
Flanagan, T. B., *263*
Flaschen, S. S., 295, *308*
Fleischer, M., 113(107), *203*
Fleitman, A. H., *265*
Fleming, I. D., 587(2), 588(2), *602*
Fletcher, P. C., *265*
Flint, E., 325(126), *433*
Flitter, D., 510, 531, *566*
Flood, H., 156(108, 109, 110), *203*
Flotow, H. E., *265*
Foëx, M., 271(124), 273, 292, 293(31), *306, 308*
Foner, S., 624 *634,*
Foote, F., 108(188), *205*, 288(66), *307*
Forestier, H., *264*
Forman, S. A., 183(111), *203*
Forsbergh, P. W., Jr., 294(32), *306*
Forscher, F., *266*
Foster, J. F., 570(28, 29, 64), 571(30), *603, 604*
Foster, P. K., *262*, 288(33), *306*
Fowler, D. L., 318(127), *433*
Fowler, R., 58(19), *95*
France, H. G., 509(4), 513(4), 536, 548, *563*
Francombe, M. H., 134(113), 138(112), 139(112, 114), 140(112), 141(112), *203, 204*, 297(34, 35), *306*
Frank, F. C., 20, *48*
Frank, G., 184(147), *204*
Frank, H. S., 542, 544, *564*
Frank, R. C., 215(82), *261, 262*
Franzen, P., 339, 340(128), *433*
Fredenhagen, K., 355(129, 130), *433*
Freeman, H. C., 616(19), *634*

French, D., 570(87), 571(6), 572(71, 72), 573(72), 578(6), 579(6, 87), 580, 581(87, 88), 583, 585(87), 587(27), 588, 589(63), 591(31, 32, 46), 592(32, 46, 86), 593(31, 86), 594(33, 46), 595(46), 598(85), 601(9), *603*, *604*, *605*
Frenkel, J., 20, *48*, 81, *95*
Frenkel, Ya. I., 104, *204*
Freudenberg, K., 496(33), *565*
Frevel, L. K., 125(116), *204*
Fricke, R., 122(176), *205*
Fritz, J. J., *263*
Frondel, C., 189(251), *207*
Frost, E. M., 317(105), *432*
Frost, G. B., 500(57), *565*
Frost, P. D., *265*
Fry, D. L., 215(82), *261*, *262*
Fuchs, L. H., 124(170), 125(170), *205*
Fukada, N., 364(252), *436*
Funston, E. S., *266*
Fyfe, W. S., 395(96, 112), *432*

G

Gable, C. M., 494(80, 81), 503(81), 504(80), 505(80), 506(80), 512(80), 516(80), 517(80), 518(80), 519(80), 523(80), 530(81), 531(81), 537(81), *566*
Gabrysh, A. F., *264*
Galasso, F., 134(119, 120), 138(120), 139(120), 140(117, 118), 141(117, 118), *204*
Galstaun, L. S., 243(25), *259*
Garbaty, E. A., 288(68), *307*
Gard, J. A., 371(238), 373(238), 376(238), *436*
Garden, L., 406(131, 132, 134), 420(113), *433*
Gardner, H. R., *265*
Gardner, W. R., 282(36), 283, 285(36), 286(36), *306*
Garikian, G., 75(52), *96*
Garner, P. J., 554, *565*
Gates, J. E., *265*
Gattow, G., 114(121, 123), *204*
Gaul, G. G., *267*
Gee, G., 343(135), *433*
Geiseler, G., 513(35), *565*
Geiser, E. M., 496(36), 510, 538(36), 540(36), 560(36), *565*
Geller, S., 173(122), 189(331), *204*, *209*

Gentile, G., 61(21), *95*
Gerasimova, N. G., 215(22), *259*
Gibb, T. R. P., Jr., 213(66), 216(24), 240(60), 242(23), *259*, *260*, *264*, *265*, *266*
Gibson, J. A., *262*
Gibson, R. A., *266*
Gilbert, B., 447(2), 469(2), *489*
Gilbert, G. A., 578(34), 579, 580, 582, 592(34), *603*
Gilbert, W. W., 153(45), *202*
Gillespie, L. J., 243(25), *259*
Gilwood, M. E., 395(211), *435*
Gingerich, K. A., 119(53), *202*
Giorgi, A. L., *265*
Glass, H. B., 545(24), *564*
Glasstone, S., 64(22), 94, *95*
Glazunov, S. G., *265*
Glemser, O., 114(121, 123), 126(124, 126), 162(127), *204*
Glew, D. N., 319(136), 413(136), *433*, 544, *565*
Glikman, L. A., *262*
Gnichtel, H., 597(53), 598(53), *604*
Go, Y., 495, 538(37), *565*
Goldberg, N. N., 508(56a), 558(56a), *565*, 632(22), *634*
Gol'der, G. A., 157(249), *207*
Goldfarb, T. D., 620, *634*
Goldkoop, J. A., *261*
Goldman, K. M., 216(84), *261*
Goldsbrough, L. N., 554(34), *565*
Goldschmidt, H. J., 300(38), *306*
Goldsmith, J. R., 367(137), *433*
Gomberg, M., 495, 496(38), 538(38), *565*
Gomer, R., *263*
Goode, W. D., 248(1), *258*, *263*
Goodman, G., 137, 138(129), *204*, 297(39), 304(40), *306*
Goon, E. J., *261*
Gordon, W. A., 215(21), *259*
Gorin, E., 510, *565*
Gorin, M. H., 500(40), 530, 558(40), *565*
Gorter, E. W., 135, 147(130), 178(196), *204*, *206*
Goswami, A., 181(306), *208*
Gradinger, H., 115(54), *202*
Gränicher, H., 296(41), *306*
Graf, P., 112(66), *202*
Graham, J., 140(133), 188(132), *204*
Gray, A. J., *263*

Gray, T. J., 269(42), *306*
Green, H. S., 78(5), *95*
Greenberg, I. N., 292(102), *308*
Greene-Kelly, R., 356(138), *433*
Greenwood, C. T., 570(36), 578(1), 582(35), 586, 587(35), *602, 603*
Gresham, T. L., 545(24), *564*
Grey, N. R., 626(13), 627, 633(14), *634*
Greyson, J., 420(11), *430*
Griffel, M., 286(126), 287(126), *308*
Griffin, H. L., 570, *603*
Grimes, H. H., *263*
Grimm, L., 105(201), 106, *206*
Groeneveld, J., 78(37), *96*
Groennings, S., 560(25), *564*
Grønvold, F., 122(135), 167(157), 171(136, 137), 173(134, 157), 174(134), 177, 178(134), 183(136), *204, 205*
Grütter, W. F., 370(39), *431*
Gruner, J. W., 398(139), *433*
Guggenheim, E. A., 58(19), *95*
Guittard, M., 105(105), 171(104), 185(41), *202, 203*, 292(94), *307*
Gulbransen, E. A., 211(27, 28, 29, 30), 216(27, 31), 219(29), 220(28), 222(27), 227(29), 233(27, 28, 29, 30, 52), 239(28), 240(52), 243(26, 50, 51, 52), 245(50), 246(50), 257, *259, 260, 264, 266*
Gurney, R. W., 81, 89, *96*
Gurry, R. W., 275(20), 288(20), 289(20), *305*
Gushee, B. E., 146(139), *204*
Guth, E. D., 119(103), 120(103, 140), *203, 204*
Gutowsky, H. S., 242(80), *261, 265*
Gwinn, W. D., 627, *634*

H

Haag, R. M., *265*
Habgood, H. W., 427, *433*
Hägg, G., 100(143), 132(142), 133(142), 136, 147, 148(146), 171(144), 179(145), 182, 183(144), *204*, 212, 252, 257, *259*, 282(44), 304(46), *306*
Haes, E. J., *263*
Hagberg, O., 173(134), 174(134), 178(134), *204*

Hahn, H., 105(149, 152), 106(149), 167(153), 174(148), 175(148), 177(151), 178(150, 151), 179(149, 151, 152, 153), 183(149, 152, 153), 184(147, 150), *204, 205*
Hahn, T., 197(65), *202*
Hall, M. N. A., 226, 252, *259*
Hall, W. K., *264*
Hammerschmidt, E. G., 321, *433*
Hanic, F., 157(256), *207*
Hansen, M., 186(155), 187(154), *205*, 211(38), 215(38), 244, *259*
Hanson, N. W., 511, *565*
Haraldsen, H., 122(135), 167(157), 170(156, 158, 159), 171(136, 156), 173(134, 157), 174(134), 178(134, 159), 183(136), *204, 205*, 304(47), *306*
Harbard, E. H., 109(71), *202*
Hardcastle, K., *263*
Harder, B., 105(149), 106(149), 174(148), 175(148), 179(149), 183(149), *204*
Hardie, D., *266*
Hardt, H. D., 364, *433*
Hare, A. W., *267*
Harker, D., 37, *48*
Harris, P. G., 372(143), *433*
Harris, W. F., 215(39), *259*
Harrison, E. R., *263*
Harrison, F. W., 141(160), *205*
Hartl, K., 343, 345(279, 280), 346(279), *437*
Hartley, G. S., 421(144), 422(144), *433*
Hartley, H., 449(12), *490*, 495, 496(42), 538(42), *565*
Harvey, C. A., 215(77), *261*
Harwood, M. G., 304(48), *306*
Hassel, O., 122(161), *205*
Hassid, W. Z., 571(4), *602*
Hauffe, K., 92, 93, *95*, 109, *205*, 269(49), *306*
Hauptman, H., 37(16), *48*
Hausner, H. H., *266*
Haworth, W. N., 571(4), 577(38), *602, 603*
Hayashi, A., 373(230), *436*
Hayes, E. T., 214(83), *261*
Hayes, H. F., 240(60), *260*
Haynes, R., *265*
Hazoni, Y., 563(42a), *565*, 627, *634*

Heaton, L., *265*
Hegedüs, A. J., 137(235), *207*
Heikes, R. R., 291(50), *306*
Heller, W. R., *262*
Hellner, E., 189(96, 329), 190(163, 165), 191(163, 165), 192(166), 195(50, 96, 164, 166, 264), 197(50), *202*, *203*, *205*, *207*, *209*
Henglein, F. M., 394(98), *432*, 593(21), 594(21), 600, *603*
Hennig, G. R., 354(146), 361(145), *433*
Hennrich, N., 600(39), *603*
Hepworth, M. T., 240(40), *259*, *265*
Herbst, W., 585, *603*
Herdle, L. E., 602(67), *604*
Herenguel, J., *263*, *267*
Hermann, C., 494, 495, 497, 531, *565*
Hermans, P. H., 601(40), 602(41), *603*, *604*
Herzog, E., *262*
Hess, H. V., 496(44), 538(44), 540(44), *565*
Hexter, R. M., 620, *634*
Hey, M. H., 373(147, 148, 149), *433*
Heyding, R. D., 151(279), *208*
Hickmott, T. W., *265*
Higgenbotham, R. S., 588, *604*
Hilbert, G. E., 577(91), *605*
Hill, D. C., 275(75), 276(75), 277(75), 278(75), 290(75), *307*
Hill, M. L., 215(45), 227(45), *260*, *262*, *263*
Hill, T. L., 72(49), 75(26), 77, *96*
Hiller, L. A., Jr., 94(62), *97*
Hillman, P., 563(42a), *565*, 627(14a), *634*
Himmel, L., 289, 290(51), 300(51, 52), *306*
Hino, J., 216(84), *261*
Hirahara, E., 304(53), *306*
Hirai, N., 78(17), *95*
Hirakawa, K., 171(244), *207*
Hiroike, K., 78(45), *96*
Hirone, T., 304(54), *306*
Hirschfelder, J. O., 69(29), 72(14), 75(63), 77(63), 93, 94(28), *95*, *96*, *97*, 404(151), 406(150), *433*, *434*
Hixon, R. M., 495(61), 496(61), *565*, 572(56), 575(56), *604*
Hoare, F. E., 287(11), *305*
Hoare, J. P., *264*
Hobbis, L. C. W., *263*
Hobson, J. D., *262*

Hodge, E. S., *267*
Hoekstra, H. R., 116(167), 123(168), 124(170), 125(170), *205*
Hölley, C. E., *262*
Hoff, R. E., 508(56a), 558(56a), *565*, 632(22), *634*
Hoffman, W., 190(171), 191(171), *205*
Hoffmann, J. D., 614, 629(18), *634*
Hofmann, K. A., 443, *490*
Hofmann, U., 339(281), 343, 345(279, 280), 346(279), 351(287), 354(91), 361(218), *432*, *435*, *437*
Holden, J. R., 120(140), *204*
Holey, C. E., Jr., 213(42), *260*
Holley, J. G., 359(152), 360(154), 363, *434*
Holló, J., 570(43), *604*
Holman, R. T., 494(85), 556, *566*
Holmes, P. J., 185(336), *209*
Holtz, F. C., 216(84), *261*
Hopkins, A. K., *267*
Hopkinson, B. E., *265*, *267*
Horie, T., 132(173), *205*
Hornaday, J. R., *262*
Hoschek, E., 109(174), 167(175), 171(175), 173(175), *205*
Houston, D. M., 292(55), *306*
Hsieh, Y. C., 585, *604*
Hsu, K. H., 585, *604*
Hsu, S. S., 133(296), *208*
Hu, Y. C., 553(7), *564*
Huber, A., *267*
Huber, O. J., *265*
Hudson, R. M., *262*
Huggins, M. L., 502(45), *565*
Hughes, E. W., 616, *634*
Hughes, P. C., *265*
Hugo, M., *262*
Huibregtse, E. J., 282(56), 286(56), *306*
Hull, A. W., 29(11), *47*
Hume-Rothery, W., 211(43), *260*
Hund, F., 122(176), 123(177, 178), *205*, 271(57, 58), 272, 273(58), 275(58), 276(58), 278, 279, *306*
Hunt, P. D., 505(77), *566*, 631, *634*
Hurlbert, R. C., *264*
Hurlen, T., 109, 111, 167(157), 173(157), *205*
Hurst, R. P., 77, *96*
Hyvonen, L. J., 213(54), 248(54), *260*

I

Ibbitson, D. A., 390(44), *431*
Ibers, J. A., 362(97), *432*
Iitaka, V., 195(240), 197(240), *207*
Ikeda, T., 296(62), *306*
Ingerson, E., 395(181), *434*
Ingold, J. H., 132(180), *205*, 282(63), 283(63), *306*
Insley, H., 398(117), *433*
Iovov, N. I., *263*
Isenberg, I., 586, *603*
Ishii, D., 125(278), *208*
Ismailzade, I. G., 296(64), *307*
Isupov, V. A., 116(181), 134(292), 143(293), *205*, *208*, 295(114), 296(115), *307*, *308*
Ivanova, T. F., 215(22), *259*
Iwai, T., 132(173), *205*

J

Jackson, R., 371(247), 373(247), *436*
Jackson, W. W., 371(248), 373(248), 380(248), *436*
Jacobsen, E., 171(137), *204*
Jaeger, F. M., 326(156), 327(156), *434*
Jaeger, J. C., 219, 220(9), *259*
Jaffee, R. I., *265*
Jagodzinski, H., 148(182, 277), *205*, *208*
Jahnberg, L., 110(14), *201*
Jahns, W., 317(265), *436*, *437*, 495(98), 544(98), *567*
Jakits, O., 296(41), *306*
James, W. J., 109(295), *208*, 591(46), 592(46), 594(46), 595(46), 601, *604*
Janer, C., 508(63), *566*
Janko, A., *263*
Jansen, E. F., 602(47), *604*
Janssens, P., 77, *96*
Jasinski, R. J., 215(21), *259*
Jeannin, Y., 173(184), 175(183), *205*
Jeffrey, G. A., 318(157, 176), *434*, 482(11, 16), 483(4), *490*, 544, *565*
Jellinek, F., 168, 170(185), 174, 175(187), 176(186), 179(187), *205*
Jellinek, M. H., 137(60), 140(60), *202*, 282(10), *305*
Jette, E. R., 108(188), *205*, 288(66), *307*
Johnson, E. W., 215(45), 227(45), *260*, *262*, *263*

Johnson, H., 297(30), *306*
Johnson, H. H., 215(46), *260*
Johnson, J. R., 278, *305*, *307*
Johnson, K. D. B., 116(7), *201*
Johnson, S., *261*
Johnston, W. D., 133, *205*, 291(50), *306*
Johnston, W. V., *266*
Johnstone, N. B., 544, *566*
Jona, F., 117(189), *205*
Jones, D. W., *265*
Jones, W. H., Jr., 288, *307*
Jonker, G. H., 141(191), 149(190), *206*, 304(69), *307*
Jorgensen, B. B., 582(35), 587(35), *603*
Jorgensen, O. B., 582(35), 587(35), *603*
Jost, W., 83(31, 32), *96*, 224(47, 48), 225, *260*
Juenker, D. W., *264*
Juretschke, H. J., 283, *307*
Juza, R., 304(71), *307*, 361(158), *434*

K

Känzig, W., 294(73), *307*
Kahn, S., 549, *567*, 631, 635
Kainz, J., 296(72), *307*
Kalish, H. S., *266*
Kamb, W. B., 373(159), *434*
Karle, J., 37(16), *48*
Karpenko, G. V., *262*
Karr, C., 560(46), *565*
Kasper, J. S., 37, *48*, 107(192), *206*
Kass, S., *266*
Katz, J. J., 116(167), 124(170), 125(170), *205*
Katz, J. R., 364, *434*
Katz, L., 118(72), 134(119, 120), 138(120), 139(120), 140(117, 118), 141(117, 118), 146(139), 147(85), *202*, *203*, *204*
Katz, O. M., 233(52), 240(52), 243(50, 51, 52), 245(50), 246(50), *260*, *264*, *266*
Katz, T., 109(193), *206*
Kaufmann, A. R., *266*
Kavtaradze, N. N., *263*
Kedesdy, H., 146(233), *207*
Keller, J. M., 288(74), *307*
Kelsey, K., 332, 339(46), 341, 343(46), 344(46), 356(45), 410(46), *431*
Kemula, W., 352(161), *434*, 548(47), 560(47), 565